THE **Liberty** YEARS

1924-1950

MAY 31
1924

5¢

Liberty

A Weekly for Everybody

In this Issue
JOHN
TAINTOR FOOTE
ARNOLD BENNETT
FRANK CONDON
SAMUEL MERWIN

The First Rose of Summer

THE Liberty
YEARS
1924-1950

AN ANTHOLOGY

Edited and with Commentary by

ALLEN CHURCHILL

PRENTICE-HALL, INC. Englewood Cliffs, New Jersey

The Liberty Years 1924 – 1950
edited by Allen Churchill
Commentary © 1969 by Allen Churchill
Other material © 1969 by Liberty Corporation
Copyright 1924, 1925, Coloroto Corp.
Copyright 1926, 1927, 1928, 1929, 1930, 1931, Liberty Weekly, Inc.
Copyright 1932, 1933, 1934, 1935, Liberty Publishing Corp.
Copyright 1936, 1937, 1938, 1939, 1940, 1941, 1942,
Macfadden Publications Inc.
Copyright 1942, 1943, 1944, 1945, 1946, 1947, 1948, 1949, 1950,
Liberty Magazine Inc.
13–535807–8
Library of Congress Catalog Card Number: 72–80773
Printed in the United States of America ● *T*
Prentice-Hall International, Inc., London
Prentice-Hall of Australia, Pty. Ltd., Sydney
Prentice-Hall of Canada, Ltd., Toronto
Prentice-Hall of India Private Ltd., New Delhi
Prentice-Hall of Japan, Inc., Tokyo

"In Conference" is reprinted with the permission of
Charles Scribner's Sons from *WHAT OF IT?* by Ring Lardner.
Copyright 1925 Charles Scribner's Sons; renewal copyright
1953 Ellis A. Lardner.
"What Makes Sammy Run" by
Budd Schulberg is reprinted
by permission of Ad Schulberg.

The editor wishes to express his
thanks for the warm cooperation of Lorraine Lester,
George Lessner, and Robert Whiteman, of the
Liberty Library in New York.

Contents

V—PEACE, IT'S WONDERFUL (1946–1950)   379

THE **Liberty** YEARS

1924-1950

I

The Magazine
for Everybody

(1924-1929)

THE MAGAZINE KNOWN as *Liberty* burst upon the American scene with the issue of May 4, 1924.

This was—of course—midway in the Roaring Twenties, that glorious decade when for the first time in history a young generation thrust off the domination of the old to behave in its own wild, uninhibited way. Boys with slick, shiny hair, attired in the looping knickers known as plus fours, toted hip flasks filled with Prohibition gin. These flasks were freely offered to girls of the day, flappers who rolled stockings just below the knee, bobbed hair, puffed cigarettes, used lipstick, shed underwear, and donned skimpy dresses that looked no bigger than handkerchiefs.

The flapper and her boyfriend—sometimes referred to as her sheik—were adept in the use of such snappy expressions as "So's your old man," "He's the cat's meow," and "She's the bee's knees." Like everything else in this jumping era, slang attained a new colorful dimension—as we shall see later on in these pages.

At the beginning older folk looked with horror at the antics of this Flaming Youth, a phrase which—believe it or not—is first found in Hamlet. Then the old generation made note of the fact that the young seemed to be enjoying a fine and frolicsome time. With this, Pop set out to buy his own plus fours and Stacomb, while keeping an ear attuned for the address of the nearest bootlegger. Mom rolled her stockings, made a bonfire of her corsets, shingled her hair, learned to like cocktails, and began making goo-goo-googly eyes at her dancing daughter's dates.

Behind all this contemporary whoopee lay the high prosperity of a stock market which made it oh-so-easy to get rich on paper. Just as important, however, was Prohibition, the law of the land which supposedly prevented citizens from drinking alcoholic beverages. For a time Americans expected this law to work. Then, suddenly, it was obvious it wouldn't. Men who had never before broken a law cheerfully contacted bootleggers or beat knuckles on the iron doors of Charlie-sent-me speakeasies. The rum runner, boot-legger, and racketeer emerged as prominent figures on the American scene. At country-club dances, bootleg gin was as important as the saxophone that wailed Doo-Wacka-Doo.

In May 1924, a decade already jazz-mad was gathering forces to turn into the Era of Wonderful Nonsense. Wisecracking, debonair James J. Walker was soon to be elected Mayor of the City of New York. In that exalted office he was the Night Mayor, fox-trotting the early hours away in liquor-serving Broadway night clubs and arriving at City Hall, if at all, late the next afternoon. To millions of his envious countrymen, the Night Mayor was "Jimmy." Europeans topped this by calling him "Jazz" J. Walker.

Also a stolid girl named Gertrude "Trudy" Ederle was in hard train-ing to swim the English Channel, a feat not yet accomplished by a female. Up to now thoughts of flying the Atlantic in a frail airplane had not occurred to the young airmail pilot Charles "Slim" Lindbergh—but in 1927 they would. Eye-popping Rudolph Valentino, the Sheik of Sheiks, was tops at the movie box office. Queen of the films was Glorious Gloria Swanson. Jack Dempsey, the fearsome Manassa Mauler, was heavyweight champ of the world. Babe Ruth, Sultan of Swat, dominated baseball.

Young couples danced the fox-trot while clinging warmly to one another, pausing only to take swigs from flasks. Shortly, however, their cheek-to-cheek dancing would give way to a wild, swinging Charleston. Hit songs of the moment ran from Irving Berlin's deeply sentimental "All Alone," to "Sleepy Time Gal," to "Memory Lane" (why has no one revived this one?). Especially popular were such nonsense tunes as "When the Pussy-willow Whispers to the Catnip," "Who Takes Care of the Caretaker's Daughter?," "Hay, Hay, Farmer Gray," and "When It's Nighttime in Italy It's Wednesday Over Here." John Held-type sheiks and shebas strummed ukuleles while chanting the infinite couplets of a song called "Crazy Words, Crazy Tune," the refrain of which was a simple Vo-Do-Dee-O-Do. At the Paul Whiteman concert where "Rhapsody in Blue" got its first hearing, composer Zez Confrey ("Kitten on the Keys") got bigger billing than George Gershwin.

It was wild, it was wonderful . . . America had been made safe for democracy by World War I, leaving citizens free to make whoopee and enjoy paper profits. Everything seemed new—Wall Street, cocktails, jazz, sex, rumble seats, aviation, slang, you name it.

What, then, was so surprising about the appearance of a magazine called *Liberty*? Nothing really, except that the *Saturday Evening Post* and *Collier's* were so well entrenched as weekly, mass circulation publications. Not to mention the *Ladies' Home Journal, McCall's*, and others that came out once a month.

But the masterminds behind *Liberty* had it figured out—or believed they did. More than its two established rivals, or any other going periodical, *Liberty* was prepared to show an awareness of the events and trends, fads and moods impinging on the great mass of Americans. *Liberty* planned to hew close to the basics of contemporary life, to be guide, philosopher, and friend to the magazine public—to have what a later generation called Immediacy.

In announcing this, a pre-publication prospectus shot up a series of arrows from a quiver full of glowing promises.

One said the upcoming magazine would be beamed at the millions of Americans who swarmed to silent films in such numbers that Hollywood movie making had become a major industry. "People in the movie audiences are exactly the kind we are trying to reach," the prospectus burbled. Each issue, it was forecast, would be a happy mixture of thrills, romance, suspense, nostalgia, and laughter—precisely the ingredients in a gripping movie.

The magazine also intended to appeal to the young people of the era. This did not mean Flaming Youth flappers, for unlike the teen-agers and teeny-boppers of a later age, they did not constitute a group which bought advertised products. Rather, the pristine publication directed itself at young marrieds and those-in-love-and-about-to marry, a status in the best tradition of the periodical's romantic stories and serials.

"Our deliberate aim is to make young people fall for us," the prospectus continued. "If they, as they grow older, become our friends, our future is assured."

Finally, the impending blessed event stated its intention of becoming the Bad Boy of the weekly field. This, we hasten to add, indicated an irreverent, devilish attitude rather than moral looseness.

From these revelations of purpose and breeziness one fact emerges: the new publication would adopt something of a newspaper approach to magazines.

This is hardly surprising, for the men behind *Liberty* were the two top journalistic figures of a flamboyant decade. One was Colonel Robert Rutherford "Bertie" McCormick, publisher of the Chicago *Tribune*, then and now called the World's Greatest Newspaper. Beside him stood his first cousin, Captain Joseph Medill Patterson, a most rugged individualist who had broken away from Windy City newspaperdom to found the New York *Daily News*. This, America's first tabloid newspaper, had been an instant success, forever altering the contours of domestic journalism.

The Patterson-McCormick axis stood forth as a strong editorial link between the two major cities of the land. It is hardly unusual, therefore, that these two men, each wealthy, vigorous, ambitious, and tough-minded, considered themselves ready to challenge the magazine universe.

In this, Colonel Bertie and Captain Joe were inevitably guided by the huge success of the *Daily News*. If a newspaper livelier than other newspapers had been a success, the pair reasoned, why not a magazine livelier than other magazines? Thus *Liberty* was projected as a magazine of infinite variety, each issue jumping in stimulating brain-stretching fashion (like a high-class *Daily News*) between the serious, the sprightly, the indiscreet, the revealing, and the absurd. "The *Daily News* set out to be different, and *Liberty* will be different," the two men vowed.

With this settled, they turned to practical matters. Patterson and McCormick—one in New York, the other in Chicago—decided to occupy the post of active publisher during alternate months. They picked John Wheeler as their Executive Editor—a man of rich experience in magazines, newspapers, and news syndicates who had many famous writers as close friends. Despite the importance of Chicago in the magazine's inception, New York would be its editorial headquarters, and so it remained.

Like the *Saturday Evening Post* and *Collier's*, *Liberty* would appear once a week and cost its readers the sum of five cents. In format it would be similar to its two main rivals, enabling it to accept the same "poster-size" advertising plates. In the tried and true formula established by George

Horace Lorimer of the *Saturday Evening Post, Liberty* would feature big-name writers and illustrators. By paying prices a trifle higher than other magazines, the new magazine hoped to attract top talent to its pages.

Liberty got its name in a manner gently redolent of the Teeming Twenties.

At first Colonel McCormick had insisted on calling the project the *Coloroto Magazine*, in honor of several large presses just imported from Germany. (It has been surmised that the true genesis of *Liberty* did not lie in the desire to offer the United States a better magazine, but rather in the need to feed these ravenous Coloroto presses.)

Editor Wheeler and staff objected to the title, branding it lackluster. When Captain Patterson's month as publisher rolled around, he joined the opposition. Colonel McCormick then agreed to a contest for a title, the prizes amounting to $25,000.

This was blazoned in the columns of the *News* and *Tribune* as the "most remarkable offer in magazine history." Perhaps it was. Over a period of seventy-nine days, 1,395,322 names poured in from thirty-one countries. Among the people who sent their suggestions were Queen Marie of Roumania (like other Europeans she read of the contest in the Paris edition of the Chicago *Tribune*); Admiral William S. Sims, outstanding naval hero of World War I; Chief Buffalo of the Cherokees; evangelist Billy Sunday; Anton Lang, who played the Savior in the Oberammergau Passion Play; vaudeville headliner Jack Norworth; and Henry Pratt Judson, president of the University of Chicago.

Of the million-plus entries, no less than 3,017 came from a single man—Charles A. Elwell, of Youngstown, Ohio. It is a tribute to homegrown grit and inspiration that the winning name—"*Liberty*: A Weekly for Everybody"—was Mr. Elwell's. It was chosen, the judges explained, "because Liberty is the first word in the American consciousness." Winner Elwell got $20,000, with the remaining $5,000 split between one runner-up who sent in "*Vision*: For Young and Old" and another who suggested "*Tomorrow*: A Weekly of Universal Appeal." The *Tomorrow* title came from André de Casanove, well-known French novelist.

Liberty's debut on May 4, 1924 was not altogether triumphant. Colonel McCormick's Coloroto presses proved faulty and more than half the first run of 500,000 had to be destroyed. Nor had a name been decided upon by publication day. Probably for the first time in history, a magazine made its first appearance on newsstands without a name. But the second issue, which rolled from American presses, proudly announced itself as *Liberty*.

Thus launched, the publication ran on for the next twenty-six years. *Liberty* satisfied a large segment of the American reading public, with a circulation that usually remained between 2 and 3,000,000. Yet it is sad to report that national advertisers, the men whose financial support really counts, never regarded the enterprise with visible enthusiasm. *Liberty* always carried advertisements, some of them quite colorful. But there were never enough to take the magazine to the top of the money mountain, or even far from the bottom. In only three years out of twenty-six did *Liberty* boast a financial profit.

Nonetheless, its editors were allowed to pay top prices to writers and artists, and consequently obtained the work of the best in both fields. The roster of *Liberty* names—some of them literary greats, others the workaday writers who formed the backbone of the mass circulation field—includes almost every remembered and half-remembered author of the time. Here are a few contributors during the first five years of the magazine's life.

Fannie Hurst, Ring Lardner, F. Scott Fitzgerald, Ben Hecht, Michael Arlen, Arnold Bennett, Rosita Forbes, Larry Barretto, J. P. McEvoy, Dana Burnet, Stephen Vincent Benét, Ben Ames Williams, Royal Brown, Julian Street, Robert W. Chambers, Homer Croy, Samuel Merwin, Elmer Davis, Sax Rohmer, O. O. McIntyre, John Erskine, Heywood Broun, Westbrook Pegler, Floyd Gibbons, Leonard H. Nason, Arthur Somers Roche, Rupert Hughes, Paul Gallico, Edwin Balmer.

The roster of early *Liberty* artists is no less distinguished or encompassing. Included are the top illustrators of an Era of Illustrators, among them:

James Montgomery Flagg, McClelland Barclay, Neysa McMein, Peter Arno, Arthur William Brown, Wallace Morgan, Robert Edgren, Ralph Barton, W. T. Benda, Cesare, John T. McCutcheon, Willy Pogany, Herb Roth, Rollin Kirby, Addison Burbank.

After the first few issues, and for more than five years thereafter, artist Leslie Thrasher was the man who drew all *Liberty* front covers. These were so-called "Continuity covers," done in color and with a set of characters whose activities were featured from week to week. Actually Thrasher's series was no more than a glorified comic strip, of the sort known as single-panel. His covers bore the overall title "For the Love o' Lil," and it is perhaps indicative of *Liberty* aims that our heroine was no gin-slurping flapper. Lil herself was a pleasant, average, and somewhat flighty girl, with a hovering family and a silly boy friend who in time became her spouse. On cover after cover, Lil & Co. were pictured in situations embarrassing, amusing or heartwarming. Readers gobbled them up.

Liberty pioneered in the one-page, short-short story, said to be the most difficult form of all to write. The short fiction in this volume belongs to that unique genre.

With most stories, articles, and features in *Liberty* went a gimmick that became a trademark. From 1927 on, nearly every contribution was preceded by the solemn accounting "Reading Time: 12 minutes, 42 seconds" —or whatever it happened to be.

Liberty's original promise to be the Bad Boy of American magazines came closest to fulfillment in illustrations. Flappers drawn for *Liberty* always seemed to cross legs a trifle more daringly than those in other publications. Over the years, the magazine specialized in backstage and night-club romances, giving artists a chance to draw girls in skimpy costumes which exposed an unusual amount of bare feminine thigh. So, in its way, *Liberty* was a precursor of *Playboy*. . . .

Through all its years, *Liberty* remained particularly a magazine of the Twenties. It was as if, having opened its eyes in the midst of this hectic era, it liked what it saw and continued to view matters that way. Liberty expected this planet to be exciting, or at least jazzy. When it wasn't, the magazine bravely tried to make it seem so.

So the Era of Wonderful Nonsense fit *Liberty* like a flapper's tight frock. Jimmy Walker was duly elected New York's Mayor and his follies and virtues were caught in a lively *Liberty* piece by Frederick L. Collins. Trudy Ederle swam the awesome English channel and her touching letter home to Mom was enshrined on the editorial page. Eight months later Westbrook Pegler finds Trudy in the throes of disillusionment.

Flappers were still viewed with alarm, and older folk wondered if these thrill-seeking girls made good daughters-in-law. Best-selling novelist Kathleen Norris tried to provide an answer. The most popular fiction theme of the day was the one which gave assurance that the sheiks and shebas of the Jazz Age were not so bad after all: give them a taste of truly adult responsibility and these heedless kids settled down (wisecracking as they did) to become folks just like Mom and Dad. This formula is found in Royal Brown's "Love—a Tale of This Terrible Generation," which also brings comforting, if somewhat baffling, assurance that legal liquor remained a staple commodity during the frenzies of Prohibition.

In Hollywood, Glorious Gloria was rudely elbowed aside by flapper Clara Bow, also known as the It Girl. In an unsparing profile by Adela Rogers St. Johns, this redhead flapper of flappers appears in moods as clashing as her hair and garb. Then, with the emergence of Talkies, the career of the It Girl began to slip.

Lindbergh duly flew the Atlantic, a deed that purified the murky atmosphere of the time. Yet sorry aviation spectacles like the Dole Race to Honolulu were as much a part of the mixed-up decade as the heroism of Lucky Lindy.

In the midst of Prosperity some young couples had difficulty making a living, and Viña Delmar's "It's a Great Life" points up possible consequences. However, the handsome country club types in Elliott White Springs' "Steeple-chase Pier" got along only too well on the crest of a Prohibition wave. (Young Mrs. Delmar and Elliott Springs were the first exceptional writing talents to be discovered by *Liberty*. Hardly an issue appeared in the zestful Twenties without fiction by one or both.)

And so it went . . . . *Liberty* reflected an exciting era in history and, as best it could, went on perpetuating that spirit.

Liberty cost five cents at your favorite newsstand. So let us say you have just put down a nickel, picked up your copy, and now you are ready to join me in a sentimental journey through twenty-six years of the magazine called *Liberty*, which set out to be the liveliest in America, and very often succeeded. . .

Does a Flapper Make a Good Wife?

by Kathleen Norris

Painted Lips, Flush of Liquor, Scanty Raiment, Dash, and High Speed—How do They Mix with Happy Marriage?

YESTERDAY AFTERNOON I was watching some young girls dancing. They were dancing in a hotel, in the cleared space of a tearoom, just as girls will be dancing in the hotels of your city today, just as they were dancing yesterday and will be dancing tomorrow.

For five years now the little girls have been dancing—not as we danced twenty and twenty-five years ago. Not rarely, occasionally, with a great sense of the fun of being "dressed up," being at a "party," having a good time that had been long anticipated and would serve as an event to date from for months ahead.

No, they dance now with the casualness with which we used to take walks, gathering wild flowers—does any one do this any more?—or as our grandmothers used to meet in the quiet afternoons to make samplers and "sew pieces" for bedspreads.

They dance every day. Every day is a party. Every lunch time, every afternoon, late afternoon, dinner time, and evening sees the modern girl with an engagement.

Not every girl—no. But so many hundreds of them, so many thousands of them that their mothers are seriously worried and the national vocabulary has gained the new term "flapper."

The word flapper has so many definitions that one is constantly worried for fear of misunderstanding. I asked a young college man if every young girl he knew was a flapper. He said, "No; the flappers are the girls who go too far."

"Too far with smoke and flasks and almost no clothes and dancing and the night life clubs and late joy riding," the college man elucidated when I pressed him.

It sounds dangerous. Yesterday afternoon when one of the little girls sat near me, panting, powdering, reddening her lips, and quite composedly arranging her bobbed and marcelled hair, I asked her just how she would define the word "flapper."

Eyeing herself abstractedly in the lid of her vanity case, she said, smilingly:

"A flapper is only what you used to call a sport. It's the same thing."

But I, who remember the '90s, know it is not the same thing at all. The "sport" of those days was usually a man, anyway. To call a girl a "sport" would have been to insult her.

And after some years of watching the flapper—the "girl who goes too far"—I am left with a feeling of profound pity for her. I don't think we have a class of persons in the entire nation as fundamentally wronged and cheated as these same little girls.

I remember a certain baby, years ago, who was a phenomenon. When he was only an infant he talked quite intelligibly; I heard him several times. He was the pride of his neighborhood. He said:

"I don't like it. Is that your dog? What's your name? Where's my elephant? Two and two make four," and a score of other things when he was eight months old.

His mother said that he had spoken clearly at seven weeks. At two years he wanted to read; he had an owlish little stare, and his precocious little voice saying, "Why don't you teach me?" rings in my ear to this day. It would have been wonderful in a five-year-old; in a baby of twenty-four months it was horrible. He died when he was less than three.

The flapper is in his class. She is burning out her soul, mind, and body, as unconsciously as the baby was. She is crowding all the happy times of her life—all that she can possibly have—into a few years. She thinks that this feverish rushing, this ridiculous doubling up of engagements, this paint thick on her face, and these artificial waves in her hair are but the anteroom to life.

And because she is young, and loves excitement, and because we have an indulgent attitude to her teens she vaguely believes us when she hears us saying:

"She'll be settled down fast enough."

But, as a matter of fact, these years of racing, of chattering, of drinking and dancing, of unnatural lights and daring jokes, little satin dresses soaked with perspiration, young mouths smeared with red paint and burned with strong drinks, soft mops of young hair twisted and scorched and marred, these years of manicuring and dress buying, of perfumes and telephoning and overeating, of leaping from hot rooms into low-slung motors—are all her life. What is left isn't worth talking about.

Marriage? No, she is spoiled for that. How can she possibly marry and manage a home on a few hundreds a month when she is accustomed to having those hundreds all to herself for a rabbit-skin jacket which does not make her young beauty any prettier, for costly perfumes that her youthful freshness does not need, for beauty creams and night creams, for hairdresser and milliner, bridge and mah jongg debts and luncheons downtown?

More than that. The right sort of man is not marrying the flapper these days. After all, self-preservation, unconscious or deliberate, is the first law of nature, and under all his nonsense and extravagance the decent boy feels it. Nature, which is having a lot more to do with these young persons than they have any idea, warns him.

He has had this girl—only a quarter dressed, boneless, spineless, corsetless—in his arms. He has felt the damp and the warmth of her body, smelled the liquor on her breath, wiped the red lip paint of her lips off his own; he knows what shops the perfume and the natural looking ringlets and the rosy color and the powdery fragrance come from; he hears the jokes, hears the bored comments, hears the silly surface chatter about things that are—or ought to be—sacred to her. And if he has the making of a real husband and father, a real homekeeper and good citizen in him, he doesn't marry her.

There is only one type of young man who marries the flapper, as every judge of a divorce court knows when these tearful children present themselves, sullen and disillusioned, before him a year or two later.

"The girls shock the boys these days" a woman who manages a certain series of fortnightly dances told me one day: The boys keep up, perhaps. But, over and over again, I hear them saying, 'Cut it out, Margaret,' 'You don't know what you're talking about, Isabel,' 'Gosh, you girls are the limit!' "

A mother I knew followed the course—a course, by the way, that is so old-fashioned as to have become the very latest thing again—of telling her little girl everything and permitting her to do nothing. The little girl at eighteen, nineteen, twenty was extremely pretty and extremely busy, very much aggrieved, and—she said to herself—"treated simply rottenly." However, she was young, and there is always a glory over youth, and so she went to picnics, and played the piano, and grumbled somewhat—not but what they grumble anyway!—and took a short Italian course, and a short nursing course, and eventually met a good man, who also chanced to be an extremely clever and rich young man, and married him.

She has never been to a tea dance, to a big cotillon, to an unchaperoned dinner at a roadhouse; she actually knows nothing, except by hearsay, of hip flasks and makeup and "necking" and "petting" and all the rest of it, and at twenty-four she is bursting with life and joy and happiness, a radiant mother, an adored wife, and a woman who, during the next twenty years, can enjoy a dance at the country club, an evening at the theater, or a few quiet hours with a book beside the fire with equal enthusiasm and freshness.

But which one of us would ask a group of the dancing rushing modern girls and boys to spend an evening with us without supplying a very definite entertainment in advance? Does it not take a good deal of courage for the average young man to say to any one of these girls:

"Will you marry me? We can't have a car just at first, you know, and perhaps we'll have only one servant. There'll be times, perhaps four or five evenings a week, when there won't be parties, of course, and if we're always to meet the crowd for dancing at five and then stand the others to sandwiches and cocktails and so on we may get into money difficulties. I can tip with five dollar bills now, and pay another five all around for cover charges, but maybe I can't keep that up. Do you think we could begin to live reasonably, and read books, and you could wash your own hair, and manicure your own nails, and wear your furs two seasons?"

I met a friend buying mah jongg prizes.

"They're for the night of the big dance," she said. "Jean is having about twenty of her crowd in for dinner first."

"But where does the mah jongg come in?"

"Well, they'll dine at eight, and they won't want to go on to the dance until about eleven. They'll have an hour or an hour and a half in between there when they can't sit around and twiddle their thumbs, don't you know."

Doesn't it seem a horrible waste and a horrible pity? For these young creatures aren't having a good time really, aren't really adding anything to the fundamental facts which always make youth so glorious and so happy a time. They are only staining it and spoiling it with unrestraint, just as any other time or period of life would be ruined by excesses and extravagances. It isn't a happy and innocent prelude to normal living, any more than turning a baby loose in a candy shop for six months, or giving a twelve-year-old the private circus, the yacht, the airship, and the machine gun he wants, would be to prepare both reasonably for life.

No man wishes to marry an exhausted, weary, sophisticated, physically burned-out wife to cure her of cigaret smoking and cocktail drinking and excessive rouging in the very beginning of their lives together. Years ago— thirty years ago—a certain type of reckless girlhood used to marry dissipated men, roués and alcoholics, "to reform them." But after half a generation of experiments along this line this became deservedly unpopular. Only the gray, lined, heartsick women who survived the trial, perhaps, could fully explain exactly how it worked—or didn't work.

My own explanation of the flapper is that as the general freedom and independence which has been affecting womanhood everywhere reached her, as wage earning, and self-expression, and the vote, and the single code, and all the rest of the changes gradually released her from the old prison bars of her mother's and her grandmother's youth, she somewhat lost her head. Men had always been free to do, say, and think certain things, argued the flapper, and girls forbidden anything but obedience and restraint.

Now all bars were down and there were no laws anywhere to worry about!

But from all sides, as I write, I get the impression that it is the girls themselves who are going to end all this. Not the mothers and fathers who have so signally failed them, but the girls themselves. They themselves will now find the third kingdom; not the prudish and forbidden kingdom which used to be so mysterious and so fascinating to their puffed-sleeved and bustled mothers; not the universal lawlessness and license they have experienced in this first untrammeled rush into the open; but their own kingdom: the kingdom of self-ruled girlhood.

There are hundreds of girls, all over the Union, banding themselves into little groups: groups definitely opposed to lawbreaking and the attendant speeding and gambling and hip flask. Decency, a real old puritan decency of speech, manner, and action, is actually being made fashionable once more among them. Hundreds of them write to me, denying in the first phrase that they are flappers—in the sense in which I have used the word here—and in the second reproaching me that I can ever criticize the flapper.

Criticize her? Far from it. But if it should happen—and it seems likely to happen—that the girls who are coming along, the girls who are sixteen and eighteen now, as contrasted with the flapper's rather jaded twenty-three and twenty-five, if this new group should stand out for a cleaner, nicer, saner way of doing things, then it will go hard with the flapper.

The mothers will no nothing—they have proved that. The new girls will be just as free as our girls today. Nobody will go into hysterics and lock doors and disinherit them when they come home semi-intoxicated and daubed with paint, half dressed and hardly able to give an account of themselves.

But suppose they don't do it? Suppose that, even being free as air, they choose to be gentlewomen and to hold their men friends and themselves up to an old-fashioned ideal of refinement in speech, dignity in action, temperance in amusement?

Not because Dad and Mother are bullying them. Not because they are ignorant of life. Not because they are without interest in the other sex, and enjoying their youth.

But because they really want to make something of these golden hours and these opening friendships. Because they want the twenties and the thirties—and even the far away, dim forties and fifties—to be something more than mere spoiled, wasted, unwelcome years.

If free, wise, unafraid girlhood ever does that . . .! Then the new type of American girl, the successor to the flapper, will be the actual glory of the world.

Please May I Bob My Hair?

by Mary Pickford

Everybody Says Don't—What Do YOU Say?

RECENTLY, IN AN unguarded moment I expressed a desire to bob my hair. I don't suppose it was so much a definite intention as it was idle speculation in which those of us who still have long hair occasionally indulge. But this statement brought back such a deluge of criticism, ranging all the way from mild reproof to violent denunciation, that it seemed that even in this private matter I was again expected to defer to the wishes of others.

I would not care to have anyone think that I take either myself or my hair too seriously. I am prepared to admit that there are probably two or three issues of more vital importance to the world than the question of bobbing my hair, I doubt very much if my decision will disturb the balance of power among nations, or more than temporarily upset the stock market.

All I mean to say is that there seems to be a perfectly amazing number of people who would like to settle this question for me—and all in the negative. And it is to these people that this article or petition is humbly but earnestly addressed.

If only one person had written saying: "I am awfully glad to hear that you are going to bob your hair," just to break the terrifying unanimity of disapproval, my case wouldn't seem quite so hopeless. As it is, all I can do is to present as convincingly as possible my reasons for wanting to cut my hair and see if I may win a reversal of judgment. If so, being a woman and therefore contrary minded, I may be satisfied with this concession and do nothing about it. Instead of changing my hair I am just as likely to change my mind.

As for reasons, I am not betraying any dark, feminine secret when I say that a woman does not cut her hair or do many other things as a result of pure reason. The way to the hairdresser is not paved with logic. She does not say to herself: "There are six reasons why it would be better for me to bob my hair, and only five for keeping it as it is; therefore I will bob it." She does it because she wants to, or because her friends want her to, or in a few obstinate cases, as I have hinted, because they don't want her to.

But if we *are* to marshal the arguments, I cannot see but that most of them will be on the side of the short-haired. In fact, except for sentiment and tradition, I cannot think of a single argument in favor of long hair. People who like to cling to the fashions of the past, who sigh mournfully over "the good old days," who think that the music and literature and art of the past were better than the offerings of today, and that human nature and charm are on a steady decline, leaving each period a little worse than the one before, will of course always become aroused over the sacrilege of destroying old idols, and deplore the loss of woman's "crowning glory." One always finds this reactionary minority tugging at the procession of progress, but the procession goes on just the same.

One can imagine some of the more old-fashioned and conservative members of a cannibal tribe clinging obstinately to their nose rings after the smart set had discarded them, sentimentally fingering these badges of beauty, hallowed by memory and tradition. And think of the Chinaman and his queue. In our eyes, his queue is hardly a thing of beauty, but I suppose no woman ever parted with her long hair with greater pangs.

For comfort and convenience, the arguments certainly all favor short hair. It is easier to wash, easier to keep clean and well groomed. In these outdoor days of swimming, golf, and motoring, a woman is relieved of that constant nagging anxiety of how her hair is standing the strain. Her hair, so to speak, is no longer on her mind to the exclusion of possibly more important matters.

But this question of comfort has never been one of paramount importance to our sex. Generations of tight-corseted ladies who were willing to sacrifice ease, health, and almost the act of breathing itself to achieve what they considered beauty of figure, attest the contrary—although I think we are growing a little more sensible on this point and are coming to the conclusion that comfort and beauty are not necessarily irreconcilable qualities.

Still, since a woman's appearance in most cases is so much more important to her than any other consideration, and since there is scarcely any form of torture to which she will not submit in order to improve it, we must waive this point of comfort as immaterial and attack the question solely on this sacred ground of her appearance.

I feel that I am too small a person to wear as much hair as I have. It is thick and massive and, if allowed to have its own way, will fall below my waist. I have learned to dress it fairly skillfully, and compress it into a comparatively small coil at the back of my neck, but even then it seems out of scale, too great a burden for a small person to carry around. This seems to me an unanswerable argument.

I am sure that a sense of proportion, which is certainly one of the chief requirements of beauty, demands short hair today just as strongly as it demanded long hair in other days.

Of course, there are exceptions. There always are. There are women with heads so small that they can stand a little padding in the way of hair. There are heads whose outlines do not look well if too clearly revealed. There is the occasional Junoesque and imposing woman who with too closely trimmed locks would look inadequate—slightly indecent. Small bodies, small heads; large bodies, large heads.

It seems a natural law of proportion from which there is no logical escape, unless one aims at the bizarre and the eccentric.

Speaking of exceptions, I am one myself. And you may wonder why, if I hold such definite views on the merits of short hair, I have thus far clung to long hair. I may seem to fall into that very exasperating class of people who wisely prescribe a course for other people, but fail to take their own prescription, like the gourmet who pauses in the midest of a feast to rhapsodize over the great virtues of dieting.

But I have had a rather compelling reason up to the present time for keeping my long hair. My small-girl parts which I have done on the screen have demanded a luxuriant growth of curls. I could not very well have got along without them, for young girlhood is the one age that, until recently anyway, has remained unshorn.

But now that I am thinking of doing slightly older parts, say the girl of seventeen or eighteen, the reason for bobbing it seems just as impelling. For if I am going to represent the modern girl, the first thing I have got to do is to look like her. I cannot very well interrupt the picture with a long subtitle explaining why, although I am a modern young woman, I don't look like one.

I know when the moment comes to confront the hairdresser, I won't be as calm about it as I sound. I suppose I have even better reasons than the average woman for feeling sentimental about my hair and panicky about parting with it. I have lived with it a long time, and I have always washed and cared for it myself. In more ways than one I am attached to it. In the early days I have no doubt it impressed people from whom I sought work. People have been kind enough to say that it was the symbol of some individual thing I had to offer the screen. At any rate, it is an old friend, certainly not deserving the punish-

ment I am planning for it. But I will spare the reader the further spectacle of a woman growing sentimental over her hair. These are feelings, not reasons, and I am trying to be convincing, not emotional.

To make my case as strong as I can, I should like to explain that I plan no wholesale destruction. If such a thing is possible, I am going to cut my hair and have it. It is always the violent extremists who bring a cause into disrepute. I think it is those women who have pared their hair to the quick, who have reduced it to an absurd minimum, who wear it plastered to their heads until it looks like something painted on the scalp—I think it is these fanatics who have created whatever prejudice there is against bobbed hair.

Just because we revolt from one ugly extreme of wearing too much hair, there is no reason why we should fly to another extreme which is just as ugly and instruct a hairdresser to fall ruthlessly upon our hair as if it were a blight upon womanhood.

Let us bob with moderation. From extreme boyish bobs, from ultra shingles, from closely cropped heads resembling a harvest field just after reaping, and in particular from shaved necks, Heaven defend us!

What I want to do is to get rid of the weight, the inconvenience, the wholly disproportionate length of the back hair. But I do not intend to be too drastic even with this.

I do not take very seriously the humor that long hair is coming back into vogue, although I wouldn't be surprised to see some of the young girls who are growing up today try the experiment, since, never having had long hair, the novelty may appeal to them. But I do not believe the mode, if it comes in at all, will be more than temporary.

I haven't yet met the woman who has enjoyed the freedom and comfort of short hair and wants to return to hairpins and all the annoyances of long hair. Besides, you will notice that when fashion in its unceasing cycle comes to a vogue that is comfortable and sensible, it sticks at that point for a long time. Short hair and short skirts are due, I think, for a long stay.

I have just thought of one advantage in having long hair. While it is long you can amuse yourself with all kinds of pleasant plans of when and how you will bob it. You can convert the dream into a reality any time you want.

But once it is short you are denied all this speculation.

You can no longer play with the two alternatives. If you decide you want it long again, no hairdresser has the magic to restore it. Only time—a long, long time—can perform the transformation.

But since I do not mean this as a serious consideration, and I have found no real arguments against it, I ask you again: Please may I bob my hair?

How to Be a Success in the Younger Set

by Elisabeth Cobb

Learn the Lingo!

A FEW WEEKS AGO an English girl came to our apartment to tea, and I invited five young Americans to meet her. Now, the little girl from across the pond was very charming. We decided at first sight that here was a young lady to be reckoned with, for she had danced with the Prince of Wales and the manner in which she wore her Bond Street clothes completely revolutionized our opinion of English women's chic, or rather lack of it; but the poor child sat dumbly through the afternoon with an expression of helpless wonder on her face; and when the other guests had found their gloves and cigaret cases and so departed, she begged me to translate their conversation for her. I think she suspected that she had been slumming.

Even after a lengthy and lucid explanation she seemed bemused, and after six weeks of being kept in as constant a state of circulation as a brand-new "hot-stuff-on-the-burning-sands" novel, I hear that she still carries around with her a notebook in which she writes any odd or unusual slang that she may hear. At the latest report she had filled eight notebooks and had started on the ninth.

Now, the poor child is in practically the same predicament as most of our elders, and so, for the benefit of parents and those unfortunates who have allowed themselves to become old-fashioned, but would sometimes like to know what it is that their children and their friends are talking about, I have written the conversation that took place at that tea, with a translation—necessarily a very free translation—in a parallel column so that Mother and Grandmother need but cast their eyes down the page to find the meaning of all those expressions that have been puzzling them so. And I do hope it won't be too much of a shock!

Miss Pittsburgh started it indignantly:

"If I ever step out with that wet smack again! He gets my vote as the flattest flat tire who ever tried to crash a party. He is so damp he drips."

"I never will attend another affair with that disagreeable person. I think him the most intolerable boy who ever essayed to attend a party to which he had not received an invitation."

Miss Park Avenue, soothingly:

"He certainly is a dumb-bell but I would not high-hat him to such an extent if he wasn't such a holy roller."

"He certainly is dull but I wouldn't be so aloof with him if he were not such a terrible religious hypocrite."

Miss San Francisco, very surprised:

"Why, my Lord, I thought he was God's greatest gift to women."

"Goodness gracious! Why, I always thought him very attractive."

Miss Riverside Drive:

"You've got the wrong dope on that snake. He is a would-be necker and a sad bird, but you could stand him if he didn't pull a shut-eye at each and every party. I was cured on the last loop we swung. Why, he went out like a light and stayed cold for hours."

"Someone has been misleading you as to the real character of that dance-mad person. He wants to kiss you all the time and is absolutely lacking in allure; but one would not mind that so much if he did not become so intoxicated that he is rendered unconscious at every party. . . . On the last social affair we attended he stayed drunk for hours.

(NOTE: *If the young man in question had not only danced but played football, he might have been everything else they said of him, but he would not have been a "snake." "Lounge-lizard" is the Old World phrase that my elder sisters use to describe his prototype.*)

Miss Washington Square, with the greatest enthusiasm:

"Holy cats! You girls are certainly dishing the dirt."

"My goodness! You girls are having a good gossip."

Miss Pittsburgh:

"Straight dope, not dirt. One smell of the cork and he passes out."

"Truth, not gossip. One taste of intoxicating liquor and he is drunk."

Miss San Francisco:

"He goes bad on himself in New York all right, but he got by pretty big in New Haven; they seemed to think he was the berries up there."

"It seems strange that he is so careless in New York and yet he was quite popular at Yale. His college mates seemed to think him a very nice lad."

Miss Riverside Drive, emphatically:

"He may be a wonder in his home town, but here I give him plenty of air."

"He may be a fine boy in his home, but I don't know him here."

Miss Park Avenue, thoughtfully:

"He used to rush a very snappy little wambi and she gave him lots of time, too, and I never saw how he rated it, for she high-hatted a lot of slick boys."

"He used to be very attentive to a very sweet little girl and she allowed him to see a great deal of her and I never saw how he achieved that distinction, for she was very aloof with a number of fine boys."

Miss San Francisco:

"I told you he was the Pola Negri of his sex."

"I told you girls thought him very attractive."

Miss Pittsburgh, assuming a virtuous expression:

"Well, she was kinda cute, I guess; I've heard lots of boys tell the world, and I always thought she was a knock-out myself, but she visited in Pitts-

"Well, she was rather fascinating, I suppose; I've heard lots of young men say so and I always thought her charming myself, but she visited in

burgh and went bushwacking around to an awful extent and no one who pulls that stuff rates such a lot.

Pittsburgh and let anyone who wished kiss her, and no one who permits that is thought a great deal of."

(NOTE: *I have heard some quaint old folk, girls who made their débuts in 1911, or so, use the expressions "peach" and "spoon," and I gather these take the places for them of "wambi" and "bushwack."*)

Miss Washington Square, giggling:

"This from our own little petter."

"This from the little girl who has been kissed so much."

Miss Pittsburgh, indignantly:

"Well, I've never been a prom-trotter or a jazz-hound, and anyhow that is what she was; nothing else but."

"Well, I have never existed for college parties nor wanted to dance continually, anyhow, and that is all she cared for."

(NOTE: *In the days of long ago, before the great draught, I am given to understand that the term "college widow" was used for "prom-trotter."*)

Miss Park Avenue:

"Why not, honey? Didn't you ever make the grade?"

"Why not, honey? Were you never popular enough to be asked?"

Miss San Francisco, yawning:

"Say, don't you think we have burped on enough people for this afternoon? I'm in an awful fog."

"Don't you think we have been a bit severe on a lot of people this afternoon? I am getting very bored."

Miss Riverside Drive:

"O, my dear, don't snout us. The trouble with you is that you have been sitting pretty too long out where men are men and women are God's greatest handicaps. Why, you ain't putting your heart in your work any more."

"O, my dear, don't be superior. The trouble is that you have been too comfortable, too long out West, and you cannot be enthusiastic over our fun."

Miss Washington Square (Miss San Francisco's very best friend), laughing:

"Don't let her kid you. If the way you get by on some of the benders we have been on lately is any sign of what you can do when you aren't half trying, I should hate to see you really strutting your stuff. You have been knocking New York for a tall green loop."

"Do not allow her to joke with you. If the attention you receive on the parties we have been on lately is any sign of your popularity when you are not in the spirit, I should hate to see you really trying. Truly you have received an enormous amount of attention."

Miss Great Britain, steadily gasping through the conversation, for it was a conversation, you know, puts her teacup down with a bang.

"O, really now, I say!"

She realized that without a good line you are a dead duck in New York, which means the necessity of entertaining conversation.

Gertie Makes a Hot Decision

by Gordon Seagrove

I TELL YOU, PEARL, I'm givin' the air
  To the cookie-dusters and parlor snakes,
An' all them sheiks with the patent hair—
  How could they keep a mamma in cakes?
All they can do is spoon and dance—
  A rush of brains to the feet beneath.
I'm kissin' em out! I want a chance
  At a ploddin' guy with three gold teeth!

A steady guy with his pants cut raw.
  You get me, Pearl—your Al's that way.
An' a strong man's bust an' a fireman's jaw.
  Lead me to him, is all I say!
A thrifty bozo that's after the gilt
  An' asks for bids on his bridal wreath.
Show me that kind and' I'll chirp, "I wilt."
  Gimme a plodder with three gold teeth.

Honest, Pearl, if you'll read the books,
  You'll find that guys that gathered the gelt
Was mainly weak when it come to looks,
  But terrible strong in the business belt!
Me, I'm for 'em! Give me 'em plain!
  Bury the cake-eaters deep in Lethe
(That means "fini"). I'll say it again—
  Gimme a plodder with three gold teeth!

Sparking
When I Was a Boy

by Chauncey M. Depew

New York's Ninety-Year-Old Ex-Senator
Is Sorry for the Boys of Today

THE OTHER DAY I saw a young whippersnapper driving along a country road in a high-powered contraption with eight cylinders. One hand was on the wheel. One arm was around a girl beside him.

"The young fools," gritted my companion. "Don't they know they're liable to run into something and be killed?"

"They won't," I responded, "Now, when I was young—"

But, by that time, the loving pair had disappeared down the broad highway. I did not put into words what I had intended saying. It would have taken my companion back into distant years . . . seventy-odd years to the days when I was a lad, sparking the girls.

The young fellows of today are handicapped. They have to keep one hand on the wheel of the automobile. We young squirts of yesterday took our girls out in the family buggies, tossed the reins over the dashboards, and started from scratch—with no handicaps.

Seventy-odd years ago——

We took the girls to church on Sunday evenings. We sat and we held hands while the minister was preaching. We made calf eyes at each other while singing the hymns, and after church it was a walk home in the moonlight, to the lilting accompaniment of croaking frogs and chirping crickets. If a girl liked a fellow in those days she invited him indoors after the walk; if she didn't, he took the shortcut home so the townspeople wouldn't see him and chuckle:

"Well, Mary gave Harry the mitten."

We didn't have dances, movies, theaters, and the other diversions which are now so commonplace. Those amusements of today were yesterday's wicked thoughts.

When I was a young squirt we had lecture courses. One week it would be Ralph Waldo Emerson; another week it would be Oliver Wendell Holmes, or Whittier, Longfellow, Bryant, or that famous old temperance lecturer, John B. Goff.

I recall one night when the young lady I thought to be the prettiest girl in Peekskill (that is, at that particular time I thought so, although, later, she faded in the sunlight of another's charms) was with me.

One of the city dudes from New York had come to Peekskill a few days previously. He also had become a pest to the village boys. City manners, city clothes, city ways, city small talk of the wicked opera. . . . Peekskill girls were crazy over him. What made me crazy was that he picked out my girl as a focus for his attentions. Being in charge of the lecture course that night, I was kept busy attending to details, and this city dude kept himself busy with my girl.

I had fully intended taking her home, but as I watched from a point of vantage I saw myself being hopelessly cut out. I saw the silly smirks of the other girls—intended for me—and the worded condolences of the village companions didn't help at all.

There I stood . . . miserable in jealousy and horror.

But it is out of the chaos of despondency that brilliant thoughts sometimes come.

My girl's father, like all old men, had a hobby. His hobby was in reciting his personal opinion as to the cause of Napoleon's defeat at Waterloo. The recitation of his personal findings always required an hour of patient listening. That is, if you didn't interrupt him. If you asked questions—heavens, it was an evening gone! I knew that from experience.

After the lecture I hastened to where a little group was standing—my girl, her father, and that city dude.

"By the way, Mr. S.," I offered, "have you ever told Mr. B. (indicating my city rival) of the real reason for Napoleon's defeat at Waterloo? I know he would be interested."

The old man's eyes sparkled.

"Really, now, Chauncey, I'm glad you reminded me of that. I don't believe I have taken up that matter with this young man. I'll do so. Step this way, sir, and you will learn something that will be of use to you."

He took my rival by the arm and led him aside. I took my girl by the arm and led her home.

I never saw him afterward. Guess he made up his mind that a country bumpkin wasn't so short on ideas after all.

Then there was boating on the Hudson. That was another place where we had it all over the youngster of today who takes his girl out in a motor boat. Today's youngster has a lot of things to worry about, to distract him. We young fellows in Peekskill, when I was a boy, just grabbed the family rowboat, shoved it out into the stream, and let her drift. Sometimes it drifted into matrimony.

As I recall it, I was well along into manhood before I really learned what oars were for.

Which just goes to show, as I said in the beginning, that boys and girls are always the same. The environment is different; that is all. Today the young fellow on the East Side takes his girl to a dance; the young fellow from Fifth Avenue takes his girl to a ball. The same thing—the East Side clinches and the West Side hugs. What's the difference?

Love - - - With a Dash of Whisky

a story by Royal Brown

A Tale of This Terrible Generation

ERRANT DAUGHTERS ARE no longer the topic of breathless interest they once were; people are now inclined to yawn when they are mentioned. Except, that is, the people who happen to have one in their home. Their mouths must continue to open.

Not soporifically, but in amazement, anger, and expostulation. As on this February afternoon Samuel Winslow's mouth opened.

It was not quite six; he had just run his personal car, referred to as "the Coop," into the Winslow garage. The other car was out, and so, Samuel Winslow surmised, his wife must be.

That, however, his daughter Phyllis—so baptized but for some obscure reason known to her intimates as Jigger—was at home, another car drawn up at the curb suggested.

This was a notable car. Across the back was scrawled the legend: "Positively last week."

"The Egg Beater" was the name Jigger had given it.

It was not her car. Which was why, perhaps, she felt no sense of shame, no worry about lost social prestige in riding about in it at any hour of the day or night.

The owner of the Egg Beater, according to his birth certificate, its license, and the collegiate rolls of Dartmouth from which he had recently been dropped, was Thomas Gaskill Jones.

Everybody, however, referred to him as Gas, and it was Samuel Winslow's grim impression that he was full of it.

"And nothing *but* gas," was the way he had summed it up to Jigger's mother at one o'clock in the morning just a week before.

"This," Samuel Winslow had informed his daughter at dinner, "is the fifth time you've been out this week. If you're not home at midnight—"

"The Egg Beater will turn into a pumpkin, I suppose," Jigger had suggested helpfully.

It had been a bad day in the stock market—Samuel Winslow was a broker.

"You heard what I said!" he had thundered.

"And so," she had commented, "did the neighbors, probably."

At two o'clock Jigger had yet to appear. At two minutes past two he had informed his wife that he was going to put his foot down.

At half past three a car had stopped outside.

Thereupon, grim visaged, Jigger's father had risen, scuffed his feet into bed slippers, donned his bathrobe, and departed downstairs.

The Egg Beater was parked at the curb and its occupants were parked therein.

This much Jigger's father had seen through one of the little diamond-paned windows that flanked the door. He had stood there, balked.

No matter how irate a man may be, he does not, unless he has taken all leave of his senses, venture outdoors of a chill February morning in bathrobe and slippers.

It was a quarter to four when Jigger tripped lightly up the steps. The door was opened to her, swiftly, explosively.

"Well?" he had said in the voice of Jehovah.

She had remained unperturbed. "Service at all hours," she had commented.

He had slammed the door. "Didn't I tell you to be home at midnight?" he had demanded.

"We went for a ride after the dance," she had explained, in a tone that suggested that he was a querulous child to be humored. "And then a tire blew, twenty miles from nowhere, and the Egg Beater carries no life buoys, you know. We came home on a flat and—"

She had yawned, letting her cloak slip from her slim shoulders. Her frock, the propriety of which her father had challenged without avail, was rumpled and one of the shoulder straps needed readjustment.

She attended to that while her eyes met his, cool and unabashed.

"Have you any idea what time it is?" he had demanded, savagely sarcastic. "It's a quarter to four and—"

"Time we were both abed," she had inserted deftly. "I'm on my way—"

"One minute!" he had commanded, as she had retrieved her coat.

Her lips were flagrantly scarlet, but her teeth were pretty. They and her hair were her best points. Especially her hair, a bright chestnut with some red in it.

She was not beautiful, merely lithe, vividly alive, and clear-eyed. She was only nineteen, yet he had felt a little afraid of her.

He had made it clear, nevertheless, that Gas was everything that no father cared to see striving to monopolize the attention of his daughter and that the time had come to—

"To give him the gate?" Jigger had suggested. She had grinned up at him and then added serenely, "Well, I have. And the box hedge and the key to the nearest exit of the city."

He had stared at her. "What?" he had gasped.

"You see," Jigger had explained, "he wants to marry me. Imagine!"

"Marry you!" he had exploded. "Marry you—"

"Oh, good gosh—why have apoplexy?" Jigger had protested. "I told him myself he was all wet. I haven't any intention of marrying, thank you—"

"I should hope not!" her father had remarked. And had added, "He'll be around tomorrow—"

"Probably," she had conceded, "but I won't be. We'll give James orders to tell him I'm 'not at 'ome'!"

Her father had stared at her slightly goggle-eyed. The interview had not gone at all as he had expected.

To his wife he had given only a censored report of it.

"She's at least got sense enough to see that he's all gas," he had grunted.

Yet here, precisely a week later, was the Egg Beater again.

Samuel Winslow entered the house. From the rear came sounds that indicated dinner was being prepared; from a room off the hall that had once been known as his den came a light.

Thither Jigger's father turned his steps. He reached the threshold and stopped.

The chair in which he read his evening papers was occupied. Doubly so. Jigger was there, unquestionably, though his impression of her consisted mainly of slim extremities sheathed in silk and shamelessly exposed as she snuggled against him on whose lap she sat. Their lips were joined; had been joined for some time, he suspected.

"Well!" he exploded.

They did not jump guiltily. Jigger merely raised a tousled head, turned a rosy face toward her father, and blinked twice.

"Oh—hello!" she said cordially. "It's all right; we're going to be married."

"Married!" His head reeled. "But you said—"

"Oh, I changed my mind," cut in Jigger coolly.

Gas remained seated, which was unpardonable perhaps, but not inexplicable, inasmuch as Jigger was still in his lap. Samuel Winslow glared at her.

"May I ask what you propose to get married on?" he demanded, savagely sarcastic.

"Oh, I'm going to get a job," Gas informed him promptly.

"You! You'd be lucky if you got eighteen dollars a week. You aren't in any position to marry—won't be for years. Unless"—contemptuously—"you expect me—or your father—to support you. And I, at least, won't. That's flat and final.

"It certainly sounds so," agreed Gas equably.

His eyes met Jigger's and then, swiftly, he gave her a kiss and set her on her feet as he came to his.

He was an attractive youngster, clear-eyed and ever so well poised. But these attributes, though they might weigh heavily with Jigger, failed to impress her father.

"No man with a spark of decency in him," he blazed anew, "would ask a girl to marry him until—"

"Oh, I asked *him* this time," Jigger informed him frankly.

"You—you asked him!" stuttered her father.

"I knew he wanted to, of course, and—well, we're not asking anybody's consent, anyway. It's a matter that concerns only us, you see. Gas will get a job and so will I—"

"You? What on earth can you do?"

"I don't know—but I'll find something. Want to make a bet on it?"

He didn't, somehow. Instead, "I may," he evaded, "be old-fashioned. But my idea of marriage was a home where—"

"The lord of creation is attended by a female slave who ministers to his every whim and keeps the children quiet? Well, *that's* not mine. I expect to be ministered to, and we won't be able to afford children for a while, anyway. You see, we're going in for companionate marriage—at the first, anyway," added Jigger.

About companionate marriage he knew nothing save that the very term was an affront to him. He preferred, however, not to discuss it with his daughter. Her penchant for abysmal frankness frightened him.

Instead, "Nobody except a pair of idiots would consider getting married without any money or any prospects," he began, and was again interrupted.

"Oh, Gas has two thousand his grandmother left him," Jigger informed him.

"I know it's not much," Gas apologized, "but I had an idea that with the stock market as it is now I might take a little flier and run it up a bit. If you happen to know of anything hot—"

To Samuel Winslow nothing could have pointed Gas' utter worthlessness more than this casual assumption that he could make money effortlessly in the stock market.

"The best thing you can do with your two thousand," he replied, savagely sarcastic, "is to buy yourself a decent car. Then take what is left and buy—whisky."

"Whisky?" echoed Gas, puzzled. "What stock—"

But that, so far as Jigger's father was concerned, was his exit line.

There was one recourse left to him. The inevitable recourse of any married man, that is. To find his wife and do his best to give her a bad quarter of an hour.

She sat at her dressing table in their room—a slim attractive promise of what Jigger might hope to be at forty—while he raged.

"If you had kept your eye on her, done your duty as a mother—"

"Oh, Sam—don't be ridiculous!" she protested there. "Jigger is no worse than most girls of her age. In fact, I think she's better—"

"Better! She has no respect for anybody or anything—"

"Well, that's the spirit of the times. And she's not unreasonable—"

"Do you call getting married at nineteen reasonable?"

"From the standpoint of biology it's perfectly reasonable. From that of economics, of course, it isn't. I'll speak to her, of course—"

"I wish you luck," he flung at her grimly.

With that he stalked to the bathroom. Jigger's mother smiled faintly as she freshened her hair. She ached to spank Jigger at times. But then, she also ached to spank Jigger's father.

After dinner Jigger went straight to her room, where her mother found her pulling her hat down over her ears.

"I suppose Father has been at you," suggested Jigger sympathetically. And wrinkling her impudent, inadequate nose added, "Aren't you ashamed of yourself, bringing up a daughter like me?"

Ann Winslow smiled. At least they could talk this way.

"Going to meet Gas?" she asked equably.

Jigger nodded. "And get the latest bulletin from his sector," she explained. "I suspect he's been having another scene with his father. What makes the paternal male so absolutely impossible, Ann?"

"Well—if you and Gas get married you *will* have an economic problem to face and—"

Jigger paused in the application of a lipstick to lips already too scarlet.

"As if *we* didn't know that" she commented scornfully. "Why don't they help—instead of howling their heads off? Oh, I know Father couldn't—much. But Gas's father could some."

"But that," ventured Ann temperately, "would make it a bit too easy for Gas, wouldn't it? Life isn't exactly easy —nor is marriage, Jigger. I do think Gas ought to show some signs of being able to take care of you—"

"I'll see to that," Jigger promised her definitely. She grinned at her mother unexpectedly, deliciously. "I'll make a man of him yet, Ann."

"I know I haven't been asked to advise you, Jigger, but I'd hate, naturally, to have you make a mistake—"

"Well, if I do it's my mistake," Jigger reminded her philosophically. "At the worst, it wouldn't prove fatal, anyway."

And there spoke this amazing generation, Ann realized. What could one say?

"What made you change your mind about Gas, anyway?" was what she did say.

"Pure jealousy," confessed Jigger unconcernedly. "Sally Stimson went after him the moment I dropped him and— well, I wasn't so darned sure she wouldn't get him. The idea of that didn't appeal to me at all, so I hauled him back. For better or worse—but I won't tell him *that* for a while."

A horn sounded outside.

"There's Gas now," announced Jigger, snatching up her coat and planting a swift kiss on her mother's mouth before adding, "I leave you to your sins—you really should have brought Father up better."

And off she went. To keep her date with Gas—and destiny.

To Gas she was saying a few minutes later, "I suppose fathers just can't help acting that way. What else did yours say?"

Gas grinned. "Plenty," he assured her, edging the Egg Beater by the car ahead. "He was in good voice and his delivery was excellent. I thought when I came home after being chucked from Dartmouth he had established a record. But I was wrong—all wrong. He surpassed himself tonight. Especially when I suggested he come across with some cash. I guess it's the help wanted columns for yours truly."

"It would have been that too, anyway, you know," Jigger reminded him. "We expected—"

Her voice trailed off as, impulsively, she snuggled up to him. They had reached the open road with the Egg Beater's uncertain headlights piercing the chill February night.

"Let's park—and give the neighbors something to talk about," she suggested shamelessly.

His eyes met hers and the Egg Beater seemed permeated with magic and mystery. Then it shook from stem to stern as the brakes were applied.

"Oh, Jigger," he breathed huskily, hungrily, as he swept her quiescence into his arms. "I guess I'm pretty much of a washout. But if you'll stick—"

"Of course I'll stick," Jigger promised staunchly and lifted eager lips to his.

Eleven o'clock, however, found the Egg Beater back at Jigger's home.

"You've got to get to bed early from now on, you see," she had informed him. "You're out for a job, and bright and early does it."

It was Jigger who got a job first.

"I'm to start Monday," she pealed when Gas arrived next evening. "I'm a model—a perfect sixteen. Twenty a week just for dressing up in the slickest clothes ever. Oh, Gas—"

She broke off there. The Egg Beater—where was the Egg Beater? The car parked at the curb was new and gleaming, one of those spiffy affairs, black, with a collapsible coupé top.

"Good gracious!" she gasped. "Where did you get that?"

"I bought it," he confessed. "I suppose I shouldn't have, but a chap I know is selling them. I dropped in to see if he knew of a job in his line and he didn't. But he gave me a ride in one of these and—get in and I'll demonstrate it to you."

Jigger got in, still a bit stunned.

"Didn't—didn't it cost an awful lot?" she asked.

"They allowed me a hundred on the Egg Beater and I paid a thousand down," he explained. "I—close your eyes, Jigger, and tell me how fast we're going?"

Jigger obeyed. "Thirty," she hazarded after a moment.

"Fifty-seven!" he told her triumphantly, and he was like a small boy, but an exultant one. "That got me. I was driving fifty-five before I realized it. It's got eight cylinders, you see, and—do you like it, Jigger?"

Jigger hesitated. But only for a second. So swiftly she had learned the first lesson that every woman must. And that is that all men, at all ages, are apt to surrender to the eternal boy in them at unexpected moments.

"I love it," she assured him.

"Don't you think it will make a wonderful honeymoon car, Jigger? I could just see you in it!"

Her eyes met his; a little thrill ran through them both. Why worry? That had always been Jigger's slogan and—

"Oh, by the way," he broke out. "I took your father's tip and bought whisky too.

"Went down to see a chap in the stock market about a job—I have been trying hard, Jigger, to land something—and asked him about it. Whisky is the board room name for National Distillers. He said it was a good buy and so I bought a thousand dollars' worth on margin."

Jigger could not credit it. Did he—did he really think her father had meant to give him a tip? *She* certainly didn't. She started to tell him so and then changed her mind. Jigger was learning fast this evening.

"Supposing it—should go down," she suggested.

"It can't very much—not from seventeen," he retorted cheerfully. And added, "This car handles one-hand beautifully too!"

And he proved it.

Nevertheless, Jigger returned to her home that night feeling like a wiser if not older girl. She was ready to admit, at least to herself, that there was more to this life and marriage proposition than she had anticipated.

The advent of March—a mild, guileless March this year—did at least find things a bit better. Whisky had not slumped; it had, in fact, risen a bit. But Gas stubbornly refused to sell. Even though Jigger, forced to it, told him that her father hadn't really meant it as a tip.

Gas grinned. "I suspected as much," he assured her calmly. "But the chap I asked about it said it had possibilities and I thought it would be a darned good one on your father if I did clean up a bit that way."

March also found Gas selling bonds. Every morning he drove Jigger to work. Every evening he drove her home again. They even lunched together whenever they could. It was like marriage in many ways—only it wasn't marriage at all.

"When we are married," had been a phrase familiar to their lips, at first.

As the weeks passed, with March giving way to April and April in turn surrendering to May, they talked less and less about marriage. Not because they, as their elders hoped, were getting over all this confounded nonsense, but because even their youth was not proof against a growing sense of what they confronted.

In June the salon through which Jigger had moved daily became almost deserted and one day the blow fell.

"And of course I was the last to come and so am the first to go," she explained to Gas. "They were very nice about it, said they hoped I'd come back in September—"

"They didn't even tell *me that*," broke in Gas abruptly.

"Oh, Gas!" she wailed. "You don't mean—"

"Oh, they were decent enough. Said they thought I was a bit young and probably didn't inspire confidence in prospects. The truth is"—his voice became savage—"that they had everything to gain and nothing to lose. If I'd sold more than enough to keep me in gas I'd have been a miracle man."

The Egg Beater's successor was waiting at the moment at the junction of Tremont and Boylston streets for the traffic officer's signal.

As it came, the car slipped out ahead and Gas added grimly, "They're after me for the installment due on the car, too—I suppose they'll be taking that away next."

"Oh, Gas!" she protested. "They wouldn't. Why—why, you practically sold two cars for them!"

This was true. Next to her, Gas loved his car more than anything on earth. He was forever puttering around it; always welcomed a chance to demonstrate it to his friends. Hence the two sales she spoke of.

She couldn't, wouldn't have Gas deprived of his beloved car. "What's Whisky selling at now?" she asked abruptly.

The stock had been the one thing that had not failed them. It had mounted steadily. Gas had 250 shares on margin, so each added point meant—miraculously enough—$250 profit.

"Forty-eight," he replied briefly.

"Forty-eight. Then you've made—"

"About seventy-five hundred net," he computed, but with no enthusiasm.

"Gas dear—why couldn't you sell—well, just enough to pay for the car, anyway?" she pleaded.

But his clean-cut young profile simply set stubbornly. "Nothing doing! That's the only luck we've had and—I'm not going to touch it. If—well, if I can't earn enough to even pay my own way, what's the use, Jigger?"

Jigger's heart missed a beat. "You mean—about everything?" she asked.

"I mean—about everything," he replied. With an effort, through his teeth.

Jigger sat very still for a second while Gas threaded his way through the traffic. Then:

"Oh, very well," she said airily. "Too bad. I—I haven't even a ring to give back to you."

It was cruel and she knew it. He hadn't given her a ring simply because she had assured him he couldn't

afford it and she didn't care. But now he had hurt her—hurt her horribly. And she had to strike back.

They exchanged not a single word through the rest of the trip. But as the car stopped in front of her house Gas faced her.

"Jigger," he began desperately, "you must know that—"

But Jigger shot out of the car without a word, marched into the house and, encountering her mother in the hall, removed her hat from her bright head and said, coolly enough:

"This has been a large day. I've lost my job, Gas has lost his, and—we've decided that marriage is permanently out."

Ann gave her daughter a swift glance. One might have believed that she was as unconcerned as she seemed. But Ann suspected otherwise.

It was five weeks to a day when Gas reappeared. Ann let him in, her first swift surprise dissolving into sincere cordiality.

Jigger might try to fool the world with her hard-eyed, brilliant-surfaced gayety, but she could not fool her mother. She called for Jigger.

"Oh," said Jigger to Gas coldly, "I—I see you still have your car."

"Why is it," thought Ann, "that a woman can always hide her emotions so much better than a man?"

The lines of his young mouth were so tense, his eyes so obviously hungry. Nevertheless, his voice at least matched Jigger's.

"Oh, yes," he said, "I took your tip and—"

"My tip?" echoed Jigger uncertainly.

"And told them I'd bring a customer in if they'd credit me with the amount due on the installment. I had a hunch I could land the order—a man I'd tried to sell a bond to had been a darned sight more interested in the car. And I did land him—thanks to you—"

"Oh, don't mention it," suggested Jigger, but not quite so coldly.

They stood so, neither quite meeting the other's eyes. Then:

"And—and I've got another job," he announced impetuously.

"Another job?" repeated Jigger, quite forgetting to keep her voice cold.

"It's—it's not much of a job," he confessed. "It's just—selling vacuum cleaners." He hesitated for an instant before adding, "House to house, you know—"

He grinned a bit uncertainly, looking absurdly like a very small boy.

Jigger slanted a glance up at him. She didn't care what he did, what he sold. And yet:

"I should think you'd sort of hate—" she began and hesitated.

"Breezing into a house?" he hazarded. "Oh, that's what they call the wrong mental attitude. We are trained to call ourselves"—he grimaced slightly—"household efficiency experts. We carry the gospel of efficient cleanliness to still darkened places, you see, and—want a demonstration?"

Jigger nodded.

"Wait a jiff—I'll get the cleaner," he promised, and disappeared through the screen door.

A moment later he reappeared. "Madam," he began, "I—

But she never got *that* demonstration. The cleaner fell from his hands as he opened his arms and gathered her in.

"Oh, Jigger!" he murmured desperately. "I've been through hell!"

"So have I—you didn't even write," she all but sobbed. "I—"

They were again in her father's chair when her father arrived home. The vacuum cleaner lay where Gas had let it fall, as Samuel Winslow discovered, coming out of the bright sunshine into the comparative murk of the hall.

"Blank, dash, and sixteen asterisks," announced he, in effect, as he rubbed his shin. "What's this blankety-blank thing doing here, anyway?"

Jigger appeared to explain. A soft-mouthed, starry-eyed Jigger who, on the finger so reserved for the purpose, wore an engagement ring.

"I made up my mind I'd never see you again until I got you one—and out of money I'd earned," Gas had told her as he slipped it on and kissed the finger.

"You were darned sure of me, weren't you?" she suggested.

"No, I wasn't," he confessed. "Anything but."

"Well, you should have been!" she announced impulsively. "I—oh, Gas!"

The engagement ring failed to impress her father and Gas' new occupation impressed him even less. And that, apparently, went double for Gas' father.

"He's all but chucked me out," confessed Gas as they rode through the heady dusk that same night. "He seems to think I ought to be doing something better than peddling—that's what he calls it. But when I ask him what, the best he can offer is to go back to college and—"

"Don't—don't you think perhaps you ought to?" asked Jigger, but with no enthusiasm.

He drew her to him swiftly. "And wait four years—perhaps six if I go into law and in with the governor!" he said. "Never!"

He meant, of course, that he wasn't willing to face the prospect of waiting that long before marrying her. And yet he had no intention of marrying her now or even in the immediate future.

This terrible generation, as personified by Gas and Jigger, discussed that too, this July night.

"I want you like the devil," he confessed, his eyes, his face, and every last atom of him corroborating the words. "But—until I've got something to offer, something worth while—"

"You've still got Whisky, haven't you?" she asked. And, realizing from his expression that he had, went on with: "See where it sold today?"

He nodded, but soberly.

"You dead fish!" she protested. "I should think that—"

"That's luck—not me!" he maintained stubbornly. "I can't seem to get a kick out of it. I'd give every last cent of it for—well, for a good job and you."

"You've got *me*, anyway," she reminded him. "And you'll get a good job yet—something is bound to happen. I—I feel it in my bones that something is going to."

This was not quite true. But Jigger was still learning. After a girl got her man she also had to keep him bucked up. And from that will to help, perhaps, is where women get their reputation for intuition.

Because something did happen. Gas had said he would be around just after dinner the next night, but eight o'clock came and passed. She couldn't imagine what had happened. Just before nine as the July twilight was setting in, he came.

"You," he announced exultantly, "have some bones!"

To Jigger, naturally, that meant nothing. Save that something had happened.

"Let's go for a ride—I'll tell you all about it," he added.

The headlights pierced the growing murk, the road unreeled before them. Gas took a deep breath.

"This," he began, "is going to be a long story. I started out this morning as usual, but everything went dead wrong. I had just had the third door in succession slammed in my face and had gone back to the car. I found an old codger there looking it over."

He paused, let his eyes meet hers. But she was breathless with interest.

"He asked me forty-eleven questions and I invited him to take a spin," he went on. "Well—to make a long story short, he was thinking of buying a car for his granddaughter and I sold it to him."

Jigger felt let down. "You mean—you mean you've got another commission," she suggested, trying to make her voice match his for enthusiasm but not quite succeeding. She had, somehow, hoped for something more.

"No—that's only the beginning. The old codger asked me a million questions or so. About vacuum cleaners and how I liked to sell them and things like that—the way old people do, you know. I told him I gave no three cheers for that job and he said right off to chuck it; that it was no use trying to do something I hated. I said that sounded fine but that I had to do something and—"

He took another deep breath. "Then," added Gas, "he asked how I'd like to go partners with him—just like that!"

"Partners?" echoed Jigger, bewildered.

"He's retired—and darned near eighty, I guess," said Gas. "One of those old boys whose family tell them it's time to give up business and enjoy life. He quit two years ago and he doesn't know what to do with himself. He's got all the money he needs but he wants some excitement. A place he can drop into and look over the books and see how things are going. He'll be sort of a sleeping partner, you see—"

"Sleeping partner?" echoed Jigger, uncertainly.

"Oh, that's what they call men who put in capital but don't take an active part in the concern. Although I have a hunch *he* will, at that. You ought to see the old boy move today after we once got started."

"But you haven't told me yet what you're going to do!" protested Jigger.

"Gosh—so I haven't," realized Gas. He grinned exultantly. "I'm going to start selling cars—this car."

Jigger blinked. Then: "Why—why, that is what you should have been doing all the time!" she gasped. "Why—you have been doing it without half trying. You're such a kid about it, so full of enthusiasm that—"

"That's what *he* said," corroborated Gas.

"He—he won't change his mind?" suggested Jigger, fearfully.

"Change his mind?" echoed Gas. "We have already bought an exclusive territory franchise, signed up a combination garage and show room—wait until you see that, Jigger! He wanted the whole thing sewed up before his family got wind of it, you see. He's about the shrewdest old boy you ever met. He wouldn't have gone on with it unless I had some capital. Said every young man ought to have some capital—"

"Capital? Where did you get the capital?" demanded Jigger.

"Whisky—sold that too today," Gas explained. "Oh, I told him the truth—where the capital came from. I thought for a moment he was going to back out, but he didn't. He just said I seemed to be a fool for luck and he hoped it would continue—"

"You aren't a fool at all," protested Jigger vehemently. "You're—"

He kissed her, swiftly. "I am," he assured her huskily. "The luckiest fool for luck that ever happened. Because if I hadn't gotten you I *would* have been a washout. I—oh, Jigger, I'll make it up to you. I'll work like the devil now."

He paused, his eyes trying to fathom something in hers. "What are you thinking of now?" he demanded.

"That—that it's not considered so very swell to get married in August," she informed him, being nothing if not frank. "But perhaps if *you* wanted to, too—a lot, I—"

He all but crushed the life out of her.

Nevertheless she seemed quite recovered—very much her usual self save for the starry, irrepressible triumph in her eyes—when she returned home that night. She saw that her father was still up, hesitated a second, and then paused to speak to him.

"Oh, by the way," she announced. "Much obliged for the advice you gave Gas."

"What advice?" he asked suspiciously.

"About buying a car—and investing the rest in Whisky," she explained airily. "It worked out rather well, you know."

He knew, at least, where Whisky was selling now. But:

"What's the car got to do with it?" he asked.

Jigger was leading up to that. She had come into the house feeling victorious. But now, suddenly she reconsidered, stopped and kissed the tip of his nose.

"I'll bet you love me in your way—even if it is a darned funny way," was all she said.

The next instant she was gone, leaving him to ponder once more on this inexplicable generation.

"What is she up to now?" he wondered.

He was without a clue. This generation was so different—

But Jigger's mother, at least, was glimpsing the truth. Jigger had burst into her room as she sat, in negligee, preparing for bed. She flung her arms around her mother.

"Oh, Ann!" she peaned. "We're going to get married. In August. I—Oh, if you only knew how I felt! How happy—"

She dropped swiftly to her knees, buried her bright head in her mother's lap. And her mother, patting her head softly, smiled—the faintest, tender curving of her flexible lips.

As if she, Ann Winslow, didn't know! As if she didn't realize that no generation could so conduct—or misconduct—itself as to escape the eternal, changeless rhythm of life.

And—love.

Lenin

by Maxim Gorky

MAXIM GORKY LIVES now in Capri and he came to Rome for a few days. There he gave this interview.

"It is no longer a secret to anyone," said Gorky, "that I am at present in opposition to the present rulers of my native land. It is known that I left them for good.

"Since I am taking advantage of the hospitality of a foreign country, I am away from politics and I am following the fate of my homeland from far away. What I will say here does not concern any political sphere, but I think it will explain some matters in this sphere. If Bolshevism was born in Russia or if Fascism found a fertile soil in Italy, it happened just because there were deep psychological roots there. These roots are not noticed by the European eye, just as many have not noticed them who are prophesying in the shadow of trees not grown of these roots. Those Russians who consider Lenin only from the viewpoint of Bolshevism, do not understand the sense of his appearance in the national arena. The true meaning of Lenin must be looked for in different spheres and if we would find it, we would have to consider it from a viewpoint of a great Oriental revolution.

"Russia is a country of pessimism. Life was never easy there. The future always seemed hopeless and the present always sad. Troubles, suffering, poverty, persecution, drunkenness, drunken speeches, and prison. The one who was not at least once exiled into Siberia was not a real Russian.

"Literature is always a true picture of a peoples' souls. On the palettes of Dostoevski, Turgenev, Goncharov, Tolstoy, and Andreieff, we find its saddest colors. Their works are full of tears and complaints. They write about death and the filth of life, of its privations and atrocities. All of them are pessimists. If one of the Russian writers happens to write a comedy, it always culminates with a tragedy. A smile reminds one of a bitter grimace. No one ever laughed in Russia with a sane, happy laugh.

"Russia has not produced a poet or a philosopher who could, with soulful clearness, present life to people. There has not been a writer yet who dared to speak in the tones of happiness and who dared to be optimistic. If such a man were to come, everyone would follow him.

"And he came. This was Lenin. There appeared a man who had the courage to laugh. He actually did not laugh, but he embodied in himself hope; in the reign of curses, he spoke of life. He had an optimist's philosophy. I shall call it a 'belligerent' philosophy. He was the only brave man in Russia, daring and powerful, and he brought hope and promise and spread optimism everywhere. But he himself never laughed. I knew him and I was very close to him. But I never saw a man who suffered as he did.

"We became enemies. We always had differences of opinion. Now, that he is dead, I can say that never before nor ever in the future, will I love and respect a man as deeply as I did him. But never did I fight anyone as I fought him. Lenin turned the reins of power into the hands of the people. This I did not want.

"I knew that a Russian peasant is illiterate, brutal, uncultured, and cannot rule. Lenin took away the reins of power from the hands of the intelligentsia and the educated industrial class, and turned it over to those who are only now awakening from a brutal state, to those who did not participate in the slightest way in the creation of new Russia, and to those who were and still remain uncultured.

"This was a big point on which our ways parted. But no matter how bad this policy was, its possible consequences are that Lenin has awakened Russia from a dead stupor. In this 'belligerent' optimism consists the actual meaning of Lenin. This was the only thing that could have saved my native land.

"But this 'belligerent' optimism in Russia means more than Bolshevism in Europe. Bolshevism as a political formula has deep psychological roots in Russia, but without roots, there cannot be any flowers. I am not Italian and I cannot feel from what the political roots of Fascism are derived. But I know that Mussolini, who reminds me of Lenin, could not descend from the Roman forum to England and France and call for his departed ancestors.

"Therefore, those who would imitate Bolshevism, Fascism, and other similar ideas, must find, first of all, their meaning."

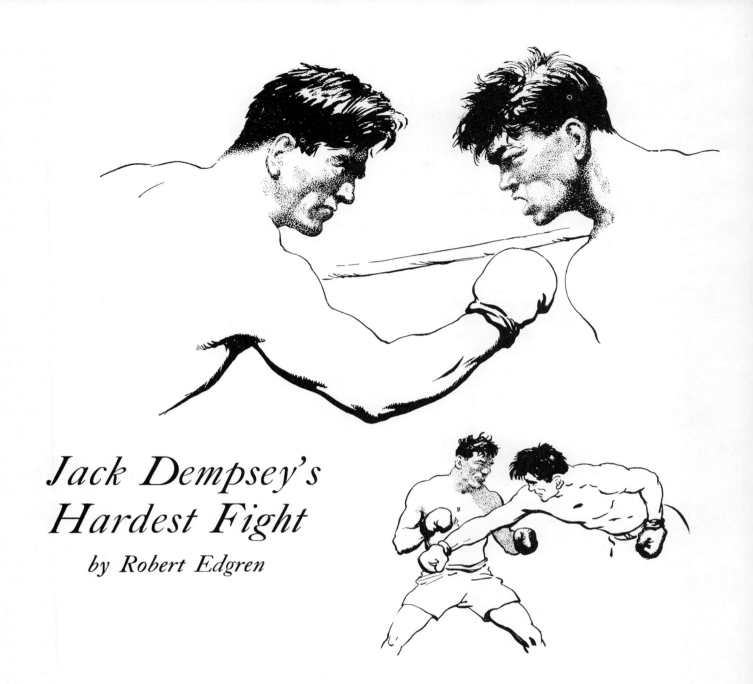

Jack Dempsey's Hardest Fight

by Robert Edgren

Jack Dempsey Tells His Intimate Sensations During One of the Roughest Periods in His Career—When His Million Dollar Championship Hung by a Slender Thread

"YES," SAID JACK DEMPSEY, "you can say the Firpo fight was my hardest. But use your own judgment. They're all hard when the other fellow manages to pop you on the button. The only easy fight is where you walk out and let one punch go and the bird in front of you hits the floor and stretches out for a ten count the way Carl Morris did at New Orleans. Sometimes you hit the other fellow and think it's all over, and then he lands on you like a ton of coal tossed off a skyscraper in a piano case. That's what makes fighting tough.

"You never know what will happen until they ring the last gong.

"There was that fight at Toledo when I won the championship. In the second round poor Jess Willard was a sight. He was all beaten up like an egg, and he wouldn't quit. I was just thinking it was tough, but I'd have to finish

29

him, when I saw his right arm coming up slowly, like the walking beam on a ferryboat engine. I didn't even take the trouble to dodge.

"That big glove landed on my chin and nearly took my head off. It was the heaviest punch I ever felt. Like running into the edge of a big oak door in the dark. For about ten seconds I was so bad Jess could have knocked me for a loop if he'd had anything left. Of course, he was too far gone.

"This Firpo fight, now—if coming within an eyelash of being knocked out of a title worth a couple of million dollars makes a fight hard, I'll admit Luis handed me the marble-lined chocolate drops.

"Did you know I was knocked out in that fight, by the first punch? Well, I was. That is, my head was knocked out, but my legs weren't. They're all that saved me. The old bean was out for maybe half a minute, but the old legs kept traveling around under me, and the old arms kept working instinctively, until Luis was on the floor.

"The first thing I remember after that punch is Luis rolling over and me hunting a corner. I looked at the pictures next day, and I had to sit there and laugh at myself. There was a lot of fighting in those pictures that I didn't know anything about. It was like some other guy fighting—some guy who looked like me—my double.

"I did two months' road work before I met Firpo. If Firpo had done two months of road work, the kind I did, he might have won the championship of the world. We were both down a few times. My legs bounced me right up again. Firpo's legs didn't have any bounce in them. He got up so slowly I could move half across the ring to get at him before he was set to hit.

"That was the main difference between us, although, of course, there were other things. But my good legs saved me the title, and believe me they're going to get good treatment any time I ever train for another battle.

"You remember," Dempsey went on, "one day up at Saratoga before the fight when we sat down and talked it over, and I told you how I spent a couple of hours every day thinking up everything that could possibly happen and figuring what to do if it did happen? I must have had all that stored in my subconscious mind, where it wasn't knocked out of me, and that's what won the fight.

"My plans worked out even when I didn't know what I was doing. Down inside me something was pushing the right buttons just the way I'd planned to push them if Firpo happened to land on me and knock me woozy. It was that and my legs.

"I train the same way for every fight, whether I'm going to meet a champion or a dub. I did two months of road work for Firpo. When I'm knocked out some day it isn't going to be because I wasn't in shape. The other fellow is going to be better than I am, that's all.

"What you want is my mental picture of my hardest fight. Is that it? Well, I'll tell you; it isn't much of a picture. The beginning is clear and the end is clear, but the middle is just a fog. Before the fight, in the afternoon, I was down along Riverside Drive, in New York City, playing on the grass with a lot of kids. I wasn't any more nervous about the fight than I would have been over shooting a squirrel with a buffalo gun.

"My plans were all made. I intended to watch Firpo's right hand like a hawk—watch his left hand, too. I was going to move fast, feint, and make him miss. Then when he'd missed me a few times and was floundering and leaving a good, clean opening you could toss a flower pot through—sock!—right on the button! Doc Kearns had it figured I couldn't miss getting him in the first round if I didn't slip on a banana peel and break my leg, and you know how Doc picks 'em.

"I got up there in the ring, and the crowd didn't bother me half as much as two waiters at my table during lunch. I'm getting used to crowds. I was sitting there looking over at Firpo and wondering whether he'd rush me at the start or wait for me to come to him when I began to notice something. I didn't get it at first. There was a lot of yelling and cheering and crowd noises and telegraph instruments going, and all that sort of thing, same as usual.

"Then, all of a sudden, it struck me. I wasn't being razzed. Nobody at all razzed me. Nobody in all that crowd! They weren't yelling at me; they were yelling for me. For the first time since Toledo I had all the crowd with me. Not like Jersey City, where a lot of people wanted the Frenchman to knock me dead, or Shelby, where I half expected some nut to take a shot at me.

"Then Joe Humphreys gave me that fine introduction, and the crowd yelled so all I could hear was the air shaking, like being under Niagara Falls. Then I got it. I wasn't only Jack Dempsey fighting for a lot of money. I was an American defending a title and I had to make good.

"Funny, that cheer nearly got me licked. If I'd been razzed, being used to that, I'd have gone out thinking of nothing but Jack Dempsey's own private interests and how to make Firpo miss a couple of times and leave the opening I wanted. Now I forgot my plans and decided to make good for that cheer by knocking Firpo out with the first punch. The first punch! Get that!

"I leaned over and looked for Firpo's softest spot and figured how to sock him there with the first sock.

"The bell rang. Firpo got up and started toward me, slowly. I was, maybe, two steps from Luis when I saw his arm raised too high and his body left wide open—a mark like a barn door. I could see the edge of his ribs bordering the old solar plexus Fitz discovered—the surest knock-out spot there is. Hit 'em on the jaw and they may get up and crown you, but hit 'em in the pit of the stomach, right, and they stay where they drop.

"I jumped in to get Firpo before he could lower his guard.

"I threw everything from my shoestrings up into a left hook.

"I missed.

"Something smacked me, from somewhere. I felt my knees hit the floor and kind of bounce. No, I didn't slip that first time. I was knocked down. That's where I told you my head was knocked out and my legs weren't. I saw in the pictures afterward that I bounced up against him and went on fighting. But if you want to tell about that you'll have to do it yourself. What I remember is nothing—just nothing at all—a blank.

"Next I knew I was looking through a thick fog and Firpo was on the floor. I can't remember how many times he went down—seven, they say—but I know it was more than once, because I saw him on his stomach, and rolling on his back, and on his hands and knees—all different pictures—through the fog.

"I heard the referee telling me to go to my corner, and the ring was spinning around so fast I'd dive for the first corner I saw and grab the ropes to steady myself, and look for Doc Kearns. Only once I saw a flat, white face, kind of hazy, through the ropes, and I knew that was Doc, but I couldn't get any message over. And then I was fighting again.

"I don't remember when Firpo knocked me down the second time. I remember I felt the ropes against my back, and I was ducking punches, and I knew Firpo was throwing them at me, but the fog was so thick I couldn't see him. The fog, of course, was just local, you might say. I got that way from being socked. But I guess Luis Angel wasn't much better off.

"I didn't feel the punch that knocked me out of the ring. It must have been half a push, for if I'd been hit right with a snappy blow I'd never have been able to climb back. I felt the back of my head hit something. Luckily, it wasn't a typewriter.

"Then the fog turned black and a big yellow glow came through it, like the sun rising over a mountain ridge and shining down into a deep canyon. Then two black lines came across the sun, and all of a sudden I knew they were the ropes and the sun was the overhead picture lights, and the big black blur that moved between me and the sun was Firpo looking down on me, and I'd been knocked out of the ring and had to hustle fast to get back in there in time to win.

"So I grabbed something and scrambled up and slid through the ropes and away while Firpo was punching at me. My head was clearing and the fog half lifted, but I couldn't see him very plainly. I saw his punches coming, slow, slow, and thought I was swaying, fast and clever, getting away from them, but he kept pushing me back and I couldn't stop and stand against him. That made me mad. I felt the strength coming back into my arms and hooked him a good one that jarred my shoulder.

"I drop something there, because the next thing I remember I had an awful whiff of the smelling salts that nearly took the top off my head, and half jumped out of my chair and found I was sitting in my corner. Doc Kearns was talking to me.

" 'You're slipping, Jack; you're slipping. Go get him,' Doc said.

"So I knew something serious must have happened, to worry Doc. Then my head was clear and it was just like starting the fight again. That ends the story."

"Well, go on," I said to Dempsey. "Give us your picture of the second round. There was a second round, you know."

"O, that," said Dempsey indifferently. "I just went back to my original plan; made him miss, and knocked him out. I ought to have done it the first time."

To Succeed, Be Enthusiastic

by Hugh Fullerton

So Say the Men Who Have Made Their Mark

"WHAT," I ASKED Colonel E. E. Arison, efficiency engineer, who in the last twenty-five years has taken thousands of industries apart and hunted through their works to locate trouble, "is the greatest cause of failure of workers?"

"Lack of enthusiasm," he replied instantly.

"What," I inquired of William Wrigley, Jr., the chewing-gum maker, "is the greatest asset of a business man?"

"Enthusiasm," he answered without hesitation.

"What," I asked Otis A. Glazebrook, Jr., president of the American Thermos Bottle Company and half a dozen other corporations, "is the best qualification for success a young man may have?"

"Enthusiasm," he said.

"Enthusiasm," said Col. Arison, "is based on faith in what you are doing, confidence in yourself and in your associates, and belief in future success. If that is lost—through destruction of faith, or confidence, or through weariness, or lack of health, or lack of ambition—a man's usefulness is finished.

"It applies as well to the head of a great concern as it does to the clerk, except that the head of a concern may lose his enthusiasm and delegate his work, or the greater part of it, to subordinates who possess the quality, and he may retain it by proxy. The worker, salesman, office man, or anything else, who loses enthusiasm is worthless.

"Enthusiasm is the driving power of business. No man can do his best work unless he has that quality. You have, perhaps, seen a man, by his own push and energy, build up a business, inspire his staff and his workers with his own spirit, and then, perhaps after he has gained wealth, his concern begins to lose, to slump. That type of business is encountered most frequently by men who study sick businesses and strive to find the cause of the illness. Sometimes it requires time to locate that sort of trouble, because of the fact that when he calls in an expert to diagnose his business, the head has waked up to the fact that something is wrong and has stirred things up for a time.

"Loss of enthusiasm by the head of a concern spreads through the entire force quickly.

"We have seen businesses built up, flourish and prosper, suddenly lose enthusiasm, and begin to slump.

"I have in mind a firm that manufactured a fine line of goods—perhaps the best. It was nationally advertised and a staple trade article. The salesmen had pride and enthusiasm, believed their product the best, and built up the biggest sales in the country. During the war the manufacturer decided to cut the quality. He got away with it because during that period such a course was common. But later, when raw material prices fell, he became greedy, and continued to manufacture the lower grade.

"So far as the buyers were concerned the firm could have got away with it for a time, but it destroyed the enthusiasm of the salesmen. Sales fell off. The head of the concern called in a student of business troubles to find the cause. He could have learned by asking one of his salesmen. If they had told him the truth—which is that no man can become enthusiastic and push sales of something in which he has no faith."

The truth of Colonel Arison's analysis was forcefully demonstrated to me in one case. A New York man invented a bulletproof vest and was employing salesmen to go on the road and sell it.

The article was a good proposition and did what was claimed for it.

While I was in the plant a young man who had applied for a job as salesman came in with the inventor. They had agreed on everything.

"Put on the vest and I'll show you how it works," the inventor remarked.

The young man adjusted the light vest, made of thin metal plates, a trifle nervously. When the inventor drew out a police service revolver shooting a jacketed bullet, the young man turned pale.

"You can't sell these vests unless you believe in them yourself," said the manager, calmly, as he placed the muzzle of the gun four inches from the heart of the salesman. "I've got to shoot you."

The salesman was scared, but he had courage. His eyes became glassy, and, as the revolver was fired, he died several deaths. An instant later he gave a yell of astonishment, relief, and joy.

"I—I—scarcely felt it!" he exclaimed. "Say—I can go out and sell that vest now! Let me get started!"

He broke the sales records of the firm in the next month.

The causes of loss of enthusiasm are many, but lack of confidence in the firm and in the product is the principal reason. No matter how hard he may try, no salesman can put entire enthusiasm into selling anything in which he does not have confidence. He must sell himself first—and if he can do that the rest of the job will be found to be easy.

Liberty's First Crossword Puzzle

by J. W. White

HORIZONTAL

1 Reed musical instruments
5 To exist
6 A pronoun and possessive adjective, meaning: "belonging to us"
7 A preposition and adverb meaning: "toward a higher position"
9 Thus or therefore
10 A public lodging place
12 The (Spanish)
14 Not fresh
16 One who indulges his appetite
19 A meadow
20 Commanded
23 A large receptacle
25 Shrine of the great mosque of Mecca
27 Something spoken so as not to be heard by others
30 Shut up within
31 A small rug
33 A kind of fish with very long bodies (plural)
36 The eggs of fishes
38 Definite article (English)
40 Merriment, or a good time
41 A man's name found in the Bible
43 A recently developed means of electrical communication
44 A kind of fur, used in fashionable garments

45 Narratives
46 A man's name found in the Bible
47 Immature insect
49 Epoch
51 A grain
52 Places (verb), or puts down (verb)
54 A money introduced into England by the Danes
56 A kind of type, used for emphasis (abbrev.)
59 Likeness, or statue
61 Beaten with a straight, slender stick
64 Degree awarded doctors who specialize in teeth
66 Submits to the action of air
68 Simpleton
70 To choose from a number of persons
72 Brings to maturity, or brings up
74 For example (Latin abbrev.)
75 The simultaneous discharge of several cannon, as a salute
78 A preposition denoting situation or direction
79 Leave
80 A Portuguese money
81 The first person singular, present indicative of the verb "be"
82 Nether world

VERTICAL

2 Hoot or deride, as at a theatrical performance
3 Extravagant
4 Before (in point of time)
5 A scarf of fur or feathers, for the neck
8 Fit of peevishness
9 To wager
10 A plant
11 Dregs
13 To make flat, or even
14 Selenium (chemical symbol)
15 Reluctant
17 Farewell (French)
18 Egyptian god
19 A note of the scale
21 A wall to stop water from flowing
22 A rodent
24 A preposition indicating *motion toward*
26 A word of opposite meaning —contrasted with "synonym"
28 To supply with notches or teeth
29 A variety of iris, the root of which is used as a perfume
30 A foot lever, as on a bicycle
32 A bower
34 A remedy, used for rheumatism

35 Abstains from food
37 A wooden implement for propelling a boat
39 Familiar Latin verb, meaning "he is" or "it is"
40 To pay or to give a gratuity to
42 A vast body of water
48 A man's name—also that of a Hebrew patriarch
50 To wash out with a liquid
53 A passageway in a theater
54 A contraction of "over"
55 Division of a drama
57 Decorate
58 Abbreviation of "edition"
60 Obtains
62 Pertaining to air (prefix)
63 Provided that, or, supposing that
65 Prefix, with the sense of "down"
67 Suffered illness
69 In like manner
71 The oval or round reproductive body produced by birds
73 To point (as a gun)
76 A southern constellation
77 Strive for superiority

HERE'S A CHANCE for *Liberty* readers to take part in the most popular indoor sport; cross-word puzzle solving.

This opening puzzle should present no difficulties, even to a beginner, for all the words are to be found in ordinary reference books— such as unabridged dictionaries—and all are "crossed" often enough to give some pretty liberal clews.

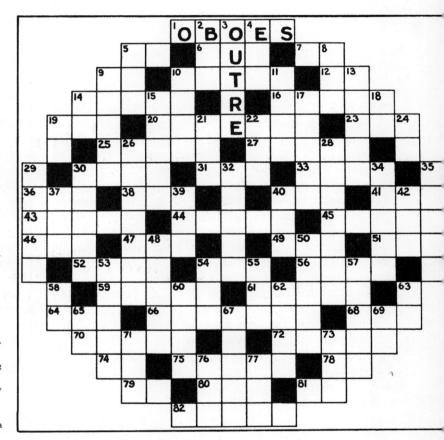

DIRECTIONS

If you are a beginner, you can get the idea from the filled-in spaces. For instance, our definition for the horizontal word starting at Square No. 1 is "reed musical instruments." Now a flute is a reed musical instrument and *flutes* would answer the definition, but there are only five spaces for letters and *flutes* has six. Therefore we must hunt around for another musical instrument and finally hit on *oboe*—the plural of which is *oboes*, fulfilling the requirements of the definition.

With the middle "o" of *oboes* for a starter we eventually find that *outré* is the vertical word running downward from Square No. 3, defined as "extravagant."

Of course you can start anywhere and use all the easier crossing and adjoining words to help find the more difficult ones.

Remember that only the white spaces are to take letters. The black spaces simply mark the beginning and end of words.

Next week we'll print the solution and another puzzle. Don't send in your solutions. [*Rather, look on page 34*]

Laugh, Town, Laugh:
The Private Life of Jimmy Walker

by Frederick L. Collins

THERE IS A fairly accurate picture of the real Jimmy Walker in these half hundred or more adjectives, chosen for the frequency of their appearance in the newspaper accounts of his character and conduct:

Jimmy was little, glib, dapper, carefree, witty, gay— these lead all the rest; then, without regard to the order of frequency, he was also jaunty, sleek, debonair, swagger, trig, slim, neat, irrepressible, bubbling, wise-cracking, and alert; smart, agile, slick, vivacious, assured, brilliant, adroit, lighthearted, scintillant, astonishing, insouciant, and nice; he was casual, fascinating, genial, likable, friendly, flashy, cynical, theatrical, spiffy, and wise.

He was nimble, sentimental, pliant, adaptable, disillusioned, buoyant, engaging, reckless, and spry; silly, dressy, diminutive, dandified, imperturbable, and fresh; youthful, charming, amusing, immaculate, well dressed, able, handsome, generous, peripatetic, and quick; winning, versatile, humorous, cool, spendthrift, jolly, chipper, darling, and late.

By his adjectives ye shall know him!

(Solution to puzzle on page 33)

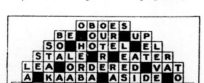

A good deal of friendly fun was poked at him because of the gradual manner in which he was inducted into office. Technically his term began on the stroke of midnight, New Year's Eve; but New Year's in 1926 got itself all tied up with the weekend in such a manner that it was decided that he should take a preliminary oath of office three days earlier, to avoid the possibility of an hiatus in the mayoralty. The idea of Jimmy's being three days early for anything was in itself amusing; but he did the best he could to neutralize the effect. He was an hour and a half late for the performance.

He had, he said, been attending a funeral!

Still later the new mayor appeared at the City Hall for the public ceremonies of inauguration. The crowd, which filled the park, fairly mobbed his automobile.

"Let me in," he grinned. "I want to go to work."

The cheering crowd opened for him to pass.

"Hey, Jimmy!"

"Attaboy, Jimmy!"

The mayor acknowledged every greeting, shook hands endlessly, grinned continuously. Finally he held up his own hand in signal that the show was over.

"I understand," he said, "that there's some serious swearing to be done now, but that will take place in the mayor's office."

The crowd laughed. And that laugh handed Jimmy the keys of the city. He was, as someone later remarked, the only mayor ever to have possessed them!

It was the Era of Easy Money.

Tex Guinan, at five dollars a cover, titillated Broadway. Belle Livingstone devastated the upper East Side. Nobody in New York gave a damn to see the Sesquicentennial, but a lot of people gave two million dollars to see Jack Dempsey, Gene Tunney, and the rain.

The opening night of George White's Scandals grossed $28,000—$28,000 in a single evening to watch a hundred all-but-naked women and Willie Howard! Peggy Joyce reached the glittering apex of her career. Arnold Rothstein became a sort of king. Raquel Meller, at grand-opera prices, made the Broadway grade. Marion Talley, with grand-opera pretensions, made $300,000. Daddy Browning picked his Peaches.

"Gentlemen preferred blondes." The other kind danced the black bottom.

In the excitement Jimmy got off to a very good start. The contrast between him and his predecessor, which had been so refreshing on the stump, was even more stimulating in the City Hall.

"Although no mighty thinker," admitted Critic Heywood Broun, "he is palpably more agile in his mental processes than his ill-tempered predecessor."

And he was vastly more entertaining. Anything might happen at City Hall at any moment. A good deal of this official activity was on the surface. "This job," the mayor himself said at the time, "is fifty percent shop window." But a good deal of it was work—as the mayor soon found out. It wasn't many months before he was calling it a headache.

It is a big town, New York, no matter how you look at it. And not all of its needs are physical. For its spiritual ones the city demands a confessional; for its social needs, a complaint department—and, for lack of a better place to look, it seeks for both at City Hall. The mayor's office becomes a sort of city-wide Lost and Found.

"There are six million people surrounding this City Hall," is the way Jimmy himself sized it up, "and if you don't happen to be within walking distance, you can get here on a five-cent ride."

The new mayor's visitors ranged all the way from pot-bellied solemnities to newsboys who were sore because Commissioner Gallatin ruled them out of City Hall Park. To the solemnities Jimmy said: "There is no man in any given activity, no representative of any interest, that I am afraid of and that I do not welcome an opportunity to sit down with and talk over the business of the City of New York."

And to the newsboys: "Go on back into the park, and to hell with Gallatin!"

Of course, the citizen with the legitimate kick was only half the story. "Every day some deluded, half-cracked soul comes to the mayor's office with his incoherent jabbering plea to right the wrongs of this sorry old world."

Orators on both sides of every conceivable question were incessantly vocal. The professional reformer was as busy as a bootlegger.

Jimmy, with his constitutional inability to say "No"—which any amount of practicing before a mirror could not alter!—was ill fitted to stand up against this pressure. But he had surrounded himself with a capable and knowing staff; and it was the staff which gradually succeeded in systematizing, if not the mayor himself, at least his office.

The City Hall in which these capable officials worked, often while Jimmy slept, dates back to 1803. It is one of the few monuments to permanence in the Greater City. Incidentally, it is that rare thing, a municipal monument to art. Jimmy usually arrived at its northern, or back, entrance. But there was nothing back-doorish about Jimmy himself. "He wears spats, a soft or hard-boiled hat, carries a cane and a carnation," wrote one observer. "Not a gray hair peeps among the smooth black of the compact boyish head. He might be a manicured featherweight champion."

There wasn't anything back-doorish, either, about the style in which Jimmy arrived. The subways might remain crowded, and did. Large sections of the city might remain busless, and did. But one hundred and nineteen Tammany officeholders went about their labors in city-owned cars, most of them expensive; and one—the Hon. James J. Walker—in a $17,000 specially designed, custom-bodied imported limousine.

"This is as it should be," wrote a critic, "nothing but the best for the boys. Good work must be well compensated. It might not be a bad idea, however, to have the city's insignia painted conspicuously on every municipal car. It would permit citizens to recognize the best speakeasies by the cars parked in front of them."

On everyday occasions, such as arrivals at City Hall, the mayor would be accompanied in his limousine by Paddy Hogan, his personal attendant; on larger occasions, by handsome Tom O'Connor, his personal captain of police, known journalistically as the mayor's bodyguard.

"The mayor likes to approach all problems physically," was the way one student phrased it. "His typical method of attacking the park, hospital, or subway problems is to summon one of his limousines and fill another with cameramen, so that the tabloid patrons may see their hardworking mayor in action."

This statement is literally true. When Jimmy announced that he was going to address himself seriously to the solution of the subway problem, it is recorded that he traveled forty-five miles the first day—by automobile!

There were no photographic formalities attending the mayor's daily progress from the back door to the throne room, but there was plenty of stir.

"Good morning, George!"

"Hello, Charlie!"

"Well, boys, what's on? Anything important?"

"Who's this bird I've got to greet today?"

The final inquiry referred to the practice of receiving distinguished visitors on the front step of the City Hall, which from the moment of Walker's election became almost a daily custom.

Jimmy would be attending an important meeting when word would reach him that someone or something was waiting to be welcomed out front. Immediately he would turn the gavel over to Joseph V. McKee, the solemn president of the Board of Aldermen, and slip out of the room.

"Presently," wrote Joseph McGoldrick, "he is on the steps outside the City Hall. The battery of stills advance. His Honor smiles, holding up the hockey stick, sirup, or cheese, as the case may be. The stills drop back to reload.

The movies rattle into place. The mayor swings the stick, tilts the can, or otherwise gestures appropriately. Then a second round of stills, then a parting shot from the movies; and, five minutes having elapsed, the mayor slips unobtrusively into his seat in the board. This is an almost daily occurrence. It may occur twice or even three times in a single day. Of course, when Queen Marie, or the cardinals, or Lindbergh, or some other splendid dignitary arrives, the city business is put completely aside for the pageantry of a Roman triumph."

Not too Roman, however, as far as dignity went! To Lindbergh, referring to the latter's use of "we," he said: "You have given to the world a flying pronoun." And to Admiral Byrd when, after his antarctic trip, he came to the Hall for his third welcome: "Dick, this has got to stop. It's getting to be a habit!"

He was equally informal in his remarks to foreign guests, especially those who, he knew, couldn't understand a word he said. To Marshal Pétain, after struggling in vain to pin a medal on the soldier's tough army coat, he said with a smile, the friendliness of which his guest could not fail to understand: "Marshal, you have been reading the newspapers and have been misinformed. You didn't need to wear a bullet-proof coat to this reception."

To a Polish chief of staff whose chest was already so covered with military medals that there was hardly room for a peacetime one, Jimmy said: "General, if we had another war I wouldn't know where to put this." And to the President-elect of Brazil who was delayed by a fog down the bay and was four hours late in reaching City Hall, Jimmy solemnly remarked: "Sir, I concede to you a championship which heretofore has been given to me."

Even when the mayor strove for dignity, the crowd wouldn't let him get away with it. He had no sooner bundled Queen Marie of Roumania into the waiting motor and popped in beside her than a standee yelled:

"Hey, Jimmy, dated her up yet?"

Jimmy shivered. The queen, ignoring the sally, tucked the robe more securely around him. The crowd cheered the gesture of intimacy.

"Oh, you queen!" someone cried. "How d'ye like our Jimmy?"

But we left "our Jimmy" arriving at City Hall, bowing to a stenographer here and a reporter there as he picked his dapper way to his private office. In this room were only three pictures: one of Jimmy's mother, one of his father, and one of Alfred E. Smith.

What, you say, no picture of his wife? No one seemed surprised. In fact, it was now generally taken for granted that the mayor and his wife had little or nothing to do with each other except on state occasions. Everybody at the Hall knew then that Jimmy and Allie were through.

It was about the only thing they did know about Jimmy. Least of all did they know when, if at all, he would show up at City Hall.

"Good evening, gentlemen!" would be his formula when so late that he realized it. "How goes the battle?" At which everybody would indulgently smile.

In this matter of tardiness the man was incorrigible. One night he arrived nearly two hours behind time for an important gabfest at the Tammany wigwam.

"We've been waiting for you," complained one of the older sachems, "since eight o'clock."

Jimmy's eyebrows went up and his hands went out.

"And what for, pray? Surely a gathering like this needs to wait on no man. Have more faith in yourselves, boys."

Sometimes he wasn't so successful in turning away the watchful waiters' wrath. One Saturday noon, just before one o'clock, Governor Smith called to pay his respects. Jimmy's day had not yet begun. The governor waited until after two. Then he went away. The loyal reporters wrote in their papers that the mayor had been "absent at a conference." But nobody believed it—least of all Al! Some said this incident was the occasion for the first of many fatherly admonitions from Albany to "cut the nonsense and get to work!"

Jimmy's own comment was characteristic: "I expect to be judged by the yardstick, not by the time clock."

Measured by either standard Jimmy worked hard. He not only helped to open several new night clubs but he attended twenty-one public banquets in twenty-four working days. At each banquet—although in competition with the world's best oratorical talent—he had acquitted himself bravely.

Yes, the mayor worked hard; and, contrary to the general belief, he had done some of his work at City Hall. Not in his office. Jimmy's legs, which fitted so neatly under a table with a cloth on it, cramped distressingly under one ornamented by a blotter. Only when criticisms of his playfulness became too persistent would he sit long at that desk—and then only to be photographed for tabloid consumption, disguised as a hard-working mayor with a pair of horn-rimmed glasses perched piously on his perky little nose. The room where he did work is a large cheerful one, seating about five hundred, on the second floor of the hall, referred to in previous administrations as the meeting room of the Board of Estimate and Apportionment, but known to those of us who survived the Walker age as "the Municipal Theater." It is, as a matter of fact, very like a theater, with a stage for the actors and rows of benches for the audience.

It is a gay white-and-red typically Jimmy Walker room with high ceilings and flashing chandeliers.

On the stage, in semicircular symmetry, sit the Mayor of New York and the members of his cabinet: the president of the Board of Aldermen, the comptroller, and the presidents of the boroughs of Manhattan, Brooklyn, Richmond, Queens, and the Bronx. These men constitute the real government of New York City.

In the auditorium sit those citizens of New York who have business to transact with their government, representatives of the various watch-and-ward societies and committees whose business it is to watch proceedings with a suspicious eye, representatives of traction and other vested interests—City Hall lobbyists they really are—who watch with equal vigilance for any impingement on the rights and privileges of their clients, a liberal sprinkling of those crack-brained cranks who bring to the board complaints which they should take only to their God; and in Walker's time there was added to these worthies a steady attendance of smart New Yorkers who had discovered that in this municipal playhouse, for two gala performances each week, the World's Greatest Showman was putting on the World's Greatest Show.

The resemblance to an old-time minstrel act was inescapable. The mayor, gay as a primrose and breezy as an electric fan, sitting in the center of the horseshoe with a red silk curtain behind him and a microphone on the desk in front of him, was every slim-waisted inch the interlocutor. Aldermanic President McKee and Comptroller Berry were the solemn-faced end men. The borough presidents were the singing ensemble.

In these surroundings, with hecklers heckling and friends cheering, with everybody—hecklers and friends alike—leaning forward in their seats on the white hard benches lest they miss a syllable from the mayor's loudspeaker, Jimmy was at his best.

"You experience nothing like it," wrote Foster Ware, "outside the theater."

The Walker Follies, in the first years of their run, were devoted chiefly to glorifying the American wise crack.

It went this way: A great many people went to the Rodeo, and said they were going. Jimmy went too; but Jimmy said he was "going to see the bull thrown in the open." A long-winded citizen took up the time of the board for the better part of an hour. Jimmy became restless. "Listen," he said finally. "Can't we two boys play after hours?" An angry man rose from the front-row bench and demanded to know why Jimmy hadn't answered his letter. "I don't write letters," snapped the mayor, "and I don't read 'em, either!"

Retorts like these invariably convulsed his hearers. Others moved them to cheers. For example, when a delegation took him to task for jumping the annual budget up to nearly $700,000,000, Jimmy shouted into his microphone: "I don't care what the budget amounts to in dollars and cents. If we're going to improve New York, we've got to pay for it." The resulting applause rattled through the crowded corridors of the dignified old Hall and reached the astonished ears of MacMonnies' giant statue of Civic Virtue in the park outside.

Sometimes Jimmy wasn't looking for applause. He was looking for action. On such occasions he did not hesitate to use his reputation for being able to say anything and get away with it in ways that would have been in anyone else downright insulting.

Under cover of the mayor's nifties an unprecedented amount of business was actually transacted.

"Despite his attacks of wanderlust and his devotion to pleasure," observed Henry F. Pringle, "he has been making definite progress."

One reason for his progress was his gift for "skimming lightly through the blooming fields of municipal minutiæ, never missing a daisy"; another—and, in these critical days, a too-often-forgotten reason—was that "he knew, within a few months after taking office, as much as the diligent Hylan had been able to accumulate in years of grinding toil."

Jimmy is himself to blame if we forget, as we sometimes do, that beneath his cleverness there is real intelligence. It is only fair, however, to record that his quickness was not confined to repartee but extended to his grasp of the city's business.

Even so solemn a critic as the Outlook conceded that "Jimmy translates the problems of municipal government into simple, musical-comedy terms that the average person understands. In his hands they become problems that can be solved with a jig and a jest."

Of course all this City Hall stuff cut into Jimmy's time terribly. The weekend was little more than a thin slit between a Saturday-night banquet and a Monday-morning "greet." And during the week it was difficult to find time for relaxation, even at night. Often he was obliged to attend three and four banquets in an evening. Invariably arriving late at the first one, he seldom escaped from the last until after midnight. So it was pretty late—or early—when what might be called his private life began.

The newspaper boys knew all this. They knew that the mayor was burning the electric light at both switches, and they did their best to "cover up" for him. It was sporting of them to try to conceal the unfortunate results of the mayor's attempts to observe the twenty-four-hour day. It was fun, too, to joke about it. But it wasn't so good for citizens who had business to transact with the city; and, in time, it wouldn't be so good for Jimmy's reputation with those citizens.

"Often," complained the Nation, "he appeared so tired and cross from his labors of the previous day or night that he hardly seemed to know what was going on."

Even the mayor realized that things couldn't run on like this indefinitely. "I'm not as young as I was," he sighed, as he arrived at four o'clock in the afternoon, after an all-night celebration, to begin his day's work. Then, with a quick return to the lifted eyebrow and the irrepressible sideways smile, he added: "However, I am glad to be of service."

Whereupon he went to Europe!

There was a good deal of "bunk" about that trip to Europe; and a fair share of it concerned his wife.

For some time now Jimmy and Allie had borne up wonderfully under the pangs of what appeared to be virtual separation. It is hard to see how an ocean or two between them would have made much difference. But perhaps Jimmy was a little self-conscious about his impending inauguration as Mayor of Europe. Anyhow, he dug up Allie and took her with him.

The next move, naturally, was to let the world know through the tabloids just how domestic the trip was to be. Allie and Jimmy must be photographed side by side at the boatdeck rail in the very act of waving united farewells to friends and neighbors. This wasn't so easy as it seems; for the Berengaria sailed at one o'clock in the morning, when news photographs are not so good. The situation would have stumped a less devoted husband and mayor; but not Jimmy. He had Allie down there for nearly an hour the day before the actual sailing, waving farewells for the benefit of the assembled cameramen and an otherwise empty dock.

"What is this?" the good-natured Allie complained at last. "A permanent wave?"

Mrs. Jimmy, as you see, was not so slow at pulling nifties herself. Another thing she had in common with her husband was a passionate fear lest she have to say:

"I haven't a thing to wear—not a thing!"

Hattie Carnegie, New York dressmaker de luxe, sued Jimmy for $14,000 worth of clothing allegedly purchased by his wife; and Sommers the shoeman put in a little bill for $2,141.20, which was said to be part of Mrs. Walker's purchases over a period of about a year and four months.

One day, according to Sommers, Mrs. Walker's purchases totaled $790—for eighteen pairs of shoes and two pairs of mules. Only two pairs of mules, you say? Yes; but they cost seventy dollars!

Mules at thirty-five dollars a pair and linen sandals at the same figure were apparently Allie's all-time lows. White lizard shoes were listed at forty-two dollars; white satin ones at seventy-five.

It is not important to follow her footsteps on their European tour. Except for certain official and photographic appearances, it was chiefly a shopping tour. The spotlight, as usual, followed the mayor, who relapsed straightway into normalcy.

Sitting in the ship's smoking room, where he presided over the nightly gamble on the day's run, he radioed his friend George Silzer, ex-Governor of New Jersey, to "have another." Deputed to give out the prizes for the girls' deck sports, he kissed the first winner, who happened to be a little girl of ten.

"It wasn't his fault," someone remarked, "that the next nine prize winners were pretty young women!"

Mata Hari's Fatal Error

by Leyla Georgie

Why the Famous Spy Was Willing to Die

IT WAS IN the Blue Train rushing madly from Brussels to Paris that the man spoke to me. Traveling was dull, and so we had cocktails together.

With a kind, understanding look in his eyes, he asked why I seemed so depressed. I told him how my show had failed in Paris.

He smiled and took my hand.

"Little girl, don't be childish. You are so young, so many things can happen to you yet. Why, the life of a woman lasts as long as she is fascinating! Yes; just about as long as that."

Let me tell you [he continued] a story of one whom we all know of. I mean Mata Hari, the most colorful of spies, who in the end was court-martialed and shot.

Throughout Europe, before she was revealed as a spy, that glamorous creature—half Javanese, half Dutch—was renowned as a dancer and a charmer. She was in Spain when it became known in diplomatic circles that a warrant had been issued for her arrest.

She was just leaving the Palace Hotel in Madrid when the Dutch *chargé d'affaires* stepped up to her car and whispered in her ear that it would be safer not to go to France—now.

She laughed, her white teeth flashing, and put one of her jewel-covered hands on the young diplomat's shoulder. She looked into his eyes.

"My young friend," she said. "Tell me. What can happen to me?"

"Madame, they will arrest you. They will court-martial you," he insisted. "Please—oh, please don't go!"

She patted his hand.

"Don't be upset, young man. Explain. What does it mean—court-martial?"

"Madame, in your case it means death. They must already have the proof, to be able to arrest you. Nothing can save you. And—oh, you are so beautiful and young!"

Mata Hari's face became serious for a moment.

"Tell me, what is a court-martial like? Is it a trial? Is there a jury? Whom does the jury consist of?"

"Of twelve hard-boiled soldiers," he told her. "Twelve who think nothing of loveliness. All they know is duty." Mata Hari lit a Russian cigarette. He awaited her decision with anxious eyes.

"Listen," she said at last, between smoke puffs. "Twelve *men*, eh? There are no twelve *men* in the world who would let Mata Hari be shot to death. Go back to your embassy and make your mind easy, as mine is. Mata Hari's life is always safe when it depends upon men."

The young Dutchman knew it would be useless to say more. His eyes glistened; perhaps there were tears in them. "Pleasant journey, madame," he murmured; and the car rolled off toward the depot.

The nearer her train got to France, the surer Mata Hari was of herself. Arriving, she hurried to her apartment, glad to be home again. She was about to plunge into a perfumed hot bath when her maid entered.

"Madame, there are gentlemen from the police. What shall I say to them?"

She calmly slipped on a brocade negligee and went in to receive these policemen. *Men*, were they not? Well, that was all that mattered.

At first, not even the stony-faced sergeant could utter the words to tell her she was under arrest. Finally they managed, among them, to let her know it.

She smiled graciously and bade the maid bring her sable coat.

She drove to the station in her own limousine, and was shown to a cell as if she had been a princess honoring some hovel with a visit.

She was going on trial soon, they said; just when, they did not know. All the time they were talking she, with her charm, was smiling.

The trial was postponed and the postponement was repeated. A year went by. Then came the day, at last.

The year in prison had left its mark upon Mata Hari. She was still beautiful, but the glorious light was gone from her almond eyes.

Throughout the trial she remained calm. The jury? The young Dutchman had been right. They were all hard, cold soldiers. But they were men. She knew her power over men. It had yet to fail her.

And then the jury brought in a verdict. She was bidden to stand up to hear it. "Guilty." To be shot at sunrise!

She did not need the formal pronouncing of sentence to tell her this verdict meant that.

A roar of sympathy was heard—there were many men in the room. One juryman approached her. He gave her a handshake. He had been the youngest of the twelve; a young captain.

He whispered: "I tried to save you—"

She opened those lips that almost any man would have given much to kiss, and her voice was composed and cool.

"It's all right, captain. I don't mind dying. My life is ended, anyway, the moment that any twelve *men* can find *me* guilty. That is the real end of me; not what will happen at sunrise. I have lost something, something that was my life—my charm. But thank you."

.   .   .   .   .

"You see?" the man on the Blue Train concluded. "Her charm's failure *is* the real end of a woman. And don't you see how childish *your* tiny troubles are?"

"But how do you know her story so well?" I asked.

He smiled with resignation.

"Well, little girl, if you must be told, I was that man—that captain on the jury."

I Have Been to Hollywood

by Fannie Hurst

*Vainglorious Strutting and Half-Baked Make-Believe, Dreams and
a Gorgeous Promise—An Impression of America's Picture City*

I HAVE BEEN to Hollywood, and it is as fearfully as it
is wonderfully made.

It hath not precedent and, since it cannot be compared
to anything in the way of previous similar performances,
must be compared to a little of everything.

It comes dangerously near to being something new
under the sun. Like grapefruit and relativity and radium.

Yes, I have been to Hollywood.

I have tasted of avocado; learned to prefer my figs
fresh; agreed with four thousand, six hundred and seventy-

one boosters from Iowa that Spanish architecture "lends" itself to southern California; gazed upon the superb spectacle of the Hollywood Bowl by moonlight and Moonlight Sonata, and sent the folks back home picture postcard views of Ben Grauman's million-dollar moving picture Egyptian Theater and the two-hundred-and-forty-eight-thousand-six-hundred-and-seventy-six-dollars-and-twenty-three-cent Beverly Hills home of Miss Tottie Cough Drop, movie queen.

I have learned that in Hollywood the length of Nita Naldi's fingernails, the birthday of Baby Peggy's poodle dog, and the tattooed knee of aforementioned Tottie Cough Drop are first-page items.

I have dined with "Doug and Mary," young Olympians, in their home on the top of the world. I have walked with Lillian Gish, who is herself moonlight, in moonlight. I have stood in a ballroom with the matchless Pola and beheld the gilded, the shellacked, the No. 2 grease-painted, the manicured, the pedicured, the celluloid youth of this Athens-on-the-Santa Fe vie for the privilege of hanging their patent leather scalps about her fair and Polish waist.

I have beheld Valentino at close enough range to set the composite flapper spine of America to ringing like a bell. I have dined at Hollywood's Montmartre beside Adolphe Menjou straight "off the set" and still in the make-up and silk dressing gown demanded by his role. I have sat between Ramon Novarro and Rod La Rocque at luncheon and enjoyed the ecstatic and vicarious indigestion of all their fans.

I have chatted with Gloria Swanson in her drawing room, swapped cookbook recipes with Theda Bara in her garden, banqueted at the home of Bebe Daniels, listened to Montague Glass play Chopin in the drawing room of William de Mille, spent tea time with Nazimova in the heart of a house in the heart of a garden that should cause fourteen Chinese emperors to turn in their graves, of envy.

I have sucked artichoke leaves across the same table from Montagu Love; gone in to dinner with Ernest Torrence; sat on the edge of the green tile and Carrara marble swimming pool of the Charles Rays, and talked "climate" and Akeley cameras to the Bert Lytells and the Lionel Barrymores over the head of a lotus flower in full white bloom.

I have seen geraniums climb trees. Sunshine for seventy-five consecutive days. Percy Marmont dive off the rail of a moving ocean liner. Tom Mix. Flaming eucalyptus. Dry irrigation. Walnut groves. Forest fires. Motion-picture-money mansions in more architectures than there are human languages, including Lettish and Hochlich.

And in the language of the "big open spaces" I want to say to you that, compared to that spectacle of the cinema world out there on the edge of the desert, the glory that was Rome's must cause Cecil de Mille to laugh up his fine linen sleeve and the Byzantine splendor of biblical empires cause the scene builders for the most casual Keystone comedy to snigger.

How Charles Ray, when he steps into his black Pompeian bath, must smile at handsome Lorenzo de Medici, who once boasted a bath carved out of natural pink granite. And behold Gloria Swanson in her white and silver Rolls-Royce, putting it all over Cleopatra, who plied the Nile in a flatboat rigged up in bunting.

And, how did it get that way?

It got that way because for the first time in the history of the world, perhaps, an art, instead of writhing itself slowly into birth, was shunted into the midst of things on the tip of a skyrocket. An industrial skyrocket.

Never in the history of the world has a community been so dominated by an industry. And that an *art*-industry. A curious two-headed monster art-industry, one continually yapping at the other.

Bethlehem and her steel, Sheffield and her factories, Sparta and her militia. As nothing. Hollywood *is* pictures.

Its homes are furnished in "sets" bought up after the completion of a picture.

Its sight-seeing busses are entirely devoted to shouting out the rococo Spanish-Italian manses and mansions of the movie rich.

The first and editorial pages of its daily press are dominated by motion picture news. Sky-scraping office buildings shoot up on motion picture capital. Motion picture limousines, the fifteen-thousand-dollar-without-accessories kind, clog up traffic.

Excuse my STAR dust, says Hollywood.

Tom Mix walks down Seventh Street and brokers drop their ticker tapes and run to windows.

Norma Shearer changes the style of her coiffure and the beauty parlors are crammed with ladies from Iowa who want their ears exposed, too.

Mary Pickford heads a Greater Motion Picture Parade and stops traffic for two hours.

Nothing short of a world war—if that—could crowd the Valentino divorce off a Hollywood front page.

Cecil de Mille, with three thousand "extras," two miles of chariots, four hundred pounds of butter, forty-eight freight cars of costumes, twenty-five tubs of theatrical cold cream, thirty-five cooks, twenty-nine sleeping coaches, two freight cars of Egyptian bracelets and shields, three hundred Arabian horses, a leopard, a lemur, and an adder, ten pounds of sweet butter for a dyspeptic star, six hundred and fifty pairs of gilt sandals, twenty-one hundred spears, four hundred loin cloths, a canvas Red Sea and a papier-mâché Egyptian temple, starts across the desert to do a "spectacle" picture, and Hollywood, accustomed as she is to public manifestations, stands thrilled. And well she may.

The man at the head of an expedition such as this is a Napoleon in his way.

Hollywood is, thinks, breathes, dreams, lives, eats, smokes, walks, talks—pictures.

Mothers paint their six-year-old little girls' lips in the image of Gloria's and keep them home from reading and writing and arithmetic to study pantomime.

Tow-haired children in artificial marcel waves or Jackie Coogan bobs sit through long hours in outer offices with fond mammas who have lugged their offerings from as far as Bangor, Maine, and as wide as Montreal, Canada, to offer them up at the motion picture shrine.

Young imitation Valentinos walk the streets with the moss of eight unshaven days along their jowls in the name of a casting director's hint that Negri's next picture will demand a handsome, bearded "lead."

Laundresses go to their day's work with their eyebrows vaselined and arching, but clipped to the shape of Bebe's.

School children in Mary Pickford curls and Lord Fauntleroy suits spend their recesses dancing the "Charleston."

There is the Baby Peggy pencil box. The Jackie Coogan sailor suit. The Betty Bronson poke bonnet.

Old men in white beards sit on curbstones all day in the hope of being discovered by a casting director intent on producing a film by some such name as the Return of the Patriarch.

Tootsies with dimpled knees do likewise—except with the hope that Mack Sennett may come riding past.

The conversation of Hollywood is *Pictures*.

The literature the fan magazine.

Hollywood is jammed with Cinderellas who have come out overnight from the fireside. He ones. She ones. Hollywood is the answer to what you would do if you had a thousand dollars a day to spend.

Patsy Fitzgibbons, who used to carry her carfare and lunch money tied in a corner of her handkerchief when she clerked in the Brazil, Indiana, Five-and-Ten, woke up one morning about three years after a local beauty contest had won her a free trip to Atlantic City, with a contract to play "Cuties" in Kingsley Productions at One Hundred Thousand Dollars a year.

Turk Spordoni, who used to drive a milk cart until he fell off one day and got up looking cross-eyed from seeing stars, walked out of a motion picture office one year later with a Two Thousand Dollar a week-signed-on-the-dotted-line contract to play eccentric comedy.

But these youngsters gauche with money, dolled up with money, Rolls-Royced with money, manicured with money, pedicured with it, epicured, haven't developed many of the classic symptoms supposed to go with the acquisition of great wealth.

Patsy Fitzgibbons, who used to wash out her own handkerchiefs and paste them on the window pane, has not changed much except in pocketbook. She has kept sweet and generous. Come easy. Go easy.

These young things, many of whom have scraped their way to fame on grit, talent, and a certain infallible kind of personal charm, and others who have bumped their way to recognition on a pair of crossed or blue eyes, a dimpled knee or just the certain right amount of comedy-

avoirdupois, make up a joyous civilization of generosity and good will.

They are as grateful about it all as they are surprised.

Patsy Fitzgibbons keeps pinching herself for fear it may be a dream. Externally she is very grand. You need only to see Patsy "on the set" with a maid coddling her, a director wheedling her, a cast deferring to her, a production depending upon her, to realize this. Well, it is difficult unless you are one of the really great who grow big simply, instead of simply big, not to be grand about the gesture of stooping to jam yourself into a Rolls-Royce or being interviewed for the *Success Gazette* or signing the deed to a thirty-room house in Beverly Hills.

But, deep down inside her, Patsy is not grand at all. There is within her, rather, the feeling of ascending swiftly in an elevator. Scare. It is a grim struggle for motion picture existence. Even after your existence is a movie-success one. A miss is only as good as her smile. Patsy knows this, and goes furiously while the going and her teeth are good.

I want to tell you about another little movie queen.

She is all blue and gold. You have wept with her, laughed with her night after night in your "favorite motion picture theater—check the babies with our matron" and always and with invariable beatitude beheld her emerge from her celluloid vicissitudes into the ever-evergreen role of virtue rewarded.

At eleven o'clock one Hollywood forenoon this little movie queen, who lives in the biggest house in the world on top of a hill around which sight-seeing busses megaphone all day, clapped her hands with a pretty petulance and said:

"I would a desert party give!"

"Yes, yes," said all the couriers and retainers, bending closer that they might hear. "Yes. Yes. But what is a desert party?"

"Why, a party in the desert."

"Yes, yes," cried the retainers whose yes-yes-es a day to little movie queen, if placed end on end, would yes-yes the road to Hellespont, "but such a thing has never been done. Yes. Yes. A party in the desert?"

"Then I would do it," cried the little movie queen; "but alas, I have only four silken tents, seven limousines and a portable kitchen large enough to feast a party of twenty on a sand beach. And I would a desert party in the heart of the desert give for eight and forty!"

"Yes, yes," cried the couriers and the retainers, and while the little movie queen, reclining on her couch, was having her face packed in white mud and her spine massaged for kinks and her fingernails enameled in mauve, the word was passed along from butler to butler, from secretary to secretary, from head gardener to head carpenter, from head carpenter to general supervisor.

Yes. Yes. A desert party. For eight and forty.

Now it so chanced that seismic conditions, variously known as "fire" and "tremble" and never referred to as earthquake by the solidarity of native sons, had just laid low as to chimney, roof, portal, and lintel the fair city of Santa Barbara.

So that for miles around the carpenters and the builders, the cabinetmakers and the joiners were busy at rebuilding the glory that had been Santa Barbara.

And when little movie queen, clapping her lovely hands, cried, "I would a desert party give in forty-eight hours, but alas, I have only four silken tents and a portable beach kitchen large enough to feast twenty," the vassals and the couriers, the ladies-in-waiting and the first, second, third, and fourth secretaries were hard put.

Gone to Santa Barbara were the carpenters and the strong men tried and true, who build kitchens overnight for desert feasts to forty-eight, and my little lady who was blue and gold wanted to give a party.

And clap-clap went her pretty movie hands and, oh-my-my-yes-yes, said the scurrying retainers.

That was of a sunny California Thursday morning and at seven o'clock that evening, what with the scurrying of the retainers, there sped out of San Francisco, on a special train, one hundred workingmen who build portable kitchens per union wages, plus, and on Saturday morning, in all the incredible blue and gold light of California, there moved out toward the grandeur of the desert, headed by blue and gold little movie queen, such a caravan as rivaled in splendor the whole Sheban performance.

Sixteen mauve upholstered limousines turned shining snouts toward desolation. A desolation that, by the time the limousine caravan arrived, was to be enlivened by a vanguard of the kind of draped silk tents shahs pitch.

By the time the little movie queen and her party thundered in, Persian silk rugs were spread between the prickle of sagebrush and her own pretty feet, a cook's tent, with a dome of purple and a festoon of doorway held back with a gilt cord the thickness of a man's arm, stood off at respectful distance from the shining silken rows of sleeping tents. Beach chairs, transformed into desert chairs by great cowls of silk swathings to keep out the dust, were spread along the rugs under lavender and orange umbrellas. A radio mounted on a gilt-legged Empire table jerked the world into the heart of that desert. By the miracle of the workingmen imported from San Francisco, a swimming pool, pink concrete and with a pink and white awning, was sunk into the sand.

A blue and gold little movie queen had paddy-caked dainty palms together, and lo, had appeared an oasis in the desert.

In a dining tent, hung in orange sateen, forty-eight guests enjoyed their mountain trout *meunière*, their extra-dry, *frappé*, and their breasts of Long Island duckling, *sauté*.

Forty-eight guests retired to hair mattresses and awoke to chilled honeydew.

Greased slaves ran up Cleopatra's tents. Greased palms put up little movie queen's.

The desert party departed in the glory in which it had arrived. Leaving not bones to bleach and empty tins to rust, but such addenda as must have startled even the desert out of its well-known state of atrophy.

Remnants such as these to bleach their way into eternity: one pair pink satin mules with ermine pompons; one small mountain of stout-looking bottles with concavous bottoms; eight unopened tins of imported *pâté de foie gras*; one gentleman's dress shirt with five-color monogram embroidered on each sleeve; fourteen jazz phonograph records; fifteen motion picture magazines containing photographs of all but three of the forty-eight guests; one pink silk lap-dog's pillow; one gentleman's safety razor with sapphire encrusted handle; one malachite cigar box containing one lady's one-piece bathing suit; fourteen empty brilliantine bottles; eleven gold, platinum, and enameled lipsticks; two dozen ice cream brick containers; one matrix and filigree anklet; one monocle; one tortoise-shell-back hair brush; one rabbit's foot mounted in diamonds.

Stunned, incredulous desert! Shades of sardine tins and hardtack! That is what it means to be a movie queen in Hollywood with the kind of blue and goldness that photographs.

This same little lady, who wears a pear diamond the size of an all-day sucker and whose dressing table is a human one consisting of two French maids standing side by side holding mirror-backed trays of all the enameled, the platinum, the rock crystal, the gold engraved objects of loveliness in the world, and whose bath is a sunken one with a jade green floor and a green jade frog spouting shower in the middle of it, sends checks every month aggregating thousands of dollars to the folks on the McMurtry side of the family back in Simmons Corner, Idaho, to say nothing of Ma's branch of the family that lies in splatters along most of the railroad-tie towns in Kansas.

Then there is a pension line list of those-who-knew-her-when that is almost half a yard long and to whom the second secretary remits monthly. There are a couple of endowed hospital beds, a special fund for disabled actors, a dog and cat hospital, a ballet school, a motion picture training school, and a veteran acrobat fund that all owe their being to the check book that lies on little blue and gold movie queen's Boule writing desk.

Little blue and gold movie queen invites four people to dinner and regales them with a six-piece orchestra in the alcove, but at the same moment, because of the heart inside little movie queen and that check book inside the Boule writing desk, a family named McMurtry, eleven of them, are eating fried ham, candied sweets, beaten biscuit, and corn pudding back in Simmons Corner, Idaho; in Los Angeles a couple of youngsters are getting the benefit of a very expensive radium treatment down a couple of maimed and poverty-stricken spines, and ten or a dozen I-knew-her-whens are blessing the ground she walks on.

Capitalism like little blue and gold movie queen's is not going to unseat empires.

It is actually and, paradoxical as it may sound, a benign capitalism.

The university that accepts little blue and gold movie queen's endowment need not be afraid of money tainted with anything more pernicious than the grateful and naive delight of the donor; a desire to please, and some of Lady Gay Spanker's impulse to wish the world had but one mouth that she might kiss it.

Kiss it back for making a darling of her. Throw her arms around it for throwing its arms around her.

Grateful! That's what Hollywood is.

Movie Subtitles — A Forgotten Art

That morning a country boy left home. He evidently expected to be gone for years —because he packed two shirts.

> George Marion, Jr., for the silent film *Warning Up*

"If you'd done as I told you this wouldn't have happened, you corpuscle!" "Corpuscle, my eye—I was a top sergeant!"

> Herman Mankiewicz, for *The Big Killing*

"Your eyes are like moonlit pools—your laughter like tinkling brooks—your wavy hair—your stream lines— . . . Pools, brooks, waves, streams! I seem to be all wet!"

> George Marion, Jr., for *The Fifty-fifty Girl*

Greg Lee, a dancer. His mother was a good soul, and his father was a heel.

> Joe Farnham, for *Rookies*

Scent o' the Blossom

by R. J. Denby

An Idyll of Springtime and Dawn and Everything

DORIS WINSLOW, a ravishing debutante, was the pampered daughter of millionaire Thermos K. Winslow.

As she was leaving her father's palatial New York home on Park Avenue one morning she collided with a tramp.

"Why the hell don't you look where you're going?" he said.

And as Doris raised her eyes to his she realized, for the first time, the meaning of love—love at first sight. For a moment she regarded the tramp's cute pink toes, peeping shyly through his shoes, and then, with a glad little cry, threw herself into his arms.

"I love you," she murmured, stroking the three days' growth of beard on his chin. She clung closely to him. The scent of his hair intoxicated her.

The tramp pushed her roughly aside, and hurried away in the direction of New Zealand.

[CAME DAWN.]

One day Doris decided to turn to music for consolation, and that afternoon took her first violin lesson. By four o'clock she had completely mastered the instrument.

The following night she gave a concert. The audience went wild, for never before had they heard the violin played with such skill.

Just about this time gold was discovered on Fifth Avenue.

Red Mike, the outlaw, was in Los Angeles when he heard of the rush. He immediately leaped into his saddle and rode for New York, reaching there about eight-thirty the same evening. Being a great lover of music, he parked his broncho in a drug store and strolled into the Deerfoot Opera House just as Doris was playing Jack Dempsey's "Lullaby in L, Op. 10 seconds." After the performance he waited for Doris at the stage door. As she emerged he removed his two-gallon hat and spurs, and, taking a diamond about the size of a coconut from his pocket, offered it to her.

Doris told him that she was not in the habit of accepting presents from strange bums.

Red Mike was enraged. He screwed his monocle into his eye and galloped off to his hotel and went to bed.

Now Red Mike had a sweetheart, an Italian named Listerina Cascara Sagrada, and she had seen him offer the diamond to Doris. Seething with jealousy, she crept up to Red Mike's room, and, following an old Italian custom, plunged a stiletto into his heart while he slept.

When Red Mike woke the following morning and found the stiletto in him he called loudly for help, and one of the bellhops went up and removed the dagger.

Later he wandered about, hoping to catch a glimpse of Doris. At last he saw her emerge from a bootlegger's store. He noted that she was delicately drying her mouth on the back of her hand.

Just as he was approaching her, he was accosted by a poor old man, who said, "Could you spare me a dime, sir? I haven't eaten in four years. I'm getting so hungry."

Without answering, Red Mike intercepted Doris.

At this moment an exhausted old dray horse fell on the road near them.

Sobbing with pity, Doris ran over, picked the tired animal up in her arms and carried it tenderly into the nearest hotel. She put it to bed, and, under her careful nursing, it commenced to grow strong.

During the horse's convalescence Red Mike contrived to see much of Doris.

Doris eventually became so attached to the horse she had befriended that she decided to adopt it. She took him South and entered him for the Kentucky Derby. Red Mike accompanied them.

Doris named the horse Southern Melody, because in the movies she had never seen a mustang bearing that name fail to win the Kentucky Derby.

At last the day of the great race arrived.

When Doris found that one hundred to one was the price on offer against her horse she put a million dollars on him. Now the bookmakers scorned the possibility of Southern Melody being able to win, but they did not feel inclined to take *any* risk about losing so much as a hundred million dollars, so just as the horses were going to the post one of the bookmakers rushed out and killed Southern Melody's jockey with a piece of lead pipe.

Doris dashed about frantically in search of another jockey, but none could be found. When she told her horse this he burst into tears. She was leading him back to his stable when his heartrending sobs attracted the attention of an old gentleman.

"I will ride your horse, miss," he said.

And without waiting to remove his silk hat, morning coat, or white spats, he leaped on Southern Melody and galloped to the post.

Now the starter was a bad man and had backed a horse called Teapot Dome to win him a large stake. Cunningly, he sent the jockeys off into the woods to gather wild flowers; all except the jockey of Teapot Dome. When the jockeys were some distance away from their horses the starter gave the signal to go, thus giving Teapot Dome an unfair advantage.

By the time Southern Melody started, Teapot Dome was leading the field by about three-quarters of a mile, but the courageous Southern Melody hurried after the leader, wore him down, and, amid indescribable excitement, crossed the tape a head in front of the animal that had been so favored by the starter.

The following day Doris, Red Mike, and Southern Melody were returning to New York on a special train with their vast winnings stowed away in two baggage cars when a man on the track signaled them to stop. Then some two hundred armed Mexican bandits suddenly sprang out of the bushes and demanded the money carried in the baggage cars.

Quick as lightning, Red Mike drew his sword and attacked the robbers. The battle lasted nearly three hours, but eventually Red Mike put them all to death. As he shook the last bandit from his sword a smiled played over his features, for he felt that after fighting so gallantly for her, Doris would at last consent to be his. He tried to take her in his arms, but she told him she had given her heart to another; a tramp she had once seen outside her father's house in New York.

Disappointed, Red Mike went to bed.

Later on a figure wriggled out from beneath one of the seats. It was the tramp with whom Doris had fallen in love. He explained that he had joined the Mexican bandits, but when he saw they were being beaten he deserted them and hid in the train. He said he had now decided to marry her and let her keep him for the rest of his life.

Doris ran to him and the tramp gathered her to him in a bear-like hug.

Hearing their ecstatic gasps, Red Mike peeped out of his berth, and the spectacle filled him with a paroxysm of jealous rage.

He leaped out and engaged the tramp in combat. They were both expert swordsmen and fought like wildcats, but eventually the tramp managed to fasten his teeth in the calf of his adversary's leg and render him powerless. And then, as the train was crossing a bridge, Doris held the door of the car open while the tramp hurled Red Mike into the rapids a thousand feet below.

"And that's that," remarked Doris, with quiet dignity.

[*FADE-OUT:*]

Doris and tramp in one long, clinging, clutching, suffocating, frenzied, devastating, catch-as-catch-can embrace.

THE END

"In Conference"

by Ring Lardner

HARVEY HESTER ENTERED the outer office of Kramer & Company, Efficiency Engineers. He approached the girl at the desk.

"I want to see Mr. Lansing," he said.

"A. M. or A. T.?" inquired the girl.

"Mr. A. T. Lansing," Hester replied.

"What is your name?"

"Harvey Hester."

The girl pressed a button and wrote something on a slip of paper. A boy appeared. She gave him the paper.

"For Mr. A. T. Lansing," she said.

The boy went away. Presently a young lady in mannish attire came out.

"I am Mr. Lansing's secretary," she said. "Did you want to see him personally?"

"I did and do," said Hester.

"Well, just now he's in conference," said the secretary. "Perhaps you would like to wait."

"Listen. This is pretty important——"

"I'm sorry, but it's against the rules to disturb any of the officers in conference."

"How long will the conference last?"

"It's hard to say," replied the secretary. "They just got through one conference and they're beginning another. It may be ten minutes and it may be an hour."

"But listen——"

"I'm sorry, but there's nothing for you to do but call again, or else wait."

"I'll wait," snapped Hester, "but I won't wait long!"

The conferees were sitting around the big table in the conference room. At the head of the table was J. H. Carlisle, president of the firm.

"Where is L. M.?" he inquired crossly. "This is the fifth conference he's been late to this morning. And we've had only six."

"Well, J. H. C.," said R. L. Jamieson, a vice president, "I don't think we ought to wait for him. If we drag along this way we won't be able to get in a dozen conferences all day. And a dozen was the absolute minimum agreed on."

"That's all right, R. L.," said K. M. Dewey, another vice president, "but it happens that L. M. is the one that asked for this conference, and he's the only one that knows what it's about. So we'd——"

At this moment the door opened and the tardy one entered. He was L. M. Croft, one of the vice presidents.

"I'm sorry to be late," he apologized, addressing J. H. C.

"I was talking over the phone to J. P. The reason I asked for this conference," he continued, "was to get your thought on a proposition that came up about twenty minutes ago. There was a post card in the mail addressed to the firm. It was from the main post office. It says they are holding a letter for us which reached them unstamped. If we sign the card and send it to them, together with a two-cent stamp, they will forward us the letter. Otherwise they will send it to the Dead Letter Office. The question is, is the letter worth the time and expense of sending for it?"

"Who is the letter from, L. M.?" The inquirer was S. P. Daniels, one of the vice presidents.

"The card didn't say, S. P.," replied Croft.

"My suggestion, J. H. C. and gentlemen," said A. M. Lansing, a vice president, "is to write to whoever is in charge of that office, authorize him to open the letter, see who it's from and what it's about, and if he thinks it important, to let us know, and then we can mail the required stamp."

"It's a mighty ticklish business, gentlemen," ventured Vice President T. W. Havers. "I have a brother, G. K. Havers. He's a pharmaceutical dispenser at a drug store on upper Broadway. He received a card like this from a branch post office. He signed the card and sent the stamp, and the letter turned out to be nothing but advertising matter from a realtor."

"Why, T. W.," said A. T. Lansing, "you never told any one of us you had a brother."

"O, yes, A. T.," replied Havers. "I've got two other brothers besides G. K. One of them, N. D., is a mortuary artisan and the other, V. F., is a garbage practitioner in Harrisburg."

"I'm one of a family of seven boys," put in Vice President B. B. Nordyke.

"I was born in Michigan," said H. J. Milton, the firm's secretary, "in a little bit of town called Watervliet."

"I'm a Yankee myself," said S. P. Daniels, "born and raised in Hingham, Massachusetts."

"How far is that from North Attleboro?" asked K. M. Dewey.

"It's right near Boston, K. M.," answered S. P. "It's a suburb of Boston."

"Philadelphia has some mighty pretty suburbs," said A. M. Lansing. "Don't you think so, R. L.?"

"I haven't been there for fifteen years, A. M.," replied R. L. Jamieson. "Last time I was there was in 1909."

"That was fifteen years ago, R. L.," remarked T. W. Havers.

"That's what I say, T. W., fifteen years," said Jamieson.

"I thought you said fourteen years," rejoined Havers.

"Let's see," put in C. T. Miller, treasurer of the firm. "Where was I fifteen years ago? O, yes, I was a bibliopolistic actuary in southern Ohio. I was selling Balzac complete for twenty-six dollars."

"Did you read Jimmie Montague's poem in the *Record* this morning, Z. H.?" inquired F. X. Murphy of Z. H. Holt.

"No, F. X.," replied Holt. "I don't go in for that highbrow stuff and anyways, when I get through my day's work here, I'm too tired to read."

"What do you do with yourself evenings, Z. H.?" asked A. T., the younger of the Lansings.

"O, maybe play the player piano or go to a movie or go to bed," said Holt.

"I bet there's none of you spends your evenings like I do," said young Lansing. "Right after dinner, the wife and I sit down in the living room and I tell her everything that I've done down here during the day."

"Don't she get bored?" asked S. P. Daniels.

"I should say not, S. P.!" replied young Lansing. "She loves it!"

"My sister Minnie—she married L. F. Wilcox, the tire people—she was over to the house last night," announced L. M. Croft. "She was reading us a poem by this Amy Leslie, the woman that got up this free verse. I couldn't make much out of it."

"Gentlemen," said J. H. C. at this juncture, "have you any more suggestions in regards to this unstamped letter? How about you, Z. H.?" he added, turning to Holt.

"Well, I'll tell you, J. H. C.," replied Holt, "a thing like this has got to be handled mighty careful. It may be all right, and it may be a hoax, and it may be out and out blackmail. I remember a somewhat similar case that occured in my home town, Marengo, Illinois."

"Did you know the Lundgrens there?" asked L. M. Croft.

"Yes, indeed, L. M.," answered Holt. "I used to go into Chicago to see Carl pitch. He was quite a card player, too.

But this case I speak of, why, it seems that S. W. Kline— he was a grass truncater around town—why, he received an anonymous post card with no name signed to it. It didn't even say who it was from. All it said was that if he would be at a certain corner at a certain hour on a certain day, he would find out something that he'd like to know."

"What?" interrupted the elder Lansing.

"I was saying," said Holt, "that in my home town, Marengo, Illinois, there was a man named S. W. Kline who got an anonymous post card with no name signed to it and it said that if he would be at a certain corner at a certain hour on a certain day, he would find out something that he'd like to know."

"What?" repeated the elder Lansing.

"Never mind, Z. H.," said J. H. C. "Tell us what happened."

"Nothing," said Holt. "Kline never went near the place."

"That reminds me," put in K. M. Dewey, "of a funny thing that came off in St. Louis. That's when I was with the P. D. advertising department. One afternoon the postman brought the mail to our house and my wife looked it over and found a letter addressed to some name like Jennings or Galt or something like that. It wasn't for us at all. So she laid for the postman next day and gave him back the letter. She said, 'Look here, here's a letter that don't belong to us at all. It's for somebody else.' I forget now just what the name was. Anyway, he took the letter and I guess he delivered it to the right people."

"I got some pretty good Scotch myself for fifty-six dollars a case," said S. P. Daniels. "It's old James Buchanan."

"Where did you get it, S. P.?" inquired Paul Sickles.

"I've got the phone number home," replied Daniels. "I'll bring it to you tomorrow, Paul."

Sickles was the only man in the outfit who was not an officer, so they called him Paul instead of by his initials.

"Prohibition's a joke!" said T. W. Havers.

"People drink now'days that never drank before," said S. P. Daniels.

"Even nice women are drinking," said L. M. Croft.

"I think you'll see light wines and beer before it's over," said K. M. Dewey.

J. H. C. spoke again.

"But what about this letter?"

"It seems funny to me," said A. T. Lansing, "that the people in the post office don't open it and find out what it's all about. Why, my wife opens my personal mail, and when I'm home I open hers."

"Don't she care?" asked S. P. Daniels.

"No, S. P.," said the younger Lansing. "She thinks everything I do is all right."

"My wife got a letter last week with no stamp on it at all," said Sickles. "The stamp must have dropped off. All it was anyways was a circular about mah jongg sets."

"Do you play with flowers, Paul?" asked K. M. Dewey. "Why——"

Harvey Hester, in the outer office, looked at his watch for the twentieth time; then got up and went to the girl at the desk.

"Please have Mr. Lansing's secretary come out here again," he said.

"A. M. or A. T.?" asked the girl.

"A. T.," said Hester.

The secretary came out.

"Listen," said Hester, "If I can't see Mr. Lansing right this minute it'll be too late."

"I'm sorry, but I can't interrupt him when he's in conference."

"All right," said Hester. "Will you please give him this message? You've got my name. Mr. Lansing and I were in school together and were more or less friendly. Well, I was tipped off this morning—I don't need to tell you how—I was tipped off that Mrs. Lansing is leaving for Chicago on the 12:05 train. And she isn't leaving alone. She's eloping. I thought Mr. Lansing might want to try to stop her."

"What time is it now?"

"Seven minutes of twelve," said Hester. "He can just make it."

"But he's still in conference," said the secretary.

Gertrude Ederle's Letter to Mom

IN THE ISSUE of September 25, 1926, *Liberty*'s editorial page was turned over to Trudy Ederle's letter home to Mom, after the New York girl had conquered the English Channel—

"My dearest loving Mother:

"We did it, Mother! We did it! The trick is turned and aren't you just so proud? We are all so happy. England and France are rejoicing in the glory. Oh, what crowds follow us here and there! The paper people are just impossible, but grand.

"Mom, I had that feeling of sure success—just wouldn't give up. Not once was I on the point of abandoning the swim. The good God led me on safely. It all went so quick. On Thursday night we decided to go, it looked so wonderful. And Friday, off we were, but soon to discover the weather was going back on us. Yet nevertheless I kept my mind clear. Then, when Julia Harpman told me that my family at home was at *The News* office to get the returns, oh, I suddenly became so thrilled. Could just picture you, dear Mother, waiting anxiously.

"Just couldn't give up then. You were with me on every stroke over. I did so much want to do it for you and make you feel proud of me.

" 'Get there or die; this day or never,' was my motto. Onto the pebbled beach of England I walked, no signs of weakness. Really, Mom, I can't dope it all out yet. To finish so easily was never in my mind.

"When they told me I still had three hours to go, away I went. The sea was terrible, but the small crowd I had on board was half my victory. They sang and cheered, pushed me on.

"Artie Sorenson didn't leave me a minute. He walked up and down the tug. No matter where I went, he was there.

"Margaret too was just lovely. Did everything in her power to help me get over. Didn't I say I need people like her? Pop, too, was helping me on, only he felt bad, I mean sorry, for me. He just had to cry and, Mommie, he wants to say that you are too soft!

"How happy and proud Pa is! No man could feel prouder. All he kept saying was 'You did it, MY KID!'

"Well, Mother, pray to God to see us home safely in your arms once again!

"Coming back from England yesterday they buried me in flowers.

"How happy everyone is.

"Last night Pop gave a party. We did it. No more worrying.

"Love and kisses galore for you, dear Mother. I am only your—

"Trudy."

What For?

by Westbrook Pegler

Counting Up the Fortune that Trudy Ederle Didn't Get

THERE SEEMS TO have been some mistake. When Trudy Ederle came home from France that day last August, to ride up Broadway through a public hullabaloo that left the gutters ankle-deep in ticker tape and kindred festive debris, there was talk of a career that would make her rich by Christmas.

But, as I say, there seems to have been some mistake; because when I saw Trudy the other day, pretty weary from trouping across the country and back in a fish-bowl vaudeville act, she was wondering how that fortune had got away from her. She was being paid $6,000 a week for her act on the stage, and she had been out nine weeks. But she said she didn't know just how to answer the amiable people who still greeted her along her way as America's own Trudy and asked her how it felt to be rich, because all is not gold that glitters, nor velvet either.

"But," I said, "six thousand a week is not bad."

"It's a lot, if you get it," said Trudy in that bawling voice of hers, she being somewhat deaf from the hammering of the water against her eardrums, "but I don't get it."

"Who does, then?"

"Well," she said, "William Morris, the agent for my act, takes ten percent."

"That's only six hundred dollars," I remarked brightly.

"Then there's a thousand a week for Dudley Field Malone, my lawyer—"

"What for?"

"He put up twenty-five hundred dollars to help pay my expenses when I went to France, and he acted as my lawyer and legal guardian."

"That's one thousand six hundred dollars," I said. "What else?"

"Then, there's another thousand a week for my father."

Trudy's father is wealthy. He owns a block of buildings on Amsterdam Avenue, New York,—or so he told me—and a thriving frankfurter factory, besides which he won a lot of money betting on Trudy against the Channel.

I mentioned this. Trudy was a little apologetic about Pop's insistence on a one-sixth share of her earnings, so I didn't crowd her.

We had marked off $2,600 of the $6,000 thus far.

"Then," she went on, "I have to pay one hundred and seventy-five dollars a week for a press agent. I don't know why I need a press agent, because everybody knows who I am, and if there has to be a press agent, I should think the theaters would pay him, because it's up to them to get the business into the house. And if there has to be a press agent and I have to pay him, I don't see why I have to pay him one hundred and seventy-five dollars a week, because it seems like an easy job to me. But they tell me I have to carry this man, so that's another hundred and seventy-five a week."

The $6,000 had now dwindled to $3,225.

"I've got to carry a manager, too," said Trudy. "He gets two hundred dollars a week."

"But," I interrupted, "I thought William Morris was managing you. What service do you pay him six hundred dollars a week for?"

"You see," Trudy admitted, with a baffled gesture of her pudgy hands, "I don't know much about this theatrical business; but, the way I understand it, Mr. Morris gets ten percent for getting me the bookings. This manager arranges about shipping the baggage and paying the hotel bills and buying the railroad tickets, and during the act he makes a little speech on the stage telling the people what's going on."

The $6,000 a week was now $3,025.

"What else?"

"Helen Wainwright and Aileen Riggin do a couple of dives in the tank to keep the people interested while I'm changing my clothes, and they get two hundred and fifty dollars each."

"Isn't that pretty good pay for divers in vaudeville?"

"I know of some who get only fifty or a hundred a week, but Helen and Aileen are former amateur champions."

"Does the girl who swam the English Channel in a gale need ex-champion divers to bolster up her act?"

"I didn't get up the act," Trudy said. "I guess I could get divers for less. But I'm not the manager, although it's my act and I pay off. The stage hand who sets up the tank gets one hundred dollars a week, too; but he earns his money."

There was $2,425 left of that magnificent $6,000 a week now.

"How much are you getting, yourself?" I asked her.

"Sometimes I think I cannot be making anything. I have to pay all the railroad fares, and we have seven people, because I carry my sister, Helen, along for company. And there are a lot of extras for stuff to use on the stage, and baggage charges for shipping the trunks and the tank, and bills for water to fill the tank. And out in California I was invited to a luncheon given by some newspaper men, and when we were leaving I got a voucher for sixty dollars. Then I discovered that I gave the luncheon!"

I recalled the anguish of Charlie Pyle, the promoter of Red Grange and Suzanne Lenglen, one day last fall as he totaled up Trudy's potential earning capacity on the back of a laundry list, and deplored the fact that she had not come under his management.

Pyle's grief was picturesque as he contemplated the amateurish handling of Trudy Ederle while the weeks slipped away and the public enthusiasm cooled.

"I would have snatched that kid home the minute she came out of the water on Kingsdown Beach, without even waiting to send her back to France for her clothes," said Pyle. "And when she landed in New York I would have rushed her straight uptown to the Yankee Stadium. I would have had a big glass tank on the infield, and I would have had fifty thousand people there at from three to five dollars a head.

"I would have sold testimonials to chocolate companies and bathing-suit and bouillon companies. I would have turned out a Trudy Ederle doll and a Trudy Ederle powder puff and a lipstick and brassiere and a step-in and a bathing-shoe, and I would have taken her over the jumps on one-night hops to the Coast, where I would have had a job in the movies waiting for her.

"That girl and I could have made five hundred thousand dollars. But I never would have let her old man take her to Germany to show her off to his old pals in the roadside *gasthäuse* for two weeks."

That part of it can't be remedied. Trudy did delay her start for home two weeks to visit her grandmother in Germany, and she did turn down a great deal of trade in Europe.

For instance, there was an offer of $3,000 for three days in Berlin. A London concern wanted to give her $500 for speaking a few words on the radio. A London theater asked her to name her own price for an appearance there. And Carl Laemmle, the American moving-picture producer, who chanced to be in Carlsbad at the time, sent his secretary over to interview Trudy in Stuttgart, with the idea of engaging her for a movie.

Trudy could have had this money, but she turned it all down because Mr. Malone, back in New York, had suddenly become very much alive and had cautioned her to do no business until she saw him.

The change in Mr. Malone after Trudy swam the Channel was remarkable to see. Weeks before she went into the water there had been a worrisome row on the beach there at Cape Gris-Nez, where Trudy was training, because old Bill Burgess, her trainer, had jumped his contract. Then, if ever, Trudy had need of Mr. Malone's legal services. The hotel at Cape Gris-Nez was a wretched place. The food was dreary, there was no bath, and the nearest barber was 300 francs away as the taxicab plies.

Trudy sent word of her distress to Mr. Malone, who was then in Paris; but Mr. Malone did not go to Gris-Nez, and the party on the beach, unversed in the laws of France, bought Burgess back with a bonus of 20,000 francs, and covered him with a homespun contract drawn up by hand, so to speak.

The American Bar Association really ought to have the original of that contract as a museum piece for its archives. But, though it was crude—like George Washington's bric-a-brac teeth, now to be seen among the knickknacks on the parlor whatnot in Mount Vernon, Virginia—the contract did the work. Burgess never got away again.

Up to this time I was what you might have called a member of the party without portfolio, as I had gone along to Europe with the expedition and up to Cape Gris-Nez. I didn't stay for the swim. But I hurled a few random *whereases* and *aforesaids* into that legal plum pudding that we got up for old Bill Burgess, and I know how badly Trudy needed some help from Mr. Malone about then.

I understood that Mr. Malone had put up $2,500 toward Trudy's expenses, but she never mentioned the fact that he had been granted one-sixth of her gross receipts. And as for Pop Ederle, the bighearted, bluff daddy of the kid who was going to swim the Channel, there was never any idea that he was going to take a sixth for himself.

Pop gave off the idea that he was a sportsman in this thing, and he let it be understood that he had put up $2,500 to match Malone's contribution.

I learned recently that Pop's contribution consisted of $1,500 of his own money and $1,000 that Trudy had earned and saved—which means, of course, that she is now paying him a royalty for putting up her own money.

In my experience among prize fighters and professional athletes in other lines, Trudy is the first one who ever paid her backers or managers a percentage of the gross receipts. Others invariably deduct the expenses before declaring dividends; and, of course, in Trudy's case, she would do much better if she were paying Mr. Malone and Pop each one-sixth of the net. Their shares would be about $660 a week at that rate, and they would have borne a share of the cost of the swimming tank.

I don't know what these loose-leaf glass bathtubs sell for as a rule, but Trudy paid $6,000 for hers, and she was told that this was a bargain. It seems that people were always willing to let Trudy have things cheap, like that, because they can't help liking her. That $6,000 came out of her net earnings.

In order to be sure of doing no injustice to Mr. Malone or Pop, I called on Mr. Malone and checked up.

Trudy's gross earnings to date had amounted to $64,-000. This included an advance of $5,000 from the New York *Daily News*, which came in as a third backer of the swim, and a further $2,500 from the *News* as a reward for her success.

The original $5,000 from the *News* was intended as expense money, but now it develops that the entire $7,500 was lumped in Trudy's account as earnings, subject to the usual deductions.

The gross account is composed of $54,000 for nine weeks in vaudeville, including one week at the Philadelphia Sesquicentennial; $7,500 from the New York *Daily News*, $1,000 from a manufacturer of bathing-suits, and $1,500 for an appearance in Tacoma in an otherwise idle week.

Now you begin to subtract. You deduct one-sixth for Mr. Malone, and one-sixth for big-hearted, sporting Pop Ederle, who backed Trudy partially with her own money —or $21,332. Then you deduct $6,000 for the tank, and

$8,775 as wages to the other members of the act, and $5,400 as a commission to Mr. Morris.

I have no details as to the traveling expenses of the troupe or other deductions from Trudy's $6,000 a week; but, inasmuch as the party crossed the country twice, I believe an average of $300 a week would not be unduly pessimistic. That would be another item of $2,700.

So the deductions amount to $44,207, and the remainder is Trudy Ederle's great fortune of $19,793. These figures are not exact; but the proportions are right, because Mr. Malone told me Trudy's own share of the money to date was about $20,000.

He said his share up to this time had been about $8,800; but this figure does not tally with the account of Trudy's gross earnings.

But there the girl was. She did the greatest athletic feat ever performed by a woman when she plugged on through the storm long after her own trainer and her father, with tears in his eyes, begged her to quit.

I have an idea that Trudy was "managed" out of a great opportunity. When she came home from France there were great possibilities in her for promotion; but her numerous family rallied around the kid and fought off friend and foe alike. They had money hysteria. They thought someone ought to pay Trudy $1,000 a whiff for breathing the air.

I don't know just where the errors in management occurred, but here you have the result. She swam the Channel on August 6, and on January 16 of the following year she had had just nine weeks' work in vaudeville. She is a pretty girl, but she has had no work in the movies; and the return from the so-called by-products that Red Grange, Babe Ruth, and so many others turned to a pleasant profit has amounted to just $1,000 from the bathing-suit concern.

Mr. Malone gave several weeks of his time, which certainly is worth money, and he advanced $2,500 without knowing whether he would ever get back the money, so I suppose he is entitled to a profit. The question in his case, then, is one of proportion.

His contract expires in May, although he says he could have taken the same share of her earnings for three years instead of for only one year.

I don't quite understand Pop Ederle's idea. He was wealthy and the father of the greatest girl athlete in the world. He had a pleasant summer among the Pilsner, the Würzburger, and the schnapps. He won enough money to repay all his expenditures and leave a profit, and also Trudy's achievement was a great advertisement for his frankfurter studio.

So the thought of bighearted Pop taking one-sixth of his kid's gross earnings, reduced as they are to a meager fraction of her expectations, brings back the cry that Trudy bawled through the wind and spray, that afternoon when old Bill Burgess and Pop were yelling for her to quit:

"What for?"

53

It's a Tough Life

a story by Viña Delmar

A Story of a Prodigal Husband Who
Found He Had a Prodigal Wife

HE WAS IN Jerry's garage when the call came. Damn it, why had he said where he was going? An interruption just when the dice were running his way. Eleven dollars ahead and Pinky, all smiles, telling him that he was wanted on the telephone. Pinky knew he was superstitious about interruptions.

"Hello." His voice was sharp and suggested that the party at the other end of the wire would state his business hurriedly if he knew what was good for him.

"Hello," said a woman's voice. "Mr. Russell?"

"Yeah."

"This is Mrs. Klein."

"Who?"

"Mrs. Klein. I got the apartment next door to you."

"Well, what about it?"

"Say, who you yelling at? I'm doing you a favor. I called to tell you your wife's got a bad pain."

"My wife's got a bad pain? Well?"

"Well, the doctor's there and he says it'll be all over in an hour. Maybe you'd like me to call and tell you whether it's a boy or a girl, you loafer, you!"

"Who are you calling a loafer, you damn meddler? It's a false alarm. Nothing'll happen for about two months yet."

"Oh, you're so smart, you Mr. Russell."

"And tell my wife to let me alone for a minute."

Dan hung up the receiver and strolled back to the boys.

"Make you sick," he mumbled. "If she complains of a toothache the whole doggone neighborhood's excited."

"What's the matter? Wife sick?" Jerry Sloane looked up from the dice with a kind, solicitous glance.

"Aw, I don't know. Maybe she's not feeling just right. But, hell, they think the kid's gonna be born right away and it can't happen before October."

Jerry Sloane smiled. "You got a contract to that effect?" he asked.

"No, but I can count."

Jerry's smile broadened to a good-natured laugh. "Gee, you're young, Dan," he said. "We got four kids and two of them were two months before their time."

"No kidding?" said Dan, astonished.

"So was my sister's kid," spoke up Pinky. "Gosh, I'll never forget it. I had her to a ball game when it started. I had her to a hospital and the kid was there before the game was over."

Dan thoughtfully lighted a cigarette.

Phil Harris, picking up the dice, rattled them impatiently. "You oughta go home," he said. "But if you're not the sort that goes home when your wife is having a baby, then for Pete's sake let the game go on."

"You think I oughta go, Jerry? Think it's really possible that—"

"Of course it's possible. Even if she only thinks it's her time, you oughta be there. Gee, Dan, don't nothing make you feel like going home?" Jerry's blue eyes were not accusing—merely curious.

Dan fled before that honest curiosity in Jerry's glance, the contempt in Phil's, and the uneasiness in Pinky's. He didn't want to go home. Colleen had a doctor, a nurse, and her mother. What help would he be? Besides, he was eleven dollars ahead.

But home he went, with a sulky frown on his good-looking face. Why the devil did women have babies the first year they were married? Here he was only twenty-three years old and a father—or would be shortly. Colleen was only twenty, but she was more settled. She wouldn't mind having to stay home nights. But he'd probably have to stay, too. Twenty-three years old and cooped up already! Dan Russell shook his head and his tawny mass of wavy hair.

At home, all was confusion. The nurse, starched and crinkling, hurried past him without a word. He heard the rumble of Dr. Porter's voice behind a closed door. Once he heard Colleen moan. An hour passed. Dan rose from his chair and walked to the window. An hour sitting still, doing nothing, and he had been eleven dollars ahead!

Colleen's mother rushed into the room. She was a small, frail woman with black bobbed hair.

"It's a boy," she said, wiping her eyes with a little important flutter.

"A boy?" said Dan. "How is Colleen?"

"Oh, she came through it beautifully."

"That's fine," said Dan.

He hoped he was saying the right things. He was a bit afraid of Colleen's mother. She paid the rent and furnished a twenty-dollar bill each Monday morning. He called her Mrs. Mayo and never swore in her presence.

"Would you like to see the baby?"

"Sure."

Dan followed her down the hall to Colleen's room. He wished Jerry were there to give him a few pointers on how to act with the kid. Colleen wouldn't know whether or not his technique was wrong; but there was Mrs. Mayo with her sharp, darting eyes and her twenty dollars every Monday morning.

Would they stick the kid right in his arms? Did you try to make it laugh, or did you look solemn and sort of impressed with the greatness of nature? Of course he could drop on his knees at Colleen's side and gaze at her adoringly, as he had seen it done in the movies; but that would be a little hard to put over convincingly. He didn't feel like dropping to his knees; he felt like running back to Jerry's garage.

Mrs. Mayo opened the bedroom door. A whiff of medicated air took his breath from him. Lengths of cotton were coiled in their blue paper skins on the table. Bottles stood around the room. A cotton pad hung over the window sill. Drying? Already?

Colleen smiled up at him from the bed. Dan said nothing. Could you speak to your wife so soon afterward? He stood still, watching Colleen's smile broaden into a little laugh.

"What's the matter, Dannie?" she asked.

"Nothing. How do you feel?"

"Fine. How do you feel?"

"Oh, I'm fine."

Mrs. Mayo sent him a look that would have shriveled an obelisk.

"Fine nothing," she informed Colleen. "The poor boy's been worried to death about you."

"Oh, of course," said Dan.

He managed a rather sickly smile. Could he mention the baby now? Was the baby a taboo subject? He supposed not. Mrs. Mayo herself had admitted that there was a baby.

"Where's the kid—er—the baby?"

Dr. Porter drew himself out of a conference with Colleen's nurse. The smile he turned on Dan was hardly heart-warming.

"The kid—er—the baby," he said, "is usually exhibited by the tactful nurse after the kiss that the happy father spontaneously and instinctively gives the young mother."

Dan felt a little sick. Doctors said such things and you just didn't ask them how they got that way. Dan remembered that Mrs. Mayo had said that Dr. Porter was gruff, but "such a darling."

"Such a darling" strapped his bag and departed.

Miss Connor moved starchily across the floor with a new blue blanket held with absurd carefulness in her arms. Oh, the baby was inside!

It was red and small and had its eyes closed. When blanket and contents had returned whence they had come, these were the only impressions retained by Dan—these and one other. It was red and small and had its eyes closed—and something else.

"Isn't he a darling?" asked Mrs. Mayo rapturously.

Just to answer "yes" seemed inadequate.

To say he was red would bring disaster.

To say he had his eyes closed would bring laughter, even from the prostrate Colleen.

To say that the baby looked as if it might at any minute remark on the fact that Dan had not yet kissed Colleen would bring the ambulance from the insane asylum.

"Yes," said Dan.

And the rolls of cotton rustled disapprovingly and the bottles clinked their scorn at the figure of young Dan Russell running down the hall away from his wife and her new-born babe.

Well, anyhow, on bright, sunny mornings, once a fellow got outside the house, it wasn't so bad. Inside, of course, it was terrible. If Colleen wasn't diapering the baby she was sterilizing his bottles. If she wasn't doing that, she was fixing his food—a mystic ritual that in some strange way upset the whole apartment.

It seemed to Dan that, regardless of what Colleen was doing, the brat was howling. Dan knew a guy whose wife had had a kid the same week little Bobby was born, and now, after eight months, the poor guy was still paying the doctor. Dan had never even seen the doctor's bill. He wondered idly just how much money Colleen's mother had. Enough, anyhow, to keep Colleen and the kid in clothes and to pay the rent and come across with the weekly assurance that, in any case, the Russell family wouldn't starve.

Dan wondered if he ought to be ashamed of taking Mrs. Mayo's money. Well, Colleen was her daughter, wasn't she? And if the old lady hadn't come through with a heavy coat that winter, daughter Colleen would have had to freeze.

Dan had had a hard time getting a job. People had to allow for those things. If his father had lived they'd all have been on Easy Street. His father had been a very important man in politics. Repeatedly Dan's father had told him so. Dan hadn't had to work. There'd always been decent clothes and a ten-spot now and again.

But the old man had died, and Dan, wearing his last decent suit, had met Colleen in a dance hall on 110th Street. She was beautiful—no doubt about that. Even guys who trailed around town in big cars took a second look at Colleen.

Dan had been thrilled when she had returned his experimental kiss with unexpected warmth. He'd been a little crazy to speak of marriage, perhaps, when he hadn't a job and was living "off" his sister, who taught school. But Colleen was a nice girl—affectionate, but nice. When you thought of borrowing ten bucks from your sister for a night at a hotel, you thought of a wedding ring, too, where Colleen was concerned. Colleen took care of that.

Within two days he had married her. She wouldn't take promises. He'd had to marry her, and had to look for an apartment, and had to look for a job, and had to listen to Mrs. Mayo describe what a generous soul she was going to be, and how she'd support Colleen grandly as long as Colleen's husband continued to be of absolutely no account.

And, after all that, what had he got? A baby the first year. And had Colleen broken the news to him gently with a half-finished bootie dangling from a knitting-needle? She had not. She had been violently sick at her stomach one morning, and had called him a fool because he hadn't been married before and didn't know from her actions that they were going to have a precious little baby.

Dan had found a job quickly enough after that. There isn't much fun around a house where a precious little baby is expected. Less fun after it arrives, thought Dan grimly as he turned the smart yellow roadster one door east of Fifth Avenue and stopped in front of a huge apartment house.

He had managed to get a job demonstrating Gillem-Prime roadsters. A straight commission job. Tough luck on the old lady. If Dan's success held out she'd still be supporting his grandchildren.

He had himself announced to a new prospect, and waited politely, hat in hand, for the prospect to arrive. The old lady had had to kick in last week with a suit of clothes for papa Dannie. A shabby demonstrator couldn't last in his firm, she had at length been made to understand.

Dannie smiled; and Dannie's smile, when it was a mixture of wicked glee and pleasant reminiscence, was a wonderful thing to behold. That smile of Dannie's was the first thing the new prospect saw.

She came toward him wearing a lovely shadow of Dannie's infectious smile.

"How do you do?"

Dannie said, "Miss Gordon?" and looked properly dazzled by Miss Gordon's oriental beauty. Of course, to some people, oriental beauty and a blaze of diamonds totaling somewhere in the neighborhood of forty-four carats seem a bit out of place at 10:30 o'clock in the morning. But Dannie's soul did not cringe, even at a smart sports outfit topped off with high-heeled satin pumps and a diamond anklet.

Dannie lifted Miss Gordon into the Gillem-Prime roadster. No, there wasn't any place she'd like to drive particularly. Yes, it was a beautiful day. Morning, had he said? No, she didn't remember having seen a morning before.

She took deep, appalling drags on a cigarette and sat back in the roadster.

"We've just made a car like this for Princess Valechevelli," said Dannie. "It is particularly adaptable for young ladies to drive because of—"

Miss Gordon turned huge, burning black eyes on Dannie's face.

"Don't do your act," she said. "My buying or not buying doesn't depend on the car. It depends entirely upon what mood I'm in."

Dannie laughed and plunged into the park.

"Anyhow, it's a good car," he said.

Miss Gordon closed her eyes, and even then didn't fail to wave back a cheery salute to a very chic and ugly girl who passed in a foreign car.

"I never miss anything," she remarked idly.

"Then you'll surely not miss the excellence of the Gillem-Prime roadster," Dannie answered, like a figure in a program advertisement.

"All the girls who walk back from automobile rides are sensible, self-respecting girls who won't permit themselves the boredom of listening to a demonstrator praising his car," said Miss Gordon warningly.

"Is that the only thing that would make you walk back?" asked Dannie.

"The only thing," replied Miss Gordon. "And I'm also a heavy drinker, in case it's my habits you're inquiring into."

They got along swiftly after that. Miss Gordon found out his first name and heard about Colleen and the baby.

"Such a model young American," she said mockingly. "A wife and a baby and an apartment uptown. Goodness, don't tell me you're not forging rapidly ahead through a correspondence course!"

"Did anybody ever forge rapidly ahead with a wife and baby hanging on his neck?" asked Dan.

Miss Gordon's eyes sought the topmost point of a faraway tree. She was older than Dannie. She had just remembered something that must have happened about the time when Dannie was getting into long trousers. She laughed the memory away.

Dannie had luncheon with Miss Gordon. Her apartment was tinted an exquisite pale green, and seemed at first glance to be furnished with ash trays and parrakeets. After a few minutes your bewilderment died away and you saw a golden divan, a chair with a back that reached its delicate carvings halfway to the ceiling, a marble nymph. Over puzzling edibles that a silent beige-colored woman served, Miss Gordon announced that she would buy the car if Dannie would teach her to drive.

"Colleen, I swear if that damn kid lets one more yip out of him, I'm going to choke him. I gotta go to work tomorrow. I can't lie here all night and listen to him shout."

"Honey, he's sick. That tooth—"

"Well, if he's sick, get Doc Porter or a dose of arsenic or something."

"Dr. Porter is in midocean with his wife and children."

"Then give the janitress a dollar to keep him in her place again tonight."

"I'm superstitious about that crib of hers, Dan. Her baby died in it, you know."

"Well, take our kid down there and see if we have any luck."

Colleen's mother was furious because Dan hadn't remembered the baby's birthday. She herself had arrived with a little white glimmering cake bearing with absurd dignity its one small candle, a woolly bathrobe, a cow that could utter a mournful *moo*, a Teddy bear, a silver spoon, and a jack-in-the-box.

Bobby stood up in his high chair and screamed lustily with delight.

"You poor baby," said Mrs. Mayo. "Grandmother and poor little mamma have to make up to it for its father's thoughtlessness."

"I got him a kiddie car," said Colleen listlessly.

Mrs. Mayo's lips tightened. "I don't suppose Dan has telephoned or anything," she said.

Colleen flushed. "No," she said. "He's busy, I guess."

"Yes—busy with that woman. I give you my word of honor, Colleen, if your father had ever brought a woman like that into our house, I would have put them both out."

"Oh, mother, it's different now than when you were young. All women look bad. It's the style to wear rouge and extreme clothes."

"I know." Mrs. Mayo paused to prepare the cow for a mighty *moo* and continued:

"The way she acted toward Dan, though—as if she owned him! And he calls her by her first name, whatever it is."

"Adorée," Colleen supplied.

"Yes, Adorée."

Bobby went off into a gale of laughter. Mrs. Mayo plucked him from his throne and held him against her heart.

"Poor baby, you don't realize now, but some day you'll know that your father is the scum of the earth."

Colleen found her mother's eyes and their gazes locked.

"Don't you tell him that—even now," she said tightly. "I don't care what you think, but Bobby's impressions are important."

"Oh, well—" Mrs. Mayo retired defeated. "You picked him and you have him. Thank God, I hadn't one like him."

Later, when Bobby had been tucked into his crib with the jack-in-the-box and his silver spoon for company, Mrs. Mayo took her departure.

"Don't jump on me," she counseled with her parting kiss; "but, daughter, don't take too much from that yellow-haired bum."

Colleen smiled and promised. She kissed her mother affectionately and listened till the street door slammed. Then she threw herself on the divan—which was not golden, but gray and old rose (ninety-eight dollars, with two chairs to match)—and gave herself up to despair.

At midnight Dan came in. Colleen jumped up quickly from the fretful doze into which she had fallen and ran to the door. Adorée Gordon followed Dan down the hall.

Premonition clutched at Colleen's throat. Climax! There was climax stamped on the overcasual way in which Dan greeted her; climax in the friendly smirk on Miss Gordon's face.

"Are you alone?" Dan asked.

"Yes, I am," answered Colleen. "Mother was here. It's the baby's birthday, you know."

"Oh, yes," said Dan.

Miss Gordon settled herself on the divan and tore her tight turban off her glistening black hair. Dan sat precariously on the arm of a chair.

"Colleen," he said, "I have something to tell you—in fact, we have something to tell you. Did you ever think that perhaps we—"

Miss Gordon coughed into the fur at her throat.

"He'll go by way of China to tell you, Mrs. Russell," she said. "Briefly, Dan and I are in love with each other, and it's up to you whether you'll give Dan a divorce and let us marry, or whether we'll have to continue as we've been doing for the past few weeks."

It occurred to Colleen, with cool irrelevance, that Miss Gordon was accustomed to telling servants, without loss of breath, exactly what she wanted done.

Dan was obviously embarrassed. He would have preferred a more roundabout method of explanation. He remembered the morning he had seen Adorée buy 100 acres of land: her expression at this moment reminded him of the real-estate transaction.

Colleen's fingers toyed nervously with the tie on her sweater. She admired Adorée. It would have been impossible for Colleen to have held the situation under full control if she had been a woman calmly asking for another woman's husband! Colleen admired Adorée and gave a short consideration to the dollar sign that brought moral support as well as material luxuries.

"Why, you've rather stunned me," she said. Her hand wandered from the tie to her brown hair. Her fingers raked through it aimlessly. "Understand, I'm not terribly grief-stricken. Dan hasn't been a model husband to me. If you'll just stay awhile and try to act natural—that's for you, Dan—I'll be myself in a minute and we can talk this over."

Miss Gordon's eyes said "Good girl," and Dan developed a sudden thirst that sent him to the kitchen for a glass of water. Colleen sat thinking over her short married life.

Her mother would be glad that she was rid of him. The baby wouldn't miss Dan. And as for herself—she was young yet. She wasn't in love with Dan now. Many a time she had hated him.

Dan returned from the kitchen with a glass of water for Colleen. The slogan from an undertaker's advertisement flitted through Colleen's brain: "A comforting thought that the last service has been done correctly."

She drank the water. Miss Gordon lighted a cigarette. Dan sat down and crossed his legs with painful nonchalance.

"I'm myself again." Colleen smiled across at Adorée. "Of course I haven't been debating whether or not Dan could be free. That goes without saying. He's as free as he likes. It was details I was considering."

"Well, of course," said Dan, "you may keep the baby."

A paroxysm of laughter shattered Colleen's poise. "And the picture of my mother?" she asked. "Oh, Dan, please say I may keep that picture."

Dan colored with annoyance. Some people couldn't keep on talking with impersonal ease.

"I was about to say," said Miss Gordon, "just before Dan made an ass of himself, that I'd like to give your baby a birthday present of ten thousand dollars. Would that be acceptable, Mrs. Russell?"

Colleen shook her head. "That would be profiteering, Miss Gordon," she replied.

"Mayn't I make a settlement on him or you?" Adorée's tone was full of awe.

"No, thank you," said Colleen.

Miss Gordon admired Colleen. It would have been impossible for Miss Gordon to refuse $10,000, even in her present financial state, and to be situated like Colleen and still have the strength to refuse. Miss Gordon admired Colleen!

The divorce would be arranged without any inconvenience to Mrs. Russell. "Thank you, Mrs. Russell, for being such a beautiful sport." "Don't mention it, Miss Gordon; I don't believe in making difficult situations more difficult." "Good-by, Colleen, you were wonderful. Lots of luck." "Good-by, Dan; be happy; and lots of luck to you, too."

Alone once again. Colleen did not fling herself on the divan this time. She tiptoed into the bedroom and looked down at Bobby. A tear should have dropped tragically on his little upturned, slumber-flushed face. But nary a tear put in its appearance. Colleen slipped out of her clothes and slid between the cool white sheets of her bed. She was asleep in five minutes.

"Adorée, if that damn mutt of yours don't stop barking I'm going to break his neck. I haven't had any sleep for three nights."

"Dan, you're too funny. After two years of being married to me, don't you know yet that if any neck on these premises gets broken it will be yours?"

"Is that so?"

"Oh, absolutely. I had Binxie before I had you, and I'll have Binxie after you're gone. Now, shut up. I can sleep through his barking, but not through your whining."

Dannie didn't think Europe was so wonderful. Adorée met people whom she knew in every city—as, indeed, she would have in the Sahara Desert. These people were very apt to forget all about Dan and to carry Adorée off somewhere for hours. When he was along he didn't have such a good time, either, for these old friends of Adorée's were always recalling wonderful evenings that had been spent with Adorée and Charles.

"Poor Charles," they would say. "So young to die!"

Adorée would shrug those shoulders and mention the fact that younger men than Charles had perished by the thousands a few years before, and probably none of them had left a woman as happily placed as Charles had left his beloved Adorée.

It made Dan a bit uncomfortable. Not that Dan was jealous of poor deceased Charles. There were too many rivals this side of Purgatory for Dan to be nursing any grudge against Adorée's former husband, or whatever had been the gentleman's status.

Rivals indeed, and by the carload. Young and very English Craig was by far the most dangerous. He was Dan's age, but so polished that he radiated little well groomed points of light. Also, he was poverty-stricken; and the way he could ease smooth wedges of flattery into Adorée's consciousness was a never-ending source of dismay to Dan. Craig was fond of Adorée's dog. Dan began to write finis to this chapter of his life when he discovered that Craig and Binxie were inseparable pals.

When Adorée broke the terrible news to him, he grew cold and sick all over.

She had young Craig with her when she told him. Dannie considered it wretched taste for her to bring Craig along.

"I don't even like you any more, Dan," she said. "I don't intend to marry Richard, so you won't have the chance to hold me up for a nice, stiff price for freedom. If you want to divorce me when you get enough money to do so, go ahead. It's immaterial to me."

"But, Adorée, I'm broke. I haven't a cent."

"That's the way you were when I got you."

"But at least I was in America."

"So you were. Well, I'll give you your passage."

Dan glared at Richard Craig. "And you—I could murder you, you damn wife-stealer."

"Ah, don't murder him, Dannie. Think of all the effort it would take to get manhood enough for that."

"Don't talk so mean to me, Adorée; I love you."

"Yes, you do." Harsh irony was in Adorée's voice. "You love my bank book. A long while ago, Dannie Russell, when you didn't know yet that I was going to own you, I put you wise to the little fact that I miss nothing. You were too dumb to profit by my tip. I know about Helen Banks in London, and that bow-legged brunette in Munich, and the other two also. That's where my money went."

"Why, Adorée!"

"Why, Dan!"

Adorée vanished then, with a gay whisk of a gold-lace flounce and a metallic sparkle of slim, perilous heels. Dan could hear her and Richard Craig laughing at the foot of the stairs.

It was funny to be back in America and to be unattached. Nothing to do—nowhere to go. Adorée had relented at the last moment and given him $100 over his passage. That wouldn't last long. He had to get a job. Thank God, he had clothes.

Maybe they'd take him back at the Gillem-Prime place. A job would give him a chance to see people, to make friends. It was as lonesome as the devil, sitting around at nights in a furnished room without a soul to talk to.

They were very sorry at the Gillem-Prime office, but they couldn't take him on now. Oh, yes, they remembered him. He'd left without a notice, hadn't he?

He found that jobs were a little scarce. Of course one would arrive in time, but for the present he'd have to be very careful of his money. It was the cursed loneliness that he minded most, a loneliness that gripped him when night began to fall over the city and lights flamed in a million windows.

He thought of Colleen and Bobby then. Bobby must be almost four years old now. And Colleen—had she married again? He was curious to know what changes the months had brought to her, and he was hungry for companionship.

She had moved from the place where they had lived together. A blonde, curly-haired girl with a sticky child clinging to her skirt lived in that apartment now. She had never heard of Mrs. Dan Russell.

He thought of his sister. He knew he didn't have the nerve to get in touch with her. He owed her money, borrowed in the days before his marriage to Colleen, that he had not repaid during his days of splendor with Adorée. But it would be some comfort to search for her name in the telephone book and just look at it. She had been a good scout. Poor Catherine, he hadn't treated her right.

He took the book from the floor beneath the community telephone and carried it over to the light. "Russell. Carl Russell. Carrie Russell." There it was—"Catherine Russell." Still at the same address.

That had been a cozy apartment—a lot better than a furnished room. He took his finger off the space directly under Catherine's name and jumped a little. "Colleen Russell." Was it possible? Then she hadn't married again. Where was she living? Holy Mother! On Riverside Drive. What was she doing there?

He rushed impetuously to the telephone—then paused. Perhaps, if he telephoned first, she wouldn't see him. She was probably hitting the high spots—going in for easy money. And what about Bobby? A wave of indignation swept over Dan. The idea of her being loose-moraled when she had her child to think about!

He decided that he'd go over there. If she was out he wouldn't leave his name. He'd just keep going till he found her at home.

It was a private house, and a typical stage butler opened the door. Dan was admitted to a room which he recognized as the type that always angered Adorée. Adorée hadn't known how to make rooms look spacious and expensive at the same time.

A tall lady with eyes like perfectly matched topazes entered the room with his card in her hand.

"You're—Daniel Russell?" she asked.

"I am."

"How do you do? I'm Mrs. Norris. I've heard about you, of course. Colleen and Bobby are staying here for the season with my husband and me. I intercepted the butler because Colleen has been rather ill and I don't want her upset. Is this to be a strictly social call or do you mean to be unpleasant?"

Meddling, of course, but sweet. Rather beautiful and vaguely familiar. The photograph that hung above her head, of a tragic-looking young man with sideburns, was familiar, too. What was this place?

Dan smiled his winning smile.

"I assure you, Mrs. Norris, I'm only anxious to chat for a pleasant minute or two with Colleen. May I not see her?"

Mrs. Norris melted. "I guess you might," she said with an answering smile.

She turned to go.

"Mrs. Norris, may I ask who is that man?"

She followed Dan's eyes to the photograph. "Why, that's my husband—Newton Norris."

If Dan had not known, he felt that her tone would have informed him that Newton Norris was the world's most famous film comedian. It was said that he earned $1,000,000 a year. Dan blinked.

The lovely lady trailed gracefully up the staircase. Abovestairs he heard voices—women's voices. One belonged to Mrs. Norris; the other was Colleen's. It reached across the years and recalled Jerry's garage, Colleen leaning out the window watching for him, dinner steaming on the table. He pulled his hand suddenly out of his pocket. He had been fondling his last twenty-dollar bill.

Mrs. Norris' words could be understood now. She had evidently escorted Colleen to the head of the stairs.

"I told Newt not to let you put your name in the phone book. Everybody who matters knows that you live with us."

Dan stiffened. Everybody who matters, indeed! Then an ex-husband didn't matter to Mrs. Norris. Dan had always heard that moving-picture people held loose views on the matrimonial state.

Before he was fully prepared for it, Colleen bounded into the room. She looked like a child of sixteen. Her hair was cut close to her head and it waved intriguingly. Her figure was slim and boyish.

"Hello, Dan." She seemed to bounce toward him with one hand extended in a friendly yet casual fashion.

Mrs. Norris had reckoned mistakenly when she had pictured a tremulous reunion.

"Hello, Colleen. How're tricks?"

"Fine. And with you?"

"Not so good. Adorée and I split."

Sincere sympathy spread over Colleen's face. She would have been delighted, thought Dan, if she herself were unhappy.

"Too bad, Dannie."

Colleen seated herself.

"How's Bobby?" Dan asked.

"He's fine."

"You're in the movies, eh?"

"I?" Colleen looked shocked. "Goodness, no. What could I do?"

"Well, you're beautiful."

"That isn't enough," said Colleen, "despite public opinion. I'm not deep like Mrs. Norris or brilliant like her husband."

"Oh, you're just staying here?"

"Yes, till Bobby and I go back to Hollywood. The Norrises are going then, too. Bobby has one more picture to finish with Mr. Norris, and then he begins to star in his own right."

"What! Bobby!"

"Why, Dan, haven't you even heard of Bobby Russell? Where have you been? Why, Mr. Norris thinks Bobby hogged all the honors in their last picture."

"I've been in Europe," said Dan absently.

"So has the picture."

"Adorée didn't care for Mr. Norris," said Dan.

He was stunned. Bobby starring in his own pictures! Colleen looking beautiful and expensive. Dan fingered his last twenty-dollar bill thoughtfully.

"Say, Colleen, I'd like to see the kid."

"He's out driving just now with his governess, and when he comes back he has to take a nap. There's a dinner tonight he must go to."

"You're not trying to keep me from seeing him, are you?" asked Dan suspiciously.

Colleen arose from the chair. "And if I am?"

"Well, look here. If it comes right down to it, you can't keep me from seeing him or from cashing in on his beauty or cleverness or whatever the hell he's got. I'm that kid's father."

The nymph Colleen shook her pretty head gently.

"Dannie, old boy," she said, "you're not. Sorry to break it so crudely, but, you see, Bobby was not premature."

"Why, you little—" An obscene word died on Dannie's lips. Newton Norris strolled past the portieres—a careless, quiet reminder that Colleen was among friends.

Colleen threw her head back proudly.

"Your instinct knew he wasn't yours. Did you ever love him? Were you ever even as kind as a stranger might be?"

"I could murder you for this."

"Wait. What have I done to you, after all? You wanted me. I didn't force myself on you. I gave myself unstintingly and was faithful to you throughout our married life. Never a cent of your money was spent on Bobby or me, and I released you when you wanted to go. Now what do I owe you?"

A new thought struck Dan.

"You're a liar," he said decidedly. "You're afraid of me touching Bobby's money. He *is* mine."

"Ask Dr. Porter," advised Colleen. "He knew about it before I even met you."

"Yes; and I'll bet that Dr. Porter—"

Newton Norris stuck his famous head between the portieres.

"Have you seen my book, Colleen?" he asked.

"No," said Colleen.

Newton Norris withdrew. Dan smiled. It had been so obvious a little trick. If Colleen had wanted Dan thrown out, she was to have answered "yes" to Norris' question.

He drew himself together. "Well, I guess I'll be going," he said.

He walked toward the door and Colleen followed.

"Dan, are you in any trouble?"

"What do you mean, trouble?"

"I mean money trouble."

Dan looked down at his shoes and registered refined reticence. "Well, to tell the truth, Colleen—"

A glimmer of jewels as a tiny purse flashed out of Colleen's pocket.

So she had come to meet him prepared. The little—! She'd expected him to ask for money. Well, he'd be damned if he'd—

"Here's fifty, Dan," said Colleen.

"Gee, thanks, Col."

Dan's hand closed over the bill. The door slammed behind him.

Tongue Twisters

*For every Tongue Twister published in
these columns LIBERTY will pay $5*

*A Tongue Twister is something that makes your tongue
stumble. "Around the Rugged Rock the Ragged Ruffian
Ran" is a Tongue Twister. What's your favorite? Address
Tongue Twister Editor, LIBERTY, Tribune Sq., Chicago*

Five fearless, feathered flamingoes flew from fiercely fuming forest fires.—*Jack Mariner, Chicago.*

Winsome Winnie Winkle willingly whistles wistfully.—*W. C. Kumpfer, Chicago.*

Terrible twisting tongue tanglers twist tangled tongues terribly.—*Marie Falkenthal, Chicago.*

Tilly Titter tried to teach Tommy Taylor tricks.—*Mrs. C. B. Anderson, Chicago.*

Funny Fanny's father finds Ford for Fanny's father family Ford.—*Miss Loretta Finn, Chicago.*

Busy bluebirds brightly build between big blooming branches.—*Edward Kurth, Chicago.*

Tiffany Taft's tanks thank Tammany Tiff's tramping tommies.—*Mrs. John Dittsworth, Freeport, Ill.*

Sammy Shannon shivered shining slim Sylvester Slocum's shoes Sunday.—*Margaret Austin, Chicago.*

Prudy Prexie puffed profusely picking pears.—*Margaret Braun, Cincinnati, O.*

Pretty Polly preserved peaches Peter Prichard picked.—*Robert Kiener, Johnstown, N. Y.*

Peter painted Polly's pretty parrot pink.—*Catherine Cassin, Chicago.*

Balmy breezes blew Billie's big blue bubbles.—*Lloyd Lewis, Chicago.*

Fair Fannie's father fought furiously for freedom.—*Helen Weber, Oshkosh, Wis.*

Samuel Sylvester shut Sarah's single shingled shutters.—*M. McFall, Germantown, Pa.*

Many manufacturing manufacturers manufacture merchantable merchandise.—*W. Pietraszek, Hammond, Ind.*

Proper Polly petulantly prohibits Peter Plopper's petting.—*Mrs. Francis Morrissey, West Brooklyn, Ill.*

Arthur's Adam's apple attracts Alice's assiduous attention. —*Miss K. Ryan, Clayton, Mo.*

Salvation Sally served several shell-shocked soldiers sandwiches.—*Mary McFall, Philadelphia, Pa.*

When will Winnie Winkle wed, we wonder?—*Billy Fitzgerald, Chicago.*

Sociable Sally Sachs spends Sundays swimming.—*Mrs. R. E. Hadley, Chicago.*

Sandy Sammy Samson saw Sally Sanders sew socks.— *Samuel L. Hane, Wheeling, W. Va.*

Betsy Brown bakes bigger biscuits by buying better butter. —*George Plankenhorn, Erindale, Ont.*

Sue Shedd saw Simon Seths' shed.—*Robert O'Neill, Stamford, Conn.*

Cousin Clarence censored coquette Constance's costly costume.—*Lona Machler, Chicago.*

Shy Susie sat singing sea songs sweetly.—*G. Mariner, Chicago.*

Red ruffles raise ructions round royal Russian rosters.— *I. Travers, Chicago.*

Sarah Shannon sold six silk shawls.—*M. Sullivan, Chicago.*

Hatty Hixom's husband's horse hurt his hoof.—*Martin Bowes, West Philadelphia, Pa.*

Friendly, fleshy Flossie fed Farmer Fred's father flounder fish.—*Marie Lawrence, Chicago.*

Faithful, forlorn Freddy followed fair, frivolous, flitting Freda.—*Anna Gentry, Maywood, Ill.*

Gloomy Gussie's glazed glasses glittered glaringly.—*Gertrude Anderson, Chicago.*

Pretty Patsy Pumpernickel preferred pickled pretzels picked promptly.—*W. Carnelli, Chicago.*

Pretty Patty Parker practices prelude pieces patiently.— *Helen Dupont, Fall River, Mass.*

Some silly saps save sloppy soap suds.—*Frances Kingsley, Chicago.*

Laughing lively, little Lillie lisps lots.—*Mrs. J. O'Brien, Chicago.*

Silly Sally Saucer sits sewing Sammy's stockings.—*Josephine Wezeman, Chicago.*

Bertha's big brother Ben bowled big balls breathlessly.— *Mrs. William Barry, Chicago.*

Dan dangled dazzling daggers dangerously.—*Jean Neill, Chicago.*

Terrence tried till twelve to teach Tommy typing.—*Harris Persons, Marshall, Minn.*

Frantic Florence finished Flora's fussy frock Friday.— *Agnes Moore, Los Angeles, Cal.*

Prudent Polly politely pardoned Peter's perky pun.—*Mrs. Louis Renschlein, Burlington, Wis.*

Peter pawned Polly Pepper's pretty pink pearls.—*Hazel Unverzagt, New York City.*

Four ferocious foxes fought five furious ferrets.—*Mary Pastoret, St. Paul, Minn.*

Sunday Simple Simon sat solving sums.—*Josephine Costigan, Chicago.*

Surely Shirley shall see Saul's show.—*George Blumenthal, Detroit, Mich.*

Peter purchased Pansy's priceless pup, Pal.—*Grace Kiener, Melvin, Ill.*

Silk socks soaked soapily sometimes save splitting seams. —*Mrs. I. Cunningham, Chicago.*

Six sleek, slick shaven sheiks sent Shebas silk stockings.— *Mrs. M. S. Ensrud, Rushford, Minn.*

Thousands thronged Tillie Tooley's theater Tuesday.— *Patsy Finn, Austin, Ill.*

Many mathematicians make mathematical mistakes.—*Ben Stolarz, Hammond, Ind.*

"Razor Rastus" raced rarin' running, ragged rascal.— *Walter G. Horton, Chicago.*

Sweet Sylvia served several shrimp sandwiches Sunday.— *Catherine McGuire, Chicago.*

Billy Brooks bought buxom Beatrice beautiful beads.— *Mrs. M. Byron, Litchfield, Ill.*

Fair French fashion fascinates foreign females.—*Mrs. L. Constant, Hartsdale, N. Y.*

Bright Sayings of Children

Bright Sayings of Children

SHE WAS WILLING TO TRADE
My neighbor the other day took her baby that had for the last week always been fretful and crying to the Childs' Welfare Bureau. Her little daughter, Mary, went with her, prattling all the way. In the office half a dozen babies reposed on cots, some awake, and some sleeping. When her turn came and the nurse took the little one on her lap and asked a few questions, Mary sidled up to the nurse and in a low tone said, "I would like to have one of these other babies; they are so much nicer to play with and smile when I look at them, and don't cry."—*F. A. D., South Bend, Ind.*

KIND O' TOUGH ON THE DOG
My little nephew and niece were told that the little dog their father brought home belonged to them jointly. During a terrible racket one day his mother found little Everett grinding the dog's tail with his heel. When reprimanded he replied defiantly: "I'm standing on my part and it's her part that's making all the noise."—*B. M., Pawtucket, R. I.*

PIE WITH BUTTONHOLES
I made a pie and as usual put little slashes in the crust to let out steam while baking. In serving the pie, I cut a small piece for Helen and it was quite smooth on top, while some of the other pieces had these little openings. Helen said: "I don't see why I can't have buttonholes in my pie, like daddy has."—*Mrs. E. J. M., Joliet, Ill.*

WHAT'S AN "IWWEGGALIE" DOG?
Coming in from a stroll along the street four-year-old George told his mother he saw a nice dog. Trying to appear interested she asked, "What kind of a dog?" and he answered, "Oh, just a weggalie (regular) dog, two feet afront and two feet ahind."—*J. I. C., Milwaukee, Wis.*

SHE'D FIX HIM!
Anna Katherine, aged five, became very much disgusted with the disobedience and unseemly conduct of another child toward his mother. She stated emphatically, "If he were my child I'd spank his pants, with him in 'em."—*O. W. D., Evanston, Ill.*

HE WASN'T "SECOND HAND"!
Little Mary was chatting with one of the visitors who had come to see the new baby that had arrived the day before.
"And how old is the little man?" asked the visitor.
"Why," said Mary in astonishment, "he isn't old at all. He's brand new!"—*L. G., Montreal, Can.*

"TUMMY" WAS HIS CLOCK
"Mamma, is it lunch time yet?"
"No, darling, not for another hour."
"Well, then, my tummy must be fast."—*F. A. S., Omaha, Neb.*

THAT'S AS PLAIN AS CAN BE
Mary had been watching her mother plant seeds in a flower pot filled with dirt. Finally she spoke up:
"I know why the seeds grow, mamma."
"Why is it then?" asked her mother.
"Because they want to get up out of the dirt."—*F. W. B., Cincinnati, O.*

IT WAS A PUZZLE!
Wynona, my kiddie of four, insisted one day on giving herself her own bath, unaided. I consented, but told her to remember her neck and ears. After a while a troubled little voice called, "Mother, how you 'pects me to wash my neck when it's behind and I'm in front?"—*Mrs. S. H., Fort Worth, Tex.*

WELL—WHY DON'T THEY?
Billy had been tucked in bed on a cold night. Asked if the bed felt cold, he replied, "Yes, daddy; but isn't it funny that the covers don't keep the bed warm?"—*B. F. B., Riverdale, Md.*

HOW DID HE GUESS THAT?
Michael's mother was eager to have her son speak correctly. One day she heard him talking to his dog, and his English was not standard. She called Michael's attention to the fact. "Aw, mother," said the little fellow. "Capers doesn't care."—*R. D. Van H., Denver, Colo.*

Flying Against Death

by Bogart Rogers

The Story Behind the Tragic Air Race to Honolulu

[EDITOR's NOTE: Captain Bogart Rogers, author of this article, was a combat flight officer with the British Army from April, 1918, until the Armistice. He has since done considerable flying along the Pacific Coast and was in close touch with the conditions of which he writes. Much has been published of the trans-Atlantic flights in which, from the disappearance of Nungesser and Coli to the present writing, ten lives have been lost. But little has been told of the reasons that brought failure and tragedy to seven fliers in the Honolulu air race. Captain Rogers tells about it here.]

FIFTEEN GAMBLERS ENTERED a mad scramble for fame and fortune. Nine men and one woman died, the latter and six of the men in the ocean.

A naval lieutenant was abused and strenuously opposed in his efforts to prevent them from committing suicide.

There was no law to keep them from killing themselves if they cared to.

Eight airplanes, representing a considerable outlay of capital, were destroyed.

The United States navy spent a small fortune in a vain attempt at rescue.

The brilliant successes of Lindbergh, Chamberlin, Byrd, and Maitland were practically nullified. Public confidence in the airplane was shaken. The nation was profoundly shocked.

The future of aerial transportation was plunged back into the doubt from which it was just emerging. Flying received a black eye it might have avoided.

And so the race from San Francisco to Hawaii for the Dole prizes will go down in the books as the "Great What-Was-It" of aviation.

The records of hazardous sport show no event that claimed so many lives and accomplished so little. It is a black page in flying history.

How did it happen, and why? Who was to blame? Could it have been avoided? What did it accomplish? Was it worth the cost to lives and money? What was it all about?

Let's check back and see if we can discover.

The average American aviator is the most optimistic cuss on earth. He will try anything once—try it if he has a chance of succeeding; try it if he hasn't—for glory, for the advancement of his calling, for money, marbles, or chalk.

He is living proof that "hope springs eternal in the human breast," that "fools rush in where angels fear to tread," and, sometimes, that "perseverance conquers all."

He will succeed or die in the attempt—as the Dole race demonstrated.

Four succeeded, ten died, in the attempt. Never, since the Wrights soared aloft at Kitty Hawk, have so many men rushed blindly in to take a desperate gamble, to throw their lives in the scales against glory and money, with such a slim chance of winning, as they did in the Hawaiian contest.

Fliers will try anything once, but whether or not they should be permitted to is a question due for serious discussion.

It all began with Lindbergh. When he arrived in Paris, aviation in America suddenly emerged from a state of coma. While he was being acclaimed a world hero and shaking hands with kings and potentates, several hundred aviators concluded they were saps.

"I might have been Lindbergh," was their doleful meditation. They knew he had performed a tremendous task, but if he could do it, they could have done it.

There were other long faces. A considerable number of inventors, designers, and builders of planes felt the same way about it. The winning plane might have been their plane.

They all wanted to be Lindberghs, so they started looking for new aerial worlds to conquer—for a cash prize if possible.

Like a messenger from the gods to comfort these mournful spirits came James D. Dole of Honolulu. Dole, who probably owns more pineapples than the rest of the world together, was a public-spirited citizen of the islands and a fine sportsman to boot.

He was interested in flying and enthused by Lindbergh's success. He also thought that anything which might reduce traveling time between the mainland and the islands was worth encouraging.

Furthermore, being a member in good standing of the Chamber of Commerce of Honolulu, he had never shied away from anything that might advertise the Pearl of the Pacific.

On May 25, while Lindbergh was still the toast of Europe, Dole laid $35,000 on the table and announced that it belonged to the first two fliers who would make a non-stop flight from North America to Hawaii, or, more specifically, to the Island of Oahu and preferably the John Rodgers Airport at Honolulu. The first flier to arrive could pocket $25,000 and the rest of the money would go to the second.

The Bank of Hawaii held the money. The Honolulu chapter of the National Aeronautic Association, the body authorized by the Department of Commerce to govern all aerial sporting events, was to handle the competition.

Concurrent with the Dole announcement, the report was printed that members of the Chamber of Commerce of San Francisco had expressed willingness to underwrite additional prize-money for the winner, providing he started from San Francisco.

The report said the prize-money might total $100,000, including the Dole offer and a rumored $50,000 from San Francisco.

When the boys read this they gave three rousing cheers, decided they should eat more pineapples, and wired for entry blanks. Rumors sprang up like mushrooms after a rain.

Lindbergh would enter. So would Chamberlin and his Columbia monoplane, and Byrd and the America. Dozens of others expressed their intention of competing. The National Aeronautic Association, or N. A. A., was besieged with inquiries.

When the rules were drawn up they disclosed that the flight could start any time after noon, August 12, which was eleven weeks away. It could be made either with landplanes or seaplanes. The offer was open for one year. There were certain inspection, fuel, and safety requirements.

The start could be made from any point on the North American continent. Every one planned, of course, to hop off from San Francisco and grab the extra $50,000.

The rules said landplanes or seaplanes. Well? Would you try to fly from Los Angeles to New York in a seaplane? Would you attempt to cross Lake Michigan in an automobile, or to float down the Mississippi on a bicycle?

It's solid water every inch of the way from North America to Hawaii. The infallible airplane engine has yet to be built. Then why add to the risks of an already difficult flight by making it in the wrong type of plane?

John Rodgers and his crew floated safely for nine days off the islands in a seaplane and were rescued. Records show that more than two-thirds of the landplanes attempting to alight on water are wrecked.

Seaplanes or landplanes! Perhaps that was the first mistake.

The fliers and builders snapped at this opportunity. The definite cash prize for the Paris flight was only $25,000, but Lindbergh was receiving princely offers to do a number of things. The Hawaiian winner would get close to $100,000 cash, with fat gleanings thereafter. It was almost too good to believe.

Then started the insane scramble. Lindbergh had proved a transoceanic flight could be made cheaply. It was said his total investment for the Paris trip was around $15,000. All the prospective entrants thought they could get by for a reasonable sum by using a single-motored plane.

The persons who were approached to help finance entrants in the Hawaii race couldn't be jammed into the Yale Bowl. Fliers, for the most part, are not affluent. Wealthy individuals by the score and clubs and societies were solicited.

Even cities were asked to scrape together enough cash to equip and enter some favorite flying son. If the necessary wherewithal had been forthcoming, there would have been twenty times the final fifteen entries.

The whole aviation world was burning with fly-to-Hawaii fever.

A stereotyped method was employed to lure the bashful dollars. The prospective entrant pushed the prospective backer in a corner and explained how easy it would be. He needed $12,000—might do it for less. There was a gamble for you! Twelve thousand dollars to win $100,000 or more.

And it wasn't really a gamble—it was a cinch. His plane would be speedy, and the speediest plane would win the prize.

Seaplanes were not being considered—they were too slow. They might be safer, but nobody was giving much thought to safety.

These fellows thought they couldn't fail. They knew the time was short—that thorough and adequate testing would be impossible—but it didn't dim their enthusiasm. Naturally, all of them couldn't raise the money, but some fifteen or twenty did.

Dole, in sunny Honolulu, was amazed. He had expected his offer to arouse interest, but he didn't anticipate any one would be trampled in the rush.

The Orteig Prize, which Lindbergh won by flying to Paris, had been up for eight years. Dole had made his offer good for a year. A week would have been sufficient.

For three or four weeks everything was serene. The successful money-raisers were working day and night on their planes. The N. A. A. was preparing to handle the start and finish.

And then, on June 28, a horrible thing happened—horrible for the pursuers of fame and fortune. Lieutenants Lester J. Maitland and Albert F. Hegenberger, of the Army Air Service, hopped off from Oakland and a day later arrived at Honolulu.

Experienced and clever fliers and navigators, splendidly equipped with a tri-motored and proven plane, they made the trip look foolishly simple. But, far worse than that, when they glided down to Wheeler Field, the potential rewards to the winner of the Dole race disappeared. They were the first to fly from North America to Hawaii.

Offhand it looked as if the Maitland flight came under the general heading of a dirty trick. The Dole race promised to be a great sporting event. The Air Service sneaked in and stole the glory.

If sufficient pressure had been brought to bear, the Air Service might have agreed, as a sporting proposition, to at least wait and start with the others on August 12. But the Air Service is jealous of its reputation.

It has pioneered long-distance flying. A flight to Honolulu had been under consideration for some time. And the people who might have brought pressure to bear couldn't ask the Air Service not to start until August 12 without being able to guarantee no civilian flier would make the trip in the meantime.

Maitland cost the prospective Dole flight-winner a lot of money. Strangely enough, while the Hawaiian flight was 400 miles longer than the Atlantic crossing, from land to land, and fully as hazardous, Maitland and Hegenberger did not become second Lindberghs.

They were royally welcomed in the islands, and enthusiastically greeted when they returned, and that was about all.

On July 14 came another punch in the nose. Ernest Smith and Elmer Bronte, his navigator, flew from Oakland to the islands. They didn't reach Honolulu—they crashed in a forced landing on the leper island of Molokai—but they had successfully spanned the Pacific in a single-motored plane and stolen another clap of thunder from the Dole fliers.

When they returned home, the police reserves were not required to handle the crowds that greeted them.

Then, either as a result of the flight having been made successfully or for other reasons, the San Francisco contributors who were being counted on for $50,000 prize-money followed the quaint old Arabian custom of folding their tents and silently stealing away.

The money just simply failed to materialize. The planes were all going to start from San Francisco anyway. It offered the best facilities.

Their prospective rewards reduced from a handsome fortune to comparative small change, it was too late for the entrants to back out. Planes were contracted for and half built. Pride and prestige were involved. And the Dole prizes were still in the vaults of the Bank of Hawaii.

Ten days before the start, fifteen entries said they would be ready to push off at noon, August 12. A number of candidates dropped out at the last moment. Several of the entered planes were not completed and wouldn't have time for adequate testing, but they'd start just the same.

"Ready or not, here I come!"—that was the slogan.

They assembled at San Francisco slowly and with difficulty. A couple of planes were on hand early. The others were flying in from everywhere and having trouble doing it.

Lieutenant Covell's plane landed twice during a short trip to San Diego. Bennett Griffin's motor failed flying from Oklahoma. The Miss Doran was forced down between Los Angeles and San Francisco.

Captain W. P. Erwin flew away from Dallas and had to go back for repairs. They couldn't even get to the starting-point without misfortune.

The starting committee has been functioning through Major Clarence M. Young, inspector of aeronautics for the Department of Commerce, and Captain Walter Parkin and Major N. W. Breingan, aircraft experts assigned to inspect the planes and issue the required licenses.

As the entries arrived, the committee and the inspectors began to get nervous. The planes weren't ready; they hadn't been properly tested; they weren't properly equipped; their navigation instruments were inaccurate, and some of the navigators didn't look so good.

None of the planes had been tested with a full load. Very few of the pilots had had extensive night-flying experience.

Some of them had flown in darkness, but had found their way by landmarks and ground lights—not by relying solely on navigation instruments and that delicate feel of balance that comes only with hours of practise at night. Every plane was dependent on a single motor, and some of them had been acting badly.

Commander Byrd crossed the Atlantic with the experience of a flight to the North Pole under his belt, a splendid plane, and a crew of three fliers and navigators as capable as himself. Chamberlin was highly trained and had a world's endurance record to his credit, made with the same plane he was flying to Europe.

Lindbergh had never made a mistake from the time his flight was contemplated until the day he finished it. "We" had been through the crucible test of two long, perfect trips—from San Diego to St. Louis and from there to New York.

The most meticulous preparation and planning preceded the flights of all three across the Atlantic. No less could be said about Maitland.

The plans of fifteen aviators and navigators to cross 2,100 miles of open water to Honolulu were so different. There scarcely would be time to assemble some of the planes and fill them with gasoline.

Some of the pilots had no navigators—they even failed to realize that success would rest with accurate navigation as largely as with skillful flying.

Enter then the villain, dressed in the uniform of the United States navy. His name was Lieutenant Ben H. Wyatt. A navigator by training and instinct, he was an expert on compasses and destinations.

Wyatt had been flying and navigating long enough not to believe in Santa Claus. He was a pessimist in a beehive of optimists.

The lieutenant had been loaned by the navy to help the starting committee with navigation problems. It took him about twenty minutes to conclude that a lot of the entrants stood a first-class chance of starting for Hawaii and finishing almost anywhere from Alaska to Panama—or on the bottom of the sea.

He drew up a list of seventeen questions. Some of them were easy. The others were headaches.

He wanted to know, "Do you intend to make celestial observations? If so, what instruments have you for this purpose? What method of working out your sights will you use?"

Another question was, "Assuming a wind of seventeen miles from fifty minutes true 600 miles from Honolulu, what will be your compass course? Give compass error on this heading."

A lot of the boys didn't know the answers and didn't care. They had come to fly to Hawaii, not to answer foolish questions.

Young, Parkin, and Breingan inspected the planes. Some of them were really excellent examples of design and construction. As they were all powered with the same type of Wright Whirlwind motor used by the trans-Atlantic fliers, their chances were equal in this respect.

With one exception, the planes had fuel capacity 15 percent in excess of the amount necessary for the distance, as the rules required. Martin Jensen's plane was a bit shy on fuel-tanks, but he said he'd carry his gasoline in five-gallon cans and dump it in as it was needed.

All this was preliminary. Two days before the start, August 10, the first fatalities occurred. Lieutenants George D. Covell and R. S. Waggener were killed at San Diego when their Tremaine monoplane, embodying radical ideas of design, crashed in flames as they were starting from San Francisco. The machine had performed badly from the first day it was flown, but the two naval lieutenants were willing to start to the islands with it.

Fully alarmed over the situation, officials of the N. A. A., the starting committee, the inspectors, and Wyatt met at the Athens Club, in Oakland, that night to decide what could be done to prevent an impending disaster.

Wyatt said it would be plain first-degree murder to let these fellows start. One or two of them were ready. The rest absolutely were not. Everyone present knew Wyatt was right.

Something had to be done and done immediately. Death and disaster were in the air. Fifteen men and a very pretty girl were intent on committing suicide. There must be some way to prevent them.

Why couldn't they stop the flight? They had no legal means. Dole had made his offer in good faith and probably wouldn't withdraw it.

He was justified in assuming nobody would be silly enough to start without adequate preparation. The backers had to be considered. They had put up somewhere around $300,000 on the guaranty that prize-money would be available.

The result of the meeting was a cablegram to the Honolulu chapter of the N. A. A., the only body that could authorize a postponement. Wyatt thought he could get the navigators straightened out in a few days, and a two weeks' delay was requested on the grounds that a start on August 12 would be hazardous and "the result could easily be unfavorable."

When the pilots and their backers heard of the committee's cable, they filled the air with wailing and moaning. Wyatt was the target for a dozen salvos of protest, objection, and strong language. He didn't seem to mind. He was fortified with the knowledge that he was fighting for their lives.

The backers, whose money was in jeopardy, squawked louder than the fliers whose lives were at stake.

Some backers concentrated their protests on the San Francisco committee. The planes that were ready should not be penalized because others were not.

The Honolulu committee turned down the request for a postponement with a curt cablegram.

While everybody was busy being mad at everybody else, the International Triplane, fresh from the factory, arrived at Bayfarm Field, Oakland, piloted by Captain J. L. Griffin and carrying two passengers. The huge plane, which resembled a flying layer cake, bounced down on the runway, bounced off again, and crashed into San Francisco Bay, a total wreck. The occupants were uninjured.

Their request for a delay denied, the starting committee refused to give up. They insisted on disqualification of all planes that had not passed Wyatt's tests.

Not a single plane had passed. Major Young threatened to revoke the flying license of any pilot who started without Wyatt's approval.

The fliers who had not qualified said they would start anyway. They raved about personal honor, the disgrace of not starting, and obligations to their backers.

Wyatt tried to convince the boys they would be foolish to start when they were so obviously unable to navigate correctly, but they wouldn't listen to him.

Then the Lockheed Vega monoplane, known as the Golden Eagle, piloted by Jack Frost, and the El Encanto, Lieutenant Norman A. Goddard's plane, successfully passed their navigation tests. Frost, with a splendid and very speedy plane, looked like a winner. The boys at the field were betting Goddard's plane would never get off the ground.

Major Irving and Bennett Griffin had some slight adjustments to make, but it was rumored they would qualify in the morning. The rest of the pilots wouldn't be able to pass their tests in time to start with the others.

Then somebody had a bright idea. They called a sportsman's conference of pilots.

The committee put the facts up to the boys, who listened long enough for Wyatt to convince them he wasn't making them take navigation tests just to be aggravating. And the entrants finally saw the light.

A gentleman's agreement was suggested whereby the start would be postponed four days. Frost and Goddard, the only two who could have started, consented. The others could do no less.

The following day the third fatality occurred. Captain Arthur V. Rodgers, flying a twin-motored Bryant monoplane, crashed to death near Los Angeles.

Frank Clark and Charles H. Babb, who was to make the flight with him, withdrew. A lot of people said Clark was yellow. You can judge for yourself. He and Babb decided they were risking a $20,000 plane and their lives to win a $25,000 prize. They realized the hazards of the trip and figured that if they made it they would have accomplished nothing new, so they politely bowed out of the picture.

Wyatt and the inspectors disqualified the City of Peoria plane. When it had passed its navigation tests the inspectors rechecked its fuel capacity. It couldn't carry enough gas to get it to Honolulu.

The owners insisted it could get there. The pilot, Charles R. Parkhurst, finally said he doubted if it carried enough fuel to cross the Pacific.

But he was a dead game sport. He had signed to make the flight and if the owners insisted, he'd try to go through with it! The inspectors saved him from what might very possibly have been a watery grave.

Eight planes lined up for the start. Two of them crashed taking off—they couldn't lift their heavy loads.

Two more returned. One of these, flown by Captain Erwin, departed two days later in a heroic and fatal attempt to find his lost rivals. Two planes reached Honolulu. Two disappeared at sea, leaving no clue to their fate.

What happened to them? A thousand things might have. Captain Erwin almost certainly lost his balance in the dark, fell in a tail spin, and crashed into the sea. The same fate may have claimed the Golden Eagle and the Miss Doran.

Engine failure might have forced a landing, almost impossible to accomplish successfully with a landplane in the open sea. None of them, with the possible exception of the Golden Eagle, would have remained long afloat.

They might have miscalculated their courses and missed the islands entirely, dropping into the sea when their fuel gave out. Only one thing is certain—they are gone.

Who was to blame? Certainly not James D. Dole, who offered the prizes. Not the starting committee or the inspectors, who did everything in their power to postpone or entirely cancel the flight. Not Lieutenant Wyatt, who worked day and night to convince the fliers of the dangers confronting them.

The rules might have been more stringent; but the pilots and their backers were most at fault. They would have departed with no preparation at all had Wyatt let them. They were too greedy for fame and money.

The flight accomplished nothing. Those most closely connected with it admit that. It was a step backward.

Nothing new was achieved. On the contrary, it nullified Maitland's splendid success.

But it will never happen again; because the Department of Commerce, the N. A. A., and other governing bodies will, by one means or another, render a recurrence impossible. Congress may even devise some way to prevent fliers from committing suicide.

Prizes for other strange and remarkable aerial accomplishments are now being offered, some because of the publicity they will bring their donors rather than for the good they will do aviation.

The N. A. A. is shying gingerly away from them. They've had enough of prize flights.

But if the new contests are ever held, you may be sure they will be held under the most rigid regulations.

So perhaps ten people did not die entirely in vain, after all—not if their shocking deaths will drive home the point that flying over great distances is a serious, highly hazardous business when entered upon without proper equipment and preparation, and will start some sort of movement that will eventually protect aviators from themselves. A lot of them need it.

A 1928 Pioneer

A Movie Review by Frederick James Smith

Making History with 7,000 Feet of Crash and Chatter

"IT'S AS MUCH a screen milestone as *The Great Train Robbery*," declared a man who sat ahead of me at the Manhattan opening of the Warner Brothers' all talkie film, *Lights of New York*.

Lights of New York is likely to be a landmark of the talkie. Heretofore we have had a number of full length films with patches of dialogue and music. Like these, *Lights of New York* comes from the Warners' studio and is a Vitaphone product. Unlike these, however, it is 100 percent noise for every inch of its seven reels.

Most of the celluloid reviewers pronounced *Lights of New York* to be crude of story and amateurish of acting. Doubtless it is—but it is also an arresting experiment.

Lights of New York is another story of gangsters, bootleggers, cabaret scoundrels, and plainclothesmen. Two young people come to the wicked city. EDDIE innocently buys a barber shop that turns out to be a camouflaged den of booze peddlers. KITTY develops into one of those innocent cabaret cuties who inspire an evil proprietor to all sorts of dire deeds. This HAWK MILLER, the big bad boy of Manhattan, frames EDDIE in his efforts to possess KITTY. Then HAWK is killed.

I won't tell you who did it, but EDDIE does have a hard time explaining.

This picture started out to be a brief fifteen minute sound film, to be called The Roaring Forties. The Warners were so enthusiastic that they elaborated the thing into a feature. It was directed by Bryan Foy, one of the late Eddie Foy's numerous sons.

Lights of New York is told with some captions and 7,000 feet of crash and chatter. Right now Hollywood is worrying about the voices of its actors. It ought to start worrying about what the voices are compelled to put over. The talkie needs dramatists who know how to write dialogue.

Lights of New York is at its best when it shows such items as a cabaret in full swing and night views of the Great White Way, which, by the way, were neatly done in the Warners' Hollywood studios.

This all talkie will disclose to you the exact plop caused by a kiss and by a dead body hitting the floor. The last comes in the big scene of the film, when an attempt is made to hide a killing from the police. The body is propped up in a barber's chair and a shave is faked. But the body flops to the feet of the surprised plainclothesmen.

The talkie, of course, is in its infancy, although you cannot say the surface has not been scratched. The difficulties are obvious. Photography has to be sacrificed for sound. Close-ups are paralyzing. And the players appear to be worried continually about their voices. When they get together they group as if about to harmonize "Sweet Adeline."

I am not one of those who think that the sound film is just a novelty. Of course, it has a ghastly quality right now. It shows up Hollywood's voices in all their raucity, magnifying every weakness.

The talkie pioneers are trying still to fit the usual film yarns to sound. They should build for sound. For instance, the Warners might have made EDDIE, hero of *Lights of New York*, the bass drummer of his town band. When he hits New York, he would have walked up and down Broadway seeking a cabaret orchestra job.

A tornado would be shrieking over New York. EDDIE would take a temporary job in an iron foundry, make good, and become a prize fight announcer. Thus, a business success, he could return home with KITTY, who meanwhile had worked her way up from cabaret dancer to hostess. The final shot would show them practicing their voices in a rose garden.

In the cast of *Lights of New York* you will find Helene Costello as the girl and Cullen Landis as the boy. They fall into the clutches of the evil night-club boss, played by Wheeler Oakman. Then there is the boss' cast-off sweetie, done by Gladys Rockwell.

These players meet their microphones with varying success. I decline to place any blame or praise, not knowing whether to hand it to Miss Costello, Miss Brockwell, Mr. Landis, Mr. Oakman, the Western Electric, the Bell Telephone, or the Warners.

Clara Bow

by Adela Rogers St. Johns

The Playgirl of Hollywood

YOU CAN LOVE Clara and hate her. You can feel sorry for her and at the same time be furious enough to spank her. You can be thrilled by her and disgusted with her. You would trust her with your life, your money, and your good name, but never with your husband. You are fascinated and interested every moment you are with her and yet you heave a long sigh of relief when she is gone, because the tension is too great for everyday living.

You must either like or dislike Clara intensely. I defy any human being to come in contact with her and feel indifference. It simply can't be done. Any emotion in the deck might be produced by knowing her, but not indifference.

The greatest box-office attraction the motion-picture industry has ever known, in point of the number of people who in one year go into theaters to see her pictures, is a twenty-four-year-old Brooklyn girl whose mother died when she was very young and who had very little education and oftentimes not enough to eat.

Her fan mail is bigger than any other star has ever received. Everyone who comes to Hollywood wants above everything else to meet Clara Bow, or, failing that, to be told what she is like.

But you cannot describe Clara Bow in one sentence. If you could, I think it would be "Her whim is her law."

I have heard men say that you can live in the desert for a lifetime and never know half its beauties, half its terrors. I think you could live with Clara Bow for years and never begin to fathom her strange and complex nature. For just as you begin to believe that you understand her, she slips through your fingers like quicksilver and comes out in some entirely new shape.

That is why everything which has been written about the most popular girl in the United States is superficial. No man could write about her with an unprejudiced pen once he knew her well. And only one or two women have ever known her well enough to be anything but superficial about her. Most of them are too much afraid of her vaunted lure for men.

Conflicting possibilities vibrate in Clara Bow like the crash of cymbals. She knows it. But she never has time to decide for herself which shall be uppermost. Life drives her swiftly.

I met her first several years ago and I saw a very young girl, with amazing red hair obviously but beautifully and effectively dyed, and the most restless, brilliant, and arresting black eyes I had ever encountered. Under an exquisite kimono, her figure looked a trifle plump but—if you will forgive me—luscious. It made you wonder what started women on this fad of being flat and skinny. The two hands that reached out for mine were hot and electric, but soft as a baby's.

"Darling," she said, in a throaty, vibrant voice, "I'm so glad you've come. I forgot all about you. Do come in and see the rushes. You'll like them."

We saw the rushes—studio name for the day's work—and Clara talked all the time in the darkness, telling me the story of this picture, explaining to the director what

Back in her dressing room, which was gorgeous and disordered as a night club at 3 A. M., she said, "I'm so sorry. I don't think there is any dinner. I'll phone and see."

But unfortunately they had just changed her telephone number again because too many people knew the old one, and she couldn't remember what the new one was. No amount of cajoling Central could extract it, and no one else around the studio—not even Tui—knew it.

No story of Clara could be complete without Tui, so we might as well introduce her right now. Tui is Clara's chum who has lived with her for years. She is an Australian chorus girl and recently married Clara's father—chiefly, one gathers, to avoid an immigration law which would otherwise have sent her back to her native land, her allotted time in America being up. Clara didn't want Tui to go back to Australia. Tui has the vocabulary of a London cab driver, the wit of Oscar Wilde, and the broad education of a girl who has known her ups and downs and read everything worthwhile she could get her hands on. She does amazing imitations and dialect songs and reminds me constantly of Beatrice Lillie.

Tui stood in one corner of the dressing room, her blonde hair on end, a cigarette in her fingers, and her brows lifted in quizzical contemplation.

"It's no good phoning anyhow," she said. "You can't take Adela home to dinner, Clara. It's the blank cook's night out and I ate the last can of blank sardines for my blank breakfast. Also, there's nothing but blank-blank gin and no lady ever drinks gin."

She grinned at me with engaging frankness.

Clara gave up calling wrong telephone numbers and said, "Darling, do you mind coming tomorrow night? I'm sorry, but I forgot. I'd take you to the Ambassador, but we couldn't talk there, and besides I have a date with a gorgeous man. At least, I think he's gorgeous. He'll probably turn out to be a dud."

"He turned out to be that a week ago," said Tui, "but Clara's so damn optimistic."

"He's a divine dancer," said Clara.

"But," said Tui, "as Michael Arlen would say, is life all dancing?"

"If you happen to be dancing it is," said Clara and went into a perfect gale of laughter.

Then she told me that I was to come straight to her house the next evening and she'd be home as soon as she got through at the studio. She wrote down an address, which turned out to be two blocks wrong, and I went home, debating in my own mind as to whether or not I would go back.

The next morning my phone rang. It was Clara. "Don't forget about tonight," she said.

I finally located the house, and after much parley with a suspicious maid—Clara had forgotten to tell her I was expected—was admitted.

was wrong with her work and everyone else's, and giggling throatily over the bad takes.

When we came out she looked at me with startled eyes and exclaimed, "Oh, you were to come to dinner!"

It is a small house in Beverly Hills, down near Santa Monica Boulevard instead of up in the fashionable hillside district. A big living room with a sun porch behind, opening into a little garden. A dining room and kitchen. Two small bedrooms. A maid's room. Clara's Chinese room, which was originally a den. Just an ordinary stucco bungalow. But inside it is exactly like Clara.

The beautiful and the bizarre, the exquisite and the commonplace—mingled in hopeless confusion.

A gaudy doll in frowsy skirts and wig leans against a wonderful Ming lamp. A huge fuzzy Teddy bear with a pink bow around his neck occupies a corner of the luxurious brocaded davenport. The center table is a really fine thing of carved oak and the rugs are awful imitation Chinese. The lamps look as if they had come from the five-and-ten-cent store, but the shawl on the piano might be worn by a Spanish Infanta.

The Chinese room—which is Clara's lounging room—is one of those things you read about in novels of flaming youth and never see. The walls are gleaming gold. An entire side is taken up by a huge soft couch of black velvet heaped with pillows of lacquer red and gold embroidery and jade silk. A Chinese god looks down from a carved pedestal. The lights are so dim it is five minutes before you can really see, and the place smells of some strange incense rising in clouds from a brass burner. The curtains are full length black satin and they are always closed.

Yet next door is Clara's bedroom—as simple and unpretentious a room as you would find belonging to any high-school girl in Cleveland or St. Louis or Atlanta.

I waited in the living room, unable to read because I couldn't find any books. Papa Bow came in finally. My presence apparently failed to register. He got up and went out without discovering me at all.

Pretty soon Clara and Tui arrived. Clara looked horribly tired. Her eyes were pitiful.

"She has no sense," said Tui, impersonally. "She's rehearsed a scene forty times with some sap leading man. *I* say if they're so dumb they have to keep at it that long, let them go alone. But she runs errands for almost everybody over there."

"You got to be regular, Tui," said Clara wearily. "Even more, when you're up. I remember, when I was scratching for a job. I remember, too, when I first came around here as a star and Pola Negri and Florence Vidor used to high-hat me. Well, I'm not above getting even if I get a chance. Pola used to ride by me in her limousine like I was part of the roadbed. Yesterday I made them stop the music on her set because it bothered me when I was trying to do a big scene.

"But I'm not going to be high-hatting anybody. First, because I know how it feels. Second, because this is a funny game—you're here today and gone tomorrow. How about a drink?"

We had one highball, which Clara informed me is all she ever allows herself while she is working. Then we went in to dinner, Papa Bow having popped up again like a jack-in-the-box. The fat and friendly cook served it, with appropriate comments. The food was marvelous. Real French vintage champagne was served in glasses of Venetian crystal. Clara didn't touch it. Instead she drank three large cups of strong tea. She hardly spoke throughout the meal. She just ate.

Tui and Papa Bow vanished, and Clara and I settled down on the davenport to talk. I was worried. Clara slumped in a corner. It seemed to me that she would give me nothing. She looked tired and almost stupid, in spite of the feverish glitter in her eyes.

Then, as we started to talk, she came alive.

There followed a night—for we talked until dawn filled the room with cold sunlight—which I shall never forget. My business has taken me to talk with many great and strange and famous people. But I think I shall always remember that night with Clara Bow—who had come from nothing to be the greatest drawing card in her own game—as the peak of my experiences.

Clara turned on the radio at its loudest and the jazz beat against the walls of the room until I felt quite deaf. I asked her to turn it off and she did, with the sweetest apology, and ten minutes later forgot and turned it on again. It isn't only on the screen that Clara is jazz-mad. Jazz is her national anthem. Her idea of a real party is to get Earl Burnett's famous trio to come out after they are through at the Biltmore and play and sing to her.

I cannot describe the tension of that room as we talked. The clash of its furnishings, the dynamic colorings, the throbbing jazz from the radio, and Clara. I cannot explain why she keys you up as she does—why she gives you the feeling that the world may come to an end before you can finish what you are doing unless you hurry—why you find yourself talking breathlessly and more loudly than is your habit.

Her own tension is catching; that must be what it is. No matter how long you know her, you will never see Clara relaxed. Even when she is dropping with fatigue, there is no peace in her. She fights fatigue with all her glorious young strength.

During that first night's talk it was possible to gain a complete view of Clara's mind. I do not know why she talked as she did. It was as though a dam had broken and the words poured out without volition; as though she had not for years talked to anyone who might sympathize and understand.

Once started, she could not stop. I had the feeling that never before had she reviewed her life as a whole, even to herself.

She talked about her birth, a birth which the doctor had predicted would surely cause her mother's death.

She talked about her childhood in a Brooklyn tenement, marked by indelible tragedies—her grandfather dropping dead at her feet as he pushed her in a little swing; the dear little boy downstairs who was burned to death before her eyes; the poverty brought on by her father's bad luck and failures. She talked about the delicate mother whom she worshiped, and her own agony when she saw that mother's mind gradually give way beneath illness caused by bringing into the world children who did not live.

"As I grew up," she said slowly, "Mother began to be afraid of me. When I first wanted to go into pictures, she was so distressed that I gave it up. One night she came into my room while I was sleeping. She had long hair, and the first thing I knew the great braids of it struck against my face. As my eyes opened, I saw that she held a long knife against my throat. She told me she was going to kill me because I would be better off dead. She said life was brutal and terrible and death was better.

"Her eyes blazed. I grew cold with fear. I didn't want to die. And my heart was breaking for her—her suffering. I gathered myself and sprang past her and out the door. I locked her in and lay sobbing against the door outside until my father came home at dawn."

When her mother died Clara tried to jump into the open grave beside her—a child half mad with grief at losing the thing dearest to her in the whole world.

As she talked, I realized somewhere in my subconscious mind that I was listening to one of the greatest tragic actresses in the world. My face was wet with tears, though I was too fascinated to know I wept.

I realized, too, the thing that alone can give anyone even a partial understanding of Clara Bow. No success, no adulation, no amount of fame or gold, can ever wipe out the terrible scars of her childhood and adolescent years. There is hammered into her soul a fear of life, and that is why she desires to live fast and furiously, why she must seek forgetfulness in mad gayety.

Before me unrolled a mind entirely untrained, raw and strong as the mind of a primitive woman, grappling in its own way with the problems of a sophisticated and civilized world. The things which the average person has accepted as truths are not truths to her. She accepts nothing. Life is as new to her as it was to Eve.

Never before had I been conscious of how much of our thinking we have taken from books, from other minds, from traditional laws. Clara takes nothing from anybody. The effect is astounding. To watch a fresh, violent young mind tackling principles, life, God, laws of society, sex, as though they had never been touched before, and discarding axioms as so much deadwood, is like being at sea in a hurricane.

"Why, can't we *know*?" she cried. "Why is life so difficult? Why are we born with such mixed-up desires? Why are we so ignorant of where we came from and where we are going? I don't understand."

A reckless, lawless, honest, rebellious young pagan, she has a primitive mind and a beautiful body, both of them capable of every fundamental emotion at its peak.

They call her the It girl. In Clara's case there is much more than mere sex appeal back of that word. There is a primitive passion for living, there is a vividness of emotion, a vital current that has been dimmed in most of us by civilization and conformity.

When Clara makes whoopee after the manner of her generation, she has a grand and glorious time. There is none of the boredom and decadence that marks too many of the girls and boys one sees about. Her pep is inexhaustible.

I remember one party she gave for a gang of young college folks. At 4 o'clock in the morning Clara was out on the lawn being taught to tackle by a 190-pound All-American. She succeeded in spraining his thumb for him, which is more than Notre Dame ever did. She has the most amazing physical strength and aptitude. The first time she ever played tennis was on our court, and by the end of the afternoon she was playing better than many girls who have been at it for years.

Clara Bow is the only completely natural person I have ever known. It may seem a bit rowdy to be rough-housing on the lawn at 4 o'clock in the morning, but it seems to me infinitely preferable to dancing in some stinking night club. She may startle the élite by deciding to go swimming on a cold night when the rest of the party is settling down to bridge. But a midnight swim in icy water isn't such a bad thing for your constitution.

Her one law is to cheat her enemy, life, out of every moment of fun and feeling that she can get.

Of all the stars—excepting the mysterious Garbo—Clara remains most completely herself. She hasn't acquired the ways and manners, the habits and customs, of the rich and the socially elect. Her servants are her friends, and if she wants to talk to them during dinner, she does it. Her house is quite as grand as is consistent in her mind with comfort. When she gives a party she asks the people she likes and who like her, without following the usual code of Hollywood royalty and asking those who belong by right of their screen position.

When she gives a dinner party she puts all the husbands next to their own wives, books of etiquette to the contrary notwithstanding. "I don't want to start any trouble," says Clara wisely. She likes tea in a big cup with her dinner, so she has it.

Another nonconformist trait is her clothes. Her dress isn't loud; it's barbaric—and rather beautiful. Looking at Papa Bow, who is a swarthy little man with coal-black hair and high cheek bones, one sometimes wonders if there isn't a drop or two of the blood of the first Americans somewhere in Clara's lineage.

The startling make-up she puts on for the street suggests an Indian's war paint. And it is wholly suitable to Clara. Without it, her face has a baby roundness, her eyes have a wistfulness that is appealing but out of character. She takes actual pleasure in that make-up. She never has any hesitation in being seen without it, so it can't be for other people. No, she likes it; that is why she wears it.

The same with her clothes. One afternoon last year she appeared at a football game, with some 90,000 other people, wearing a sport suit of the brightest lipstick red, a red tam over one ear, no stockings, and bright red slippers with high gold heels and buckles.

It wasn't the slightest use telling her that one doesn't wear slippers with high gold heels with a sport costume to a football game.

"Why not?" says Clara Bow. "I like 'em. They make me feel good."

Well, after all, why not? Is there any sound moral or economic reason against gold heels? As for taste: "My taste suits me," said Clara. "And I have to live with myself more than anybody else does."

Her clothes express her mood. She may arrive for a simple little dinner—anywhere from an hour to two hours late—in a gleaming spangled gown that makes you catch your breath, for Clara can be beautiful when she wants to be. A week later she will come to a very formal dinner for a visiting celebrity in a quiet white frock with a huge red bow tied behind. It is impossible for her to see why it should bother anyone else, since she herself is perfectly at ease.

Whatever her own law of whims, she is quite as willing to allow others to apply theirs. It is perhaps not quite nice of her to be an hour or two late for every appointment, or to forget appointments altogether. But if *you* happen to be an hour or two late, and she remembers that you are coming, she waits sweetly and makes not the slightest comment when you arrive.

I should think that the three important things in Clara Bow's life are work, sex, and laughter. And I can well imagine the younger generation, of whom we hear so much, saying, "But what else is there?"

To her work Clara gives everything she has. No hours are too long. She has never been known to display temperament of any kind. She accepts direction happily and gratefully. The author and the supervisor can do their work without any interference from her. When she gets her teeth into a part, as the old actors say, she hits it with full steam ahead. Her days at the studio are still fun to her. In fact, she'd rather be in the middle of a picture than on a vacation. There isn't an ounce of "art" in her character. But she likes to work, likes to act, enjoys the contact and bustle and excitement of a picture set.

Laughter she will buy at any price. Anyone who can make Clara laugh is sure of her continued interest and friendship. There is a young aviator from Texas whose name has been linked with hers. He isn't quite what you would call good-looking by the greatest stretch of the imagination. But he is one of the greatest raconteurs who ever told a story. Also, he can sing and do imitations. James Montgomery Flagg once remarked that he could do everything but make a panama hat. I dare swear there has never been anything between him and Clara more romantic than laughter. That, too, is the secret of her close friendship with Tui Lorraine. Tui makes her laugh.

It is a modern characteristic, this love of laughter. Anything for a laugh, is the modern slogan. Clara, being by nature an extremist, grabs laughter with both hands, from anyone, anywhere, under any circumstances.

Portrait of a Lady with Grey Eyes on Fifth Avenue

a story by Michael Arlen

An Encounter with the Will-o'-the-Wisp Called LOVE

I WAS WALKING, thinking as I walked. Presently, however, circumstances arose that compelled me to raise my eyes, and I saw ten thousand automobiles, a host of men, a flurry of women, the sunlight sprawling across Fifth Avenue, a fire engine gayly crashing through the one-way sanctity of Forty-sixth Street, and the nose, the mouth, the chin of Carmelita Doherty.

Stern, slender, swift—Oh, Carmelita Doherty, is that you, is that really you, so very grown up, so impassive! *Hauteur,* they called this Carmelita carriage in the old, old days—*hauteur,* upon my word, when you can say "high hat" and be so funny!

Carmelita Doherty, whither do you hurry this fine sweet morning? Stern as a woman of forty at her dressing table, unabashed as a divorcee at Deauville, she strode from east to west across the pavement. A profile and a promise of delight, a profile and an ankle or two—and that's all there is of Carmelita Doherty this fine sweet morning on Fifth Avenue.

How harshly her feet broke the prancing shadows on the pavement! With what adorable indifference her eyes made holocausts of the eyes of suddenly lonely men! How masterfully she rode the confounded multitude! Ah, what a mistress for a man her equal! Alas, how grave the misdemeanor of God in having created me for no other apparent purpose than to be on exactly that square foot of Fifth Avenue which would be demanded by the sovereign feet of Carmelita Doherty in her passage to her automobile!

We bumped. I am dealing in facts. I could say that we collided. But "to collide" is merely to commit a polite misappropriation of space in charming surroundings A Vanderbilt might collide with an Astor. But for oneself, one bumps.

Abashed, I recoiled from the slender contact. A whisper of outraged Chypre filled the air. A pink pearl in a circlet of diamonds trembled between the tender breasts of Carmelita Doherty. But what am I saying! I could see nothing. A glance of her eyes had stripped me of parentage and made me the offspring of moles. I felt like a dandelion at a ball in honor of Miss Gloria Swanson. I felt inferior.

"Carmelita Doherty," I said, "I am so sorry!"

No man could say more. But did she hear me, did she see me, did she for one moment contemplate an exchange of such compliments as are seemly between gentlefolk? In point of fact, the way she gave me the air was nobody's business. With that blank, *deaf* look which adorns society like a pallid jewel and is as a thorn in the sides of butter-and-egg men who like to be hearty with a lady, she passed me by.

Carmelita Doherty, she passed me by!

Humility is a sign of grace, and no man should be entirely without grace. But what man so low that he can be put upon without a dignified attempt at protest! Wherefore I laid my hand upon the arm of Carmelita Doherty and lifted up my voice and said:

"Come, Carmelita Doherty, remember that you almost married me once! Remember, too, that you might have married me had you not already been married. Remember, again, that we were once as good as married, or maybe we were better than married, but we were certainly no worse than married, for what could be worse? Come, Carmelita, be gracious, be fair, be big! If, on the other hand, you cannot remember my name, come right out into the open and call me 'darling.' "

She smiled, and straightway the sun came over to the shady side of Fifth Avenue for to adore the teeth of Carmelita Doherty.

"It's *not* you!" she sighed. "Dar*ling*, it's not you!"

The fact that it was me lent a certain significance to a conversation that might otherwise have been too impersonal to be really enjoyable.

"I *do* remember you!" recklessly said Carmelita Doherty. Of course I remember you! In fact, I have never remembered anyone else.

She was, you understand, being just a nice girl. But the divine spark of truth was not in her. She was so slender, maybe there was no room for the divine spark of truth within the person of Carmelita Doherty. As regards slender women, it is always a question open to debate as to how much goes to God and how much to art. But that is another story. Let us stick to the point. Carmelita Doherty did not know me, she had forgotten me, that was the point. She did not know me, but she was willing to lie, and I cannot allow a woman to lie for my sake.

"Mah Jongg!" I said, since one had to say something.

With exceeding brightness her eyes conquered space, time, and place.

"But that's not the half of it!" she cried. "Mah Jongg, Marquita, Manuelo, Michael—Mich*ael!*"

"I didn't know you cared so much, Carmelita! Fancy your remembering me like that! Why, it's a good year since we met, and then we only saw each other every evening for four months!"

"Oh, but I have wonderful flashes of memory sometimes. It was in Rome, wasn't it? Oh, it all comes back to me—dar*ling!* In Rome, in a room where some people were playing Mah Jongg and a man was humming Marquita to a ukulele, when Manuelo was my lover and I met you! My, how you two did quarrel, didn't you!"

I resented that.

"Anyhow, the best man won!" I said shortly.

"Yes, Jack Doherty," said Carmelita.

At the time I met and loved this lady she was not yet married to Mr. Doherty but only engaged to him, for she had only just married someone else. But Carmelita was really very old-fashioned and still believed in divorce, and she was wealthy enough to be able to afford any amount of alimony. It is such women as Carmelita who make Reno what it is.

"And how is Jack?" I asked, playfully—you know. "As bad as ever?"

Her eyes filled with tears.

"He's not bad," said Carmelita. "He's revolting."

"You can't mean that!" I said.

"I've left him," said Carmelita.

"No!" I said.

"Certainly I've left him!" said Carmelita. "I had to. He drove me to it. He made my life a hell. He gets so violent when he's sober that I simply wrecked my nerves in trying to persuade him to get drunk. It was awful! Heavens, is it really one o'clock! Can you imagine, only meeting you saved me from being punctual for lunch! Are you lunching at the Colony? Isn't that a funny coincidence, nor am I! But, oh dear, I don't know how to get to where I *am* lunching. I had a car this morning, but I seem to have lost it. I distinctly remember coming out this morning with a car and chauffeur, but I can't *imagine* what has happened to them. It's an Italian car, darling, but I wanted to make it look American and so there's a Jewish chauffeur driving it. If you should see him as you are walking along, do *please* tell him to find me at the Ambassador. But, oh dear, however shall I get there!"

"When tired of walking," I said, "a taxi is not considered an unusual form of locomotion. Here you are—and good-bye, Carmelita."

"Good-bye, darling. It's been so nice to see you again! Good-bye, Manuelo dar*ling.*"

A Few More Words
in Answer
to Mrs. Boole

from Heywood Broun

MRS. ELLA A. BOOLE bases her argument for prohibition on the assumption that there is no middle ground. One must be either a wet or a dry. But it seems to me that millions of Americans, particularly in the big cities, are living in this middle ground which Mrs. Boole has not yet discovered. During the Smith-Hoover campaign I asked a friend of mine how he could possibly support the Republican candidate since Mr. Hoover was so definitely on record as a dry. My friend replied:

"Why should I worry about prohibition? I can get all the liquor I need, and it's beginning to improve in quality and decrease in price. Let the drys have the law and we will keep our gin. That seems to me a fair arrangement all around."

And this is the attitude of a great many New Yorkers.

My personal testimony would be that prohibition has done a vast amount to make drinking more pleasant and civilized than it was in the old days. New York restaurants have improved infinitely. The old barroom was generally a vulgar and tawdry place. The refining influence of woman was largely absent. Of course the back room existed, but it was a humiliating and ill-furnished resort. Now that the old-time saloon has largely gone, we have become accustomed to the coeducational bar. I think it is fair to say that there is less drunkenness in New York than before the days of prohibition. The speakeasy proprietor has every reason to avoid rows of any kind. And so he strives to develop a clientèle of pleasant and respectable folk. Of course the romantic element now enters in. There was no spirit of adventure in pushing through the old swinging doors. The mood is quite different when one peeps through a grille and shows a membership card or mentions the name of some acquaintance as a password. We all feel like fraternity members.

It may be that vigorous local enforcement could check the speakeasy, although Mrs. Boole herself points out that it has always been with us. I wish to assure her that the new style is ever so much more attractive, than the old. Up to this point Mrs. Boole and I are in pretty fair agreement. Prohibition has done a great deal to develop character in America. In the face of what seemed terrific obstacles, an ancient industry has not only been preserved but has flourished. Again, there is the fact, which should bring pride to every patriot, that we have at last begun to compete with France itself in the matter of making red wines. The juice of the grape was neglected in the pre-Volstead period. Now there are thousands of restaurants in New York alone where one can obtain an excellent bottle of California claret at a nominal figure.

In the beginning the fear was expressed that the benefits of prohibition would accrue only to the rich. That is no longer true. Competition and American aggressiveness have managed to bring the price of alcoholic beverages down practically to prewar levels.

In all fairness I must admit that the quality of gin and whisky is still a shade below par. That is being corrected. After all, America has always been noted for its technical skill. Anyone with faith in America can hardly doubt that some of our younger chemists will match the best alcoholic products of the Old World.

So far, so good. And yet, I am no more satisfied than Mrs. Boole with the existence of a nation half wet and half dry. Prohibitionists argue in terms of savings-bank accounts, radios, and automobiles. But what shall it avail a country to gain radio sets and automobiles if it loses its own soul?

There is the risk of prohibition. It has sufficed to make hypocrites of us all. Our politicians have never been noted for frankness and sincerity. But now there are scarcely a handful of men in Congress or state legislatures who dare to speak their minds freely. Every candidate for public office has become a wire walker. And this same disposition invades the home.

The Constitution has been riddled again and again in an effort to increase the efficiency of enforcement. Old liberties lie sick and tarnished. Free speech may be the next to go. In speaking of the tone of editorial comment Mrs. Boole remarks: "It is as vicious as it is vain. Something ought to be done to correct it."

Just what does that mean? If it means anything at all, it suggests that Mrs. Boole and her organization would like to have a clamp pressed down upon the newspapers of America. Indeed, she makes the specific suggestion that we should return to war conditions and organize a government propaganda of four-minute speakers. Everybody remembers that during the war dissent was punished. Drys are fond of saying that wet opposition is highly organized and financed entirely by brewers and distillers. I cannot speak for the press of the entire country, but I know New York newspapers and New York reporters and commentators. All of us attack prohibition with the greatest good will in the world. No one need offer us a subsidy. Granting the utter sincerity of Mrs. Boole and her associates, I think that they make a grave mistake in not allowing the same honesty of mind to their opponents.

Too much argument has been based upon statistics. For instance, Mrs. Boole takes up the replies of college presidents in regard to student drinking. Even in pre-prohibition days the president of a college was almost the last person in the community who was likely to know of high jinks within the institution. When a beer night or a cocktail party was being organized the suggestion was never made, "Let's call up Prexy and ask him to attend."

The same things hold true today. It would be unfair for me to generalize about colleges throughout the country, but I can report on Harvard, Yale, and Princeton. When I was an undergraduate at Cambridge there was a good deal of drinking. But it was done beyond the college boundaries. Now a great many undergraduates keep liquor in their rooms. This was almost unknown between 1906 and 1910. At college football games in the East the hip flask is far more openly displayed than ever before.

The test of prohibition efficiency is the retail price of gin. Gin today costs less than half what it did four years ago. And in a recent trip from New York to Los Angeles, I stopped at hotels in six of the Middle Western states. At every hotel I found a corkscrew fastened to the wall. If prohibition is really so near perfection, why do practical men such as hotel keepers embed these corkscrews in the wall? For the use of those who want to order sarsaparilla?

Confessions of a Bootlegger

by "Jimmy" as told to Paul Gallico

A Melodrama of Real Life on Rum's Roaring Road to Riches

[EDITOR'S NOTE: Jimmy, the bootlegger whose authentic experiences are related in this article, is one of the best known and most successful bootleggers in New York. His frank revelations are the fruit of several years' activity in rum running and bootlegging.]

I AM AN honest bootlegger. My business is to make and to sell liquor that is fit to drink. I couldn't exist if it weren't for the fact that I have the co-operation of the local police, the State constabulary, the municipal police, and 85 percent of the citizens. There is another 10 percent that won't help you if you get into a jam. The remaining 5 percent are fanatics. God help us if we get tangled up with any of them!

Tell the average person that you've got a load of liquor in your car, and he'll hide you, lie for you, and help you. It's a moral help as well as a physical one. I am a law-abiding citizen. I mean that I wouldn't break a law that would make me hated. It's the feeling that the people are with you that gives you the nerve to do some of the things we have to do. It you don't think it's wrong to drink, you can't expect me to think I'm breaking the law when I get the stuff for you. Especially not when 99 out of 100 of the local officers of the law are with us. The hundredth one we usually get.

There's the story of the cop who tried to pinch one of our liquor trains. I don't know whether he was an honest cop or wanted the liquor for himself. We were taking Scotch into Newark in a truck. We had a pilot car in front and a trailer in back, full of defenders.

Going through a snooty little town on the road from Highlands to Newark, a cop on a motorcycle ignored our pilot car, rode right up to the truck, blew his whistle, drove it in to the curb, and shouted, "Hey, what you got in that truck?"

Naturally, the driver patted him on the head with his blackjack. The driver was a tough egg. When I got to the truck from the trail car, the boys had him laid out on the liquor and were wondering what to do with him. Some of them wanted to drive him into the Orange Mountains and dump him.

"Why make a hero of him?" I asked. "We want to get rid of this bird. He isn't with us at all."

The boys said that was so. We broke out a bottle of Scotch and poured half of it down the cop's throat by holding his nose. The rest of it we poured over his clothing. We stuffed the bottle into his back pocket, and then took his club and broke the bottle. Then we dragged him a little on his face to dirty his uniform. Then we started his motorcycle and ran it up against a tree and smashed it up. After that, we took the cop and draped him on the ruins. That's how we left him.

The cop that found him there reported plenty. The poor devil is driving a trolley today. That's a single instance, but there were plenty more. We'd stand just so much hold-up from the officers of the law, and when they got too grasping, something had to be done. In nine cases out of ten, they were tapped over the head and then made good and drunk and tossed out on the road where they'd be sure to be found. It didn't hurt the men, but it sure fixed them.

You can't get along without friendly cops. They can tip you off to raids coming from their superiors; they can ride your load through dangerous places. They are the greatest protection in the world against hijackers. They stand watch for you when you are unloading. They can turn their traffic signals for you to let you through in a hurry. They can always tell you where to get liquor. They can and will make themselves useful to you in a hundred and one different ways.

The fee is usually one dollar a case, but it varies from twenty-five cents to two dollars and a half a case, according to the job.

Any bootlegger reading this story will think I'm crazy to pay a cop two dollars and a half. It all depends on circumstances.

I'd hate to think what bootlegging would be without cops. Maybe I ought to tell the story of what happened to Manny because he forgot about cops.

Manny is his first name. It's his real one. He'll get a great kick out of reading this. Manny always did have a sense of humor.

Manny was one of these tough babies. I didn't like his looks, in the first place. His ears didn't have lobes. He wore one of those goddam caps. The gang warned me that he was a tough egg who would put it over if he could.

He wanted to buy a load of Scotch and champagne. He wanted to make what is known as a big buy. I had the stuff. I told him I'd sell him a load. But before I delivered it to him I moved it away from the main supply to a shack about a mile off. Then I made my preparations before I went down there.

About ten o'clock at night, Manny showed up with his truck. On it were two friends of his known as Mutsy and Pokey. They were gunmen. Manny asked, "Where's the stuff?" I showed it to him. Mutsy and Pokey began to load the truck.

"You here alone?" Manny asked.

I said "Yup!" I had my coat off. All he had to do was look at me to see I wasn't heeled.

Pretty soon they had the truck all loaded. Then they got on it.

"How about paying me?" I asked.

There was $4,200 worth of Scotch and Cordon Rouge aboard that truck.

Manny just said, "You ain't got anybody here with you?"

I shook my head.

"Try and get it," Manny said.

Mutsy and Pokey began to laugh. They all had their hands in their pockets.

Well, I had to laugh too. "All right, Manny," I had to say; "go ahead and take it. This isn't the first time I've been hijacked. I guess I can laugh this one off."

Manny said: "You poor boob! Any guy that don't take care of his stuff no better than you do ain't got anything coming to him."

Then he and his outfit drove off.

I put on my coat and started off down the road after them.

When I got about half a mile down, there was the truck drawn up alongside the road, and Manny and Mutsy and Pokey were reaching up for the Milky Way. Two State cops had their guns poked halfway through 'em.

"Why, Manny," I said, "did you get into trouble? Now, isn't that too bad! Let's see: they got you for possession, transportation, and concealed weapons."

The troopers had picked the finest collection of hardware off the three you ever did see.

"Hey," Manny asked, "what the heck is this, anyway?"

"Well," I told him, "I told you I was all alone at the shack, but I didn't say anything about my friends down the road."

Well, Manny said a lot of things, and after he got through I said to him, "Don't you think you'd better pay me?"

Manny paid me. After he peeled off the $4,200 I had coming to me, I suggested, "Maybe you can do business with the boys now, Manny. About a couple of hundred apiece ought to make it square."

The boys allowed that was about right.

Manny pried himself loose from $400. The guns the boys got from the three must have been worth about forty-five dollars a throw. Then Manny and Mutsy and Pokey got on their truck again and drove off. I walked on after them again.

When I got down to where the State road came in, there was the truck over on the side of the road, and Manny and Mutsy and Pokey were feeling for the stars again. The two local cops had them lined up. Honest, that was the most beautiful sight I ever saw in my life.

"Why, Manny," I said, when I got up to them, "this is most unfortunate. I didn't expect this. Did you get grabbed again?"

Manny's face was all puckered up and red, and he was so upset that he could not say anything at all, but he was trying very hard.

"Now, Manny," I said, while he was still trying, "how much have you got?"

"He had five hundred dollars," explained the cops.

"Well, I guess that will about square it, won't it boys?"

The boys thought that it would. They kept the $500, and Manny and Pokey and Mutsy got on their truck again.

"Now, Manny," I said—and then I called him a lot of things—"you'd better take the back roads, because there may be a lot more fellows out looking for you, and I won't be around to help you out of your trouble like I have so far. I've done all I could for you, and I'm going home now. If you get into trouble again, you will have to get yourself out of it. And next time, just because a feller is alone, don't think he hasn't got any friends."

It's things like that that make the game worthwhile sometimes when things aren't breaking just right for you. You can think back over them. It took Manny all the rest of the night to get to Newark. He drove down every back road in Jersey. You've got to give a lot of credit to the cops.

By this time I was making money at the game. I was a big shot. I made money every way you could make it. The stuff was coming in over the Canadian border just as if it was being poured. It stood offshore in the boats, and it came rolling up from the Bahamas.

It was around that time I bought me my little phaeton and began making trips to Canada with my two old ladies and whiskered gentleman, movie extras, with me as their chauffeur.

Then I got my rum runner. The business was growing up, and so was I. But so was the government. At night all over the Eastern seaboard the roads were choked with these big trucks, pounding along loaded to the gunwales with liquor.

Once in a while you'd read of single cases where hijackers had swung out of a side road and boarded trucks, pitched the driver out, and driven off, but—the ones you didn't read about!

There was one time there weren't enough gunmen around you could hire for convoys. There was more money for them in hijacking. And when you did send a bunch out in a pilot car and trailer, if you didn't happen to go along there was no telling whether they wouldn't turn on you and hijack you.

I want to tell you right now that for a while thuggery was threatening to ruin the game. The very men we hired for protection were getting to be more than we could handle. If there had been any brains in the Federal outfit they'd have let us alone.

The business would have wrecked itself, just as a ship taken over by a drunken crew goes on the rocks.

Gunmen are all dumb. They don't know how to run liquor.

The government saved the game for us. A lot of the boys don't realize it yet, but when the Federal agents broke up the trucking game, they drove the gunmen out of the business back to their cheap fifty-dollar spite killings, and made possible the modern high-powered seventy-five-mile-an-hour bootlegging.

With the passing of the trucks the lowbrow element in bootlegging had to go too. The truck outfit was good for just what it did—haul liquor and shoot each other up. The Federal agents stopped the trucks, not on the road, but before they got off. Or they were waiting for them when they pulled in with their loads.

When they stopped that kind of thing, the truckmen weren't fitted for anything else. The fellow with brains began to use his head. Mutsy and Pokey and their class were out of the big dough. The bootlegger forgot all about Mack and White trucks and took to the road in runabouts.

When the trucks went, the fast small cars came in. Even the old-time Cadillac touring cars that you'd load right up to the roof were no good any more. The game called for concealment as well as speed. The boys began to use Packards, Cunninghams, Hudsons, Paiges, and Cadillacs of the runabout type—swell cars you could drive around in broad daylight. Each car carried from thirty-five to sixty cases of liquor, depending on the type of car and the arrangement.

Now, that may sound funny. But don't forget that the bootlegger never carries his stuff in cases. "Case" is just a word that has come to mean twelve bottles of something.

When you load a car, you take the bottles out of the cases and pack them neck to neck as tight as they'll fit. You'd be surprised how many will go.

There were three methods of getting cars ready for liquor transportation. One of them was a pan. That was a piece of steel, shaped a good deal like a roasting pan, which hung under the car from a point aft the flywheel to another just aft the running board.

The specialists who fixed cars for the trade drilled holes in the frame of the chassis and hung steel angle irons on which the pans rested. They were from twelve to eighteen inches deep, depending on the make of the car. You got at them from the floor boards in the front and back. Packing carefully neck to neck, and filling in the spaces with newspaper as I went along, to keep them from clinking, I've carried 732 bottles of Scotch, champagne, and Cointtreau in a Packard I had fixed that way.

Now, you know, nobody is going to hijack a swell Packard car that's moving along at from seventy to seventy-five miles an hour, minding its own business. It just can't be done.

Well, John Law found out all about the pan, and began to look underneath cars. That had to be thrown overboard.

Then you could go to certain places and get your car fixed up with false seats. That brought the fast expensive sedans back into popularity. The seats were taken out, compartments built in, and a steel shell shaped like the seat was made to fit over the compartment. This came two or three inches higher than the usual seat. Every inch was important. Over this was fitted a slip cover of very flossy and expensive velours. It looked great.

When you packed your load, you rolled back your velours cover, fastened it with a steel slide, and lifted off your shell. Then you packed your liquor. The compartments took from thirty-five to forty cases. Then you put back your steel box, pulled down the velours cover, and drove off with it in broad daylight.

But, gee, what a ride! I've stayed in bed for twenty-four hours after running with one of those.

Don't think I was sorry when the Federal agents put that one out of date.

I'm still using the third method, so I don't see any particular reason why I should give it away. It's too good. When the prohibition agents get on to that one, as they will some day, I'll be able to tell what it is. By that time it may be worth while writing another article. Bootlegging changes overnight.

I drove around, buying and selling liquor something terrific. I had learned a lot from my experience with my dear old movie extras. I got me a pretty girl, snappily dressed, awful easy to look at, a bulldog, a bag of golf sticks, and one of those college-boy fur coats. The girl got $100 a ride, and she was worth it. The bulldog could laugh right in a cop's face and make him like it. Get a cop laughing and it's ten to one he won't make a pinch.

Taken for a Ride

a short-short story by William C. Ford

JENNINGS WAS BEING taken for a ride. A man sat beside him on the front seat of his car with a gun pressed against his ribs. The gun was in the man's pocket, and was held in his left hand.

Jennings didn't feel that he had ever done any harm to anybody. True, he was a bootlegger, but he was only a little one, and he tried not to sell any poison stuff.

Still, he had trespassed on the territory of one of the big fellows, and so, when he stopped at the red traffic signal, two men had stepped into his car. The man who got into the front seat covered him with the gun. The other gave directions.

"The Boss wants to see you," he said. "Drive to Brook-ville."

"All right, boys," Jennings had answered. "I'll make it right with him."

But he knew he was going for a ride, and his captors knew he knew.

Jennings speeded up with the gun at his ribs. Once he turned to the man at his right.

"Say, friend," he ventured, "can't this be fixed up?"

"Shut up," said the man.

Jennings took one hand from the wheel and put it cupped to his ear.

"Speak a little louder," he said. "I got some trouble lately with my ears. I can't hear you very well. I said can't this be fixed up some way? I ain't a bad guy."

"Shut up!" said the man considerably louder. "We ain't got nothing to say." And Jennings shut up.

Presently they approached a fork in the road. About a hundred yards from it, Jennings said:

"You want me to take the upper or the lower road?"

The man on his right turned to his companion on the rear set.

"Which road?" he muttered.

"Upper," said his companion. "Take the upper road," said the man on Jennings' right.

"All right," said Jennings, and turned to the left.

"Hey!" yelled the man in back. "I said the upper road."

"What the hell'd you turn left for?" cried the man in the front seat. "I told you *upper!*"

Jennings slowed down. "Oh!" he said. "I didn't hear you right. Want me to turn back?"

"No," grumbled the man on the back seat. "They're both lonesome." He spoke low. He figured Jennings could not hear. "Go ahead" he shouted. Jennings went ahead.

About a mile farther on the man on Jennings' right pushed the gun a little harder into his ribs.

"Stop here a minute," he said.

Jennings slowed down; came to a stop. It was a lonely spot. No cars were coming in either direction.

"Get out," said the man.

Jennings started to obey. Then a voice came from the bushes at the side of the road.

"Move on to the inspectors," it said.

A man was standing there with a long blue revolver in his hand. He motioned forward. In front two men were spreading a printed banner across the road. In the gleam of the headlights the words stood out large and plain. They read: "Stop! United States Officers."

"The Feds!" said the man on Jennings' right.

"Hell!" said the man on the back seat.

Jennings drove the car up to the sign. All concerned knew they were covered by machine guns. Jennings stopped. The men came up.

"Got any liquor in this car?" one of them said.

"No," said Jennings.

"Get out," said the officer. "We'll look it over. That one of the number plates you got on your list, Bill?"

"Yes," said Bill.

"Stand over there," said the Federal officer in charge. "Look it over, boys."

The inspectors found twenty four-gallon tins of alcohol under the back seat. The officers walked up to the three men with drawn guns.

"Line up, and put 'em up!" they said.

Jennings and his two captors complied.

"Search them," ordered the officer. "Any booze?"

"No, but guns on two of them," said an inspector.

"All right," said the officer. "Put 'em under arrest."

Handcuffs clicked. The ferret-eyed inspector who put the handcuffs on to Jennings had a few words with him. He spoke low, but Jennings seemed to have no difficulty in hearing him.

"Say," said the inspector. "This is all off. I told you to keep off the lower road tonight. Didn't I tell you if we got you we'd have to go through? Didn't I tell you we'd be on the lower road? What's the use in doing business with a dumb-bell like you? What you paid sticks, see? You got your tip. I did my part. Gee, I thought I was doing you a favor." He snapped on the handcuffs.

"You did," said Jennings.

Scarface Al Capone – 1929

by Edward Dean Sullivan

AS A NEWSPAPER man I have known Al Capone for eight years.

I know what he was, what prohibition made him, and I know what his ingenuity, hard work, and topsy-turvy success means as an example to the very worst element in this country.

Al Capone, better known as "Scarface," is the head of one gang of the more than eight hundred powerful gangs now at work in this country under prohibition. In 1926 the gross income of his one gang was seventy million dollars. That figure is from the records of Edwin A. Olsen, United States District Attorney at Chicago. Only three years have passed since then, and do you imagine that business has decreased? On the contrary, last year, 1928, thirty million dollars was spent in Chicago *for protection alone*. The gross to the gangs was well over a hundred and fifty million.

Capone has concentration and executive ability beyond the ordinary. He is utterly fearless except when it is sensible to be afraid. He is foolishly generous. He has a fine memory and is invariably appreciative. He is intensely loyal. I have never known a person who wasted fewer words in reaching the heart of any problem. Yet he, despite his intelligence, loses all perspective when it comes to a discussion of his rights under prohibition.

Listen to him:

"Prohibition is a business. All I do is to supply a public demand. I do it in the best and least harmful way I can.

"I can't change conditions. I just meet them without backing up.

"Most of my business is in Chicago. When prohibition came in there were seven thousand five hundred saloons there. Chicago spent nearly a hundred million dollars for booze at the old prices. Nobody wanted prohibition. Chicago voted six to one against it. Somebody had to throw some liquor on that thirst. Why not me?

"My customers include some of the finest people in the city, or in the world, for that matter. But I am just a bootlegger. I violate the prohibition law. All right—so do they!"

Capone first employed a vast group of distillers and alcohol cookers in the tenement homes of the Italian areas in Chicago. This was infinitely better than a centralized distilling operation, for when one unit was raided or disturbed for any reason, the rest remained operating on all cylinders to meet the tremendous alcoholic demand of Chicago. Obscure Italian families in great number were equipped with the necessary apparatus, and the cooking-out of poisonings went on in their homes.

Picture the situation. A father employed as a laborer trying to earn a living for the notably numerous members of an Italian family. Some agent of Capone gets in touch with him. He sets up his copper equipment and starts to make real money, perhaps a minimum of $15 a day. He no longer gets up at 5 o'clock in the morning; he has leisure. He dresses and eats well. All the hopes and aspirations of his family, whether they have to do with education, good appearance, diversion, or better social status, are magically gratified.

Who provides the almost unbelievable change in the family atmosphere and circumstances?

"Mr. Capone."

But it is too good to believe! What if they are arrested and all this happiness leads to disgrace? Can anything save them?

"Mr. Capone."

How would you feel about it, if your life honestly lived had been an endless struggle with scant reward? If you were untrained and ignorant—or even intelligent? Do you think your family would appreciate this change of fortune and idolize whomsoever provided it? Yes, it would—from papa right down to the baby.

And there you have the heart of what politicians mean when they utter the word constituency.

So when Al Capone went to the Chicago City Hall on matters vital to his tangled but highly remunerative enterprises, do you think the political leaders called him "Scarface," or were insulting? I'll tell you what they called him: "Mr. Capone."

Yes, indeed, even a careless political observer can recognize the political value of Capone and all gang leaders similarly situated.

They are in a position to build friendships, and to buy down opposition with both money and power.

In 1927, when William E. Dever ran for mayor against William Hale Thompson, it was generally conceded that Mr. Dever was "the finest mayor Chicago ever had." In fact, his record was so good and the newspapers were so friendly to him that the gangsters, unabashed by his slogan, "Vote for Dever and Decency," promptly sent their emissaries to him with $100,000 for his campaign. It was just a drop in the bucket, but they were taking no chances; he might succeed. The money was in thousand-dollar bills, but, of course, that was just a habit. Mr. Dever refused it peremptorily.

William Hale Thompson, who always addressed his audiences as "fellow hoodlums" during this campaign, was elected by 83,000 votes over the best mayor who never had a chance. Immdeiately afterward Al Capone moved his entire gambling paraphernalia in from the surrounding suburbs and put gambling machines into practically every book store and drug store in Chicago. It was a great day for the hoodlums.

In the ten years of Al Capone's reign in Chicago there have been 4,000 homicides. At least half of them have had some relation to booze, gang, and racketeer activity. For every thirty men in these branches of twisted industry and slaughter there is one "Big Shot" or leader. Seventy Big Shots have been killed since 1924 in Chicago, and the only one who was nearly convicted was James J. Doherty, political gangster. The state's attorney who prosecuted him and failed to convict him, after what was assumed to be a most brilliant effort in prosecution, was subsequently found dead next to the gangster defendant after a gang battle at Cicero. They were making their twentieth visit together at a saloon which was a pay-off spot for the gangsters.

Al Capone is usually indicted for any murder in Cicero, and he was indicted in this case. Four months later, in his own good time, he gave himself up—to have it over with. He was freed of the charge.

Gyps That Pass
in the Night

by O. O. McIntyre

*The Bright Lights Glow and There Is a Laugh for the Law, but
the New York Supper Club Patron Pays and Pays and Pays*

IN ONE OF those intimate cafes in the dark lanes of the Forties just off Broadway, in New York, there is this announcement on the embossed menu:

Some time ago this cafe was padlocked. It no longer affords the raison d'etre of this padlocking to its patrons. And besides, one may obtain ginger ale, seltzer, as well as the very best brands of cracked ice. Also delicately flanged champagne glasses and tall tumblers. There is, you know, a key for every padlock!

More than thirty prominent restaurants have been adorned with padlocks—Broadway's wound stripes, they call them—but most of them, having done mock penance, are open again, some observing the law and some disregarding it as flagrantly as of yore.

So far the Broadway padlock has refused to click. The forces of law and order say it will eventually. At this Broadway smiles and lifts another glass.

When the biggest chain of cafes in town, headed by the mammoth Palais Royal, was peremptorily padlocked a shiver raced down the Broadway spine from Columbus Circle to Herald Square.

Yet today nearly all of these cafes have reopened in new dress and with new names. They say they have learned their lesson and refuse to sell drinks.

Broadway's prohibition in so far as supper clubs are concerned has become a hide-and-seek game. With the prohibitory click of the padlock the club reopens around the corner. They are merely playing tag with the Eighteenth Amendment.

An average of five new clubs opens each week. These openings are gaining almost the social recognition of the theater first night and are attended by crowds just as fashionable.

The night club has become one of the greatest of the highly specialized businesses dedicated to the American boobery. A few of them conform strictly to the law, but in the main they are a fitting monument to W. C. Fields' classic line:

"Never give a sucker an even break."

For instance, supper clubs pay rents with hat-check receipts. Thus, in the flossy decorated Hang-Over Garden of Babylon you visit four padlocks up a side street, you are victimized by a Tarzan of the Apes who snatches your hat before you pass the silk-roped portals.

He is only one of the gyps that pass in the night. The night club is the phoenix of alcoholic amiability that has risen from the ashes of prohibition.

There are more than two hundred of them as this is written, ranging from the candle-sputtering attic in Greenwich Village to the black-and-tan cellar honky-tonk in Harlem's Black Belt. The gaudiest, of course, are in that midtown section of Lobsteria.

They bloom in crevices a little off the beaten track. Sometimes an austere private home or an abandoned

garage. Topnotch interior decorators are employed to burgeon them with artistic elegance. They can afford to be lavish.

Ex-cooks, ex-chauffeurs, and ex-whatnots are garnering huge fortunes as proprietors of the gilded jazz mosques. Some own a chain of them, for if one is successful it pays for all.

An obscure cabaret performer opened up his own club, and from a theatrical boarding house—two flights up and all the way back—moved to the elegance of a Long Island estate with private yacht dock in one season. His net receipts were more than eighty thousand dollars.

A former taxi driver whose eyebrows and hair nearly meet has joined the coupon clippers.

Dozens along Mazdah Lane have jumped from sweater and cap to the Tuxedoed life overnight. The dance goes gayly on. One backer of a night club who is of some social importance was embarrassed recently when his partner, who emerged from the scullery, asked to meet a few of his high-toned friends. When it was delicately intimated there

were certain barriers, he exploded: "Well, ain't I got a full dress suit?" Many are still adding a war tax as a sublime bit of bootlegging buncombe. And in one place there is a dollar extra charge added to the regular *couvert* for tables in the range of fans. Thus do our *maestri* of chicane charge for air.

Couvert charges range from six dollars to fifty cents in the sawdust-coated emporiums that feature only a loose-lipped, sallow-faced piano pounder. Outside of high-priced orchestras and now and then professional dancers there is little to remind patrons of the old-time prewar cabaret.

The supper club is no more and no less than a gilded speakeasy, and the big receipts are from drinks of powerful voltage sold in an amazingly open manner. At almost every table is a silver wine cooler, although during occasional spasms of reform the wine is served in iced pitchers.

The highball is from seventy-five cents to one dollar and a half, depending upon the swank of the club. Wine is almost invariably twenty dollars a quart, although a few places charge thirty dollars. Cocktails are discouraged, but are sold for one dollar when demanded.

A few wilted lettuce leaves passing for salad bring one dollar and a half. A ham sandwich, paper thin, is a dollar, and scrambled eggs and bacon are often listed at two dollars.

A brief stay after theater for two leaves scarcely enough from a fifty-dollar bill to appease the itching palm of the hat checker upon departing.

Incidentally there is a shrewd bit of graft psychology in their operations. A plate in the half doorway ledge is filled by them with quarters, half dollars, and a few dollar bills. Thus the dime tip has passed entirely from night life.

The cigarette girl, charging double prices, also exhibits the same psychology in her change tray. Nothing is left undone to strip the victim of his last penny. The doorman's explanation that all cabs in sight are engaged and the obvious pause indicating he might get a conveyance for a consideration is all a part of the game.

The hostess may or may not play an important part in the success of a supper club. Her job is to greet patrons, move from table to table, encourage buying, and in some cases introduce some of her girl guests to men with heavy bank rolls who lack company.

Perhaps the most striking example of the fact that in some instances the hostess does pay is Texas Guinan.

Texas is one of the anomalies of New York's night life. She is Junoesque in stature, and a pleasing expression of perpetual holiday is topped by Titian tresses.

She neither smokes nor drinks, and at dawn, when her professional duties are over, she takes herself to Central Park's bridle path for a long gallop to clear her brain of the wine-soggy atmosphere of the night.

She lives with her father and mother, an old-fashioned couple, in a modest apartment in West Twelfth Street. Texas was born in the State whence she got her name. She was a broncho-busting movie heroine with some little success, then toured vaudeville, and passed into more or less obscurity until the supper club craze came along.

She began as a hostess in what was called the Gold Room, upstairs over the Beaux Arts Cafe. Patrons, upon receiving checks, thought the room appropriately named.

Texas created a following. So she moved to another cafe and, from two hundred dollars a week, drew five hundred dollars and a certain percentage of the *couvert* charges. Today, in a way, she is one of the attractions of New York—along with the Follies, the Aquarium, and Central Park. From five hundred dollars a week she has become the recipient of twelve hundred dollars a week and a twenty-five percent rakeoff of the gross receipts.

The places over which she ruled have been padlocked several times, but Texas bobs up serenely around the corner, wearing a necklace of tiny gold padlocks and urging the bibbers to "give this little girl a hand"—meaning her circle of performers, whom she introduces singly.

Nearly all of the supper clubs have girls who are paid certain amounts to engineer their "butter and egg men" to the resorts. These are usually show girls who have no objection to bringing along their heavy sugared boys listed under "Arrival of Buyers" daily in the press.

Now and then there is a brief hiatus in the evening's frivolity. A waiter captain scurries from table to table, requesting all flasks be removed. Two derbied figures appear in the doorway, walk solemnly about, exchange a pleasantry with the head waiter, and depart. This is the nightly reminder that there is a prohibition law in the land.

Several clubs have the sleek, suave, herring-hipped Argentine dancers, who offer themselves as dancing companions, and the host finds it added to his bill—five dollars per dance.

Every club, no matter how respectable it tries to appear, has its quota of night vultures who are there to single out women with money and jewels and report to their clan.

It is the young girl who is leading the chiffon life—an apartment on the Drive and a limousine—who is their prey. They know she is the toy of what Broadway calls "a heavy sugared daddy" and that she lives pretty much alone, save for his occasional visits.

And so they take advantage of her loneliness, find out her manner of living, where she keeps her jewels, and then one morning New York awakens to buzz over another Dot King murder. Four beautiful young girls have in the last two years been garroted in their apartments and the trails all led back to chance acquaintances while out "cafe-ing" in supper clubs.

That is the sinister side of these nocturnal haunts aside from their polite brigandage.

A curious bit of frankness to confuse the customer is printed on each check, which reads:

"Please total your bill before paying the waiter."

This is in red ink, and the warning achieves just the psychological effect desired. The patron receives an impression of honesty and does not add up his bill.

It is an easy matter to add two or three bottles of wine to the bill of a befuddled customer after his evening of gayety, and this is almost the invariable custom.

Another scheme that has brought big returns to the nightly looting is worked by young dancing girls employed by the house. It is called the "burnt dress racket."

These girls mingle at various tables where there is a suggestion of welcome. They suddenly discover a burnt place in their magenta decollete frock made by a carelessly held cigar or cigarette, apparently.

It was a new dress; a sudden shoot of tears and a big-hearted Ebert magnanimously volunteers to reimburse. Sometimes a dress is paid for three times in an evening—the house sharing a fifty-fifty split.

Then, of course, there are the men and women in pairs who try, and many times successfully, to jockey some husband who has strayed from the fireside for the evening into a blackmailing cache. These are frequent, but rarely receive publicity for obvious reasons.

Waiters are adept in what is known as the "drink switch." When the party has become a trifle befuddled by wine it is easy to serve a bottle of innocuous sparkling cider without detection at champagne prices.

Such is the power of suggestion they continue hilarious and may whoop it up for hours on a libation that is as potent as ordinary drinking water.

Because they do not open until after theater the supper clubs are the catch basin for those in a mellow mood who are not likely to dispute the gentle grafting that would bring protestations in sober senses.

Men who will stand perspiring in a telephone booth demanding return of their nickel will permit a Sicilian bandit to mulct them out of a ten-dollar overcharge in a supper club and overtip him for his trouble. This is the sort of sophistry that has made millionaires of dishwashers in after-the-war night life of the metropolis.

From midnight on they guzzle the lethal libations amid the hot draperies and rocketlike burst of jazz. And after this there comes those breakfast places—the first of which has opened up in the Fashionable Fifties.

The supper club has given a halo to New York night life it has never had before. It draws every shade of patronage from gouty old boys to college lads with gin bottle necks showing from dinner jacket pockets.

The imperious lady dowered with lorgnetted elegance rubs elbows with buoyantly bunned *nymphe du pavé* and her nightly pickup.

Out of the peaceful everglades of Florida recently came Wilson Mizner to see after twenty years the Broadway he knew so well—the Broadway of the Poodle Dog, the Haymarket, and a hundred other scabrous joints featuring knockout drops and roughneck stuff.

Mizner in the old days breakfasted at 4 P.M. and went the pace. Then he vanished and became a peaceful Main Street realtor. And when he came back he saw the new night life that sprang up in his absence. He sat at all the ringside tables.

One morning recently, after a hectic night, when dawn was pinking the sky, he was walking through a side street of the Roaring Forties with a companion. He was deep in reflection.

"What," inquired his companion, "do you think of New York's present night life?"

"It is a great life," said Mizner, "if you don't WAKEN!"

JAMES MONTGOMERY FLAGG

The Steeplechase Pier

a story by
Elliott White Springs

A Fable of a Modern Frail

"I'M BRINGING OUT an old friend for the weekend," I told my wife at dinner on Friday. "You've probably heard me speak of him—Mart Canfield. I think he sent us a silver pitcher for a wedding present."

"What—another visiting fireman to whoop and holler!" she exclaimed without any evidence of pleasure. "He's from Ohio, isn't he?"

"Yes. He just got in town today and called me up first thing."

"What's he like?"

"Big, good-natured, rotten pilot, good machine-gun shot, fine poker player, hard-boiled, but a gentleman."

"Does he drink?"

"Does he drink? Does he! He was with the British flying corps for a year. What would you expect? He'll go through our cellar like Sinclair through the navy. But he won't get obstreperous. I'll guarantee that. He's got a hollow leg."

"What's his taste in rags and bones?"

"Indifferent. He used to be rather naïve. His idea of finesse was to bow politely when he met a lady and ask her, 'Are you really a lady?' If she said 'Yes,' he'd treat her with respect the rest of her life. If she said 'No,' he'd lose further interest in the dancing."

"That sounds interesting."

"He's a good fellow and would appreciate anything we have to offer in the way of light entertainment. This is the first time he's been east since the war. Better get in some good talent for the party."

"Who'd you suggest?"

"How about the Walshes for the chorus? He and Jerry are old friends."

"All right. And Jane Stahl for him."

"Isn't she a bit young? It seems only yesterday that her mother spanked her for using rouge."

JAMES MONTGOMERY FLAGG

"Don't dwell on your age. You look old enough without trotting out your memories," my wife cautioned me. "Jane's young, all right, but you don't know the half of it. If your ancient comrade makes his customary wisecrack at her, he'll think he got into the Steeplechase Pier by mistake. She was debarred from polo once for rough play. Mike Stevenson says she hit him with a mallet harder than that Englishman. I believe she took a set from Helen Wills, and she was runner-up in the state golf championship last year.

"I didn't know she was all of that," I confessed. "How time does fly! Well, trot her out and let her do her stuff.

I haven't seen Mart since the war, but I guess he can hold his own with anything this generation has to offer. Anybody that can make money out of the lumber business has to know how to take care of himself."

"Has he made a lot of money?"

"I think so. At least, he told me he wouldn't quit until he did, and he's a determined cuss. I came back on the boat with him in March of 1919. We had a stateroom together in the sick bay. He got hit in the hip with a phosphorus bullet in August and was still in a plaster cast. God, what a time of it he had! He was in terrific pain every minute.

"But he'd lay there in his bunk and plan what he was going to do when he got well. He was particularly sore because he'd missed the celebration that followed the Armistice. That stuck in his craw worse than his broken hip. So he'd lay there and plan how he was going to celebrate the Armistice when he got on his feet again.

"First he was going back to his business and work in double shifts until he made a million dollars. His partner had stayed on the job and, I gathered, had done pretty well with it. When he got his million he was going to sell out and go back to Europe to put on the show he would have if he hadn't been in the hospital on November eleventh. I didn't have a chance to talk to him very long over the phone, but I gathered that he is sailing for Europe as soon as he gets his passport and passage. So I suppose he's made his pile."

"All right. Bring him out," my wife said. "But if he's like your other aviator friends I won't bother to lay a plate for him. They all assume the second drinking position with the caviar. And I suppose I'll get the usual line. Before dinner I'm a lucky girl to have gotten such a fine fellow as their dear old pal—God bless his heart! Then along in the cool of the evening they want to know how much longer I'm going to keep them waiting while I waste myself on such a hopeless bum. And did I ever hear about the time you got thrown out of a hotel in Edinburgh because the chambermaid was jealous? Some day the worm will turn and I'll tell a few myself. Well, bring on your retired millionaire! I'll order a couple of crates of oranges and a case of vermouth."

So we left it at that.

Saturday I had lunch with Mart at his hotel, and Joe Gish and Winnie Chappel and Jerry Walsh were there to talk over old times and drink to the king. Then Mart and I drove out for a round of golf.

"Well, Mart, did you make your million?" I asked him as we followed the traffic.

"Yes, I did, as a matter of fact," he admitted modestly. "Or rather my partner made it for me. The war didn't do our business any harm and we decided to spread out. We've got branches in ten cities now. That's how we made the money. Just recently my partner and I drew down a million each and then incorporated so our subordinates could have a share in the business. I've retired, but the business will go on."

"Aren't you pretty young to retire?" I asked.

"Yes, I guess I am," he confessed. "I'm only thirty-five, but you know I promised it to myself. After you spend a year on your back wondering whether you'll ever walk again, you get strange ideas. What's your life worth? That's the question that keeps bothering you. Who wants Rockefeller's money if they have to take his indigestion along with it? How much good was money to me when I was on my back with my leg harnessed to the ceiling? How much good was a fortune to me if I had to keep on working all my life?"

"Didn't you like your work?"

"Sure. But when I got out of that bed I found I'd lost my ambition. I didn't want to be mayor or president of the bank. I didn't want a big house with marble baths. I didn't want a yacht. I didn't want to have to play polo. I wanted to do the one thing that I had not been able to do—celebrate the Armistice.

"I wanted to push street cars off the track and kiss strange women. You boys were out raising hell all over Europe from November eleventh until blue in the face while I was lying up in bed watching the flies on the ceiling and holding my breath to keep from screaming. Now that I've got my pile I'm on my way back to take up where I left off when that Hun shot the bottom out of my seat. He was in a red triplane. I can still see him turn inside my S. E. and put a burst into me from underneath.

"Anyway, I'm going to Paris and take up my duties as a victorious aviator just back from the heat of battle. I shall be drunk and disorderly in four languages. I shall get the taste of Volstead and Blue Sunday out of my mouth. I shall pick out the most beautiful woman in France and take her with me on a tour of the old battlefields. I hear that Wipers and Albert and Bapaume are rebuilt. I don't believe it's possible, but I must have a look. I shall charter a plane and go back to visit all the old clouds I used to hide behind.

"I shall find the woman with the reddest hair in England and take her with me while I revisit all the old pubs where we used to huddle around the stove with the local politicians. I shall find the Waac in Scotland with the broadest burr in her accent and take her back to Turnberry with me to play golf on the old machine-gun range in the dunes where we used to slap each others' faces to keep them from freezing. I shall row out to Ailsa Craig where I flew once on a bet of five pounds.

"In other words, I shall purge my mind of bitter memories and redeem my soul from its travail. I shall wrestle again with fate. I am Faust in reverse gear, for I have already been in hell. Like Jacob, I have served my seven years at hard labor and now claim my reward. Better come along and hold my coat for me."

"You forget that I am married," I reminded him, "and have a business with no partners in it. Besides that, I wouldn't want to see you disappointed. I went back in nineteen twenty-one myself to do the same thing. I only stayed two weeks. I couldn't stand it. Everywhere I went there were ghosts of the men who were gone. All the women we used to know had either turned professional or reformed. The place is cluttered up with curfews and taxes. Remember God made Europe as well as America and they pay a lot of reformers to remind them of it. I'd never go back again even if I could. Better luck to you."

"You must have hit an off season," Mart told me, undiscouraged. "I've kept track of some of the old crowd. Murray's is still running. Peggy and Sheila and the Brainless Wonder and the Queen Bee and Baby Child and the Strawberry Blonde are all still tripping the light fantastic and spending the week-end at Skindle's. They still have electric punts on the river. And the girl who nursed me at the Lancaster Gate Hospital is back on the stage. I had a letter from her last month. We still have a date.

"More power to you," I wished him. "Youth fatteneth on illusions and the wisdom of old age is a hollow nut. Joe Gish says he'd rather play post office with the dumbest senior in the Gallipolis High School than be fought over by all the mistresses of the king."

"Joe ought to know. I'll guarantee he's had both experiences."

"Well, give my regards to Jack May, the Trafalgar Lions, and cold tubs," I told him. "I hope you get your money's worth. You certainly had a hard time on your last trip and deserve anything you take a fancy to now. If Mademoiselle from Armentières is your idea of Marguerite, I hope the devil delivers the goods. You've certainly surrendered your soul to him. There's the club over on that hill. We'll only have time for nine holes."

When we got home everyone was dressing for dinner. We changed and hurried down for cocktails.

Mart was able to meet the wives without a drink first, but Jane sort of stuck in his throat. She had on full regimentals. There was more of her out of her dress than in it. But it was all good, so I didn't see why he was gasping. The cocktails restored him temporarily and we went in to dinner. After dinner the conversation loosened up with the coffee and liqueurs.

"I understand you are going back to Europe," my wife said to Mart. "Isn't this an off season?"

"Yes," he agreed, "but I want to get back in time to celebrate the anniversary of the Armistice."

"Can't you do that here?"

"Not the way he wants to celebrate it," Jerry explained for him. "This is sort of a pilgrimage he's making. He's going to get drunk and disorderly all over England and France and give the wild women something to tell his grandchildren about."

Mart blushed.

"Well, hardly that," he temporized. "But I did miss the big show and I'm going back to see the sights I couldn't see the last time."

"What kind of sights?" Jane asked.

"Suppose you guess," Jerry offered. "I'm all for you, Mart, old boy."

"I suppose you'd like to go with him," Jerry's wife commented caustically.

He subsided quickly.

"Do you have to go all the way to Europe just to celebrate the Armistice?" Jane asked him.

"Well, that's not exactly the idea," Mart explained. "I expect to stay over there."

"You mean live over there?"

"I think so."

"You're too young to understand such things, Jane," Jerry admonished her, "but the European species of wild woman is far superior to the American brand."

"What do you know about either?" Jerry's wife asked him. "If Mr. Canfield is really looking for companionship in a brawl, it's a shame he has to waste money on a ticket. You ought to be able to introduce him to the right people."

Jerry subsided for good.

"I suppose that home life in a Paris bar has its charms," Jane surmised, "and those Continental women certainly have a way with men that turns our souls green with envy. They're so attractively wicked."

"What about some contract?" my wife asked to relieve Mart's embarrassment.

"You four go play your usual cutthroat game," Jane suggested. "And I'll take Mr. Canfield over to the Barlings'."

"What's over there?" asked Mart uncertainly.

"Oh, just a crowd of people celebrating Saturday night. It won't be like Paris, but the likker is good, and Peggy Watts will make immoral propositions to you. They have a regular bar in the garage and a jug band. You might just as well get into training for big game."

So Jane and Mart left us. We played bridge until late and went to bed.

About noon next day Jane came down looking fresh and cheery. Mart hadn't showed up yet.

"What did you do with my old friend last night?" I asked her.

"Oh, nothing much," she informed me. "I didn't have a chance. There was too much competition. But it was a good evening while it lasted. What that man can do to a piano! Why didn't you tell me he was the original jazz king?"

"He is good," I admitted. "I remember he used to play for us in the mess every night. But I didn't know he was good enough to excite attention around here."

"Well, he is. He was the life of the party last night. He did things to Bach and Beethoven that were statutory offenses. And he concocted a prairie oyster with chopped onions and tomato juice that made a new woman of me. He also cooked up a dish of eggs that opened the way to the hearts of all present. I had to fight for possession of him."

Mart appeared after a while looking the worse for wear and sank into a convenient chair.

"Quick," said Jane to me, "two absinthe frappés and then we've got to be going."

"Going where?" asked Mart weakly.

Jane went over and sat on his lap casually.

"Over to the Colts'," she told him. "Don't you remember? We promised to lunch with them and then go aquaplaning. We've got to hurry or miss the first round of cocktails."

She extracted a cigarette and a match from her garter.

"I'm sorry I got so tight last night," she apologized. "But that was a new drink to me you shook up when you got behind the bar. You can't expect much from us little girls over here. We're not used to strong drinks like Continental women. I'll try to do better today. Here, drink this and pull yourself together. Why speak of love when there's work to be done?"

They tossed off their frappés and started to leave in her car.

"You don't mind if I take young Lochinvar-out-of-the-West for the day, do you?" she asked my wife. "I don't dare pick on these two sedentary married men around here while you and Alice have your eyes on them. And there're half a dozen women clamoring for a chance at Irving Berlin Paderewski before he's swallowed up by the gutters of Cathay. If I didn't bring him back today they'd accuse me of taking an unfair advantage of him."

It was four that night when I heard them come in.

Next morning I learned that Mart was the casualty this time. And he looked the part. I gathered that the aquaplane and bacardi rum had proved his downfall. So the score stood at a tie. Mart said he'd get his revenge that night in town. They invited me to come along and referee, but I had sense enough to decline.

"I'm sorry I looked too long on the red wine," Mart apologized to her.

"Oh that's all right."

"Did I disgrace myself in public?"

"Not particularly, though you did try to knock down a chandelier. You said it was a triplane. And, say, if the girls in Paris don't take to your ideas readily, they're in for a hard time."

"Was I that bad?"

"You were until I tapped you with the marble ball off the gear shift."

"I was wondering where I got that knot on my head."

"Well, that's it. After that, you condescended to discuss the matter. You seemed quite surprised when I didn't fall in with your scheme. You intimated that you had wasted two evenings. You complained that I had misled you. You explained that you had left the old homestead and were going out in the world to prove Nero a piker and you didn't want any flappers around. You sounded like the old Monk of Siberia."

"Did I tell you all that?"

"You did and a lot more that I'll spare you. Well, New York hasn't much to offer, but it will serve as a starting place for you. I'll see that you don't miss anything."

And apparently she did, for when I stopped in at his hotel to see him the following Friday, he had weakened visibly. I asked him if he wanted to come out over the weekend again, but he said he already had an engagement. Jane had fixed up a party at the Worchesters' at Glen Head. I knew what would happen to him there and extended my sympathy.

"I'm worried," he confessed to me.

"Hangover?" I asked.

"No. It's about Jane."

"Probably a hangover after all," I surmised.

"She's a fine kid."

"Yes."

"But what's going to become of her?"

"Couldn't possibly guess. Ten years at hard labor or the Florence Crittenton Home."

"It's a shame for a girl like that to go to the dogs."

"Well, you're headed for hell, aren't you? Why be exclusive?"

"But she's a good kid."

"Probably. But I thought you and she were playing hare and hounds. It looks like she's won."

"You don't understand. She's just a kid, full of fun, full of life, full of pep, and going to get into trouble."

"I shouldn't be surprised. Everybody does, sooner or later."

"Why don't her parents take her in hand?"

"Can't say. Why don't you?"

"I'm sailing on Wednesday. It's none of my business, anyway. But something is sure to happen to her. She goes out and gets tight with a strange man, and what can you expect?"

"Meaning you as the strange man?"

"Yes. She didn't know a thing about me. Anything might have happened."

"Did it?"

"No. I'm not the kind to take advantage of a girl."

"Oh, aren't you? What about the second night?"

"I was tight myself then. But after the way she behaved I was entitled to think what I pleased. She certainly acted the part. She ought to learn to behave herself and not give people false impressions."

"She seemed to be able to take care of herself."

"Yes, but before long she'll pick on the wrong man and then she'll ruin her life and disgrace her family. I don't know what would have happened if we'd both been tight at the same time. Somebody ought to take her in hand before it's too late."

"Saying which, you will take her in hand tonight and fill her full of fire water and descend upon the town like the wolf on the fold. What's the program?"

"I believe we are going to try and take a drink in every speak-easy on Forty-eighth Street. Yesterday we tried to get a cocktail in every apartment house on Park Avenue. We finally passed out in Grant's Tomb."

"No wonder you feel your guilt today," I commented. "If I had done that I'd be out digging my own grave. But cheer up—you'll sail Wednesday and you can sober up when you get abroad."

"But I don't know what to do about Jane. Someone has got to take care of her. At the pace she's traveling she hasn't long to go."

"Get the beam out of your own eye and never mind the eyes of a pretty girl," I advised and left him to his misery.

Sunday afternoon Jane and Mart dropped in to call and catch a few drinks. She'd had him out on a drag hunt that morning, and what the aquaplane hadn't done to him the jumps had.

Jane followed me into the pantry as I was getting some ice.

"Your boy friend travels fast," she confided to me.

"Yes," I agreed. "He's been saving his energy for this sabbatical year."

"So he told me. He's planning to set Europe on fire with red-headed women."

"He usually does what he says he'll do," I told her.

"Him and who else?" she asked scornfully.

"Meaning you think you can stop him?" I inquired.

"Well, I'll have you know that he asked me to marry him this very morning. How do you like them apples?"

"Score one for the queen! Are you going to live in Paris or Ohio?"

"Neither. I declined his proposal," she told me with something like a catch in her voice.

"Why?" I inquired. "Isn't that what you've been after? You'll never get a better chance. Men like Mart don't grow on trees."

"I know it. But I just haven't the heart to spoil his fun. For seven years he's planned to go down with the bands playing. He told me how he lay in bed for a year and that was all he had to look forward to. Then he went to work to get the money to put on a good show. Now he's made good and has one foot on the primrose path. He's a little boy going up to the platform to get his prize. He's realized his ambition, but he's willing to forego the fruits of his

victory to fish the little girl out of the gutter and save her from the wages of sin. He's doing this for me, you see. He thinks that he could make an honest woman out of me.

"It's very nice of him and all that, but not practicable. I may be a bum sport, but I'm not that bad. I can't steal his candy. I don't blame him a bit for wanting to raise hell after what he went through.

"I'm going to put him on his boat Wednesday if my constitution will hold out that long, and then I'm going down to White Sulphur and take the cure. I'm going on the wagon for the rest of my life. I hope I never see another drop of likker as long as I live. I hope all the wild women in Paris hold a convention over him. And don't ever call me in to entertain another shell-shocked veteran."

"No one can say you aren't a good sport," I assured her. "What did you tell him?"

"Oh, I told him to run sell his papers, I wasn't interested. I kidded him along so he wouldn't have any regrets to spoil his trip. We're going to burn the island until Wednesday. I don't want the girls in Paris to think we've neglected him over here. I must uphold our reputation.

"I may not be red-headed, and my French is more sacred than profane, but when I'm through with him he'll think Gaby Deslys was the French Carrie Nation. Make mine strong, will you, please?"

Mart was lapping it up as only a rejected suitor can.

They got themselves in good shape and drove on to the next stop.

I stopped in Wednesday morning at Mart's hotel to bid him farewell. He hadn't started packing yet.

"You'd better hurry if you're going to catch that boat," I advised him.

"I'm not going to catch it," he informed me. "I just canceled my passage. I'm catching the Special back home instead."

"Business gone sour?"

"No. I've decided that I don't need a trip abroad. I'm convinced that my constitution can't stand a life of vice and crime. I've waited too long to celebrate the Armistice."

"What d'you think you've been doing for the past ten days—observing Easter?"

"Well, whatever it was, it's enough. I don't crave any more wine, women, or song. I'm going back to Ohio and try to live this down. My bruises ought to heal by Christmas. And I hope I never have to drink another cocktail. If I'm very sick I might take a little whisky medicinally, but otherwise I'm going to ride the wagon until Gabriel pulls the whistle."

"It's too bad, Mart," I sympathized with him. "I was looking forward to your report on conditions in Europe. When did you make this important decision?"

"About an hour ago."

"Have you told Jane about it?"

"No. What's it to her? She's not interested in anything but a party. I told her good-by last night."

"Don't you think you'd better call her and tell her you've changed your plans?"

"No. She's already told me what she thought of me."

"She might be planning to go down to the boat to see you off. It's only courteous to call her and save her the trip."

"That's so," he agreed. "Get her for me, will you? I can't use the telephone this morning with any degree of success."

I got Jane for him in a few minutes. She sounded pretty low.

"Hello," said Mart after I passed the instrument to him. "I just called up to say I wasn't sailing. . . . No, I'm not going abroad. I'm going back to Ohio. . . . Yes, I'm going back home. For good. . . . No, I'm not going to Europe at all. . . . Well, they'll have to get along without me. I hope I never meet another wild woman. . . . I beg your pardon. Any wild woman, then. . . . Yes. . . . Yes. . . . What's that? . . . Yes, the Anti-Saloon League has its headquarters in Ohio; it was founded near home. . . . Do I think they'll let you join it? I don't know. . . . Will I come by for a cup of tea before I go? Certainly. . . . Good-by."

"You're right, Mart," I told him. "You'd be a total loss in Paris. You'd sit around and cry into your apéritif because a little girl was going to hell in New York. Delilah certainly set a good precedent. More power to her."

Heavy Sugar Daddy

a short short story by

Frances Bolton

"H'LO!" CHIRPED THE tall blonde, drawing out a chair and planting herself in it. "Like the floor show?"

The stout old party across the table ignored her question. He said: "Did you get my letters?"

"Yes. Didn't you care for my torch song?"

"Why didn't you answer them?"

"There wasn't anything to say."

"You won't change your mind?"

"No," said the girl. "Gentlemen usually admire my boop-boop-be-doop technique."

"Damn it all, Dolly, this is serious! I'm lonesome; I need you."

"We wouldn't get along," said Dolly, lighting a cigarette. "Our ideas . . ."

"You mean our ages. I know I'm old; that's why I want youth around me."

"That's what you think. It wouldn't work out."

"I think I could see things your way," said the man slowly. "I've been trying."

"If you saw things my way you wouldn't be trying to get me away from here. This is where I belong."

"No, you don't!" he said. "You're too good for this place. I could get you in . . ."

"That's it," she interrupted. "I don't want you to get me anywhere. I got myself here. Even if it is a dump, there's a kick for me in that."

"All right," he conceded, "you can do anything you want. I won't interfere."

She looked skeptical.

"You could have your own apartment," he coaxed, "your own friends."

Dolly patted his veined hand. "It's no use."

"I'll give you a car. You can go abroad—alone, if you want."

"Let's drop it," said Dolly. "You can't give me anything I want except, maybe, a chicken sandwich."

The stout old party wiped his forehead and called a waiter. He gave his order, then drew a package from his pocket. Tenderly he unwrapped the tissue from a long leather box and laid it in front of Dolly.

"I brought this along," he said, "in case . . ."

"In case I gave in?" Dolly laughed. "An apartment, a motor, Europe, and now diamond bracelets! You've been seeing too many movies!"

"Open the box!" he commanded. "And you'll see I'm the real thing in what you cuties call sugar daddies!"

She sprung the catch with a flourish. "The family jew-ells!" she gasped. "The darling pearls! Oh, really, you are doing well by me!" She lifted them out of the box and let them dangle from her fingers.

"I'm sorry I accused you of diamond bracelets, but all the same . . ." She shook her head and folded the pearls into their bed.

"Wear them anyway," he pleaded. "Just to please me!"

Dolly snapped the box shut.

"I'm sorry, I can't." She addressed the man, but her eyes went past him. He followed her gaze to a glossy youth in a tight suit who was attending to his nails in the doorway.

"I see," said the man, looking at Dolly's eyes. His glance probed the youth and he added, "If there's ever any trouble . . ."

Dolly cut him short: "I can take care of myself!"

He shrugged his shoulders and slipped the box into his pocket. "Good-by!" he said, and went out.

The young man abandoned his nails and went out too.

When Dolly was finished with her number in the second floor show the youth was sitting where the stout old party had been.

"You gave that heavy sugar daddy his bellyful, kiddo!" he greeted her.

"Al," she started, "that man . . ."

"You don't need to tell me, baby. I saw you. You're a good kid. Here's something to show that you never lose by sticking with me." He laid a long leather box in front of Dolly.

She snatched it up. "Where did you get it?"

"Louie grabbed it while you were putting on your number. Let's see how you look in them, Doll."

"Is he hurt?" cried Dolly.

"Who, Louie? Say, that guy's the slickest dip . . ."

"No! no! Not Louie—the man he r-robbed."

"Why, sweetness, what do you care about him? You're washed up with him, ain't you?"

"Answer me! Is he hurt?"

"Naw! Doesn't even know he's lost 'em, probably. Say, Doll, you haven't thanked me . . ."

Dolly rose. She stared down at the handsome face in icy scorn.

"I thought you were a bootlegger," she said. "You're nothing but a sneak thief!"

She swept past him to the dressing room, grabbed her wrap, and made for the door. Then she paused and plunged into a phone booth. She called a number on Park Avenue and when she got it she said:

"This is Dolly. Are you all right? I'm coming home. . . ." A pause. "Yes, to stay." Then: "You left mother's pearls on the table, dad. I'm bringing them with me."

JAMES MONTGOMERY FLAGG

II

Bring Prosperity
Back!

(1930-1935)

MAY 11, 1940

Liberty

HOW TO FIND A BETTER JOB by Professor Walter B. Pitkin

TALES OUT OF SCHOOL

Startling Disclosures of Washington Society by a Senator's Daughter

JAN. 23, 1937

Liberty

5¢

UNANSWERED QUESTIONS ABOUT THE PRESIDENT-ELECT
BY Dr. STANLEY HIGH

"HAS WALL STREET Gone Wild and Whirling?" was the question above an article by Irving Fisher in the February 19, 1929, issue of *Liberty*. In roughly three thousand words Professor Fisher viewed with alarm the stock market's furious convolutions. Professor Fisher clearly refutes the popular belief that the Depression arrived without warning, but almost no one at the time seems to have paid attention to his words of wisdom.

The country was far too busy executing its own Black Bottom ("the new twister") toward October of 1929, at which time America toppled from the gin-scented pinnacle of the Twenties to the bleak depths of financial disaster. It was a strange kind of financial collapse. The rich, with their huge paper profits, felt it first. Wealthy men ended their lives by leaping from office windows, while others desperately tried to market their yachts and estates. Inevitably, the misery seeped down to the average man and by 1931, wholesale unemployment left entire families hungry, hopeless, and despondent. On big-city street corners onetime white-collar workers hawked apples for five cents apiece.

Everyone seemed confused and spiritless. Practically the only confident voice rang from the State House in Albany, where Franklin D. Roosevelt served as Governor. From his wheelchair this buoyant man began issuing a series of brief messages to the people of New York, which *Liberty* seized upon as short features.

Even so, the historian browsing through *Liberty* in search of background on the Depression years gets a rude shock. For with the advent of national disaster, magazine editors faced a problem: Did people who were directly confronted with unemployment, plummeting incomes, and breadlines wish to read more about such things in the pages of their popular magazines?

The reply seemed to be a resounding negative. Accordingly, big-circulation periodicals set about providing readers with escapist material reminiscent of the lamented Twenties. Realism, with its attendant suicides, suffering, and starvation, was left to the *Literary Digest, Time,* and the newly conceived *Newsweek.* To brighten its pages, *Liberty* subtitled one serial "The Thrilling Story of a Girl with a Jazz Age Heart." Others were "The Story of a Faithful Wife's Lover," "A Story of a Girl Who Went Hunting in the Danger Zone of Love," and "Public Sweetheart Number One."

Liberty had made its debut in the Golden Age of Magazine Fiction, when editors were making the glorious discovery that short stories and week-to-week serials running through the columns of a magazine attracted the advertisers who in turn pay the bills.

Now, with the nation substituting the song "Brother, Can You Spare a Dime?" for "Who Takes Care of the Caretaker's Daughter?" *Liberty* provided stories reminiscent of the Good Old Days. Readers of a 1931 issue were startled to find themselves facing a just-discovered piece of fiction by Count Leo Tolstoy. Other top fiction writers who cheered the magazine through dark days were Edith Wharton, Sinclair Lewis, Joseph Hergesheimer, Albert Payson Terhune, Fannie Hurst, Warwick Deeping, Cosmo Hamilton, Arthur Somers Roche, Louis Bromfield, and Ben Ames Williams.

With the Thirties, Viña Delmar had begun directing her talents to the money marts of Hollywood. Elliott White Springs turned his attention to Springmaid Fabrics. So the *Liberty* fiction mantle fell on Achmed Abdullah, Thyra Samter Winslow, Edward Hope, and other younger writers. James M. Cain's notable "Double Indemnity" first appeared in *Liberty.* Another who contributed fiction as well as everything else was Cornelius Vanderbilt, Jr., a young man of towering wealth and social position who became a surprising *Liberty* stalwart during the Thirties. One of his serials was titled "Filthy Rich."

Liberty also offered humor. Robert Benchley wrote no less than seventy-three pieces for the magazine, many of which were illustrated by Peter Arno. (Some of these turned up later as the famous Benchley movie shorts.) Especially dear to *Liberty* readers was Burt Green's column, "Love Letters of an Interior Decorator," which set a record by running for one hundred consecutive installments. J. P. McEvoy contributed his lively "Show Girl" stories—a wild amalgam of letters and telegrams which became a hard-cover book, a Ziegfeld musical comedy, and a movie. A generation of television viewers may be intrigued to learn that stories of Ed, the Talking Horse, first appeared in *Liberty.*

It's impossible to mention *Liberty* fiction without paying tribute to the serials—those jumbo week-to-week stories, many of which were promptly transferred to bookshelves and movie theaters. (Unfortunately they run too long to be included in this selection.) In the Twenties, Fannie Hurst got $50,000 for twelve installments of a story called "Mannequin." Others' piecemeal efforts ran even longer. In cooperation with Paramount Pictures, *Liberty* sponsored a serial by ten top fiction writers of the day, each of whom contributed a single installment. Authors were Rupert Hughes, Zane Grey, Sophie Kerr, J. P. McEvoy, Ursula Parrott, Polan Banks, Viña Delmar, Irvin S. Cobb, and Gertrude Atherton. The serial and later film were titled "The Woman Accused." Who remembers them now?

Those over the ledge of middle age may fondly recall the serialized "Red Napoleon," by Floyd Gibbons. In broad journalistic strokes, it merged the world of the recent past with a fantastic, dictator-ridden future. This was probably the most famous of all *Liberty* serials.

In a nation awash with Depression, *Liberty* hardly acknowledged hard times except in its editorials. Otherwise, its major notice of countrywide adversity came in a series of humorous pieces by Eddie Cantor. These later went into his best selling book *Caught Short: A Saga of Wailing on Wall Street.*

A quick word-picture of contemporary misery does appear in "Stag Lines and Breadlines," by Cornelius Vanderbilt, Jr. In this, the author reports that a few lucky folk still had money enough, and that they were still spending it in the lavish fashion of the filthy rich. This article underlined the irony—of which *Liberty* made much—that Barbara Hutton, America's Poor Little Rich Girl, came of age at a low point of the Depression. Her lavish New York debut was a four orchestra gala costing the tidy sum of $60,000. Yet people suffering hunger pangs read avidly about Babs and continued to relish her girlish extravagance as she waltzed toward a wedding with fortune-hunter Alexis Mdivani.

Though *Liberty* tried hard to picture the sunny side of life, it could not altogether avoid sober politics. Debonair James J. Walker resigned under pressure from Governor Roosevelt, who thereby consolidated his image as the man of a new era. In FDR, *Liberty* quickly saw a rising political star, yet whispers across the land said the polio-crippled Governor did not have the physical stamina to be President. In 1931, *Liberty* sent a writer to cover this delicate question—and every year into the 1940's, the magazine ran an up-to-the-minute report on the Presidential health.

European politics had also begun to intrude on the national consciousness. Even as Roosevelt took the oath of office, Adolf Hitler began his dreadful rise in Germany. *Liberty* correspondents like Floyd Gibbons, Frazier Hunt, Princess Catherine Radziwill, and the ever-present Cornelius Vanderbilt dispatched stories from Europe.

Far more exciting than politics was crime. As Prohibition became Repeal, the gang lords began to fade away. Al Capone, the greatest of them all, had been convicted of income-tax invasion and locked away in Alcatraz. Suddenly the focus of crime swung from big city racketeers to rural outlaws like Bonnie Parker, Clyde Barrow, and John Dillinger. *Liberty* already possessed a stable of hard-hitting crime reporters in Edward Doherty, Will Irwin, Al Dunlap, and Edward Dean Sullivan. It may be said that they gave the best contemporary coverage of the rip-roaring crime in the hinterlands.

No less than the world, *Liberty* was in a state of flux.

In its first seven years of existence, the magazine had performed the considerable feat of losing over $2,000,000 a year. Circulation remained good, but lack of advertising joined with the high cost of contributors to drag the magazine down financially.

Oddly enough, even the tireless zeal of *Liberty*'s circulation department brought on problems. The huge response to the magazine's prepublication name competition had so impressed the management that it was ever prone to clip-out contests and other gimmicks for offering the reader a menagerie of financial prizes. The first of these had readers cutting out and rearranging the scrambled pictures of pedigreed dogs, with the live, unscrambled animals offered as prizes. This turned out to be a disaster, since most of the dogs died en route to winners.

Undeterred, the magazine kept on promoting contests, games, and liberal rewards. Prizes were offered for titles to books and movies; for matching the borders of states; for the last line of limericks; for a varied assortment of similar challenges.

Liberty's most famous contest was the Patriotic Game of Presidents, which consisted in matching the chopped-up physiognomies of Chief Executives. This feature ran in the first Depression winter of 1929–30, and seemingly, everyone in the hard-pressed nation dreamed of winning a share of the total $25,000. Yet the extra readers only multiplied the magazine's printing costs. Meantime, advertising remained low. One expert put *Liberty's* lifetime headache succinctly when he said, "The magazine was devoured by its own circulation."

As losses mounted, the Patterson-McCormick axis quivered to deep lamentations. Why had these two successful newspaper moguls ever pushed themselves into magazines?

It's hard to believe, but at this precise moment a highly successful *magazine* publisher was cursing himself for getting involved in *newspapers.* Pioneer health faddist Bernarr Macfadden was the happy publisher of *Physical Culture, True Story*, and other periodicals which earned him millions each year. Yet he had seen fit to step into the newspaper field. "He liked to diffuse himself," explains his longtime associate Meyer Dworkin.

By 1931, Macfadden had ten newspapers including the tabloid *New York Graphic*, famed in song and story as the most outrageous newspaper of all time. But Macfadden had lost a stupendous $8,000,000 on his beloved *Graphic* and was on the verge of closing it down. As yet, he had no plans for his unprofitable newspapers in other cities.

Macfadden had a fondness for the words "Daily" and "News" in the names of his far-flung journals, as in *The Detroit Daily* and the *Automotive Daily News*. Captain Patterson found this habit annoying and personally took Macfadden to task. Inevitably, their talk turned to mutual publishing problems, and one day, Macfadden traded away his *Detroit Daily* in return for *Liberty*. No money or stock was exchanged in this most clean-cut of transactions.

How nice it would be to report that this unusual switch of management brought *Liberty* brand new life and vigor! Bernarr Macfadden was a man who in mid-Depression established soup kitchens where a hungry man got a meal for nine cents; he had also exhorted his *Graphic* editors with the cry, "Put a mother's tears on the front page—that never fails!" Yet no such inspiration was to be seen in *Liberty*.

Macfadden did contribute weekly signed editorials which were hard hitting and individualistic. In them, he espoused such causes as the New Deal, safe driving, anti-lynching, Repeal, and sane sex. But beyond this, the marvelous mind lay fallow.

As editor-in-chief, Macfadden picked a long-time associate and admirer named Fulton Oursler who was said to have "a 500,000 candle-power imagination." Yet he never gleamed too brightly in his *Liberty* capacity. Oursler dropped the "Love o' Lil" covers, but otherwise seemed content to expand the already established big-name policy. Where the big names had formerly been those of writers and artists, Oursler brought in celebrity-authors, or just plain celebrities—George Bernard Shaw, H. G. Wells, Albert Einstein, Winston Churchill.

He also stressed *Liberty*'s pet "surprise" features—short pieces calculated to bring a reader up short by an odd juxtaposition of author and subject. In this genre, Oursler—or someone—achieved a pinnacle of success with "My Sex Life," by Mahatma Gandhi.

In this fashion, *Liberty* faced (and survived) the Depression with a new publisher, a new editor, and the same old editorial policy. Making no effort to cover the harsh realities of life in this time, it chose to concentrate on events surrounding the Depression, while also offering generous helpings of escapist fiction.

It was a policy similar to those adopted by the *Saturday Evening Post, Collier's, Ladies' Home Journal, Vogue,* and *Boy's Life.*

In *Liberty*, it looked like this . . .

The Jazz Age

by Vachel Lindsay

(To be read and chanted, quite aloud, by an
open hearth-fire, with the radio turned off.)

GOOD-BY, JAZZ AGE, I'm going Home, and fish in the minnow crick,
With any old twine, a good bent pin, and a worm, and a hickory stick.

Good-bye, Jazz Age. The Wagon Bridge, broken, finds the Broken Bridge Farm.
A sign on the rail warns motors away, so stray lambs meet no harm;

And so scarab beetles take to the trail, unterrified gypsies again;
Swans cross the lane:—Greek ladies of old! And roosters are Robin Hood's men!

Good-by, Jazz Age. I'm going Home. The tottering bridge will stand
If you take it afoot, whistle a charm, a witch-hazel wand in your hand.

The minnow crick shines! Curves on the grass! The path by the bank finds the yard,
A blue iron deer, green iron dog, and a live pup that barks at you hard.

He bites only those who are togged out for golf, wear movie clothes or puttees.
Oh, you must be dressed like Josh Billings at best, to put the quaint hound at his ease.

We will never come back from the Broken Bridge Farm. Home-logs uphold every shack.
We eat what we raise, and raise what we eat, and spare any stranger a snack.

On the mantel are dream-books. They came in oak bureaus in Cumberland Gap wagon-trains.
The novelty volumes are Riley and Nye, and the Jumping Frog yarn, Mark Twain's.

Good-by, Jazz Age. I'm going Home, where Artemus Ward is still hot,
And Falstaff is quoted when pigs are in clover, and Burns, when the weasel is shot.

The Biglow Papers are cutting up capers, the whiplash of Gulliver stings,
And Widow Bedott is a friend to the fancy, and Tennyson's Camelot sings.

When the sun's on the field, the jigs of Dan Tucker will make us young yokels again;
When the rain's on the pane, the poems of Poe transform us to musical men.

Good-by, Jazz Age, I'm going Home, to a parlor with wax flowers and candles,
Spinning wheels, snuffers, Washington's picture, chromos of saints wearing sandals.

We will eat what we raise, and raise what we eat, and will not be shattered by noise;
Will dress like the pictures in dog-eared McGuffey:—Third Reader sweethearts and boys.

As Emerson sang:—"Good-by, proud world." The hill of sun burned Uncle Sam
Is a citadel set for ten thousand years yet, far from the scramble and cram.

His homestead the State, the Hearth, the Hope, The Star Spangled Banner of Power.
Good-by, Jazz Age. I'm going Home. "The Clock on the Stair" strikes the hour.

Are We Ripe for "Revolution"?

by Jay Franklin

*An Outspoken Warning to Pussyfoot
Politicians and Stuffed-Shirts in Business*

THERE WAS A time when Americans believed in political ideas so much that they were ready to fight for them. We fought for national independence, for territory, for states' rights and for the Union, and for democracy and self-determination. Men knew that when you said "politics" you were speaking of the future, and they were willing to suffer and die that the future for themselves and their children might be bright and assured. We did not feel ashamed to hold torchlight parades and to battle for the right to vote. That was the time when a wise and witty foreigner remarked that an American election amounted to a peaceful revolution, and that an American revolution would resemble a violent election.

For an entire generation, now, we have been taught otherwise by the fish-mouthed old men who have run our national affairs. We have been taught that politics don't make much difference, that it only amounts to a choice between a Republican and a Democrat. We have not had a real political election since 1912, when Wilson was elected, and we have not had a really exciting national election since 1896, when Bryan ran for the Presidency.

Even now, timid and purse-proud men in both parties writhe with horror at the idea of an American election deciding everything.

Today we are paying the price for this ostrich policy. We find ourselves facing terrible and urgent problems—problems which won't wait for elections or politicians. We have a cowardly and bewildered Congress which represents the population of the United States as it was in 1910, and which doesn't know how to deal with a post-war world. We have a President who has driven his political supporters practically crazy by his stubbornness and his thin-skinned resentment of any advice or criticism. We have a Republican Party which is held together by political shoe strings and banana oil, and which is

drifting toward a split between the East and West. We have a Democratic Party prepared to break up into a split between North and South.

We have had twenty years of government by ballyhoo and twelve years of government by boloney. And now all the accumulated problems of a generation are on our doorstep, at a time when the voters have been paralyzed.

We have at least eight million wage earners unemployed some of them for years, and Congress has but lately got through squabbling with the President as to what to do about it, and brought forth a compromise measure that he says he can approve. We have debts—not the highfalutin' war debts of which we are so sick and concerning which there is such drooling publicity, but the low common-or-garden variety of debts, mortgages, bonds, chattel mortgages, bank loans, crop loans, which impose a burden of ten billion dollars a year on the nation. As a keen English observer remarked of us: "In a country where money is the aim of all social effort, the money lender—the banker—is king!" These debts threaten every business with bankruptcy, every bank with failure, every house owner, rent payer, and farmer with eviction, every pocketbook with legalized robbery. We have a farm population which is living on the verge of misery and starvation in the greatest granary in the world—the Mississippi Valley. We have the most expensive tax system in the world and some of the heaviest taxes—thirty-one cents out of every American dollar goes to pay the cost of grafting, extravagant, and inefficient governments. We have a prohibition system which has financed crime and given to thugs and professional murderers the revenues which would support a great state. We have a tariff which has strangled trade and is destroying both foreign and domestic markets. We have grafters and lobbies who have rendered us powerless to influence or halt the greatest threat to world civilization today—the menace of war in the Far East between Japan and Russia.

And nothing can be done about it, except to mark your X under the Republican eagle or the Democratic star and hope for the best.

This is the stuff of which revolutions are made. Oh, yes! They will tell you in Washington that revolution is impossible in the United States; that all this Communistic talk is so much rot; and that everything will be pretty much as it was before. The people who talk this way are fools; for there never was a real revolution which started out to be one. There are always revolutionary groups in every country, just as the human body harbors many deadly germs which rarely succeed in causing their characteristic disease. But let the system get run down by overwork or poor nourishment, let the poison from an abscessed tooth or an infected tonsil spread, and then anything may happen. We are in just such a state today, and if there is any lesson in history it is that we should go to the operating room quickly if we wish to keep our political institutions from taking a trip to the morgue.

The English Revolution under Cromwell began in a lawsuit against a man named John Hampden who thought he was being unjustly taxed. The tax was unjust but not illegal, and the government won its case; but there was a demand for political reform, and because the king resisted he finally had his head chopped off. The American Revolution began as a well meant and entirely nonrevolutionary protest against some perfectly legal taxes and official orders, and it was only with the greatest reluctance that the colonists found themselves forced, by the refusal of King George to settle their grievances, to sign the Declaration of Independence. The French Revolution began as a move on the part of the privileged classes themselves to surrender their privileges and put the national finances in order. No body of men could have been more loyal to King Louis XVI than the Estates General which assembled in Paris in 1789. It was only when the king tried to send them home before their work was done that they became revolutionary. The Russian Revolution itself began as a move to establish constitutional government in Russia and to organize the empire for a more efficient conduct of the war against Germany. It wasn't until Kerensky discovered that what the Russian people wanted was not a successful war against the Germans but a quick peace, not constitutional reforms but food and land, that the Soviet Revolution took place.

For it is the essence of revolution that it should come from within a country and take a form which it is difficult to resist. It is easy for the general or the police commissioner to say, "Shoot 'em down!" But what happens if the soldiers won't shoot? It is easy to do as Kerensky did —surround the government buildings with troops. But what happens if the revolutionists do as Trotsky did?— seize the power plants and the telegraph offices and railway switches. There are a comparatively few spots in the United States today which, if seized by a bold group of revolutionaries, would paralyze the industrial life of the nation. And if the Railway Brotherhoods should turn Communist the country would be powerless to function. However, the powers which control the United States today, and which have milked the country dry in a generation, remember the railway strike of 1919 and the Plumb Plan. And they have taken care that the railway workers are the best paid and the best treated of all the workingmen in the country.

Yet we are ripe for "revolution." The American people are not revolutionists, but they have a lot of common sense and a burning desire to get things done quickly. Our political system makes it impossible to do anything in a hurry. Now suppose that a strongly organized, adequately financed, and well led group of Americans organized a town, a city, or a state, did it quickly and efficiently, and put through a lot of emergency rent and employment-relief laws, cut out the graft, lowered taxes, and sent all the money lenders running to the federal courts for injunctions and appeals. How long do you think it would be before the whole country followed suit? How long would the local election laws and political machines stand up against a thing like that?

It would go like wildfire. People would start yelling "Bolsheviki!" until they discovered that the new group was running the Communists out of town with short shrift. We would have a "revolution" before we knew it.

Don't forget that nobody paid much attention to the plight of the farmers during the drought until a gang of law-abiding, hundred-percent American farmers in England, Arkansas, marched into town and *took*—yes, it was just as crude as that—the food they needed for their starving families. Don't forget that neither the Republican Party nor Herbert Hoover even admitted that there was such a thing as serious unemployment in the United States until hunger marchers appeared in Washington and demanded relief. Not many weeks ago a group of jobless veterans from Oregon decided that they wanted the bonus now and that they would go to Washington and ask for it in person. They started the Bonus March, which brought thousands of miserable and hopeless veterans into Washington, where they established a camp.

They did not get the bonus, but did get something better: the realization that politics is not a game which must be played according to any rules, and that every political system must satisfy its people or face a violent threat against its own stability. Within a fortnight of the time when the bonus was rejected, both Houses of Congress had passed huge relief bills, and only the White House stood between the people and some measure of economic appeasement.

We are not only ripe for "revolution" but we are having one, and we shall have to act quickly if we are going to let it bring us something better than the waste, confusion, and suffering which revolutions usually bring. We need a real "American Revolution," led by Americans, acting in terms of American ideas and ways of doing things, rather than a foreign importation. We don't need Communism, Socialism, Fascism, or even a Labor Party. We don't need a Lenin, a Karl Marx, a Hitler, a Mussolini, or a Ramsay MacDonald. We need an American upheaval which will be led by someone as sane, practical, and American as Andrew Jackson, Abraham Lincoln, or Al Smith. And we want it, not because we have any theory of the desirability, need, or character of "revolution," but simply because we want to put this country quickly into a shape in which a man can have a job, take a drink and a smoke, own a house or a farm, marry and raise a family.

We need an upheaval which will prevent our children and their children from starving, killing themselves, emigrating, or sinking into dumb slaves of machinery simply because some future banker guesses wrong about the stock market.

That's the sort of "revolution" we are going to have, and the lengths to which we have to go to stage it will depend entirely upon whether the old boys who got us into our present mess are ready to take it lying down or will put up a fight for the divine right of the moneybags and the stuffed-shirts to make millions of Americans miserable in the name of the law and the profits.

Treachery to the People

by Governor Franklin D. Roosevelt

*A Warning to Those Who Fail to
Cooperate in This Economic Crisis*

WE MUST NOT close our eyes to the certainty that unemployment this winter will force a certain number of men over the line from honesty to dishonesty, from an orderly life to one of violence.

Unemployment relief being carried out in the State of New York at best can do no more than prevent actual hunger and suffering. It cannot do more in one winter. It cannot inspirit men in great discouragement, nor prevent their human envy of those more fortunate.

Wherever there are sharp distinctions of inequality in fortune, men will be especially tempted to get by cleverness or strength what society at such a time as this, and as now constituted, denies them. It would be decent as well as wise for those upon whom fortune has smiled to make no parade of it.

Sensational stories about the rich, fed to us by a certain type of journalism, have blurred the old-fashioned common sense of many toward vulgarity as well as silly display.

Even the substantial man is more tolerant of display than he used to be; his American sense of humor allows him to be amused at it.

But humor has worn thin when a man and his family have been out of work for months; they humanly resent all waste of money by those who still have large incomes. They know what it would buy for them, and wonder whether the rich man really understands and is doing his bit in the world of his fellow men.

Those who are human despite their fortune, who are unostentatiously meeting the emergency with practical generosity and public service, should be more appreciated than ever in our history. But there are still many in this state, as well as elsewhere, who do not realize that we are at a crisis in our national life comparable to war. The same sort of unselfishness and the same simplicity of purpose is required that we showed in 1917–18.

A state of economic war has been declared by New York. We are the first of the American commonwealths to open the engagement by attacking the problem of unemployment relief by specific and helpful legislation. Any lack of cooperation with our relief organization just created, any personal or political interference, any waste of funds, I shall consider and treat as in times of war—as treachery to the people.

"How Did This Happen?"

ANOTHER CHALLENGE TO CONTEST FANS

LIBERTY WILL PAY

$250

to the Sixty-four Winning Entrants!

INTRODUCTION:

A farm boy, walking behind the plow, picked up an Indian arrowhead.

CONCLUSION:

A millionaire's daughter eloped with the family chauffeur.

HOW did this happen? What chain of circumstances connected the two events? If you submit one of the sixty-four best explanations one of this week's cash prizes will be awarded for your effort. Why not put your inventiveness to work and capture a share of the money? All you need is your imagination, a sheet of paper, and a typewriter or pen and ink.

Do not submit a long explanation. The limit is 500 words. Use as many less as you wish.

At first glance it may seem a far cry from the plowboy and the Indian relic to the elopement, but you can undoubtedly figure out a chain of circumstances to connect them. Probably you will construct several series of events that will supply the missing action. Choose the best of your output and enter it as directed in the rules. Your chance to win is excellent if you enter. Perhaps the $50 First Prize will be awarded to you. Or one of the other major prizes may be yours. Even the smaller awards are well worth having.

Read the rules carefully so that your entry will not be voided by failure to observe all requirements.

THE RULES

1. Anyone, anywhere, may compete except employees of Macfadden Publications, Inc., and members of their families.

2. Write, using not more than 500 words, a chain of circumstances that develops the given introduction into the given conclusion.

3. It is not necessary to clip or copy the printed introduction or conclusion.

4. Write on one side of paper only. Use typewriter or pen and ink. Penciled entries will not be considered. Neatness will count. Spelling will count.

5. The entry which supplies the most logical, most concise, most entertaining chain of circumstances will be adjudged the best. The entry rating next highest in these qualifications will be adjudged second best, etc.

6. On this basis sixty-four prizes will be paid as follows: First prize, $50; second prize, $25; third prize, $15; fourth prize, $10; ten prizes, each $5; fifty prizes, each $2.

7. Address all entries to CIRCUMSTANCES EDITOR, Liberty Weekly, P. O. Box 556, Grand Central Station, New York, N. Y.

8. All entries must be received on or before Monday, October 16.

WIN ONE OF THESE CASH PRIZES!

FIRST PRIZE	$ 50
SECOND PRIZE	25
THIRD PRIZE	15
FOURTH PRIZE	10
TEN PRIZES, EACH $5	50
FIFTY PRIZES, EACH $2	100

ANOTHER $250 PRIZE CONTEST NEXT WEEK!

What the Talkies Have Done to Hollywood

by Florabel Muir

WHEN THE TALKIE cyclone first loomed up the old-time stars felt secure behind their bulwarks.

"We can't be replaced," they said in effect. "The public knows us. We are household words, even in climes where the fans can't read our names. Without us the whole movie structure will fall to pieces."

Hollywood believed them. The quaking producers were afraid it was true. As the first influx of stage people filtered into the lots, Hollywood's battle cry was:

"They may be big shots on Broadway, but who knows them out in the sticks."

A fair question, that. Jack Warner thought he would like to know the answer. He put on a picture called *Gold Diggers of Broadway,* and cast it without one prominent player from the movie ranks. The star was Winnie Lightner, a comedienne from the variety stage.

The sticks gave Warner his answer by turning out in droves to guffaw at Winnie's tricks, and *Gold Diggers* earned a most gratifying profit for Warner Brothers.

This encouraged other producers and the axes began to fall right and left. The expensive contracts that producers had been glad enough to sign in order to hold their stars were cut away as rapidly as they expired.

Hollywood had learned that pictures could be made profitably without the lure of long-established favorites. Paramount came along with *The Love Parade,* featuring Maurice Chevalier, Jeanette MacDonald, and Lillian Roth, all unheard of in the films. This was followed by *Sarah and Son*, with Ruth Chatterton and Fredric March. United Artists gave us *Puttin' on the Ritz*, in which Harry Richman, James Gleason, and Joan Bennett showed what stage folk could do on the screen.

Metro-Goldwyn-Mayer produced *The Rogue Song* with Lawrence Tibbett and Catherine Dale Owen. Fox got into the competition with *Song o' My Heart*, presenting John McCormack and an unknown colleen, Maureen O'Sullivan. The Warners followed *Gold Diggers* with *Disraeli*, an even greater triumph, which featured George Arliss and Joan Bennett.

These pictures were not only box-office successes but they won acclaim from critics throughout the land.

Here, by the way, is a list of the pictures produced in the last year or so that are thought by the studios to have earned the largest profits, as far as returns are now in— though they are not necessarily those that have grossed the largest sums: Paramount, *The Virginian, Coconuts,* and *The Wild Party*; Warners, *Gold Diggers of Broadway* and *No, No, Nanette*; Metro-Goldwyn-Mayer, *The Broadway Melody* and *Anna Christie*; Fox, *Sunny Side Up* and *Hot for Paris*; R. K. O., *Street Girl* and *Love Comes Along*; Sam Goldwyn, *Bulldog Drummond*; Columbia, *Flight.*

Of the fifty most profitable films produced within that time, four-fifths of the casts were unknown to Hollywood early in 1928.

The effect of all this in Hollywood was magical. Stars who had been collecting up to $10,000 a week and more now found themselves suddenly becoming fifth wheels.

Some saw the light and surrendered. Corinne Griffith disagreed with the Warners over the handling of a story and turned in her contract, which had three pictures to run. She received $275,000 cash and retired to a villa in France. "It was a bargain for us," Jack Warner told me. "She wasn't clicking at the box office."

As recently as 1928 Colleen Moore topped all the stars in drawing power, according to the polls of the trade papers. She made *Footlights and Fools* early in 1929 to conclude a contract with First National that had been bringing her $12,500 a week. She has done nothing since. Late this spring she was still hoping for a chance to reenter pictures and her agent Myron Selznick, was offering her services around the studios for $7,500 a week.

Jack Warner took a lot of money that he had been paying to Corinne and Colleen and tossed it into the lap of Marilyn Miller. Marilyn made *Sally* for the Warners and was paid $100,000. She returned for another picture for which Warners agreed to give her $150,000.

Constance Talmadge married Townsend Netcher, a Chicago millionaire, last summer and retired to become one of Hollywood's popular hostesses. Phyllis Haver married William Seaman and said she would not try for movie fame any more. Norma Talmadge has released one film, *New York Nights*, in more than a year and it created no sensation either at the box office or among the critics.

Benjamin P. Schulberg, Paramount's chief producing executive on the west coast, believes "Mary Pickford is all through making the sort of pictures that won her fame."

"She may do something else on the screen," Mr. Schulberg told me, "but it will not be the same old Mary."

The case of Mary Pickford is not quite the same as that of most stars. When she makes a picture she does it with her own money and all the risks of production are hers. She has studio and releasing facilities at her disposal in the United Artists organization.

Norma Talmadge is in somewhat the same situation. Her husband, Joseph M. Schenck, is president of United Artists. It's a long time since Norma has worked for a stated sum per week.

Laura La Plante, for some years Universal's main box-office reliance, cut loose to free-lance because the new situation makes her worth only a fraction of what she once earned.

Gloria Swanson, since leaving Paramount a few years ago, has produced independently. She had some disastrous experiences on her own, but achieved a notable comeback in *The Trespasser*. No actress is working more feverishly to retain public favor.

Paramount, slow to recognize the upheaval, swept away its stars when the clean-up started. Emil Jannings was the first to go. Thomas Meighan followed; likewise Adolphe Menjou, Leatrice Joy, Richard Dix, Evelyn Brent, and Bebe Daniels.

"There was a time," Mr. Schulberg told me, "when Thomas Meighan could demand $10,000 a week and get it. But there was only one Tommy Meighan then and now the woods are full of them. That condition was unhealthy for actors and producers alike.

"Movie salaries will never fall as low as stage salaries, but the $10,000-a-week days are gone forever. Five thousand dollars a week is about the top now. The law of supply and demand has done it."

That even such an astute film executive as Mr. Schulberg is known to occasionally err is evidenced by the fact that at least two of the stars dropped by Paramount have won distinguished successes under other affiliations. Bebe Daniels went to R. K. O. and triumphed in *Rio Rita* and *Love Comes Along*. Evelyn Brent did likewise, triumphing in *Framed*. Adolphe Menjou's admirers believe he will score in the talkies.

111

Betting on who would survive the change was like betting on a horse race. Ronald Colman, for example, rose to greater popularity than ever, while his co-star in several pictures, Vilma Banky, has not been able to overcome the handicap of an Austrian accent.

John Gilbert's future remains uncertain, while Greta Garbo achieved the triumph of her career in *Anna Christie*.

Ramon Novarro is another veteran who has maintained his popularity. William Powell, a character man in the silents, leaped to stardom by virtue of a vibrant personality that never found its proper medium before. Schulberg told me that Clara Bow is still popular and due to become the Anna Held of pictures. The musical abilities of Buddy Rogers have helped to keep him in the swim. Nils Asther's Danish accent doomed him for the talkies. Joseph Schildkraut's star has waned.

The public almost never hears the truth about motion-picture salaries. However, by utilizing confidential sources of information I was able to obtain some authentic figures that will illustrate why the movie magnates are laughing in their sleeves at the stars of other days.

Marjorie White, unknown to films before *Sunny Side Up*, now is regarded as one of Fox's best bets. She was starred in *Happy Days* and has important assignments ahead. She receives $750 a week. This is three times what she had earned on the stage, it comes in fifty-two weeks of the year, and yet it is about a fifth of what Fox used to pay a star. No wonder everybody's happy.

Dixie Lee, a chorus recruit, had the girl lead in *All Alone* for Fox, but she gets only $400 a week. Jeannette Loff was released by Pathé and snapped up at $300 a week by Universal. Eddie King, Paul Whiteman's sound expert, discovered that Jeannette has a voice and she will be earning much more these days.

Fifi D'Orsay gets $750 a week from Fox and is listed for heavy starring rôles. Mary Nolan, whose New York stage name was Imogene Wilson, came to Universal for $400 a week and glad to get it. Kay Johnson, a young stage actress, made one of the big hits of 1929 in *Dynamite*, and rates as a star though she draws only $750 a week. Catherine Dale Owen signed on for $600. Inez Courtney receives $700 a week at the Fox pay window and led the cast in *The Solid Gold Article*.

Nancy Carroll, whose pictures are making a mint of money for Paramount, works for $600 a week. No doubt her next contract will increase her income.

Maureen O'Sullivan is on the Fox payroll at $200 a week. Red-headed Marguerite Churchill gets $750 and is much featured. Helen Kane, "the Boop-a-Doop girl," contracted to work for $15,000 a picture. Mary Brian, former chorus beauty, has worked up to $1,250 a week with Paramount. Kay Francis has captured the allegiance of an army of fans with her slithering vampish rôles and her ability to wear clothes, but her salary check is only $750.

"The law of supply and demand," Schulberg says. Rare bargains, these, every one.

Ann Harding, a winning box-office bet for Pathé, labors for the ridiculously meager sum of $15,000 a picture—ridiculous in comparison, for example, with the $75,000 which Ina Claire got for starring in *The Awful Truth*, which wore out no turnstiles. Pathé discovered this inequality and rectified the situation to some extent by lopping Miss Claire off the payroll.

Lillian Roth worked in vaudeville and was not even a headliner for around $125 a week. Was she overjoyed to quit the two-a-day for double the money? Ask her. She is doing very well in the films, as you'll agree if you have seen *The Love Parade* or *The Vagabond King*. Jack Oakie started acting in the movies for $250 a week and within a year shot up to stardom and $1,500 a week.

Bernice Claire's is one of the few names on First National's starring list, but she has yet to receive $1,000 for a week's work. The same is true of Natalie Moorhead, a free-lance artist much in demand.

June Collyer, Mary Lawlor, Zelma O'Neal, Marion Schilling, William Janney, Russell Gleason, Loretta Young, Sally Blane, Joan Crawford, Walter Pidgeon, Sidney Blackmer, Morgan Farley, Douglas Fairbanks, Jr., Chester Morris, Stanley Smith, Fred Scott, Mitzi Green, Virginia Bruce, Helen Twelvetrees—nearly all these names were unknown in Hollywood at the beginning of 1928. Dozens of others could be mentioned. They are in the front rank of the eager young army of those who are taking the spotlight away from the old favorites and rejoicing the hearts of the movie lords.

The public, always fickle, likes them. Naturally the producers like them because the public likes them and because they are cheap at the price. The new generation of players is the reason why you see so many all-star casts billed nowadays. Formerly one highly paid star would set back a production cost sheet $100,000 or more.

What will happen when these youngsters have installed themselves in public favor as their predecessors did?

Nothing at all, says Schulberg. The producers have learned the great truth that nobody is indispensable. The law of supply and demand will take care of the employers. As long as talent keeps knocking at the movie gates as it is doing now there will be half a dozen applicants for every job and salaries will be kept down to a reasonable level.

Sam Goldwyn, a war-scarred veteran of many movie battles, sounds a pessimistic note anent the fortunes of the old stars.

"I venture to predict," he said, "that within a year fully fifty percent of the old-timers who have survived until this time will be all through and never heard of again. It's inevitable. One reason is that we're going to have fewer movies. The talkies eventually will reduce the number of pictures made by half, and these will all have to be good."

Yellow Saplings
by the Lake

a story by Leo Tolstoy, translated by M. M. Marble

A Hitherto Unknown Story, Written Forty Years Ago

Translator's Note: Just when this newly discovered short story by Leo Tolstoy originated cannot be told with certainty. The well known Tolstoy scholar, N. N. Gusew, who placed it at my disposal, believes that it was written at the beginning of 1889.

Although in itself a finished piece of work, this short story is doubtless the embryo out of which the world-renowned novel, The Kreutzer Sonata, *grew some years later. In the novel, however, not only was one of the chief characters changed from an artist to a musician, but the whole work was written in an altogether different tone from the short story.*

POSDNYSCHEW HAD MARRIED as men do. He had studied at the university; he had also gone to work after that, and he had arrived. Then the consciousness of love awoke in him. They met.

She was young, beautiful, really very beautiful, not without dowry; she had duly attended boarding school, although she did not graduate. She had curly hair and dressed modishly. She was dainty, somewhat artless, good-natured, but, above all, nice.

"Well, what about it?" he thought: "I, too, am a human being, am I not? Outside of my chemistry there are still other joys in life: beauty, love. Why should I live only as an onlooker while others take everything they can? Also, the years are passing. I, too, have a right to live."

So he thought, and so he married. He saw the whole thing through, as is necessary; he went through the whole experience.

In earlier times, when you married only according to the will of your parents and didn't see the bride until the wedding and had had no experiences at all, everything was fine and honorable: the feather beds and the linen chest and the clothes and the wedding finery. But now, when in the souls of all who get married the physical is the most important part actually, when no one believes any more in the sacrament—and Posdnyschew is a scholar, consequently he also does not believe—all of this trousseaux, linen, dressing gowns, clothes, negligees, chocolate, etc., is distasteful at least.

Well, he went through the whole business, was married, and learned that there are some very nice experiences to be had outside of chemistry. He was pleased with it, very.

He went to work and worked, came home and in his home found grace, taste, beauty, and amusement, instead of dust and ennui. What better could one want? "Why," he thought, "didn't I think about this long ago?" And so he imagined that nothing else would ever come beside these pleasures.

But something new and unexpected came, in the first few weeks. Tears came, and discontent, and her desires for something which didn't agree with what he himself needed.

Something happened as always happens; what you yourself would have experienced if you had introduced a certain convenience into your home—a fireside chair in which to rest, and suddenly the chair kicks up its legs and makes demands. What demands? Why, to play a little, and to rest.

You may wonder how a chair could wish something for itself; after all, it is only—a chair. You turn the chair around, you try to sit down, and the chair does the same. So goes it among men.

Quarrels and wrangling began—and what wrangling! Such as always comes to pass among people who don't at all understand, and don't want to understand, that another's life can have its claims as well.

At first this wrangling seems surprising. How is it possible? Only six hours ago love was so strong, and suddenly nothing remains of it—the chair was so soft and comfortable, and suddenly its legs are sticking up. Love surely couldn't have been so strong when nothing remains of it now, not the slightest sign.

Be that as it may, there isn't any of it there, not even a trace. A totally strange and hateful person stands before you, and the wrangling begins. It is a secret which everyone conceals from all others, although everyone is aware of it. Quarrels and hate began just as among animals, and at that all the stronger as what was called love before was strong. Such a hate as leads frankly to the wish that she, and he himself as well, might die. And so it goes on until once again the illusion of passion overshadows everything.

In this case, also, things went on just so. But, beside all this, there came still another unexpected situation: after he had created a pleasure for himself, he failed to take into consideration that there are many other lovers of the same pleasure, including some very clever people who know not only that it is very pleasant to live with a woman, but also that it isn't necessary to have at the same time the inconveniences and disagreeablenesses which are part and parcel of married life. They know also that it is decidedly pleasanter and freer from worry to skim the cream from the milk that others have had the trouble of milking from the cows.

His wife was very beautiful; she had, you know, such a provoking and arresting beauty! Others also, the cleverer ones, had noticed that. Furthermore, one of these cleverer ones advanced to the attack.

Oh, yes, then began for Posdnyschew all those questions: How to obtain the freedom that both desire? Why should a mutual understanding be destroyed when, if a strange gentleman feels the necessity of taking your arm, for example, it remains just a meaningless little circumstance? Why make difficulties? He can take my arm and then go on his way. He would have three arms and I only one. And I would gladly give him my arm.

Thus began what you think should have been so easy to solve. The chief hindrance to this simple solution, however, lies in the fact that the whole problem will never be clearly stated. The devil only knows if my wife is going to be unfaithful to me, or has she been so this long time? Or has she so planned things that just today she will be unfaithful? Nobody knows, neither the husband, nor the wife, nor he who lies in wait for the other's wife.

This latter says to himself: "Well, perhaps the affair can be arranged today." He always calls it "the affair." The wife says to herself: "I am in love; the feeling is strange and nice." Whom she loves, however, she herself doesn't know. But the husband thinks: "No, it only seems so to me." A minute later he thinks: "How strange that I have never noticed that they have found each other!" And another minute later: "Still . . . perhaps not. I won't think about it." And he makes a resolution not to recall this nightmare any more.

A pleasant occupation, nightmares! He who hasn't experienced them doesn't know how hideous they are.

And so it began, and so it went on, and on, and on. Two years passed by. It turned out that the pleasure—remained a pleasure; much that was beautiful and comfortable along with it, but also much that was difficult. And how difficult!

You might say she was no educated woman! She did have just that sort of an education which permits a woman to say of herself: "I am an educated woman." If a woman speaks English, she calls all people who do not speak English uneducated; and if she—God forbid!—has read about natural history, then all those about her are uneducated: *she* has read about it.

He had an eye for her development, gave her books to read, himself read with her. She read those books and loved to discuss them in detail, especially if that cleverer person who lay in wait for her were present.

Everything went on as usual, and everything was a sham. He knew why he had married her. Her development wasn't necessary to him, it was only custom; only superficially was he concerned with her development. She, too, knew what she was and why he needed her, and wherein her strength lay; but she only gave herself the air of being interested in still other things.

Interests she did have, poor thing, but only her face, her body, and the clothing of her body and of her children. There was a child. Well, you know, having a child, also, is so beautiful: a little crib, a bathtub, children's little clothes—these were always of interest, wherewith she could be so beautifully coquettish in the nursery. You could never decide: does she bathe the child in order to have the child clean, or to show her white elbows? Does she caress the child because she loves it, or merely to lay her beautiful head on the little head of the child?

So it went on and on; and then it seemed as though something had happened. But it happened in such fashion that no one could know if it had happened or not. Actually it was no secret for the husband. Were it a secret, it would be much easier for him; but it was that same nightmare about which no one should think if he would not tear his heart out.

You ask what happened. It was in the country; I was living there too. In Posdnyschew's neighborhood lived an artist: such a youthful, decorative person; one of those who are clever, one of those also who have their pleasure without getting married! He was twenty-eight, a handsome fellow with white skin and smoldering blue eyes, red lips, and a shimmering, reddish mustache. What more do you need? He was always painting trees with little yellow leaves, had his hat and rug, and with his palette was forever changing his location. He had made the acquaintance of the Posdnyschew family and often visited them.

Then the spider web began to be woven around him on all sides and he ensnared himself more and more in it. The web was fine, it would be a shame to tear it, why indeed should one? One fine thread after the other, one thread after the other; hardly had he looked around before he was snared, body and soul.

She loved painting; already in boarding school she had shown great ability, but had had no guidance. After awhile she began to paint, more and more: how could she let such a good opportunity go by? He is famous, and so generous and ready to help, and, besides, he has such a pure soul! To all appearances there is no other interest between them than high art. Oh, how beautiful this spot of color is! Ah, how green this leaf is! But should the husband show only a trace of jealousy, or begin to bare his claws, at once she is all injured innocence and asserts that she never once thought about the other one! "You, yourself, are suggesting bad thoughts to me!" The man draws in his claws, but jealousy remains.

How wonderful the attitude of these two to each other seems—their similarity of tastes, their joy of living, their joking!

The husband's presence doesn't change the simplicity of the atmosphere. He even begins to change in this atmosphere, but in his soul is hell. He can't explain all that he thinks without betraying himself. To seek an explanation from her only means unleashing all the animal instincts. To leave the question unexplained is still worse.

He had perceived the chief fact, which in all such cases is the saddest, that what she was to him—an object of pleasure for a few minutes of life—she must be in still greater degree for all other men. And what he was to her, other men offered to be in hundredfold greater degree, because of their variety and greater attractiveness. Truth to tell, then, she must prefer these others.

He, the husband, recognized no inner restraints in himself or in her. Everything pointed to the fact that if she isn't actually stupid, she must take the step. To be sure, there are hindrances: gossip, bad reputation, unpleasantnesses; hence it was obvious that she must take it so that no one should learn of it. And if she should take it, or had already done so, he, the husband, would not find it out.

No, indeed, she had not taken it! Actually, however, she had now been having an affair with the artist the whole summer long. Were he but willing to analyze his impressions exactly, he must know, know for a certainty—not as you know that of which you have visible proofs, but because of your inner impulses: a certainty, but without proofs.

I know of a characteristic episode in the life of the Posdnyschew family at that time. In order to understand it, you must try to realize their feelings as well.

One day she was going from the country into the city. She needed to get something—you know, as ladies are always needing something—very urgently. But he, the artist, was to finish painting some wonderful sapling or other by the lake. She was going to the city. She was in a hurry. She was particularly beautiful on that day, said her husband.

But she mentioned twice during the conversation that it was going to be a nuisance for her to do some sort of an errand in the city for the artist; she gave him thereby to understand that the artist was remaining in the country.

Suddenly Posdnyschew understood that everything was over. She had been unfaithful to him. He went to see the artist, but was told by a neighbor that he had gone into the city the evening before. Now he remembered her frequent trips to the city, in bad weather, and without sufficient reasons. So it had happened! She had already done it—done it just as she must have done it and remain true to her ordinary instincts.

He couldn't stay at home and decided to go to the city —not just simply to go to the city, though: he took his revolver with him to shoot his wife, and *him!*

This dreadful decision came about quite naturally; but what happened was quite otherwise. He met her on the way. He espied her from quite a distance. She was coming back home, sprightly, gay, contented. In the first moment of meeting he saw in her face that beaming happiness which was always for him the surest inner proof of her unfaithfulness. When she noticed him she smiled, and it seemed to him that she was laughing and smiling at him at the same time. But after that she became uneasy.

"What's the matter with you? Where are you going?"

He wanted to lie, but couldn't. He got into her carriage, and in so doing he crushed the pictures which she had brought from the city. She became annoyed. As though she had a right to be angry with him!

"What's the matter with you? Are you crazy?"

"I can't go along so any further."

They got out of the carriage and went home on foot.

"It's torturing me!"

"Oh, you're thinking about Leonid Nikolaevitch? Forget it! You ought to be ashamed of yourself!"

Now the game began. A happy smile played about her lips, which she could not repress. She laughed at him. She would not deny it; she would not lower herself to make denials.

"How could anyone think such a thing? How could such nonsense torture anyone? Everything is all so fine, why wreck your life? If it tortures you so, I won't meet him any more. Although it is stupid and humiliating for me. As you will. You and your peace of mind are dearer to me than anything else."

And yet she was already unfaithful to him and intended to be so again. But he believed her, and she never seemed so beautiful to him. He never loved her so passionately. When taking his revolver in his hand, he had opened the

way for the first time to animal instinct, but by so doing another animal instinct was intensified—the same, but with a different objective.

This episode was ended. She certainly didn't see the artist any more—he went traveling. The family life seemed to run smoother. Still, each was watching the other warily.

A year passed quietly. There was no jealousy, nor any grounds for it. There was only wrangling, and off and on he was in despair about it. He regretted that he had taken this torturing load upon his shoulders. There were attempts to be freed from it, and there was the consciousness that life was played out, that one must drag along with the burden to the end. Then would follow peace and reconciliation, but no inner ties. Each regarded the other as something that he needed, over which he had a right, but which had no rights of its own.

This year passed by then. Another child came. Habits took deeper root, the agreeable feelings of married life increased, but still the tortures increased also; seemingly, however, not in proportion.

Had you seen him at that time you would not have said that he was unhappy, he would not have been able to say that about himself. So it is with a man in whom a fatal disease is developing: he first learns the dreadfulness of his situation after the disease has already made its appearance.

About that which tortured him most he dared not speak, certainly not to that being who was nearest him, to his wife.

He told me later that his tortures were increased by his not knowing whether or not the last child was his or that artist's, he with the pale complexion who painted saplings on the edge of the lake. Sometimes he was persuaded one way, sometimes the other. He suffered terribly.

Why did he suffer? For this reason: because his wife was for him a sweet and tasty morsel which he greatly desired, and the sweeter the morsel was, the clearer it was to him that, logically, other men also wanted to eat up this sweet morsel, or had eaten it up, or sooner or later would eat it up.

They went traveling abroad. Her mental development seemed to progress. Still, her feelings were just the same. She knew that she was a sweet morsel and that one must preserve, protect, and augment this sweetness. That is what she did. Had she a petty and reprehensible nature? No. She was a creature like all the rest—a nice little animal, generous, sly, beautiful, and clever.

So they continued to live as average married people. Then it so happened that they spent a summer upon the estate of his brother, in quite another countryside than that of earlier days.

He began to be interested in farming. At the height of summer he was very busy.

She had acquaintances among the neighbors, among them a woman physician. A good soul, she talked much about the freedom of women.

One day he came home to fetch the flower stalks he had forgotten, being busy in the garden, and saw his wife also coming toward home.

"Where have you been?"

"I've been out walking."

"Out walking?"

He saw her face beaming, such beaming as was caused only by love, by animal love. Later he was coming from his work and met the physician; he was talking with her, one thing led to another, and she told him that the artist had arrived the week before and was living at the priest's house.

Then his wife came in to dinner, trying to conceal her expression, but she couldn't. In so doing, she seemed beautiful as never before. "She belongs to me," he thought, "yet I am not the cause of this beaming expression; but he is, the other fellow." Still he said nothing, concealed everything like a tiger; took pains to be only the more simple and natural. So he let everything remain unexplained.

"Mine, and still not mine," he thought, and she seemed still sweeter; "not mine, and yet mine!" The more he loved her, the more he hated her, and the hate began to be stronger than the love. He loved her and lay in wait for her.

The artist didn't appear. How he tortured himself! He knew nothing, but he saw that she felt that this other one was here, near by; and she was meeting him! He dared not mention his name.

In this way a week went by. He said he was going into the city, and took his departure. En route, he sent the carriage back, and late in the evening himself came home, and saw when the artist, cautiously and looking all around, came up to the balcony door, hesitated a moment, and went quickly in.

" 'No,' I thought, 'I—I—I am Posdnyschew! A garden knife isn't good enough!' I ran to my room; there I had a dagger. I hardly remember how I got into her room. Yes, mine, my wife, my wife!"

He jumped through the window. She was almost undressed; she lifted her bare arms and remained sitting on the bed. "No, what's mine I won't give away!"

"I ran to her, stabbed her with the dagger, and tore it upward. She fell, she clung to my arm, I pulled the dagger from her. The blood ran—it sickened me. 'Die, you snake!' I struck her with my fist in the face and went into the hall where the maid and the house boy were.

" 'Quick! Notify the police! I've killed my wife.'

"I sat down in my room and smoked a cigarette. The neighbor physician came in.

" 'Go to her,' she said.

" 'What for?'

" 'Go to her.'

" 'Will she die?'

" 'Yes,' said the physician.

"A shudder convulsed me. All the better! I went to the door. She lay in bed; her bruised face was swollen, her cheeks and eyes blue. For God's sake, what have I done? I wanted to fall on my knees, I don't know why, and beg for something. She motioned to me.

" 'Forgive me! Forgive me!' she said.

"I was silent.

" 'I couldn't help it. I didn't know. I'm bad, but I'm not to blame; believe me, I'm not to blame! Forgive me! Will I really die? Can't anyone help me? I'll be so good, I'll make up . . . for everything . . .'

"Where did she get those words? No one could do anything more for her. She died.

"I was put on trial. I am Posdnyschew. That stupid court acquitted me. They didn't know that I first began to love her really upon her deathbed. No, she wasn't to blame.

"Had she lived, I would have loved not only her face and her body, but herself, and have forgiven her everything. And had I always loved her for herself and not only for her body, it wouldn't have been necessary to forgive her anything, probably."

Will Americans and the English Ever Understand Each Other?

by Winston Churchill

IT IS SURELY an elevated prospect which opens to those who are born into the English-speaking world. Spread wide around the globe and in possession of many of its fairest regions and main resources are more than 150 millions of men and women speaking the same language, sprung in an overwhelming degree from a single origin, nursed by the same common law, and nourished and inspired by the same literature.

Such a vast community, abounding in wealth, power, and progress, enjoying liberal and democratic institutions and representative government, constitutes the most successful human race which has appeared since the zenith of the Roman Empire.

Although riven by the mischances of history and sundered into two branches, their joint inheritance of law and letters, the crimson thread of their kinship, the similarity of their institutions, far outweigh the discordances and even antagonisms of politics, the rivalry of flags, the variants of climate, interest, and environment. Noble indeed is the opportunity of life offered to a citizen of this great common body. He moves with ease and very little sense of alienation across enormous distances, and, unpacking his gripsack at a thousand centers of industry and culture, finds himself very speedily almost at home.

In dwelling, therefore, upon the differences which time, events, and climate have wrought in the mentality of the various branches of the English-speaking world, it is above all things important to remember that these divergences are far less in volume and importance than the ties of union of homogeneity.

The social life of the United States is built around business. In Europe business is a newcomer in society. The numerous aristocracies, overthrown but still influential, the ancient landed families, the hierarchies of the army, the navy, diplomacy, the law, and the church, frame and largely fill the Old World picture.

Successful businessmen in Europe find a society ready-made for them. They are welcomed to circles which, especially in England, existed many years before their fortunes were made or the processes and machinery which they direct were devised. In the United States, on the other hand, the struggle to subdue and utilize a continent has taken the place of dynastic, religious, and class controversies. It has absorbed the life of the American people. Everything else falls into a somewhat remote background; and business, commerce, money-making, in all their forms, occupy the center of the stage. Business dominates the scene.

By "society" I do not, of course, mean the gay world of fashion and amusement. In America, as in other countries, that is no more than an adjunct and a diversion. The society which guides and governs the United States is based not on play, but on an intense work which takes from its votaries a first charge on all their thought and energy. From the innumerable universities all their young men go into business as a matter of course. Business is to them the means of earning their living, of making money, of making a fortune. But it is much more than that. It is that career of interest, ambition, and possibly even glory which in the older world is afforded by the learned professions and state services, military and civilian.

Practically all the prizes of American life are to be gained in business. There, too, is the main path of useful service to the nation. Nearly all that is best and most active in the manhood and ability of the United States goes into business with the same sense of serving the country as a young Prussian before the war entered the army, or as a son of a noble house in England in former times sought to represent a family borough in the House of Commons. The leading men of every state are all in business. Their businesses are interlaced; they compete, they collide, they overlap. A continued struggle proceeds, but under rules which, though unwritten, are getting stronger every year.

American industry is greatly the gainer from its power to attract practically all the vital elements in the nation. It is the gainer also in an increasing degree from the intimate combination in every stage between business and social life.

For the leaders of business are also the leaders of society. They are gregarious; they band themselves together in groups, in clubs, in organizations. They do not only work together, they play together. They develop a strong corporate life carrying with it a continual rising standard of discipline and behavior. In every state and city they and their families are the nucleus of the local life; and in New York, where to a very large extent everything takes place on a superscale, the leading business men are the leading figures of the whole nation. There has developed a confraternity, the members of which help one another and stand together, and certainly have a far higher sense of comradeship and association than exists in business circles in England.

Very often it is at the golf club, or the country club, or across a private dinner table that the foundations of the largest transactions are laid. It is very important, therefore, in American business circles to be a member of the club or to be a welcome guest at the dinner, to be popular, trusted, and thought a genial companion and a good sportsman.

Of course no convention prevents anyone entering and succeeding in business if he has the qualities and the luck for making a fortune. It is done every day. New figures armed with fiercely gathered wealth advance resolutely. They require no aid. Liked or disliked, they can stand on their own feet and make their way. It is a free country; they need not bow the knee to any social clique. "No, *sir.*" Yet it would be very nice to be elected to the golf club and to be accepted into the social circles, and it would also be very helpful, and never more helpful than in times of crisis and trouble.

These subtle influences invest the business life of the United States with a quality of strength and order which it formerly lacked. They are healthy and far-reaching. They are creating a new standard of values among successful men. It is good to have a great fortune; but there is more distinction in having a fine business and in managing it well. Wealth ceases to be the aim; it becomes the means, agreeable, indispensable, but yet only the means. Freedom of action, and a sense of close contact with the practical, the elating force of large propositions—these are the elements of an interesting life. These colossal modern businesses offer a man in many ways more scope and power than he could find in a cabinet office or at the head of a squadron of the fleet or a division of the army. The prospect is no less attractive because he may become a millionaire in the process.

In all concerned with production the American displays preëminent qualities. Conditions in America have favored and fostered enterprises upon the largest scale. The American business mind turns naturally, instinctively, to bigness and boldness. In Europe many of the important manufacturing firms have grown up over generations from small beginnings, and the works as they stand today represent the makeshift contributions of many years.

On the other hand, American development has had a clear field. To plan the "layout" of businesses upon a gigantic scale, to sweep away ruthlessly all encumbrances of the past, and to crush out all rivals or merge with them, are accepted as obvious ideals. The enormous plants make no compromise with the obsolete or the inefficient in any form.

Time—even in this land of hurry—is not grudged in preparation. Indeed, so vast were the preparations and establishments set on foot on both sides of the Atlantic for the maintenance and supply of the American army that the war was over before they had really begun to function, and, according to General Pershing, hardly a single American-made cannon fired an American shell at the enemy. Still, if the war had lasted into 1919, the results of these tremendous preparations would have been irresistible.

But what business has gained by this concentration of American ability and quality upon itself has been very largely at the expense of politics and of the professions and martial services. Except in times of war, the United States military or naval man occupies only a very modest position in the public eye or social world. Politics is frankly despised and lamentably neglected as a lifelong vocation by the flower of American manhood.

In England, at any rate, the man of independent means and ability who devotes his whole life to Parliament and public affairs, forswearing the opportunities of gathering wealth and seeking only, by serving the state, to rule events, is still regarded as on a higher plane than the prosperous and successful founder of a great business.

It is, or was until recently—for things are changing— quite the contrary in the United States. Politics, dominated by the machine, has produced a caste of professional politicians, beneath whose tough sway few illusions thrive. Aspiring, ardent youth is repulsed from political life, and the aristocracy of business finds ways of solving its political problems other than by personal participation. In the result the foreigner sees little to admire in the political life of the United States except its immense mechanical stability.

The Constitution grips the American people with a strong, unyielding hand. Public opinion, so powerful in England, plays but little part in the government of the United States. Presidents, senates, congresses, state legislatures, public officers of all kinds, sustained and erected by the party machine and working for fixed terms, are not to be influenced by the day-to-day emotions of democracy or its press. At election time the strong outbursts of popular feelings are all skillfully canalized and utilized. The forces are enormous, but the men in charge know how to bridle and guide them.

The average Englishman, indignant at some scandal or ill usage, feels he can put the matter right. The average American feels quite sure that he cannot. Public opinion and the sensitive flexibility of our Parliamentary institutions will very quickly sweep away in England an unpopular law. The American resigns himself to put up with it or evade it.

The statute books (both federal and state) are crowded with laws which have fallen into what is euphemistically called "innocuous desuetude." Politics are accepted like the weather: they go on; one must make the best of them; life has to be lived, work has to be done—and there are so many other more interesting, jolly, and profitable affairs to attend to.

A certain optimistic fatalism fortifies and consoles the American citizen. He feels that his country is strong enough, and that its vital force is buoyant enough, to survive the worst that politics can do. It may be that in following democracy and universal suffrage the old controls of English politics will in their turn be destroyed. Under the mask of democratic forms great nations habituate themselves to arbitrary rules.

Having slipped into prohibition unawares, America is unable to escape from its deadly embrace. The law cannot be altered, it appears. Therefore it must be broken or evaded; and broken and evaded it has been on a scale without example in the history of self-respecting communities. But this great evil of almost universal lawbreaking has bred still more deadly diseases. An inclined plane slopes unbrokenly from the senator or magnate sipping his glass of smuggled wine in Washington or New York, through layers of diminishing respectability until the frontiers of murderous crime and blackest villainy are reached.

Here again the scale is gigantic. The worst types of European criminality find themselves banded together in formidable organizations and commanding enormous wealth. Back and up from this terrible underworld rise the ever-lengthening tentacles of graft and corruption. An attempt to interfere improperly with the rights and discretion of the citizen has carried the legislature far beyond the bounds of public opinion, and the consequences, expanded and reacting from year to year, constitute a hideous disaster to American civilization. We simply cannot imagine either such a cause or such consequences arising in England.

After all, the first characteristic of the American people is their happiness. The visitor feels himself in the presence of a race with a keen zest for life, a sure confidence in the future, and much enjoyment of things as they are. The American is more highly strung than the northern European, and in most cases this does not seem to lead to pessimism or a morbid condition. The impression of happiness is common to all classes. The people in the streets, in the shops, in the hotels, the liftman, the bell hop, the telephone operator—all are gay.

No doubt there is a material basis for this. A double income for a wage-earner means more than twice the amount of amenities and enjoyment. The old orthodox tenet of European civilization, that "money does not bring happiness," is probably only a modern adaptation of Æsop's fable of "The Fox and the Grapes." Vast wealth does not bring happiness; but that small margin of spare money after necessities have been provided for constitutes in America the structure of what is definitely a larger life.

In the United States this larger life—or, rather, larger share of life in its natural and rightful balance—is enjoyed by an incomparably greater number than in any other country in the world. "England," said Disraeli, speaking of the early years of the nineteenth century and of long centuries before it, "was for the few and the very few." Now we have broadened out. Instead of catering for "the twice two thousand" of Byron's scornful gibe, "for whom the world was made," millions of our people now participate in a wide and eventful form of existence. But in the United States the same classes are counted in scores of millions. Life there is organized not for the few, nor for the millions, but for the scores of millions. Culture, amusement, and reasonable ambitions are provided wholesale by mass production. Culture, indeed, is a standardized article; and the population is almost conscript for university education. Here is the great achievement and marvelous phenomenon of the great republic, namely, the vast numbers participating in the full life.

Because the overwhelming majority of Americans enjoy conditions which are incomparably fortunate according to European standards, opinion is hard upon failure in all its forms. The mortal sin in the American decalogue is failure; all others are venial. If a man is a failure, the American presumption is that he has himself to blame. There are no vast submerged classes in whose behalf it can be pleaded that they have never had a chance. The great majority of the United States citizens feel that those who have not been able to come up to the general standard have faults or weaknesses for which they deserve to suffer.

There is little place for pity in the schemes of the great republic for the failures, for the impoverished or the worn-out. A great chance was offered; it was fair and free; it was offered to all; and if these pitiful ones have not taken it, so much the worse for them. All this is the philosophy of an expanding prosperity and widely diffused success.

But now, swiftly, suddenly, unexpectedly, though for only a spell, misfortune, contraction, disorganization, stagnation, unemployment have swept down upon the community which two years ago had reached the highest level of material well-being yet achieved by such great numbers of folk in this world. American optimism and complacency have been violently shaken. Millions of unemployed workpeople and clerks present themselves in the great cities. There are bread queues, there are riots, there are even what are called "socialists"—a terrible symptom! And in remote country districts, as well as in the back streets of stately cities, actual famine lays its bony hand upon individuals.

This is, of course, only a passing phase from which the United States will emerge strengthened or more prosperous. It is on the rule and not the exception that we must dwell. Next to happiness, a marked heartiness characterizes the American people. This word when used in its English meaning is almost a term of opprobrium; but in America it means a genuine flow of friendly feeling. The traveler is welcomed with gusts of friendliness, expansive gestures, and every appearance of joy. Hospitality and every form of kindness are thrust upon him. To this the average British visitor makes but an inadequate return. He behaves with traditional reserve and frigidity and too often seems to lack the technique for reciprocating the welcome he receives.

There is no doubt that the English people are chary of allowing the feeling of friendliness to take root quickly, and diffident in its outward expressions. They embody a complicated mass of sensitiveness and susceptibilities, acquired or inherited, which are due to a long succession of troubles and frustrations. They are the children of a race for whom life has for many generations been less easy than the life of the last few generations in America. Since individual frustration and failure have been more common in his experience, the Englishman carries about scars and wounds which are liable to injury at the hands of another. In consequence, he is unwilling to come close to others in terms of friendliness until he has tried and tested them.

American susceptibilities are of a more childlike and superficial character. The American is more confident and free from the scars of many battles. He is less afraid of the stranger and is capable of an immediate sensation of genuine friendliness. Affability and amiability come easier to all classes of Americans.

A third characteristic of the American is his earnestness. He dwells in an atmosphere of intense earnestness and seriousness about all matters of practical concern or general interest. The American prides himself on his sense of humor, but to a transatlantic visitor his earnestness is the predominating feature. We, with our experience that the goal, whatever it be, can only be attained by wary, round-about, and imperfect methods, are reluctant to indulge in hopes of quick success. With us the cautious and plodding attitude is appropriate. A superintense or earnest Englishman always seems to have a flavor of hysteria or of the ridiculous about him. Jests and irony run through our serious discussions and even the gravest situation breeds its joke.

Such an attitude is shocking to the average American. Any flavor of levity applied to the grave affairs of life is obnoxious to his mind. He regards it in his visitor (although too polite to say so) as a sign of the corruption of the Old World.

These earnest enthusiasms and aspirations lead very readily to a habit of platitudinizing. A friend of mine who made prolonged travel with a learned delegation through the United States, far from the fashionable circles of New York, says, "They never seemed to tire of enunciating the simplest truths with all the solemnity at their command. This may partly have been due to the belief that the platitudes were good for us, and to their habit of acting quickly on what they believe to be sound."

There is no doubt that the American love of platitude has a deeper root than this. It arises from their national situation. They have had great good fortune and success. They have a tremendous and obvious task to perform. Their mixture of many races—Poles, Italians, Serbs, and other southern European emigrants—has not yet been assimilated. The hundred-percent Americans have before them a serious problem of welding the nation together. For this the platitude is a powerful instrument. Everyone must be made to think the same things in certain important matters. United sentiment must overcome diversity of racial origin. About certain important matters all must be taught to say the same thing and to repeat it until it becomes tradition itself.

To sum up this brief examination of a tremendous subject: The Americans are a frailer race with a lighter structure than their British compeers. They are less indurated by disappointment; they have more hopes and more illusions; they swing more rapidly between the poles of joy and sorrow, and the poles are wider apart. They suffer more acutely both physical and moral pain.

Their mighty finance, which two years ago soared so triumphantly to the skies, has now for the moment, with as little reason, crashed to the pavement.

These excesses, both of elation and depression, would have been avoided in England. Tough, buttoned up, with much reserve, and with many latent resources, the Englishman trudges forward, bearing his burden. He will not fail. Even if the first prizes of the future should fall to the United States, he will still remain a vast enduring force for virility, sanity, and good will.

But it is in the combination across the Atlantic of these diversified minds, and in the union of these complementary virtues and resources, that the brightest promise of the future dwells.

His Father's Wagon

a short short story by Jim Tully

THE WAGON WAS loaded with watermelons. They shone with dark green luster under the southern sun. Hitched to it was an old roan team. Patiently they waited in front of the sun-scorched house. Now and then they looked around for their master. At last he came and gave them each a withered apple. He climbed upon the seat and the slow journey began.

The horses looked neither to right nor left. They walked slowly, heads down, tails unmoving. Green flies buzzed around them. The wagon creaked. The wheels wabbled.

The driver sat moveless. His faded blue eyes squinted. His brown army shirt was open at the throat. His feet were perched on the dashboard. The leather of his shoes was worn brick-red. His heavy hand held the lines loosely at a point where they had become thin by long contact with his fingers.

His face was finely chiseled—a face inherited from inarticulate generations of mountaineers who lived sparsely on scantily yielding soil. His eyes alone gave softness to his weather-beaten face. They were the eyes of one who gave withered apples to tired horses.

He was seemingly unconscious of the beauty around him. It was, nevertheless, a part of his life. Every spring he planted a geranium bed in the corner of the timothy lawn. It remained green long after the grass turned yellow.

His mind was filled with many thoughts. They centered about Ora. He had known her all his life. He had dreamed of marrying her when they were both children.

She went to normal school; he went to the war. Now he was soon to marry her.

The boy stopped in front of the village store. He wrapped the lines about the whipstock and wiped the horses' shoulders with a piece of burlap.

The village store was also the post office. The proprietor sorted a meager mail. He glanced anxiously at two strangers who gazed out of the door as Larry entered with a large melon. Long years in the hills told him they were "revenoors."

"Excuse me, please," Larry asked pleasantly as he edged his way past the two men in the doorway.

"Certainly," both exclaimed, as they stepped back from the door and looked at each other.

"Well, here's somethin'll make you happy," the postmaster said to Larry. It was a long government envelope. "You're acomin' up in the world. This is from the old Uncle hisself. See—it says, 'Penalty for private use three hundred dollars.' "

Larry opened the envelope and pulled out something. It resembled a Liberty Bond, but had more yellow and green on it.

Martin exclaimed "That ain't so bad—your bonus insurance." He looked at it more closely. "Got it made out to your people, too. That's a fine thing of the old Uncle, now, hain't it?"

The two men looked at Larry.

"Well," he said, "it's not so bad—but I've got to die to get it."

The men followed him outside.

"What you got in that wagon, young feller?"

"Watermelons."

"I know you got watermelons, but what else?"

Larry climbed into the seat and picked up the lines.

"Wait a minute, there! Not so fast. Answer us first. Whatcha got in the wagon here?"

"I told you what I had in the wagon."

"Yeah, we heard you the first time, but we're a bit doubtin' 'bout wagons in this neck o' the woods. We'll take a look ourselves."

One man held a revolver. His partner tumbled the melons about.

The man climbed down from the wagon. His face bore an expression of puzzled disgust. Relieved, Martin walked toward his store.

Larry took up the lines once more.

One man looked at the end of the wagon. He yelled to Larry, "Wait a minute, there!"

To his partner he said, "Listen, Mike! The tail end don't come to the bottom. She's got a 'possum belly."

The man jumped into the wagon and began throwing melons out. They fell on the dusty road and broke open.

Martin stood in the doorway, his heart with Larry, his head with the government he served.

A quick yank revealed the false bottom.

Piled in straw were jugs and bottles which gave the odor of burned oatmeal.

The man laughed. "Corn licker, eh? Where'd you make this and where you takin' it?"

Larry made no answer.

"Well, we'll find out. You take him to the county seat, Mike, and I'll stick aroun' here and see what I kin see."

Larry called to Martin, "Say, Mart, will you git someone to drive the team home and tell Dad?"

"Sure I will," answered Martin confidentially. He knew that no real man of the hills ever told on another one.

"Why, don't you know we take the horses an' wagon, too? It belongs to your Uncle Sam now. It's confiscated for transportin' licker—in the name of the United States."

"But it's Dad's wagon. It's all he's got. You wouldn't take his only team an' wagon, would you?"

His whip curled over the team.

They dashed down the road.

One of the men fired twice.

Larry crumpled. His jaws were clamped tight. His eyes were open to the downward-going sun.

A bullet had pierced through the left pocket of his army shirt.

The storekeeper picked up the green-and-yellow paper.

"It's his insurance," he said. "You know, he fought against the Germans."

"Did he?" asked the men in unison. "That's too bad."

The
Turn
Is
Coming

by Eddie Cantor

Hold Out Your Hand and Take It in High

WE MUST BUILD a new road to Prosperity. So far we've been building merry-go-rounds and giving Europe free rides.

I've got the remedy for the whole thing and will sell it at twenty-five cents a bottle. After all, I've got to make a living, too. Where am I? Oh, yes!

The surest way out of the depression is to find new jobs. All the old professions are overcrowded. For the first time in years doctors have the same sickness as their patients—undernourishment.

Lawyers who used to handle thousands of cases are now lucky if they can get a single case. And then it's cut stuff.

Dentists used to give gas; now they're taking it. Even bankers have become economical. I know one who hasn't spent a dollar in two years. He'll be out in a month. But I am ready to open new roads to success. New fields for genius to explore and talent to express itself.

There is a great opportunity for a Chain-Food Coupler —one who links sausages. This is a fine art and requires the greatest skill so that the sausages don't run into each other and make one big bologna.

I have given jobs to fifty-two Poultry Upholsterers who put stuffing into chickens, and have opened a new field for Kitchen Chiropodists to prepare pigs' feet.

There is a big demand for Jig-Saw Dentists to put teeth in circular saws, and Cake Carpenters are needed to make chocolate shavings for pastry.

Spaghetti Tuners can command their own price. This art requires a real appreciation of music and a knowledge of organ building, so that the spaghetti tubes should give the same tones when you draw them up.

There is no end to new opportunities, and by this time I'd have had everybody employed if the international situation hadn't required my presence in Europe. The other night I was called on the transatlantic phone by Premier MacDonald. "Eddie," he said hoarsely, "you have to come over. And, for heaven's sake, take an English boat so we can count on one passenger!"

When I got to Number Ten Downing Street there were the heads of Europe in heated conference. Hindenburg sat in a corner going over his map with a razor. MacDonald and Briand hurled kings and queens at each other in two-handed pinochle. Mellon sat near the window throwing German Bonds to the pigeons. And Stalin was grimly solving a cross-word puzzle as part of the Five-Year Plan. I promptly took charge of the meeting.

"Deal me in," I said eagerly.

"People are panicky for no reason at all!" cried Briand, throwing down his cards in disgust. He had a very bad hand. "Why can't we learn from China? They've had a depression there since they started the country!"

"You don't say! Give me a hundred dollars' worth of chips!" said MacDonald feelingly.

"And what do the Chinese do?" exclaimed Briand, shortchanging him. "When things get very bad, they simply increase the birth rate! If the people get hungry they throw themselves to the alligators and that solves the eating problem!" And he looked significantly at Hindenburg.

"But if a man is starving," cried Hindenburg, patting his paunch, "won't you save him?"

"We gave you a moratorium," remarked MacDonald, melding four aces.

"That moratorium ruined us!" growled Hindenburg. "You wouldn't take the money, so we were stuck with it! Now, if you don't lend us a half a billion dollars, we'll go broke and see how you like it!"

"Please don't go broke, Mr. Hindenburg," pleaded Mellon, the tears streaming down his cheeks. "It was so nice of you to accept the moratorium, and now we'll lend you a half a billion dollars if you guarantee not to pay it back! Promise?"

"Well, we'll consider it," said Hindenburg sulkily. "But what'll you do for us next year? After all, you helped us and you're responsible!" he added menacingly.

"Well, maybe we can work it out for us to pay *you* reparations," suggested Mellon timidly. "If you accept, we can then vote a bonus to the German War Veterans."

"Brilliant idea!" cried Briand, dealing himself a new hand from his sleeve. "After all, if you Americans don't take care of Germany for the rest of her life, you'll have a hard time proving you didn't start the war!"

"You're in bad, Briand!" exclaimed MacDonald, leading with an ace of trump.

"Say, you're cheating!" shouted Briand indignantly. "I know every card I dealt you and I wouldn't deal you any aces!"

After the conference Mellon took me aside. "I certainly got the best of Germany, didn't I?" he said. "Now you go and tell the folks back home that I'm calling off payments as fast as I can and pretty soon I'll have it fixed so that we'll never get a cent from anybody!"

"And that'll bring back prosperity!" I chimed in enthusiastically.

"Can't fail!" said Mellon, pushing me off the dock.

I returned to America and immediately I went about to see the remarkable improvements in business that our international policy had caused. I visited one of our big department stores and strolled into the silk division. A young lady was being waited on and everybody was bringing down huge rolls of material. It felt like the good old days.

"I want twenty-two rolls of Japanese silk at $4.50 a yard," she said.

"Yes, ma'am," murmured the head man who followed her with pencil and pad. "Anything else?"

"Yes. A hundred and twenty-three yards of engraved satin at $5.30 a yard."

The man calculated the total with awe. "Will that be all?"

"Oh, no! Sixteen rolls of chiffon at $2.79 a yard; three hundred and seventy yards of lace at $1.98 a yard; five hundred and sixty-two yards of silk velours at $8.43 a yard, and thirty-eight rolls of taffeta at $1.17 a yard!"

The man perspired as he added. "It's a big order," he said huskily. "Will you pay for it now or shall we send it C .O. D.?"

"Oh, no," replied the young lady as she pocketed the neat and accurate bill. "I don't want the goods. We're a silk house ourselves. But we had to sell our adding machine and I didn't know how I'd ever figure up our inventory! Thank you so much!"

In other lines things looked equally promising. I went to buy an automobile and the place was crowded with salesmen. "How much is this car?" I inquired.

"Twenty-four hundred and sixty-five delivered," they responded in chorus.

"Do you allow discounts to actors?"

"Certainly," said the manager, stepping over six salesmen.

"I act in pictures, too—do I get an extra discount for that?"

"You do," said the manager.

"I also write books and plays—you know, that means publicity. Does that entitle me to a rebate?"

"Of course!"

"I happen to be a stockholder in this company. How about that?"

"That gives you a special stockholder's discount," came the eager reply.

"And of course you'll give me the agent's commission," I added. "Well, then, how much do I owe you?"

The manager began to figure the necessary deductions. "Well, Mr. Cantor," he said, "we owe you a hundred and fifty-three dollars!"

After all, I guess we can't be prosperous until all the other countries become prosperous. It's up to us to tell them how. Here is the program:

Let's have *World Prohibition*. Look what it has done for us! Shutting down the vineyards and breweries of the world would save billions. People wouldn't grow grapes and turn them into wines and champagnes, other millions of people wouldn't bottle them, and still more millions wouldn't be fermenting beer and distilling corn and rye. About fifty million people could be taken out of that industry and their energy conserved. All those people could be resting and doing nothing. That would be a great step toward prosperity!

The next thing we could recommend is *World Racketeering*. Think of the young men who might have remained half-wits and idiots all their lives, but thanks to the proper rackets have become figures in society and ride around in fancy cars.

Bootlegging is one of the surest roads to fame and fortune. People who can't read or write, and who shoot their mothers with machine guns, now have their talents rewarded and wield a great influence in the community. Kidnaping, arson, blackmail, and murder are all new enterprises where anybody with a yellow streak and no forehead can make himself a career.

I met a racketeer who before prohibition spent most of his time in a strait-jacket, but now he wears a pearl-handled gun to match his shirt studs.

Recently I visited his home. It was a cozy little love nest with a cannon in the parlor and gas bombs on the mantelpiece. His wife complained that their child, Egbert, didn't eat his spinach. "Now, my son," said the father quietly, "if you don't eat your spinach I'll put you on the spot!" He pulled a gun, but the child was quicker and shot him through the left eye with a forty-four.

I asked him about the depression and he smiled. "Not in my business," he remarked. "I'm so busy I don't know where I am."

He wore a little pink thread around his finger. "I wonder what that's for!" he mumbled, perplexed.

"Is it a reminder?" I asked him.

"Oh, yes! Now I know! I have to kidnap Sam Consido at five o'clock!"

He had a deep red mark on his head and I asked him how he got it. "Oh, that's nothing!" he said. "Just a bullet I once got through the skull. Six more inches and it would have reached my brain!"

Another wise measure is *World High Tariff*. There should be a wall around every country, so that nobody can trade with anybody under any circumstances. This would be a great spur to the smuggling business and give revenue officers a good side income. Bootleggers and smugglers are always well-to-do. Imagine what prosperity there'd be if the whole world were divided into these two classes!

We mustn't forget *A World Ban on Immigration*. Steamship companies are operating at a loss today. They would welcome any scheme by which they could close down altogether. Besides, people should stay where they're born. They should die and be buried there. It makes the soil very fertile. And there's nothing like fertile soil for raising wheat at a loss. This should become a world policy.

The beauty of such a constructive program is that we can predict the result. It will all lead to a *World Deficit*. We have had remarkable success with our deficit. In one year we increased it to nine hundred million. It was no easy task. It took all the forces of the administration to do this. But in the end we triumphed. At this rate our deficit next year ought to be eighteen hundred million, and if we keep up the good work our deficit will in a short time be equal to the entire wealth of the nation, so we'll be even! In the same way the whole world could get even.

In return for these ideas, Europe should do something for us. All future conferences for moratoriums should be held here. It would boost the hotel business and employ a lot of interpreters—six or seven at least. We should also get the tourist trade and arrange not to pay what *we* owe. It may be a good idea to reverse positions with Europe altogether! While we're at it let's reverse everything!

At a recent bank closing in New York, the defunct depositors stood quietly in line to collect their fifty percent. One man rushed into the crowd with a terrible outcry against the officers of the bank. "I will tear them limb from limb," he shrieked, wringing his hands and pulling his hair. "I will boil them in oil and hang them from the lamp-post!"

A policeman tried to calm him. "My poor fellow," he said sympathetically, "you must have lost your life savings in that bank."

"Who lost?" cried the man. "I wasn't even a depositor! If I was a depositor, then they'd first hear from me!"

He was a man who talked depression and enjoyed prosperity. All the others on the line smiled bravely and were broke.

By applying the Cantor Reverse System all around I'm sure prosperity would be back in no time. Instead of two nickels for a dime, let's have two dimes for a nickel. And instead of talking prosperity and having depression, let's talk depression and have prosperity!

*   *   *   *   *

I've tried to make a serious study of the economic situation. I find that if people understand what you say they don't take it seriously. For that reason I've used as many hard words as I could, and now *I* don't understand them. I'm attaching a glossary of the technical terms. If the meanings are wrong it's the printer's fault.

GLOSSARY

Prosperity—The time right before election.
Coolidge—The Sphinx wired for sound.
Moratorium—A game called on account of darkness.
Bills—First stages of confetti.

Diplomat—Soft soap in a high hat.
Bank Examiner—A coroner.
Depression—A decline or fall—as off a precipice.
Federal Reserve—A place where oxygen is kept.
Reno—Where "Liberty Bonds" are purchased.
Tariff—A Republican cover charge.

Unemployment—Appletime.
Opportunity—Applesauce.
Business—Near beer. It's now one and one-half percent.
Cabinet—A hollow thing made of wood.
Starving Armenian—A fellow American.
Millionaire—One who eats three times a day.

My Private Life

by George Bernard Shaw

I HAVE BEEN asked if it is fair for newspapers to invade the privacy of public men. Or, to put it another way—has the public any right to know anything of the domestic life of a personage?

It all depends on what the newspaper wants to know. There is such a thing as idle curiosity, and there is such a thing as intelligent curiosity. There are interviewers who know their business; and there are interviewers who are tactless idiots.

If you intrude upon me to ask how many buttons there are on my waistcoat, I can only reply: "I don't know. Get out!"

It has been said that the public has a right to *know* its public persons, since—so it is held—what they are explains what they do.

I might reply that what I do explains what I am much better than what I am explains what I do. For nobody knows what I am, least of all myself; whereas what I do is more or less ascertainable.

But the newspapers seem to want to know what I do in private.

Is it of interest to the public to know that I never have bacon for breakfast?

Yes, it is, if the newspaper is collecting material for a serious article on dietetics. No, it is not, if it has in view an article on the war in Spain.

My breakfast consists of porridge, postum, and grapefruit. What is the news value of that fact compared with that of an earthquake in Chile?

You must bear in mind that even the greatest genius—meaning today the person with the greatest publicity—is ninety-nine point nine percent exactly the same as Tom, Dick, or Harry. It is the remaining nought point one percent that matters. As long as the newspapers stick to the nought point one percent, I am at their service as a public duty.

Is it of public interest to know what exercise I take? Well, I did a good deal of bicycling at one time, but I could never see the value of athletics.

I agree with W. R. Titterton when he says that taking physical exercise merely for the sake of your muscles is as unhealthy as taking spiritual exercise merely for the sake of your soul.

Sandow once tried to get hold of me. I told him: "I know what you can do: You can lift three elephants, half a dozen pianos, and twenty men on your chest. But that's no use to me. I want to keep them *off* my chest."

I have an idea that Sandow died young.

Even I am not as young as I used to be. I like the story of the man who, on reaching his hundredth birthday, was asked by the interviewers to what he attributed his longevity, and replied: "Gentlemen, I attribute my longevity to the fact that I have abstained from spirits, wines, and beers, and from physical intercourse with women until I was fourteen."

No, I am not as young as I used to be. And old age does make a difference. For example, you can't drive a car. Or jump a fence. And there are other things.

For instance: The other day I was on a deputation to the Town Planning Department of the London County Council with regard to the site of the British National Theater. As I was once a Borough Councilor—for St. Pancras, London, N. W.—I was supposed to be the man to speak for the deputation. I spoke—and I made a fearful hash of it.

Looking back on the days when I was young, had a red beard, and spoke at street corners, I remember one failure of mine at the East India Dock Gates, Poplar (a famous street-corner forum in the East End of London).

At that time they always provided our meetings with a plain-clothes policeman. It was of course quite easy to spot him. And I determined to try to get him to listen to me.

I failed utterly.

He would pay attention to the first few words, decide that it was the usual harmless nonsense, and then turn his thoughts inward.

But once in Hyde Park I did achieve something. I delivered the best speech that I have ever made.

It was raining cats and dogs; and my audience consisted of four shrouded and dripping policemen. My chairman was occupied in trying to hold an umbrella approximately over my head.

I set myself to convert those four policemen. And I believe that I succeeded. In the improbable event of one or all of the four reading this, I admit that I should like him, or them, to own up.

There is a part of you—or anyhow of me—that does not age. My brain functions as well as ever it did. Perhaps it functions better than ever. But it can't keep on so long.

However, as I have said, you can judge what I am from what I do, and what the nought point one percent of me does is to your hand.

I Seem to Remember the Name, But...

by H. I. Phillips

A Memory Test of People in the Headlines

WHERE ARE THE headliners of yesteryear? Or those of yesterday, for that matter? If there is anything less permanent than a spotlight, you name it, mister. Believe it or Ripley, ten years from today you may be asking yourself, "Amos 'n' Andy? Let me think. They were those fellows arrested for flying over Japan, weren't they?" Or, "Al Capone? Wasn't he a crooner?"

Already you can mention the Vestris to most people and they will suggest that it was a Greek wrestling hold, or one of those Florida developments that went bad.

No farther ahead than 1940 millions of Americans will be uncertain whether Rudy Vallée was a geographical depression, a Chinese general, or the author of *Mourning Becomes Electra;* or if "Legs" Diamond was a baseball park or the fellow who tried to go under the North Pole in a submarine.

You may scoff at the notion that in 1942 if you were given three guesses at the answer to "Who was Albie Booth?" you might write: 1. The fellow who shot Lincoln. 2. A famous tenor on a cigarette hour. 3. I don't know; I'm a stranger here myself.

Yet that's just about what would happen.

You resent the intimation that you have a terrible memory? Very well, then. Who was Mumtaz Begum? Male or female? Vegetable or mineral? The name was on the front pages of every newspaper in the country. No, it wasn't the name of that hundred-and-fifty-year-old Turk who was hit by a taxicab on his trip to America.

Give up? All right. Let's have the facts about Karl Rosner. You remember Mr. Rosner, of course. He went over Niagara Falls in a barrel, or was received by Huey Long in his undershirt, or something.

Who was Moose Factory? Or what was Moose Factory? And did it have anything to do with the production of moose?

Remember Fred Beauvais? Gaston B. Means? Dot King? Happy Felsch? Aaron Ward? What was all that fuss about Willie Stevens? Did he win a World Series game for the Cardinals or carry the diphtheria serum to Nome?

Bald Jack Rose? Think hard! The man who was murdered in that Catskill beer racket? Don't be silly!

Who was Joyce Hawley and when? How straight are you on the facts about Sergeant York? Remember Guy Empey? Was he the Englishman who spent all those years going native with the Arabians and later became known as Aircraftsman Shaw?

Do you recall Epinard? In what year did Oom the Omnipotent win the Preakness? Was Dunboyne a horse or a British general? Was Papp a thoroughbred or a German restaurant? Tell in one paragraph the facts about Cirrus, Mad Hatter, Freddie Welsh, Fatty Arbuckle, William Taylor, the Great Lafayette, Old Rosebud, Clyde Fitch, Jack Britton, Harry Vardon, Champ Clark, Dr. Dumba, Count Leopold von Berchtold, Dr. Sawyer, Bronson Howard, Ward and Vokes, Jim Churchill.

By the way, who was Franz Ferdinand? No, he wasn't a wrestler or the composer of Madam Butterfly.

Remember the Arabic? What was it? Was Victoriano Huerta a billiard champion or a German admiral? Did

Commander Nobile, General Carranza, and Admiral Sims figure in the Battle of Jutland, or am I thinking of three other fellows?

Who was Captain Fryatt? Sir Cecil Spring-Rice? Theda Bara? Zev? Was Admiral Sims' first name Addison? Who was Adeline Genée? Pawnee Bill? Jim Thorpe? Sliding Billy Watson?

Dr. Albert? Did he figure in some famous mystery in New York involving a will? Or was he a chef at the old Holland House? 'Sfunny! I recall the name but the details escape me!

Marie Corelli? Used to be fired from a gun with the old Adam Forepaugh show, didn't she? Or was that Nan Britton?

Edith Wharton, Osler, Owen Wister, E. N. Westcott, F. Hopkinson Smith, E. W. Kemble? All I know is that they were in the show business or helped form the American League or something, and even then I may be wrong. Of course we all know about Laura Jean Libby. She was the woman for whom the vegetable compound was named. Or was that the Countess Cathcart?

Who slapped Theodore Dreiser's face, or whose face was it Theodore slapped? What football player ran the wrong way with the ball? Oh, well, we can't remember everything.

Was Marion Talley a golf champion or a movie star?

"Shoeless Joe" Jackson? "Kewpie" Black? "Ducky" Pond? "Stan" Keck? "Pinkie" Baker? "Don" Lourie? They were in the headlines a few years ago, and you're wrong if you think they were lawyers in the Scopes case.

By the way, what was the Scopes case?

Were Post and Gatty a tap-dancing team, a pair of radio comics, or what?

Charles Levine? Was he the Brooklyn boy who went to Spain and became a famous bullfighter? Or was that Bossy Gillis?

For what is Gertrude Ederle famous? Who was Joe Notter? Paul Berlenbach? Eddie Rickenbacker? "Butch" McDevitt? Bernt Balchen?

Who were Alcock and Brown? Hockey players? No, we're not even warm. Just a moment please. Weren't they pretty well known aviators a decade or so ago?

How familiar is the name of Commander Karl von Müller to you now? Was the Deutschland a song, a café, a submarine, or a dirigible?

Was Alexa Sterling an opera singer, a figure skater, or a golf champion? Who was Marion Hollins? Cecil Leitch? Joyce Wethered? Molla Bjurstedt?

Was Sir Barton a whippet, a prize heifer, or a great race horse? Was he ridden by Willie Hoppe? Can you place Matt McGrath, Peter Manning, Capablanca, Jess Sweetser, George Kelly, William H. Anderson, Papyrus, and tell offhand which was subject to horseflies?

Did Christabel Pankhurst lead the birth-control movement, the Lucy Stone League, or what? Who is Emma Goldman? John F. Hylan? Nurmi? Joe Moore?

I seem to recall Boca Raton, Sacco-Vanzetti, and Gunnar Kasson, but I'm not sure which was a Florida boom resort. Didn't Charles Ponzi forget to touch second? Dr. Emile Coué did a mind-reading act or something, didn't he?

Who was Cipriano Castro and in what league did he pitch?

Was it Howard Carter and the Earl of Carnarvon who first flew to Australia? Was John T. King ex-President Coolidge's shoemaker or am I thinking of Michael Collins? Or was it Jim Lucey?

Was the Shenandoah an oil tanker, a stake race, or a dirigible?

Here's a tough one: Krishnamurti? Concentrate and don't let those children outside annoy you. The leader of the Riffs? No, you're not anywhere near it.

Have you any idea in what shooting case Ethel Conrad and Lillian Graham figured, or was it Nan Patterson?

Who were Gallagher and Shean? Did they fly that plane from Nova Scotia to England?

Do you remember Mabel Hite? Emperor Cook?

Who was W. E. D. Stokes? Fred Merkel? Bugs Raymond? Dan O'Reilly? Bessie McCoy? Arthur Twining Hadley? "Dutch" Carter? "Ping" Bodie?

Was Lefty Louie a southpaw pitcher with the Brooklyn Club? Can you place Daisy Ashford? Sylvia Carmen? Who was Jane Gibson? Jake Lingle? King Boris? Captain Ross Smith? Mustapha Kemal? Leo Frank? Hugo Stinnes? Lieutenant Becker?

And here's one that will keep you up tonight: Who was that fellow Abd-el-Krim? No, he wasn't the leader of the Young Turks. Guess again. The winner of a Nobel peace award? Go to the foot! We knew that one would stick you!

"My husband sees things that way, too, but fortunately he can't draw!"

The Twilight of the Gangster

by Edward Doherty

How Much Longer Are We Going to Put Up with Him?

WE, THE PEOPLE of the United States, are a queer lot—perhaps the queerest in the world. We're a sluggish, blind, and lazy lot. We're as paradoxical as an Irish bull. But we have our moments! We call America the Cradle of Liberty, and vote it dry. We boast of our courage, and let criminals run us and rob us and kill us. We boast of our democracy. We high-hat such kingdoms as Italy, and most of us think Benito Mussolini is a despot. Italy has Fascism. But we have feudalism.

We've created a host of robber barons in the last ten years. We've let them amass enormous riches. We've let them pillage and slay. We've pampered and petted them. We've made them idols. We've cheered Alphonse "Scarface" Capone every time he was acquitted. We've cried "Persecution!" every time he went on trial. We've cheered Jack "Legs" Diamond when he was acquitted of burning the feet of a man he was charged with kidnaping.

We were glad to see these piratical figures get away with it. But we were well fed then. America, a full-stomached America, could laugh at the gunmen and their quaint and picturesque murders, could be good-natured about their kidnapings, their rackets.

"They're all right," we said. "They're out for the dollar, just as we are. And they keep us from dying of thirst. They only kill each other, anyway."

We let them go their ways. We let them establish themselves. We let them become powerful. We let them use our streets for slaughterhouses, let them turn machine guns loose on our busiest thoroughfares.

Innocent people have been killed, wounded, maimed for life—men and women and little children at play. Our rivers and our highways have been used for the dumping of grotesque bullet-riddled bodies.

We jailed women who sold a few bottles of whisky or home brew. Officers have shot down men who were carry-ing pint bottles of illicit liquor. We have hanged or electrocuted kids who made our feudal heroes their heroes, and who went out with guns to rob or to kill.

But have we hanged or electrocuted any of our feudal bootleg dukes? Name me one.

Scalice and Anselmi, killers imported from Sicily to help Capone and the Genna brothers in Chicago, were convicted of killing two policemen and wounding a third. But what happened? They got a new trial, and were acquitted.

Strange they should come from Sicily? Not at all. Sicily, the home of the Mafia, harbored the deadliest assassins in the world until the "despotic" Mussolini cleared Italy of its criminals. He jailed a lot. He killed a lot. But many of them are over here now—serving feudal liquor lords and getting rich.

Never in the history of the United States has there been such public flouting of law and order as we have permitted in the last ten years.

What other people would permit rival gangs to race recklessly down the streets of its big cities, shooting at each other with machine guns, killing each other, killing children, killing women, killing innocent men?

Hymie Weiss once took a cavalcade of motor cars past a hotel in Cicero, Illinois, a suburb of Chicago, and turned its walls into a huge Swiss cheese. The rest of the world was appalled. But America was phlegmatic. It was just a gangster gesture.

Weiss, affectionately known as "Little Hymie," lived to boast about that exploit. He lived three weeks.

Capone's machine gunners massacred seven men in a Chicago garage. Two of the murderers were dressed in the uniforms of policemen. America began to be shocked. A joke was a joke, but this was carrying a joke too far.

133

But what could be done about it? Everybody knew Capone had planned that massacre. But he was immune.

"Well," we said, "somebody will get Capone." And we let it go at that. A well-fed, busy, moneymaking America could forget a massacre and continue to wink at gangsters.

But hungry men know no jokes. And there are many hungry men in the nation today. Factories have been closed. Stores have gone out of business. Municipalities are broke. Chicago cannot pay its teachers or its policemen or its firemen. Men who were prosperous a few years ago are begging half dollars of their friends.

Hungry men have no benevolent affection for feudal dukes or barons. They see things with new eyes. The gangster kings have felt the depression too, but they were the last to feel it, and they are not suffering much. Men drink most, it seems, when they are desperate.

The glamour has been stripped from the gangsters. Even the most stupid of us see them now as they are, yellow louts, red-handed plunderers. We have begun to realize they have waged actual war upon us in this last red decade. Hunger has made us see the truth.

We realize now that they have taken billions of dollars from us. They have not only flooded the country with cut whisky and green beer and new wine, but also with poison. They have charged outrageous prices for it. They have forced business men to pay tribute. They have "muscled in" on groceries, butcher shops, restaurants, hotels, drug stores, factories, industries of all kinds—even miniature golf courses. They have peddled "protection." They have forced little men out of business. They have made big employers cut salaries and throw workmen out of jobs. They have had as much to do with the present depression as the crash in Wall Street had.

They have taken over the government in many cities. They have bought thousands of city and state police. They have corrupted judges and city officials. They have bribed members of the coast guard. They have stolen the polls, intimidated and killed honest voters, torn up ballots. They have elected to public office men sworn to protect them—not to protect us. In some districts no candidate can be elected without their aid.

The great white father in Washington has talked of the "noble experiment." Millions of pious people have given thanks to God that America is dry. And our feudal murderers have killed each other. Thousands of them have been dumped into our back yards, and still they have grown in numbers and in power and in wealth. And young America, growing to manhood, is following their example.

Last August two nineteen-year-old boys, carrying a small arsenal with them, held up a payroll messenger, stole over $4,000 from him, shot the police guard dead, and fled in a taxicab.

A motorcycle policeman tried to stop them. They killed him too.

And then the new feeling in America showed itself.

Vincent Hyde, a fireman, picked up the motorcycle policeman's pistol and cartridge belt, jumped on the running board of another cab, and gave chase. He fired at the fugitives until he dropped, wounded. Rubin Katz, that taxi's driver, though he had a wound in the throat, never faltered until the fleeing car crashed against a truck. The police showed their heroism too, as they always do in emergencies. There were cops on the running boards of every car in the pursuit, targets for the bullets of the two kids in the taxicab ahead. Six were killed in that chase, including the bandits, their driver, and a little girl who was sitting with her father and mother in an automobile.

She was the second child killed within a month in the city of New York.

The man who drove the kids who tried to ape their liege lords the gangster kings was Herbert Hasse. He seems to have been a hard-working, decent chap, a typical American citizen. He had a wife, a family. Gunmen probably didn't mean anything to him. Let them alone and they'll let you alone, he might have told you. Or he might have said, "Well, we got to get our booze somewhere, and those guys only kill each other."

The bandits jumped into his car. It might have been yours. Any car will do for a bandit making an escape. They put a gun to Hasse's head and made him speed. He didn't want to, no doubt. But he didn't want to die. His family needed him. Somebody shot Hasse dead.

If those two boys had been real gangsters, out for some quick money—and gangsters do not hesitate to rob—they would not have killed the policemen intentionally. Gangsters are careful about killing cops—they want cops to protect them. They need police friendship.

But even if they were gangsters they wouldn't have hesitated a moment to kill every *civilian* man, woman, and child who got in their way.

It isn't so long since Vincent Coll's men, hunting an enemy in Manhattan, turned a machine gun loose in a street crowded with children. They riddled a baby buggy, and the slugs tore through the body of a sleeping child and killed him. Four other children were left lying on the sidewalk, unconscious or screaming with pain, before the gun was silenced and the car drove off.

We've stood for plenty, we star-spangled flag-waving Americans. And we've had more than enough.

Commissioner Mulrooney in New York City and Commissioner Alcock in Chicago have declared war on gangsters, real war. Mulrooney has told his men to shoot first, and shoot above the waistline. And he means it.

Governor Franklin D. Roosevelt of New York did his best to send Jack Diamond to jail. He failed. A crowd cheered when Diamond was acquitted. Jack Diamond, "the clay pigeon of gangdom," "the big shot," "the much shot at," thief and murderer that he is, was cheered as though he were a national hero.

But the federal government doesn't think him a hero. It tried him in New York, and convicted him of conspiring to violate the prohibition law and of owning a still. Judge Richard J. Hopkins of Kansas gave him the limit—four years and a fine of $11,000—and directed that he be prosecuted under the Jones law.

"Under that law," the judge said, "he might be sentenced to thirty or forty years."

Paul Quattrocchi, one of Diamond's lieutenants, was sentenced with him. Diamond has appealed, and is at liberty pending a hearing on the appeal. But jail seems certain for him—unless somebody saves him with a machine gun.

Capone is going to jail too. He has been indicted by a federal grand jury. He is accused of income-tax frauds and of 5,000 specific violations of the prohibition law. Sixty-eight of his vassals are named with him. It is charged that his syndicate's income from beer alone totaled $75,000 a day.

Government agents declare the syndicate operated all over the Middle West. They believe they have broken the power of the syndicate with this indictment, bankrupted its members, and stripped Capone of all his influence.

Capone had it all fixed, he thought, to make a bargain with the prosecution. He'd plead guilty and spend a few years in a nice jail where he could have every luxury. But Federal Judge James Wilkerson wouldn't bargain with him. Capone withdrew his plea of guilty, and he and his lawyer are talking things over. But, rest assured, Capone is going to jail. Judge Wilkerson sentenced him to thirty days for contempt of court last winter. He hasn't served that term yet. But he will. Unless—as in Diamond's case—some machine gunner catches him first.

The twilight of the gangs! Capone and Diamond will go to jail. Coll will go to the chair if he's found. "Dutch" Schultz is done as a big shot since his arrest. This despite his acquittal. "Waxy" Gordon, Vannie Higgins, "Bugs" Moran—all the feudal princelings you can mention are wondering what will happen to them.

We've been fools, we Americans. But we've snapped out of our foolishness. We have been cowards. We are cowards no longer.

But have these gangsters been brave and wise?

Look at Jack Diamond. You could play him on a player piano. He's been shot four times. He's half paralyzed. He's eaten with consumption. There are bullets in him the doctors are afraid to take out. He's had money. He hasn't much left. He's only thirty-four—and speeding to his doom.

Look at Capone, who is reputed to have had $60,000,-000. He's in fear of his life every moment. He's guarded by a hundred men constantly. He rides in an armored car. His guards surround him when he's at a theater, or a prize fight, or in any crowd. He wakes up every little while and goes to another bed—he has many beds—so an assassin will have a hard time finding him. He doesn't trust any of his guards. He dares not. He once trusted Anselmi and Scalice.

He was told that Anselmi and Scalice had ambitions. They wanted to be rid of him and join forces with Joe Giunta, whom Capone had made head of the Unione Siciliano.

Capone sent two men to test Anselmi. They found Anselmi ready to betray his king. They agreed to help him.

"Don't use your gun," one of them said. "That can be identified. I'll get you one. Wait here." He went into another room, shook the cartridges out of his revolver, removed the bullets, and put the empty shells back into the chambers.

Anselmi went upstairs, the gun in his hand. He went into Capone's office. Capone stood with his back to Anselmi. Anselmi fired twice. The pin clicked on two empty shells. Anselmi turned pale and put the gun away.

Capone turned. He appeared to have noticed nothing. He greeted Anselmi with a beaming smile. He shook hands with Anselmi. He embraced him.

"I am giving a big dinner tonight for you and Scalice and Giunta," he said. "I'll have all the rest of the boys there, but you three will be guests of honor."

The banquet was held in a roadhouse south of Chicago. All the guests were searched and frisked as they came in.

Scalice, Anselmi, and Giunta ate heartily and drank well. Perhaps they knew what was to happen. If they didn't they were fools.

Capone got up at last and drank a toast to them, and made them stand in the middle of the floor. Then two men who had proved their loyalty to the king drew guns and told the guests of honor to line up against the wall.

"Here are three fine traitors," Capone said. He revealed their treachery. He reviled them in bitter words. Then he advanced slowly toward them, holding a baseball bat in his hands. He clubbed each one to death, and his men filled their bodies full of bullet holes.

"That's how we punish traitors," said Capone. "Throw them in some ditch in Indiana."

Capone may still have $60,000,000, but his life is one great nightmare of fear—the fear of being killed.

Do you call that courage?

The most cowardly rats in the world are men who live by the gun, men like Capone, Diamond and Schultz.

Capone fled from Brooklyn to Chicago years ago, to escape arrest. He lay low for a long time in the Chicago underworld. He was known as Al Brown. Johnny Torrio, who had known him in New York, taught him the art of murder. "Big Jim" Colosimo, the boss of the underworld, used him as a messenger boy, cursed and kicked him.

Big Jim put away his wife and took unto himself a beautiful young songstress, Dale Winter.

Big Jim was told that a load of booze would be delivered to him one afternoon, and he was to pay for it with cash. He had the money on him when he was killed. The killer got it. Johnny Torrio took over Colosimo's kingdom, and added to it joints all around Chicago.

Johnny Torrio and Al Capone had Dion O'Banion killed. Two men shook hands with him in his flower shop across from the Holy Name Cathedral; and while they held his hands, a third man pumped him full of lead.

George "Bugs" Moran, one of O'Banion's most fanatic friends, shot Torrio in the neck, and sent him screaming to a hospital. He was never any good to the racket after that. And Capone was king in his place.

One of the first things Capone did was to guard his person well. He brought in bandits who had fled the wrath of Mussolini. Mafiosi from Sicily, Camorristas from Neapolitan streets and alleys.

But, though they guarded him well, he was still afraid. He was afraid of Bugs Moran. He was afraid of the crazy Earl Hymie Weiss, of "Polack" Joe Saltis, of the red-faced McErlane. He was afraid of the O'Donnells.

He had good reason to fear Hymie Weiss, for that desperado had declared war on Capone "and all them grease balls," and he had bought a lot of machine guns. Weiss was the first of the bootleggers to use that weapon.

Every so often he went looking for Capone—but Capone had made himself hard to find. Hymie had neither guile nor imagination. He took a long time to make up his mind. But once he had made his plan—and it was usually the craziest he could think of—he executed it at once.

Capone had grown up to learn about forks and caviar and opera. Society women raved about the wistfulness of his voice. Weiss had remained a roughneck.

Capone kept himself in Cicero or in Florida. Weiss ruled the Chicago Loop, and made his headquarters over Dion O'Banion's flower shop across from the cathedral.

Capone tendered the olive branch to his enemies. They talked peace terms in a downtown restaurant. Weiss got very drunk—but when he sobered he doubted that Capone wanted peace, and determined to give him hell.

He learned that the Genna brothers, allies of Capone, were having him followed—him and all the other enemies of Capone. Chicago was full of Genna's, it seemed to Weiss. They were alky cookers. They employed hundreds of their countrymen to cook alky and sold it to Capone. They were rich—and getting powerful. Several high public officials attended one of their banquets.

Weiss put a police gong on one of his autos and went out hunting Gennas. He got Angelo first. And later he bagged Anthony. A cop got Mike—wounded him fatally after he and Anselmi and Scalice had killed two detectives. Jim Genna wasn't tricked by the sound of the gong into thinking Weiss was only a cop. He beat it back to Sicily. The other Gennas stayed in their homes until they could safely sneak to some spot far from Chicago.

There were more than 15,000 alky-cooking places in Chicago at the time. The Gennas owned all those on the North Side. They made millions of dollars selling this stuff —the basis of gin and whiskies. They used to "kick in" about $6,000 or $7,000 a month to be "let alone."

"They only kill each other." The Gennas had bagged their fill—especially when they were collecting for the defense fund for their friends and found men unreasonable enough to refuse them money.

Angelo, who was the head of the Unione Siciliano— ostensibly a patriotic American-Italian society, but actually a union of alky cookers, bootleggers, and killers—had slain many men before he came to power. Weiss got him shortly after he married, killed him when he was rich and happy and respected and feared.

Weiss was one of the first to organize murder on wheels —steal a car, fill it full of trigger men, and go cruising around until an enemy was sighted, then "give him the bang" and tear through the streets to safety.

He got Angelo that way. Angelo was in his own powerful new car. Weiss' machine came up from behind. The guns roared. Angelo stepped on the gas and the car tore through Chicago's streets like a scared rabbit. Weiss' car followed like a greyhound. Angelo tried to turn a corner quickly. His car skidded into a lamp-post—and the machine guns laughed as he screamed for mercy.

Weiss had to use treachery on Anthony. Anthony wouldn't go out of his house for anyone save his very good friend Antonio Spano—whom the Gennas had imported from their native town, Marsala, Sicily. Spano was known as "the Cavalier."

Weiss found the Cavalier and held a gun to his head, and bade him telephone Anthony and put him on the spot.

"Talk all the spiggoty you want," he advised the Cavalier. "The guy with me is a wop. Talk wop to him, Luigi. Luigi will understand everything you say."

Anthony Genna met Antonio Spano on the corner Weiss had designated. He greeted him effusively. Spano held his hands tightly, as a friend should. And Weiss fired.

A Genna died as O'Banion had died.

For the only time in his life Hymie Weiss had carried out a murder touched with a little imagination. It couldn't have been his own idea.

Anthony was shot in the back. He lived just long enough to breathe the name of his betrayer, the Cavalier.

Hymie was satisfied for a time. He would get Capone, but he'd have to wait. Meantime he had to help his fellow Pole, Joe Saltis. Saltis and Lefty Koncil were on trial for the murder of "Mitters" Foley.

Hymie attended every session of the trial. He put everything he had into the task of saving Joe—and so forgot to be careful.

He had no idea that six Sicilian machine gunners were waiting patiently for him to walk before their guns. They had spent days waiting. There was a machine-gun nest across from the cathedral—with three men working in eight-hour shifts. There was another nest on the corner.

Those six gunners must have heard the ringing of vesper bells, the resonant sound of the organ, the voices of the choir, the chorus of the pious repeating the words of litanies. Perhaps they even joined in the chant at times, since there was nothing better to do.

Weiss left court with his bodyguard, Pat Murray, and picked up Attorney W. W. O'Brien and his investigator, Ben Jacobs. Sam Peller drove the car. They parked the machine at the corner of the cathedral shortly after three P.M.; and the gun in the nest across the street immediately came to life. Weiss and Murray dropped dead. The other three were wounded. More than fifty slugs are still in the corner stone of the church.

What did it profit Earl Hymie Weiss to be a bootleg king with power of life and death? There was a certain glamour about him because of his loyalty to the memory of his friend O'Banion. But was it brave to kill Angelo Genna when he was helpless? Was it brave to shoot Anthony Genna in the back while a traitor held his hands? Was it brave to take a small army of armored cars into Cicero and shoot up Capone's hotel? He had glamour, but he was a coward and a fool.

Incidentally, he wounded a woman during that silly one-sided battle in Cicero. He wouldn't have cared if he had killed her and a dozen others. She was in the path of his machine-gun bullets. It was just too bad. That was all. She had no business walking the street when a gangster king was out for a bit of murder.

They only kill each other—and any innocent man or woman or child who gets in their way.

Baby Face

a short short story
by David McLaughlin

SMOKY HAD PICKED her up at a certain corner out on Wellmington Avenue. Almost every evening for the past few months that he had taken the Wellington Avenue way down to his "office" he had noticed her standing there on the same corner. She evidently worked nights somewhere and was waiting for a bus.

She didn't look as though she'd turn a fella down if he offered her a ride—or anything else. If she had stood on any other corner he'd have picked her up long ago. But Smoky was superstitious about that particular corner. The Vine Street bank stood there. And it had been in the Vine Street bank, a little over eight months ago, that he had

killed Hep Washburn—and made his get-away with the haul that they had intended to split fifty-fifty. Got away clean, too.

But, what the hell! Why be superstitious? He could feel that last shot of whisky he had taken on just before leaving his room coursing warmly through the insides of him. He'd pick her up. You could see she wanted to be picked up.

Wheeling his roadster in to the curb, Smoky slowed down to a crawl and threw the door open carelessly. "Ride downtown, sister?"

"Thanks." Without a second's hesitation the girl stepped into the car and dropped down in the seat beside him.

138

Jees, but she was pretty. Smoky slid the gears smoothly into second, into third. He liked the way her blonde hair escaped from under the narrow brim of that little black felt hat. He liked her eyes. On closer inspection there was something fresh and unsullied about her, something sort of innocent. Better drop her as soon as possible. She was just a good kid, a baby face. He tried to keep his eyes away from her.

But, cripes, that was just a trick of hers. She was old enough to know what she was doing. Must be twenty-three or four, anyway. Maybe older.

She opened the large purse she had carried hugged up under one arm, and drew out a package of cigarettes and a lighter. "Have one?" She held out the package to him. He refused. He had never used tobacco.

The girl lighted her cigarette and slid down in the seat, her head close to Smoky's shoulder. Not so slow, he thought. That kid stuff must be a pose.

" 'Sa a nice night," she offered.

"Yeah," Smoky drawled.

"Say!" said the girl. "Ain't I seen you before?"

"Not that I know of," returned Smoky. "And I usually remember a pretty face."

"Is that the best you can say for it?"

They laughed. Smoky turned the car deftly into the traffic on Roosevelt Boulevard. He could feel the girl looking him over.

A few blocks further along, she exclaimed: "Why, I do know you! You're Smoky Sutter."

"That's me, sister." Smoky wondered just how this girl happened to know him. Was she a sister or sweetheart of one of the gang? He could not seem to remember. His head felt foggy. He stepped down on the accelerator. The wind, maybe, would clear his brain.

The girl moved nearer to him and let her head rest on his shoulder. "I was at Bat Carrmody's party last winter. The fourteenth of December, it was. Remember?"

So she was the woman of one of the gang. He couldn't place her, but she must be okay. Anyone who went to Bat's parties was okay.

But the fourteenth of December! That was the night Hep and him had pulled the Vine Street bank job and he had come away and left Hep lying inside the bank on the floor. That was all the party he'd had on the night of December fourteenth.

"It couldn't of been that night, sister."

"Sure, that was the night."

"But I was pullin' a job that night," Smoky insisted.

"Say, what are you tryin' to pull now?" the girl demanded. "You know you was at Bat's that night. You took me home. Don't you remember? It was snowin', and you said you hated to go back to your room because it was so lonesome there. And I said you didn't need to go. There was no one in the flat but me. You could . . ."

"You're crazy," said Smoky. He wished he hadn't taken that last drink so his mind would have been clear. This jane was tryin' to pin somethin' onto him.

"Aw, come off it," sneered the girl.

"I tell you I was pullin' a job," Smoky stuttered. "Me and a pal of mine, Hep Washburn."

"Hep Washburn's been dead a long time," she scoffed.

"That was the night," said Smoky.

They were in the downtown traffic now. The girl smiled up at him admiringly. "Say, big shot, you must be the guy that bumped Hep off, then?"

Who in hell was this dame, anyway? Smoky glanced quickly down at her. His own eyes flickered away before her straight gaze.

"Where did you say you wanted to get out?" he asked.

"I don't intend to get out."

"You what?" Smoky faltered.

"I don't intend to get out."

What was this, a joke? Smoky pulled the roadster to a stop at the flash of a red traffic signal.

"I'm Hep Washburn's wife."

As the girl uttered the words, Smoky was aware of two sharp reports and a searing pain in his chest. Hep Washburn's wife had plugged him. She was sitting there now, calmly watching him die. Funny place to die. Anyway, he supposed this was dying.

The traffic signal showed green. Cars began to flow past. The drivers of the autos blocked behind Smoky's roadster began to honk their horns and cuss. A cop was striding swiftly forward. So this was Hep Washburn's wife. This baby face. Smoky could no longer see her sitting there with the pistol in her hands. But he knew she was there. He felt sorry for her. . . .

Liberty's
Capital Punishment
Essay Contest

Is Won by the Daughter of a Murderer
The Most Amazing Essay Which Won the $1,000 Prize
In announcing the winner of the $1,000 Essay Contest, based upon the outcome of the trial of Leopold and Loeb, Liberty publishes below the most astonishing document which has ever come to the Editor's attention.

The essay is an argument in favor of the infliction of the death penalty, written by a woman whose mother was murdered by her (the writer's) father.

The statements set forth in the essay have been verified. Both the woman and her father are living in New England.

The essay follows. Particulars concerning the contest, and Liberty's investigation of the prize winner's story, are printed below.

ESSAYS, CARE OF Liberty, P. O. Box 1123, Chicago, Ill.

In answer to "Should Capital Punishment" be abolished or not, I say no.

The reason I say no is because I come from a state where there is know capital punishment, and I am the daughter (to my sorrow) of a man that should have gotten either the chair or the noose.

Twenty-five years ago, my mother, then only twenty-two years of age, was murdered by my father.

He was sentenced to life imprisonment. After being in prison for twenty-four years he was pardoned.

This all happened in the State of Rhode Island, where there is know capital punishment.

When he was released my father-in-law insisted that I take him into my home. Hating my father as I do I did not want to, but to please the old man, I said I would try him out and see how he behaved.

Being in prison that length of time did him know good whatever.

He thinks nothing of going back there. He talks of prison as another would of a palace. The first two years of his sentence were the hardest; after that it was nothing.

When he first came to my house he couldn't understand why we don't run gambling houses or go into the bootlegging game. First thing he did was get hold of some moonshine and go from house to house and try to sell it; all he talks about is sticking up, meaning a hold-up. One day he met a crony of his that was in prison with him for a hold-up. He wanted this man to rob his (my father's) cousin's place of business, telling him that he would give him the plan of the office and they would divide fifty-fifty. He came into the house and told us this, telling us that the man refused to do it as he got married and was through with that life forever: then he said to us why do you suppose I wanted to get out. If I could get my cousin in R. I. State or some other state I would finish him up as he did something to me when I was younger and I would like to have my revenge but in this state you get the chair and I don't care for that.

When I said something to him about it he struck me and I at once put him out of my house.

Wouldn't a man like that be better off had he been put out of the way at once? He is a menace to society. Nobody has anything to do with him.

His brother went to a distant state and had his name changed as soon as my father commit the murder. My brother and I don't notice him on the street when passing by.

The crime was know accident.

It was all planned out the same as the Loeb-Leopold case.

He did not hesitate leaving two small children aged two and three.

If there had been capital punishment in the State of R. I. he would not have commit this crime, as he loves his own life dearly.

He is well and strong to-day, thinking of what crooked thing to do next.

My poor young mother went to her early grave, leaving her motherless children in the care of a poor old grandmother.

Keep up the capital punishment and save young lives as lots of criminals have a fear of it.

Every state should adopt capital punishment and not do away with it.

My story can be proved. In case this story should be printed please just use initials or sign Jean La Belle.

Is Franklin D. Roosevelt Physically Fit To Be President?

by Earle Looker

A Man to Man Answer to a Nation-Wide Challenge

IT IS AN amazing possibility that the next President of the United States may be a cripple. Franklin D. Roosevelt, Governor of the State of New York, was crippled by infantile paralysis in the epidemic of 1921 and still walks with the help of a crutch and a walking stick. Yet by all the political signs he will emerge as the Democratic nominee.

If there were only a small possibility of Roosevelt securing the nomination at the Democratic National Convention, it would seem more decent not to let the subject get into print; but at the present moment he is the four-to-one preference of the Democratic politicians who will select their candidate, and a two-to-one preference among Democratic business and professional people so far polled.

An average of one thousand editorials or editorial comments each week, published in newspapers for or against him throughout the country, testifies to the actuality of the national interest.

The political elimination of other able men who have been suggested for the nomination—apparently because of special ability in their own fields of endeavor—and the poor caliber of the "also running" have contributed to the strengthening of the Roosevelt boom. His amazing political luck, making him seem "Franklin the Fortunate" to the practical politicians who will select the candidate, has increased the impression—despite the virulence of the attacks being prepared against him through assaults on Tammany, the regular Democratic organization of New York City—that he will undoubtedly emerge as the Democratic nominee for President.

A sound mind in a sound body has more and more come to be a requirement for the Presidency. This is outside the legal requirements, but two recent breakdowns in office, those of Woodrow Wilson and Warren G. Harding—to mention merely the latest Democratic and Republican Presidents who were unable to stand the burdens and responsibilities of their office—very pertinently raise the question whether or not Franklin Roosevelt is fit to be President.

Rumors from places widespread upon the map of the United States have been for some time questioning his physical fitness.

Perhaps it was because the possibility of his nomination turned into a probability that in the last week of April these undercover whispers rose up in the first outspoken public raising of the question. At a meeting of the National Women's Democratic Law Enforcement League a speaker was nationally reported to have said, "This candidate, while mentally qualified for the Presidency, *is utterly unfit physically. . . .*" The statement, whether true or false, was not contradicted by Franklin Roosevelt.

But long before this, by a letter addressed directly and personally to the governor, I had challenged him with regard to his physical condition as follows:

MY DEAR GOVERNOR:

The proposal I am about to make may at first seem more like a challenge; but either as a proposal or a challenge it will have to be met if, as seems inevitable, your name is mentioned as the nominee of the Democratic Party for President of the United States.

I refer to the propaganda that will be set in motion to convince the voters that even though you have recovered from your attack of infantile paralysis, the strain of the Presidency will be such as seriously to raise the question as to whether or not you are physically fit to be President.

As a Republican and, as you know, an ardent admirer of the aggressively strenuous tradition of the Roosevelt name, I am writing to ask that you make a frank avowal as to whether or not, in the event of your nomination you are sufficiently recovered to assure your supporters that you could stand the strain of the Presidency.

Believe me, my dear Governor, with great respect,

Most sincerely,

EARLE LOOKER.

I awaited his answer, if any, with considerable interest. It came.

February 28, 1931.

MY DEAR MR. LOOKER:

This is to acknowledge your letter of February twenty-third.

Of course no statement from me as to my physical fitness should really be acceptable to you. Your question, however, is very distinctly a personal challenge to me, no matter what my present or future position as a public servant may be—even in the humblest of positions. Furthermore, not being in any sense a candidate for any other public office, it is equally a challenge to any business or professional work which I may assume on leaving Albany.

Being assured of your integrity, I am therefore prepared to permit you to make an investigation of my physical fitness, to give you every facility for thoroughly making it, and authority for you to publish its results without censorship from me.

Very sincerely yours,

FRANKLIN D. ROOSEVELT.

The challenge had been caught and thrown back to me within four days, despite the fact that my letter to him had been almost brutal in its tone. The tenor of his reply was startling; it was so apparently without reserve.

I lost no time in arranging for my first interview with Franklin Roosevelt at the Executive Mansion in Albany.

Arriving there, I was ushered into a room to the left of the entrance, furnished with good taste and containing ample evidences of the interests of the owner. These were mostly nautical. Upon the walls there were old prints exemplifying the traditions of the American navy.

Perhaps it was the nautical spirit of the room which for a moment caused me mentally to compare the motionless governor with a ship's figurehead, magnificently dimensioned from the waist up. Most unexpected was his width of shoulder and Dempsey-like development of chest, with muscled athlete's wrists and great vigorous hands gripping the arms of his chair. He seemed larger all around than the usually accepted scale of life size. He carried a head in proportion. His forehead was broad and high, his eyes wide-spaced and blue, his nose straight, and his lips firm. This face was undeniably fine. I saw now that the tan upon it had contributed to my first impression of a resemblance to a figurehead, for the texture of his skin suggested that it had been long exposed to the glare of the sun and the stinging of salt spray.

Franklin Roosevelt went directly to the point. Yes, he was unreservedly willing that this proposed physical investigation be made. And he was fully aware we should need medical counsel. Further, he himself suggested an all-important question.

"Do you realize," he said, "that this is infantile paralysis, and, if you are really going to make as thorough an investigation as is called for—the kind of investigation I am now challenging you to make—that while I only gave you permission to look into my physical condition, such paralysis is generally understood either to affect the brain, or to be caused by a brain condition?"

"But, governor," I protested, "I am not questioning your mental fitness as a result of infantile paralysis, because I understand that the disease is not connected with the brain.

"You're quite right," he answered, "but this fact is not generally understood, and in fairness to myself as well as to all the others who have been touched by it, you must not only make this clear but use my own case as proof."

I agreed, seeing that Roosevelt himself had broadened the scope of my investigation.

"Governor," I asked him, "do you want to be President of the United States?"

"Do I understand," he countered, "that as a Republican you are making a political thrust, with the thought that any admissions I might make will be used against me and against my party?"

"It would be well," I said, "for you to consider the question in just that spirit."

The governor threw his head back and laughed.

"It is necessary for me," he said with great seriousness, "just as it is for the several others who are being suggested for the Democratic nomination, to answer that question not only as if you were a microphone broadcasting to a very considerable number of people listening, but also to give you and them the absolute truth. So I say this: Personally, from my years in Washington and as Assistant Secretary of the Navy, I know a great deal about the responsibilities and the burdens of the Presidency; no man who understands them as I do could look forward with any intense personal desire to assuming those burdens and responsibilities.

"Ask some of the older men about the state Capitol here in Albany—men who have seen governors come and go—ask them if they'd personally like to have the job as governor. Every one of them could say decisively and with feeling, 'No!' Was I personally anxious to be governor? I was not! But I accepted that nomination in order to accept an opportunity for service. You must understand I have to use the old words, and that one particularly—'service'—because no other word exactly fits.

"I feel the same way about the Presidency. That's all there is to it. Anyone could have a great deal to say in amplification of that, but that's the complete net of it."

"Mr. Roosevelt," I said, "if you became the leading choice of the Democratic Convention and it was then a question of your personal decision, would you sacrifice your personal desires?"

Roosevelt's answer was so quick that he fairly snapped out the words: "The opportunity for service that the Presidency affords has not honestly been considered a personal sacrifice by anyone I have ever known or heard of who has had that opportunity, despite its tremendous difficulty and its great responsibility. You have as complete and as fair an answer as I can ever give anyone."

Momentarily the silence was tense. But at this instant Mrs. Roosevelt entered the room. Her interruption, she explained, was caused by an official visitor it was necessary for the governor to see personally. I excused myself and went out into the rococo hall, where Mrs. Roosevelt joined me.

As the daughter of Elliott Roosevelt, T. R.'s brother, Mrs. Franklin Roosevelt possesses the Roosevelt brow and nose, the quick smile and the occasional burst of real Rooseveltian laughter. She is politically minded, a family trait.

This tall, competent lady was now regarding me seriously. Really, she was silently questioning me as to my interview with her husband. Obviously, it was also her business.

"Mrs. Roosevelt," I said, "you know that my letter to the governor was dictated by the fact that there are a great many people concerned about the possibility of his becoming President because of the toll the office has taken among men who seemed fit when they were elected and then were broken down by the burden. The fact that Governor Roosevelt is allowing the most thorough examination to be made must indicate that he has some basis for believing that he can stand the strain."

Mrs. Roosevelt neither smiled nor frowned. As if repeating for the thousandth time a conclusion to which she had come after long and earnest thought, she said: "If the paralysis couldn't kill him, the Presidency won't."

This was the question which was now to be answered in so far as was humanly possible.

If Franklin Roosevelt was human, it would be natural for him to be on his guard with me as one of the opposition. To offset what he might easily have believed were my preconceptions regarding him it would be natural for him to act his best part before me. The risk, therefore, of getting a false impression of him from regular interviews was too dangerous.

The official visitor had gone. Returning to the governor, I said to him, "Shall I be free to come and to go wherever you happen to be for the next many months—everywhere I may judge to be helpful to a full investigation?"

"Suits me!" the governor said without hesitation.

Almost immediately that evening I had a most unusual opportunity to observe him. In the meantime as we had been talking we had been interrupted at least five times by telephone calls for the governor. Our talk had therefore been catch as catch can.

As he pushed the telephone aside for the last time, I said, "Well, I suppose your business is ended for the day?"

He grinned. "I am going to rest now," he said, "for about two hours, if I can get it, and then more work."

"It is about quarter past eight now," I said. "You don't mean to tell me that you'll rest until quarter past or half past ten, and then work again?"

"I'll work," he said, "until I have finished what there is for me to do. That will probably be about one o'clock tomorrow morning. I'm going to rest now because I should have a clear mind about the work I'm doing tonight. Pardons and commutations won't wait. They affect the lives of the many people involved more closely than do many other decisions of a governor. The decisions for and against must be made as immediately as possible, because it takes a long time for the investigation of each case prepared for my action and, after I take it, time elapses before my decision can be put into effect.

"In the meantime, no matter what the rights or wrongs of the case, there is suffering—as, for example, on the part of women and children never mentioned in the records of the case, persons who may be quite innocently involved—"

"No one," I said, "would quarrel with your working on such decisions tonight."

"If you knew the character of these cases," he said, "which are usually unknown outside the Parole Board, you would rest, if you could get the chance, before tackling them, but you certainly wouldn't delay them. I have a case tonight—But, first we're all going up to the third floor to see a movie. I believe it's *Outward Bound* tonight."

On the third floor of the Executive Mansion is a hall perhaps thirty feet square, which has been arranged as a private motion-picture theater.

As we settled in our seats and the lights were switched off, someone in the darkness close to the governor asked him a question about a state appointment. More sharply than I had yet heard him speak, he said, "Yes, I know exactly what I'm going to do about that. But this is the evening before, isn't it? I'm not considering that now, or anything else but *Outward Bound*—whatever that is."

Evidently he was trying to clear his mind of all business for these two hours before him. As I watched him in the gray light reflected back from the screen, his face relaxed and seemed to soften. That his mind entered wholly into the spirit of the play was obvious.

At the end of the film, as the lights were switched on, there was a long pause before the illusion was entirely broken by enthusiastic comments on the picture.

"Now I must get to those pardons," the governor said in a businesslike voice. "But as we were interrupted so many times by the telephone, should I not give you ten more minutes tonight?"

Since it was the first and most important question, I returned to his physical condition. "Governor," I said, "since you are willing to have a thorough examination and have, yourself, widened its scope, may I suggest that I go to the director of the New York Academy of Medicine and request him to form an experts' committee to act as my counsel? Let him suggest a medical man, an orthopedist, and a neurologist. This will give us a report on your general health, the bone condition, and the brain condition. Certainly nothing could be fairer to you and nothing could be more authoritative for the public. The manner in which these specialists will be chosen will absolutely insure an unprejudiced report and one that will be accepted by everyone in and out of the medical profession."

"I entirely agree," the governor said. "You may arrange just that; and since I am the subject—or the victim—of the examination I will write a letter giving the specific authority for those specialists to do their worst."

It seemed only fair before the actual examination to get Franklin Roosevelt's own idea of his physical fitness to perform executive functions.

With thousands of my fellow countrymen, I knew that bathing at Warm Springs, Georgia, where the governor spends an annual vacation, had worked something of a miracle for him in restoring his legs to some use. But now I learned that it was *swimming* in the blood-warm waters of these Georgia springs and not their medicinal properties that was really responsible for his remarkable improvement.

"I go in three times a day," he said, "and I stay in about two hours each time. Six hours daily out of twenty-four given up to swimming, for a period of several weeks, is giving me back the use of my legs."

"You were always a fine swimmer, I have heard," I said, "and it must have pleased you immensely to find your favorite form of exercise coming to your aid in your helpless condition."

"Yes," he replied. "At first I doubted whether I'd be able to swim at all. But the thing worked out well. You see, the buoyancy of the water removed the weight of my body from my legs. In the beginning I swam with my arms almost entirely, but now I can use my legs as well. Recent scientific investigation has proven that exercise taken while swimming in tepid water will restore nerve force to paralyzed limbs. Surely I am an example of it."

"I notice you are not wearing your leg braces now," I remarked.

"Oh, the braces," he replied. "I forget them when I take them off. I forget them most of the time anyway. I wear them all day at the office."

"They give you the opportunity to move about your office as you wish, I suppose?"

"I don't move about my office," he answered. "But I can and do move about the state. I don't see any particular advantage in moving about my office, do you? How many times do you wander about your own office, or writing room, when you are supposed to be working?"

"Not often," I answered.

"Don't you ever get the fidgets?" the governor asked.

"Yes, of course," I replied. "I get up and stretch, look out the windows into the garden—"

"Well," laughed Franklin Roosevelt, "I don't move from my desk all the time I am in my office. Do you remember the tale that Dumas had to be locked up in his workroom in order to make him finish his play, *Bonaparte*? And wasn't there some other French writer who had his valet chain and padlock his ankle to his writing table at a certain hour each morning, so that he could not get away and was forced to work, whether he wished or not?"

I had to admit that I had heard these legends.

"Isn't it better," the governor asked, "if you have a big job to do, to be held to that job and not be able to waste time indulging in fidgets? I'll say this: Staying at my desk does not make my work any more difficult, and it certainly does not waste time."

Franklin Roosevelt saw advantages to his work in his physical disability. Certainly it was a philosophic way for him to look at it, and the "out" from his point of view, but judgment of the evidence must be reserved for future opportunity to observe him independently. The functions of governor of a great state are not to be compared exactly to those of an ordinary administrative or business executive. He must not be a bureaucrat, drawing information to himself only in the form of complicated and perhaps misleading reports; he must be able to see some of the action himself and look upon the evidence, in some cases, at first hand; he must be able to form his own judgment independently of official and political influence.

No, the question of the effect of his immobility upon his capacity was not at all proved.

Franklin Roosevelt's personal charm, of which I had heard so often as a political asset, was undeniable. He was a gentleman in the sense in which we use the term in democratic America. He had stood for the questions I had to ask with an evenness of temper that showed a well disciplined mind.

Nevertheless, the experts' examination would have to be cold and dispassionate; my personal observation would have to be continued under every possible condition, favorable as well as unfavorable to Franklin Roosevelt.

This was the net of my plan of investigation, but by no means a fair outline of it. An independent lay estimate was required of the possible strains to which Franklin Roosevelt might be subjected, together with comment upon his probable ability to withstand them as indicated along lines suggested by details of the physicians' reports.

These details were to be disclosed to me, but not to Franklin Roosevelt. Observation and report were essential upon these personal traits of character which could not but be connected with Franklin Roosevelt's physical condition, whatever that was found to be.

On April 29, 1931, the three specialists selected for me by Dr. Linsly R. Williams, director of the New York Academy of Medicine, went to the governor's town house in New York City to examine him. I was also in the house, but of course I did not witness the actual examination.

The door of the governor's room was closed for an hour and a half while the medical committee put him through his physical and mental paces. Waiting, I wondered again and again what would be the final verdict. And I realized that a good many millions of my countrymen were entitled to hear it, too.

I asked for the truth the moment I entered the governor's room, just after the conclusion of the examination. The specialists refused quite bluntly to give me their answer, on the grounds that while each had made his examination, none of them was prepared to report without due consideration and time to check up on details. Moreover, they had not consulted.

Franklin Roosevelt grinned at me. The specialists smiled. The governor was as ignorant of the result as I was. The three specialists might already have formed their separate opinions—but they would not reveal them yet, even to each other, until each was absolutely sure.

But my own lay decision had been reached after some weeks of investigation and observation. I had interviewed forty-three disinterested persons in Albany and in New York who had observed the governor; the total of their report was that he seemed to be more physically able now

than he had been four years before. Personally, I had watched him working and resting. I had noted the alertness of his movements, the sparkle of his eyes, the vigor of his gestures. I had seen his strength under the strain of long working periods. In so far as I had observed him, I had come to the conclusion that he seemed able to take more punishment than many men ten years younger. Merely his legs were not much good to him. But my own conclusion was only a generalization. I did not possess scientific facts.

"When will I know?" I asked the doctors that day.

"You'll hear," I was told, "when the facts have all been checked—"

"And then checked again," was added.

The doctors looked at their watches and departed. I bowed to the governor and followed. I had nothing!

In the late afternoon of that same day, before I returned to Northampton, a telegram from New York was delivered at my home. It read as follows:

EARLE LOOKER 281 ELM STREET NORTHAMPTON MASS
WE HAVE TODAY CAREFULLY EXAMINED GOVERNOR ROOSEVELT WE BELIEVE THAT HIS HEALTH AND POWERS OF ENDURANCE ARE SUCH AS TO ALLOW HIM TO MEET ANY DEMAND OF PRIVATE AND PUBLIC LIFE
SAMUAL W LAMBERT MD RUSSELL A HIBBS MD FOSTER KENNEDY MD

So, from the specialists' examination, as well as from my own observation, I am able to say unhesitatingly that every rumor of Franklin Roosevelt's physical incapacity can be unqualifiedly defined as false.

In fairness, then, to Franklin Roosevelt, let it be said that, whether his traits of character indicate his fitness or his unfitness for the Presidency, *he is physically fit*.

Stag Lines and Bread Lines

by Cornelius Vanderbilt, Jr.

Why Spend Millions to Bring Out This Season's Debutantes?
Men Will Be Starving This Winter While the Daughters of the
Still-Rich are "Introduced" at a Total Cost of $100,000,000.

GIMME A NICKEL for a cup of coffee, lady?"
The familiar password on the thoroughfares of every metropolis today. He is a shabby, threadbare, gaunt individual with a week's growth of beard.

Her limousine has drawn up behind a line of other ponderous chauffeur-driven cars. She is small and dark and petite, and clothed in shiny, shimmery Parisian black.

She presses the buzzer with her elbow, and James signals one of a squad of burly dicks mingled in the crowd about the exclusive entrance.

A heavy hand is laid upon his shoulder.

"Scram," says The Law, "before I run you in."

Her door is opened. She steps daintily upon a red carpet under an upholstered marquee, shudders ever so perceptibly as the assembled crowd of burly, ill-kept individuals mutter something, and darts within the portals.

Upstairs in the big house all is gayety. Tall candelabra dripping gilded wax into tiny glass frames. Louis Quatorze paneling and antiques. Ladies in pale pastels with trailing gowns, and gentlemen in their white-bosomed fronts and long tails, boutonnière-bedecked in radiant dignity.

The receiving line is never-ending.

It is all a stiff, dull, formal custom, she well comprehends, handed down from Elizabethan days, endured by modernity chiefly on account of its pageantry. In a flowered niche at the end of the drawing room she sees her hosts, and just beyond them Marie-Louise, saintlike in crinkly white chiffon. In her arms the child carries a bouquet of trailing jasmine and pink rosebuds.

The effect is quite charming. Everything is perforce *de rigueur;* and although Mr. and Mrs. Post D. Pression assure her in their sincerest manner that they cannot give Marie-Louise the kind of a début she ought to have—because times are so hard, my dear—she nevertheless understands that Marie-Louise will never find herself in want!

Somewhere beyond, a stringed orchestra is playing.

A crooner almost inaudibly purrs pianissimo.

Couples entwined about each other's very beings sway and sag and bend and slouch and curve and sometimes stagger. For just a few steps farther on are carafes and goblets, punch bowls and silver sandwich dishes, and decanters, and the occasional pop of pre-1919 Pol Roget!

It is in celebration of Marie-Louise's coming out that this quiet, tasteful little affair is being thrown! For Marie-Louise is Post D. Pression's 1933 débutante daughter; and, be things as they may, regardless, she must be properly launched.

Times have been terrible for all her family's friends. The market has been falling ever since November ninth—but the slant on daddy's study chart started down when she was a mere youngster of fifteen. That was away back in October, 1929. The graph has mounted but twice since then, each time to come tumbling down again.

You couldn't call Marie-Louise a snob, exactly; yet it did do that pitter-pattery little heart of hers good when daddy promised her she'd be "introduced" properly, regardless. And if daddy had found it necessary to topple unceremoniously out of Al Smith's Empire State Building the day preceding, no doubt Marie-Louise and her fond mother would have blamed some hidden office romance for daddy's demise.

Maybe I exaggerate; only, there are people like that, a lot of them, still left in Manhattan—and elsewhere.

Their mad egotism has not been quenched. Maybe they'll have to skimp a bit this winter, but Marie-Louise is going to be launched, regardless.

"The government can care for the unemployed; that's why they tax us so," is their philosophy when they expend $30,000 this winter for Marie-Louise's début, and tell the mayor's committee they cannot afford to give and give and keep on giving.

Strange, the contrasts of life.

Two layers of brick, mortar, steel, and cement separate 1,150,000 men and women out of work in New York City alone from practically the same sort of finery as existed—

only on a little less expansive a scale—three brief years ago, when, according to the Welfare Council, there were only about 100,000 people out of work.

Twenty thousand bluecoats keep order; keep nearly a million and a quarter bread-liners from all of the many Marie-Louises who are today making their bows to society in practically the same mode as they have been doing since time immemorial, and from their parents.

True, society this year is not splurging, cannot, as it did in the late 1920s. Incomes have dwindled to a bare tenth of what they used to be. Hordes of people are living on hoarded shekels, commonly known as principal. But everything is relative in life. If the Post D. Pressions feel it necessary to expend $30,000 for Marie-Louise's début, that is their affair, they argue. There was a day, not a third of a decade ago, when three times that amount would have been considered trivial in the set in which they travel.

Out on the streets long lines of people form twice a day to be handed a bowl of gruel, a cup of lukewarm coffee, a slice of bread, and sometimes a piece of meat.

Six million dollars a month is going to be needed this winter to take care of New York's unemployed. That is the city's estimate of the times.

The Uptown Club, a well known welfare organization, has estimated that a family of five, consisting of two adults and three children, can be cared for for eight dollars and eighty-eight cents a week, and fed twice a day. Yet there are easily 300 families who have daughters of débutante age scheduled to make their curtsy this winter, and who will spend in the neighborhood of $9,000,000 for this privilege in the six weeks it takes to launch them properly before the social arbiters of the land.

Nine million dollars would feed the 1,150,000 New York unemployed for six weeks.

Out in Chicago a few weeks ago I saw a crowd of perhaps fifty standing in the middle of a block. I asked one of them what they were waiting for. The answer appeared as the back door of a well known exclusive club opened and two colored servants came forth lifting a huge garbage pail between them.

Like vultures, the men and women about me fought to get into that can. They were not poor-looking. Many of them wore overcoats and slightly shabby furs. Some of the men even had white collars and appeared shaven. I looked at their shoes, and there, and there only, could one tell the desperateness of their situations. All day long they trudged the streets answering ads and looking for jobs.

They *wanted* to work. They were ashamed to have to stand in line and beg food. A realization that once upon a time, when God was in His heaven and all was right with the world, clubs had served the better cuts, the rarer dishes, had brought them of one accord to the back doors of the places some of them may have once belonged to.

I took eight of these individuals, picked at random from among those who *couldn't* get into the garbage can, down to a nearby restaurant of the chain variety and fed them. When they were through I managed to chat with a couple of them.

One young fellow, whose cheeks were a little sallow and who coughed a lot, told me he'd been working all of his life for twenty-five dollars a week. He was twenty-eight when he caught a bad cold. The past four years he got out in the parks and along the lake front as much as possible. Slowly health had ebbed. He read somewhere that he could go to Arizona for twenty-two dollars and fifty cents, day coach, and for an additional forty dollars a month he could be hospitalized until the cough disappeared. In his savings account he had $260, deposited over a period of four years. That would take him to Arizona and keep him at least five months, and by that time he might find work on a ranch, or something.

But his sweet little old mother passed away, and after he'd finished paying for her burial he had scarcely enough left even to get to Arizona. Six months later the factory he worked in closed without notice and owing two weeks'

back pay; and how he'd kept body and soul together the past two years he couldn't even begin to tell.

A little lady in the late forties said that if she could convince them she was ten years older, she might be admitted into an old ladies' home. She said she'd called upon her former employer in his magnificent Lake Shore Drive house some months back and asked his butler to ask him if he'd contribute fifteen dollars a month (less than fifty cents a day) toward her care in this home. Her only reply was to have the iron grille doors closed in her face and the corner cop warn her to "move on."

Yet that same evening, or so she told me, his eighteen-year-old daughter Hélène made her bow to North Shore society at a cotillion in the Winter Club in Lake Forest, Chicago's exclusive suburb. And the papers the following day (she produced a clipping to show me) raved at the magnificence of the affair.

This winter men and women and little children will be starving while the still-rich parade their offspring. Not a major city in the land escapes its débutante racket. Hardly a young woman out of a $3,000-a-year finishing school avoids being presented. The hokum, the feigned necessity become a matter of major importance wherever starvation and unemployment go hand in hand.

Remember, please, these eighteen-year-olds have grown up with the people to whom they are being presented.

Could anything be more farcical?

But Mr. and Mrs. Post D. Pression feel they have their position in society to uphold. True, they are much poorer this fall than they were three years ago. But they can skimp a bit and get by. Besides, it will have a better effect on their friends, who will believe the Post D. Pressions were more sagacious than they in their investments. Also —and this is a very popular theory this winter, I find—it will be loosening a bit of cash to the butcher, the baker, the candlestick maker. Indirectly, then, it will be helping the unemployed.

Certainly to rent one of the entertaining floors of the most fashionable new hotel at $5,000 for the evening will benefit the hotel holding company! The buffet supper for 500 at five dollars a plate—$2,500—will help the *chefs de cuisine!* You can't secure a first-class nine-piece orchestra for less than $1,000 for an evening—not in New York! And the crooner, if he is anyone well known at all, gets $1,000 more. Employees in livery, detectives and so forth run to an additional $500. That's $10,000 for the evening already!

Then, of course, there are the refreshments—Pol Roget 1919 sells in these prohibited days for about $300 a case. Five hundred thirsty débutantes and collegians, with a sprinkling of mammas and papas, will consume twenty cases—$6,000.

There should be ten cases of Scotch—$1,000; and two cases of fine old liqueurs—$500. And so the refreshment problem can all be settled for about $7,500—a mere pittance, you see.

Exotic flowers from the city's smartest florists will come to no less than $2,500 more.

Marie-Louise's launching will cost perhaps $20,000, then.

The ensuing six weeks would be a nightmare to any less well primed youngster. Teas will be given for her by well meaning relatives. Grandmother will, of course, be the first to entertain. Aunts and uncles, cousins and close friends will follow.

She must go to the opera at least twice a week. A part-time box in the Metropolitan's Golden Horseshoe will cost daddy $5,000 for the season. Opera dinner parties must be made up, young people invited, tables reserved at the best restaurants and night clubs for supper and dancing afterward. You can't go to any of the better-class New York night clubs with an opera party of seven for less than $150 an evening. Twice a week for nine weeks of the opera season brings this to $2,700.

Then there are the theater parties. Marie-Louise must see every new musical comedy and not less than five of the other Broadway productions during the season. She goes to the hockey matches, to the automobile, the motor-boat, the flower, the horse, and the dog shows. She is lucky to do it all for $2,300.

We haven't even spoken of her clothes. Marie-Louise is lucky if she can be properly attired for $5,000.

Funny thing, I thought in the beginning of this yarn that her début in 1933 would cost but $30,000; now, really, I don't see how it can be accomplished for less than $35,000.

In Baltimore, at the Junior Assembly this winter, there are perhaps 100 young women making their bow to the tune of $25,000 apiece. For in Baltimore, you see, you don't have to cope with the opera, theaters, night clubs, and exhibits in the six-week launching period.

The $2,500,000 thus spent by Baltimore's first families would take care of the million and a quarter undernourished babies in this country for the same six weeks!

Nowhere, with the conditions as they are, is there as much nonsense over the social presentation as in these United States, except perhaps in the custom of getting American girls presented at the Court of St. James.

The coming-out racket will cost American families this winter in the neighborhood of $100,000,000. That would house, feed, and clothe for one week the 11,400,000 persons who President Green of the American Federation of Labor said in October were unemployed and without visible means of nourishment. But if you mentioned it that way to any of the 3,000 families who will bring their daughters out, you would immediately be met with critical glances, arched eyebrows, and what not. Wealthy parents in society are always interested in anything that will help them; entirely uninterested in the affairs of the unfortunate out of work.

My
Prince
Mdivani
and I

by Mary McCormic,
as told to Basil Woon

*The Famous Opera Star's Rueful Revelations of
Her Supporting One of These Amazing Brothers
in the Style to Which He Was Accustomed*

PRINCE ALEXIS MDIVANI did Barbara Hutton a great favor when he married her. Any Mdivani will tell you that.

The vanity of the Mdivani family is fantastic. I am quite certain Princess Nina and Princess Roussada and Princes Serge and David really and sincerely think Barbara is the lucky one, not Alexis. Of course (I can see them shrug) the money will come in handy; but then, consider how fortunate Miss Hutton is to have secured a husband so exquisitely versed in the art of spending it!

Is there anything to be said for the Mdivani point of view? To be fair to them, there is—quite a lot. If anyone should know the astonishing Mdivani philosophy, I should, for it was served to me for breakfast, lunch, and dinner during the years of my married life with Serge.

Prince Serge, whom I married, is an all-around outdoor man, a champion tennis player and rider. He was at one time called the best-dressed man in Paris.

Prince David, whom Miss Mae Murray is suing for divorce, is a trick rider and jumper, a tennis player above the ordinary, and a champion long-distance swimmer.

Prince Alexis, husband of Barbara Hutton, is one of the world's great polo players and lives for practically nothing else—except, it is to be hoped, Miss Hutton.

Serge and David, of the boys, and Nina, of the girls, possess real talents in business. Both Serge and David are trained oil men and could become rich if only they were content to work toward that end. Unfortunately they are not willing to face the years of comparative drudgery that must come before wealth.

The rest of the family was in Paris when David married. Serge, reading the Paris edition of the Chicago *Tribune*, nearly choked. There on the front page was a cabled story from Hollywood to the effect that his brother David had married Mae Murray.

A hurried family council was held and it was decided that Serge should go at once to Hollywood to find what all this was about. Serge liked life in the movie colony so well that he stayed there and married another motion-picture actress himself.

The romance of Prince Alexis and Barbara Hutton was old news to me. For more than a year there was a stock phrase used by Serge and David whenever they yearned for something they couldn't afford. The phrase was: "Wait till Alex marries Barbara Hutton!"

Long before the world had any idea of the possibility of a romance between the two, Serge and David discussed it as you or I would talk of "our ship" coming home. When Alex married Barbara, all their troubles (presumably Mae and I were among them) would be settled.

The "romance" really was the result of almost perfect planning on the part of the Mdivani family. The system followed by Serge and David had, in the view of the family, proved a complete washout. Brother Alexis was not going to do anything so foolish as work, you may be sure. He was to be a superplayboy. Some one who wouldn't have to go to work in the morning. Some one who would make his wife his profession.

So Alexis was sent to Cambridge, to which English university it had been ascertained the sons of the richest American families were sent. Care was taken over his health and he was urged to practice hard the arts and sports most likely to appeal to an idle, wealthy girl.

What an apt student he was is sufficiently proven by his success since. Not yet thirty, he has already married two of the richest girls in the world.

In the first year at Cambridge Alexis was accepted in the fashionable, fast-spending set, which included several Americans, among them the two Van Alen boys. This Georgian prince was a great lad, the Van Alens agreed. He was a gentleman, a sportsman, a good fellow generally. They invited him to visit them in America.

This fitted in with Princess Roussada's plans also. She was having a certain success as a sculptress, but in America her title might get her commissions where her undoubted talent might not.

So the time came when Roussada and Alex steamed away toward the United States.

Their titles and the Van Alen introductions proved an open sesame to the exclusive society of New York, Palm Beach, Newport, and Bar Harbor. Princess Roussada received all the commissions she could execute, and Prince Alexis was received into the Van Alen family.

The daughter of the family, who was heiress to a fortune estimated at some ten million dollars (or so Alexis wrote Serge at the time), was a shy, rather silent but sweet girl named Louise. From what I was able to learn (Serge himself was not kept fully informed), Louise adored the sporting prince from the very first. He asked her to marry him and she eagerly consented. He was her first beau! He certainly made her very happy while it lasted. And she refused him none of the luxurious playthings—ponies, motor boats, automobiles—to which, as a prince, he thought himself entitled.

Alexis himself told me how sweet and generous she was. "She would do anything to make me happy," he said. Several months after he had first met Barbara Hutton in his own home (Barbara was a friend of Louise from childhood), he wanted something else to "make him happy." And sweet Louise Van Alen Mdivani gave him—a divorce.

The divorce was secret and arranged with great care by the Van Alens and Mdivanis. It was Alexis's brother-in-law, Charles Huberich, who represented Louise!

It was then that we—Serge and I and David and Mae—began to hear about Barbara Hutton. Alexis's rare letters sang the praises of the Woolworth heiress, and "When Alexis marries Barbara" began to be heard wherever the Mdivani princes gathered together.

Shortly after his divorce from Louise, Alexis came from Paris to visit his brothers. One of the first things he did was to put $17,000 into the Pacific Shore Oil Company. That seems to indicate that his divorce from the Van Alen heiress had not left him high and dry.

One night I cornered him after dinner. "What's all this about Barbara Hutton?" I asked him.

"She is adorable. I am going to marry her."

"But supposing she won't have you?"

"She will."

"Supposing the family prevent your marrying her?"

"I shall marry her anyway. She is of age. They will have to agree."

"What will you do if she changes her mind?"

"Why," interrupted Serge airily, "in that case he'd remarry Louise! She's still staying with my sister Roussie, you know!"

Alexis didn't say anything to this. I admit that I felt a little sorry for Louise. There was quite an anxious period for the Mdivanis after that, for the Hutton family were apparently making a determined effort to prevent Barbara marrying Alexis.

The *Lurline* was about to make its maiden voyage around the world. Barbara consented to make the tour. Alexis did not take passage too. His plan, as Serge explained it to me, was to wait until Barbara was bored to death with the sameness of life on shipboard, and then join her. The fact that an Italian count, also a suitor for her hand, was making the trip did not worry Alexis.

"She'll be so fed up with that fellow," explained Serge, "that she'll be glad when she sees Alexis!"

From the day he boarded the *Lurline* Alexis apparently had the situation well in hand. Serge would receive cables from him. "Have just proposed"—this was from India; "Barbara has consented"—this from Port Said; "Marriage certain"—this from a port in North Africa.

The original idea, I was told, was for the marriage to take place in French North Africa. This alarmed the Huttons, they say, because under the laws of France a husband is entitled to half his wife's fortune if there is no prenuptial division of property. Mr. Hutton agreed to give his consent, providing the wedding was held in Paris "after a suitable arrangement between the parties concerned."

What the "suitable arrangement" was, you know as much as I do. The newspapers say Alexis was paid $250,000 in a lump sum.

When the final cablegram came that the wedding was certain there was quite a celebration in our beach house. The exuberance of the brothers was pardonable. Alexis was to marry Barbara at last. Their ship had come home!

A few weeks later General Zakhary Mdivani died, and Serge and David left for Paris. There, last June, they attended the wedding.

Well, I wish Barbara more luck with her prince than I had with mine. I hope that I meet her some day. I have a wicked notion that my greeting to her will be a phrase borrowed from a well known night-club hostess in New York: "Hello, sucker!"

Liberty
A Weekly for Everybody

Printed and entered as second class mail at Chicago, Illinois. Western Office: Tribune Square, Chicago. Superior 0100
Editorial, Executive, and Advertising Offices: 247 Park Avenue, New York City. Telephone: Ashland 4160
Please address all communications to 247 Park Avenue, New York City

The New Deal Is Here— God Be Praised!

editorial by Bernarr Macfadden

AT LAST WE have a real leader in Washington—unafraid, clear-headed—a great personality.

And he is doing things with a heavy hand! Action and more action—its realization almost makes us dizzy.

We were all demanding revolutionary changes and we are getting them. Our slow-moving, elephantine legislators have been energized and galvanized. Heretofore they appeared to have been etherized.

Much of our sanctimonious fanatical prohibition law was wiped out in a few days. For many years conscientious officials have been trying to annul this ugly source of racketeering. But the New Deal, with strong hands and a heavy tread, has mowed down the dry resistance in steam-roller fashion.

The depression has been given sledge-hammer wallops, mighty, staggering blows, and maybe—who knows?—the final knockout may be close at hand. Anyway, we are all hoping and helping the new Washington gladiator in the terrific battles he is now calmly and effectively waging. We are with him, all of us—a few straggling, bedraggled drys excepted.

The dictatorial powers placed in his hands have been used forcefully and intelligently. And with this mighty weapon to destroy the unthinking and at times fanatical opposition, the battle for an economical and forceful government is well under way.

Our new leader has already proved himself magnificently—bold, courageous, sagacious, and marvelously capable.

Before he took the reins at Washington confidence was everywhere lacking. Hopelessness, helplessness, had paralyzed the people. Our banks were tottering—all of them. Long lines of depositors were demanding their money.

But a new force intervened. Our new President came into power. He saw his duty with a clearness of vision difficult to comprehend, and revolutionary, unheard-of measures were quickly inaugurated.

Our government became human overnight. Weighty problems, terrifying emergencies, heretofore ignored or met by talk and more talk, were effectively attacked.

And a miraculous change was wrought in the public everywhere. The financial storm, the chaos with which we had been threatened, gradually abated, and confidence again appeared—peering at us out of the gloom and despair in which we were all engulfed.

And one glance was encouraging, and now it (confidence) is strutting forth here and there and everywhere.

God-given confidence, that invaluable factor so essential to remedy our woes, is on the way—is here. Self-assertiveness, belief in ourselves, in our national future—that is the divine force that will electrify our disorganized nation.

May this beneficent force soon reign supreme in the hearts and souls of our people everywhere.

—BERNARR MACFADDEN.

The Depression Is Staggering

editorial by Bernarr Macfadden

HURRAH for President Roosevelt! Hurrah for Senator Wagner—the author of the National Recovery Bill! Hurrah for all the hard-working statesmen in Washington who have dealt the demoralizing depression such smothering blows.

And save a hurrah or two for the work of the National Recovery Crusade. We recently called our readers' attention to the constructive activities of this organization. The workers in this association are still hard at work, and the most amazing results have already been accomplished.

Elmira, New York, the first city to have had the attention of this organization, maintains that the attitude of their citizens has been altered to such an extent that it almost seems as if a miracle has been performed. Business of every character in that city has reported changes for the better.

Pessimism has been replaced by optimism, and what was accomplished in Elmira can be duplicated throughout the nation. Send forth pæans of praise.

Old Man Depression is moving swiftly toward the cemetery. We can all help him on his way to oblivion.

So do your part, dear reader—and then some!

Fear is the dangling skeleton that has often scared us into feverish tremors. But this bugaboo is fast disappearing.

Confidence is returning; it is overflowing in the hearts and minds of great numbers of our people. In a few months we have changed a situation that bordered on desperation to one of hopefulness allied at times to cheery optimism.

When the World War was ended, Armistice Day was acclaimed with joyous abandon. People everywhere were thrilled and elated with exaltation. They were drunk with joy—literally a crowd of genial maniacs, happy and care-free, expressing themselves with reckless abandon. Strangers—men and women—hugged and kissed each other.

Mad crowds joined in the jubilation of rapturous indulgence. Conventional etiquette was forgotten.

What a thrilling jollification we had on that great day!

And it is about time for another such merrymaking.

All of us, everywhere, have admitted that the depression was a real war—a war that brought us business stagnation, unemployment, hunger, suffering, etc.

Everywhere it has been maintained that this war was far worse than the World War.

And if this be true, let us set the day to celebrate our splendid victory.

The war on the depression is almost won. It will be maintained in many sections of our country that victory complete in every detail is already ours.

But let us not be premature. There must be no mistake.

And it is our contention that a celebration should be inaugurated throughout the entire nation, and that we should commemorate this auspicious occasion with the same hilarious unrestraint and make this great event as thrilling as when the whole world went mad in commemorating the end of the World War.

The war brought us by depression was more terrible. It doubtless cost this country more lives, far more suffering than the World War, and the end ought to be commemorated with a flaming jollification.

Join in this demand for a great national celebration. Let us all drain deep of the joyousness of this great occasion.

After nearly four years of doubt, anxiety, suffering, can anything be more thrilling than the announcement that Old Man Depression has really been buried?

No liquor should be required on that occasion, for we should be intoxicated with happiness—the delightful character of such news should make us all drunk with joy.

—BERNARR MACFADDEN.

The New Deal Hits Washington Society

by Maxine Davis

*How the Capital's Hectic Hostesses Have Found It a Misdeal
in Place Cards—It's Playing Havoc with Caste and Precedent*

"THROW AWAY THE Blue Book and get a crystal!" This is all the advice the State Department, the White House, or Washington's professional social oracles can give the hectic hostesses of the New Deal. Washington society is a mirror that reflects the mood of America. Under the New Deal official society is like the Constitution: the old framework is still here but most of the whalebone tortures have been removed. The Roosevelts have smashed some traditions and adapted others. The result is baffling.

There used to be a law. The rules of precedence and performance were rigid as the Sixth Commandment. This is no longer true. The Roosevelts have made society sociable. Their own habit of entertaining the people they like as well as the ones they should—and making them all equally welcome; their directness, their vitality and zest have made state functions gay and dinners merry.

Now as always the White House receptions and state dinners are the spool on which the elaborate fabric of Washington entertainment is wound. Simplicity was the

Hoover plan; stark formality was the result. Mr. and Mrs. Small Official paraded solemnly through the stately rooms, were presented to the unhappy Hoovers by gold-braided aides who always looked as if they smelled bad cheese.

You peered at the notables in the Blue Room, pushed through crowds in the East Room, and departed, your clothes wrinkled and your ego shattered.

Judy O'Grady, wife of the Representative from Nochokee, had been to the Congressional reception last year. With no special pleasure she took her place in line again. In front of her a Colonel's Lady switched her train irritably. Behind her a sweating Senator's wife backed and pushed.

The line moved slowly. Judy's Hon. Husband began to complain about his feet and an early-morning committee hearing. You couldn't hear the Marine Band for the voices, or see any one.

At last a beaming aide announced them to the President in a tone that said, "Here they are—the people you've been waiting for all evening." The President shook their hands heartily. Mrs. Roosevelt greeted them as if they made all this fuss worth while. She meant it, too.

The effect was a veritable cocktail. These days the White House is a home, and it's *fun*. Strangers gossip. Isn't the roof an introduction?

See that tall couple arriving too late to greet the Chief Executive. He's one of the leading Brain Trusters. And doesn't his wife look mad! She has a new dress, her first train, all for nothing. There is Alice Longworth, still the most glamorous woman in Washington, in what she calls "NRA blue" and tremendous ancient gold Hindu earrings. There is Director of the Mint Nellie Tayloe Ross, in shell-pink satin with ruby ornaments. Oh, *dancing!* Let's!

Although cordiality, often informality, characterizes the entertainment of the Democratic Roosevelts, their state dinners are ceremonious as those of the Republican Roosevelts. The guest list is smaller; the menus are simpler. But the form is there. Battalions of White House aides, resplendent in full uniform, are on hand as decoration because, Mrs. Roosevelt explained, "it costs nothing to put them on." The Marine Band plays all during the meal. Politics, however taboo in the past, are spirited table talk. People leave regretfully from a "good party."

The Garners seconded the White House social motion in their dinner to the President and Mrs. Roosevelt. They turned the entertainment problem over to Gene Buck, who not only produced a quartet of singers and a Mexican tenor who played a guitar but also something known as a "mentalist." This dangerous character guessed that Mrs. Garner had written on a slip of paper, "Be strong and of good courage"; and that the Vice President had thought of "Home Sweet Home," but had failed to write it down. That was bad enough. When, however, he found out that the President had written, "G.O.P. ticket for President: Huey Long and Ham Fish," then Mr. Roosevelt turned to the Senate leader and said, "Joe, here's where we'd better

go *home*." Anyhow, it was an hour later than the State Department's Division of Protocol said they could stay!

As for dinner parties, the New Deal is a misdeal in place cards. Why? The confusion caused by the Alphabets. The Brain Trusters, major and minor, are more popular than an English novelist at a woman's club. But while the President has given them billions to play with, he has neglected to give them a seat at the table. Do you put the General Johnsons and the Donald Richbergs above or below the Congressman O'Gradys? Where does Jesse Jones sit? Nobody knows! With no protocol to guide it, one great embassy closed its eyes one night and seated Relief Administrator Harry Hopkins above former Ambassador Sackett.

How about the Little Cabinet? There's a headache for any hostess. In the past, assistant secretaries were insignificant as Caspar Milquetoast. Now look at them! Agriculture's Rexford Guy Tugwell! Commerce Department's John Dickinson! Labor Department's Ed McGrady! Do you dare to seat them below the salt? Everybody wants the Alphabets—but where, oh, where do they eat?

Fortunately the Brain Trusters are no sticklers for precedent. They're so important they don't have to care. Anyhow, the big thing is to get them for dinner. This is always in the nature of an achievement. "We'd like to accept tentatively," Mrs. Brain Truster tells her would-be hostess, "if you don't mind leaving it that way."

The hostess does mind, but it's the best she can do. She may say hopefully, "Dinner at eight—don't bother to dress," but she knows she can only watch and pray. Watch the clock and pray that the conference dissolves and that some higher-up won't choose that inconvenient moment to discover a new formula for the Better Life, so that her dinner guests just happily gobble sandwiches and milk in their offices.

This may be hard on the cook, but it is a great aid to digestion. The menus at Washington tables have become much simpler. No more terrapin. No more sole Marguery, or suprême of guinea hen Eugénie. Just a good nourishing soup, and a roast that won't spoil while standing in the oven keeping warm until the Alphabets arrive. And lots of vegetables.

Many of the New Deal, like Secretary Wallace and Louis Bean, are vegetarians.

The New Dealers may arrive at nine thirty for an eight-o'clock meal, but Heaven only knows when they will go home. They arrive complete with trends and charts and curves, turn your drawing room into an open forum, and continue far, far into the night. Once three of the most important of them, unable to resist the opportunity for a conference, retired to a bedroom for hours, keeping the party yawning and the room out of service.

What a contrast to the old régime! Your Brain Truster may wear a wrinkled suit, but there is no Teapot Dome oil on his waistcoat. He may wax oratorical about public utilities, but he banks no pay check from the Power Trust.

I, for one, never expected to see our national capital so overrun with honest men!

Periscope into Alice Longworth's drawing room. You may see her giving her imitation of the Blue Eagle, a peculiar flip-flop performance, for its sire, General Johnson. Poor obscure Republican "Princess Alice"! Her invitations are still accepted eagerly by both ex-plutocrats and the pick of the Alphabets. You may meet Secretary Ickes, Dr. Tugwell, and even Father Coughlin rubbing shoulders with the Robert Low Bacons, the Richard Aldriches, or the Albert Simmses.

Welfare Worker Harry Hopkins, the most popular man in the New Deal, is often encountered in, for instance, Eleanor Patterson's marble palace; General Johnson is the second most popular guest, but he is hard to snare. Dr. Tugwell runs them a very close third. Assistant Secretary of the Treasury "Chip" Roberts is beloved for his stories, often unexpurgated. And the social crystal gazers read as a sign of the times the fact that the labor leaders, including McGrady, Leo Wolman, Donald Richberg, and Senator Wagner, are now aces in anybody's hand of place cards.

The Diplomatic Corps is fascinated by the New Deal. However, its members are shy of inviting the leaders to break bread, and concentrate on the younger men. One of the rare discontented young conservatives of the administration went to a dance at the German embassy recently, saw it swarming with the junior Alphabets, indignantly decided the Nazis were trying to be far too social with our young socialists and fascists, paid perfunctory respects, and went home.

You might think these young men would be manna to husband-hunting mammas. Not at all! Mothers of débutantes, most of them of the Old Guard, keep their out-of-joint noses in the air, hug the potted palms, peer through lorgnettes and say, "Who are these people?" They rarely find out. Few of them are listed in Dun and Bradstreet's, and fewer have even heard of the Social Register. It is a bad season for Cupid in Washington. The bright young men, even when rich and blue-blooded, apparently care more for reform than romance.

If the New Deal is a blight to Cupid, it is drought and grasshoppers to the calling-card engraver. He is indeed the Forgotten Man. When the new official's wife came to the capital she read The Book, interviewed her more experienced colleagues, and often rented a social secretary to instruct her.

Whom did she call on? An apparently endless list of people. Who called on her? Just about every one whose card tray held her pasteboard. Social relations were never established until a call was returned. To fail in this courtesy was a major insult.

The first place she called was of course the White House. She left a card at the great front door, and sooner or later the First Lady invited her to tea. Now I'd hate to count the women who have been often to tea and even lunch at the Executive Mansion who do not even own calling cards. Mrs. Roosevelt doesn't care. Her housekeeper is not so pleased. Too many of these "unidentified" guests steal napkins. At a recent White House tea party the table was laid without any. When Mrs. Roosevelt inquired about this lack, she was told they were all in the wash—those that were left!

The rankless New Deal wives don't have to call, not even on each other. What is more, they do *not* call. Most of them, such as the sculptress Mrs. Leo Wolman, the poetess Mrs. Jerome Frank, the painter Mrs. Russell Lord, are too busy.

"I wondered when I should drop a card on you Brain Trust women," I told an old acquaintance who moved to town with the Roosevelts.

"A card? What for?" she inquired, baffled. Then, as a spectacular battle was raging around her husband, "Oh, of condolence?"

Regularly ranked wives still call, but there are not so many places to go. Mrs. Garner was only "at home" once, and then she confided the fact, not, as is customary, to the newspapers, but to a very few friends.

Because the Garners will assume only an irreducible minimum of social obligations, tall, race-horse-lean Mrs. Speaker Rainey has happily accepted the mantle of administration eater-in-chief. Though this social business isn't play, she insists. "It is just work, work, work, from early until late—Saturdays and Sundays included. Our position carries with it the acceptance of invitations from embassies, legations, and other important houses for dinners given in our honor."

Captain Rainey of the Girl Scouts, as she likes to be called, manages to be her husband's assistant and a butterfly as well. She loves it. She has eaten "at home" every Wednesday. The doors of the desk prominent in her drawing room are plastered, like a débutante's dressing-table mirror, with invitations.

No one else has been so meticulous. Few Senators' wives were officially at home on their traditional Thursdays, and not one single Congressman's lady told the society editors she was sitting in her parlor, card tray in one hand and teapot in the other.

The Cabinet wives have always had to bear the worst burden of the calling bore. They were supposed to, and did, receive every Wednesday. Their open houses and lavish tea tables were the fair prey of every unemployed nonentity in town. Now Mrs. Roosevelt has halved their trials by suggesting that five of them receive one Wednesday and five the next. Pruning social labors is an achievement for which every succeeding administration will thank Eleanor Roosevelt.

Even with the curtailed calling season, the social strangers have disappeared. This in spite of the fact that the Democratic Cabinet is composed chiefly of rich men living in mansions and entertaining with truly Republican elegance.

Round, clever little Mrs. Homer Cummings, wife of the Attorney-General, stands hospitably in her big hilltop house, probably conscious of having the most and best food in the Cabinet. No one leaves hungry. The Attorney-General sometimes comes home, and wanders about looking unhappy as a jobless undertaker.

Mrs. Henry Morgenthau, one of the most modest and charming of the Cabinet intellectuals, has promised her husband faithfully that she will not ask him to come to a tea party during his entire tenure of office. Fresh-faced Western Mrs. Dern is, unexpectedly, the most meticulous of the Cabinet hostesses.

There are still cocktail parties. People drop in for a drink, and sometimes stay for dinner.

The Old Guard are sure this vigor, this informality is a passing phase. They say they have seen it tried before, and always seen it fail.

The answer? Look in the crystal!

Why I Will Not Marry

by Greta Garbo

In Which the Celebrated Sphinx of the Screen
Breaks Her Silence and Tells What Is in Her Heart

WHY ARE PEOPLE so interested in the matrimonial status of the film stars?

After all, marriage is "nobody's business" except the two people concerned. It is strictly their private affair.

Moreover, it is damaging to a star's following for the more intimate details of his or her domestic life to be broadcast far and wide. It is particularly unfair—if not actually unwise—in the case of the film actor who plays great-lover rôles to stress the fact of his having a wife and children, no matter how he dotes on them in private.

Probably for this reason, if for no other, Hollywood no longer indulges in the big formal church weddings with gay banquets and dancing to follow—red-letter events like those which thrilled the film colony to the core when the nuptials of Vilma Banky and Rod La Rocque, Bebe Daniels and Ben Lyon were celebrated a few years ago.

Then, of course, there were the spectacular marriages of Gloria Swanson to her marquis, and of Mae Murray and Pola Negri to their brother princes Mdivani. Of these, Mae Murray's is the only marriage that has survived.

Despite the blaze of glory in which Gloria descended with the noble marquis upon Hollywood in 1925, and the fact that the film colony rose with one accord to do them honor, the romance was soon shattered. Not so soon, however, as that of Pola Negri. Last of the trio to wed Pola was the first to shed her spouse. She beat Gloria to the divorce courts by just six days. Incidentally, both husbands have since found consolation elsewhere—Prince Serge (Pola's ex-husband) with the Chicago opera star Mary McCormic, while the Marquis de la Falaise de la Coudraye, *alias* "Hank," is now known as "Mr. Constance Bennett."

Personally, I should hate to have my husband lose his identity to that extent. Rather than that, I should

want to retire from the screen altogether. I should want to forget I had ever been Greta Garbo.

With so many broken romances littered about the studios, Hollywood is not so keen as formerly to draw attention to the love affairs of its players.

Nowadays quiet weddings are the vogue.

It is the fashion to slip out of town by airplane, get married in far-away Mexico, and maybe or maybe not announce the fact afterward.

Ina Claire, reigning beauty of the New York stage, and John Gilbert, then prince of screen romantics, eloped by air to Las Vegas and were married there very quietly. Even so, bets were being made within two hours of the ceremony about the outcome of the marriage: that it wouldn't last a year; that it would survive six, eight, perhaps ten months.

What chance of success has the average marriage in these circumstances?

Can you wonder that film stars hesitate to exchange single blessedness for married bliss?

The particular problem that faces the film star, however, is this:

Have I the peculiar kind of genius and temperament that makes of matrimony a holy and lasting bond? Am I a fit and proper person to be anybody's "lawful wedded wife"? Can I make a success of married life?

With a male star, perhaps, it is different. When he marries, convention expects that his wife shall subordinate her interests to his, as happened recently in the case of Maurice Chevalier and Yvonne Vallée.

An artist in her own right, Yvonne relinquished her theatrical laurels gracefully, without complaint. When Maurice was invited to make pictures in Hollywood, it was as plain Mrs. Chevalier she urged him to accept,

and as Mrs. Chevalier that she accompanied this internationally accepted exponent of charm.

How embarrassing, on the other hand, is the situation of the non-film-acting husband married to a famous film star! He is bound to lose something of his own identity. Imagine a man being known as "Mr. Garbo"—just that and nothing more!

And in those sections of society still impressed by the false glitter of the limelight, and where the spectacle of a woman who has made her own way in the world is still matter for surprise and idle chatter, this is what would surely happen.

Only a fool or a hero could abide such an anomalous position.

The only good reason for two people getting married is that they can be together most of the time. That is impossible with me so long as I remain on the screen.

The marriage contract which has to make the best of whatever is left over after the film contract has been fulfilled seems rather a makeshift affair. A husband needs his wife's thoughts and spiritual support as well as her actual physical presence. Unless one marries a fellow film artist, there is little chance of this ideal union of sympathy and interests. For I am in deadly earnest when I say that a film star's career is a whole-time job.

When I first went to Hollywood under the wing of the great Mauritz Stiller, I used to go to parties regularly and attend premières. But soon I found that my work began to suffer. Also, that to make public appearances destroys the illusion that surrounds the shadows of the silver sheet. The creative artist should be a rare and solitary spirit.

Stiller's death was a great blow to me. For so long I had been his satellite. All Europe at that time regarded

Stiller as the most significant figure in the film world. Directors hurried to the projecting rooms where his prints were shown. They took with them their secretaries and, in the dim silence, they dictated breathless comments on the wide sweep of his magnificent technique.

Stiller had found me, an obscure artist in Sweden, and brought me to America. I worshiped him. There are some of course, who say it was a love story. It was more. It was the utter devotion which only the very young can know—the adoration of a student for her teacher, of a timid girl for a master mind.

In his studio Stiller taught me how to do everything: how to eat; how to turn my head; how to express love—and hate.

Off the screen I studied his every whim, wish, and demand. I lived my life according to the plans he laid down. He told me what to say and what to do.

When Stiller died I foud myself like a ship without a rudder. I was bewildered—lost—and very lonely. I resolutely refused to talk to reporters because I didn't know what to say.

By degrees I dropped out of the social whirl of Hollywood. I retired into my shell. I built a wall of repression around my real self, and I lived—and still live—behind it.

In the gayest, maddest colony in the world, I became a hermit.

I did not go to parties any more. I was too tired. I went to bed when my work at the studio was done.

If I needed recreation, I liked to be out of doors: to trudge about in a boy's coat and boy's shoes; to ride horseback, or shoot craps with the stable boys, or watch the sun set in a blaze of glory over the Pacific Ocean. You see, I am still a bit of a tomboy.

Most hostesses disapprove of this trousered attitude to life, so I do not inflict it upon them. Besides, I am still a little nervous, a little self-conscious about my English. I cannot express myself well at parties. I speak haltingly.

I feel awkward, shy, afraid.

In Hollywood, where every tea table bristles with gossip-writers, what I say might be misunderstood. So I am silent as the grave about my private affairs.

Rumors fly about. I am mum.

My private affairs are *strictly* private.

Hitler Shows His Hand

by George Sylvester Viereck

*The Fascist Platform—Its Threat to Bolshevism,
and What It Means to the Rest of the World*

"WHEN I TAKE charge of Germany, I shall end tribute abroad and Bolshevism at home."

Adolf Hitler drained his cup as if it contained not tea, but the life blood of Bolshevism.

"Bolshevism," the chief of the Brown Shirts, the Fascists of Germany, continued, gazing at me balefully, "is our greatest menace. Kill Bolshevism in Germany and you restore seventy million people to power. France owes her strength not to her armies but to the forces of Bolshevism and dissension in our midst.

"The Treaty of Versailles and the Treaty of St. Germain are kept alive by Bolshevism in Germany. The Peace Treaty and Bolshevism are two heads of one monster. We must decapitate both."

When Adolf Hitler announced this program, the advent of the Third Empire which he proclaims seemed still at the end of the rainbow. Then came election after election. Each time the power of Hitler grew. While unable to dislodge Hindenburg from the presidency, Hitler today heads the largest party in Germany. Unless Hindenburg assumes dictatorial measures, or some unexpected development completely upsets all present calculations, Hitler's party will organize the Reichstag and dominate the government. Hitler's fight was not against Hindenburg but against Chancellor Bruening. It is doubtful if Bruening's successor can sustain himself without the support of the National Socialists.

Many who voted for Hindenburg were at heart with Hitler, but some deep-rooted sense of loyalty impelled them nevertheless to cast their vote for the old field marshal. Unless overnight a new leader arises, there is no one in Germany, with the exception of Hindenburg, who could defeat Hitler—and Hindenburg is eighty-five! Time and the recalcitrance of the French fight for Hitler, unless some blunder on his own part, or dissension within the ranks of the party, deprives him of his opportunity to play the part of Germany's Mussolini.

The First German Empire came to an end when Napoleon forced the Austrian emperor to surrender his imperial crown. The Second Empire came to an end when William II, on the advice of Hindenburg, sought refuge in Holland. The Third Empire is emerging slowly but surely, although it may dispense with scepters and crowns.

I met Hitler not in his headquarters, the Brown House in Munich, but in a private home—the dwelling of a former admiral of the German Navy. We discussed the fate of Germany over the teacups.

"Why," I asked Hitler, "do you call yourself a National Socialist, since your party program is the very antithesis of that commonly accredited to Socialism?"

"Socialism," he retorted, putting down his cup of tea, pugnaciously, "is the science of dealing with the common weal. Communism is not Socialism. Marxism is not Socialism. The Marxians have stolen the term and confused its meaning. I shall take Socialism away from the Socialists.

"Socialism is an ancient Aryan, Germanic institution. Our German ancestors held certain lands in common. They cultivated the idea of the common weal. Marxism has no right to disguise itself as Socialism. Socialism, unlike Marxism, does not repudiate private property. Unlike Marxism, it involves no negation of personality, and unlike Marxism, it is patriotic.

"We might have called ourselves the Liberal Party. We chose to call ourselves the National Socialists. We are not internationalists. Our Socialism is national. We demand the fulfillment of the just claims of the productive classes by the State on the basis of race solidarity. To us State and race are one."

Hitler himself it not a purely Germanic type. His dark hair betrays some Alpine ancestor. For years he refused to be photographed. That was part of his strategy —to be known only to his friends so that, in the hour of crisis, he could appear here, there, and everywhere without detection. Today he could no longer pass unrecognized through the obscurest hamlet in Germany. His appearance contrasts strangely with the aggressiveness of his opinions. No milder-mannered reformer ever scuttled ship of state or cut political throat.

"What," I continued my cross-examination, "are the fundamental planks of your platform?"

"We believe in a healthy mind in a healthy body. The body politic must be sound if the soul is to be healthy. Moral and physical health are synonymous."

"Mussolini," I interjected, "said the same to me."

Hitler beamed.

"The slums," he added, "are responsible for nine-tenths, alcohol for one-tenth, of all human depravity. No healthy man is a Marxian. Healthy men recognize the value of personality. We contend against the forces of disaster and degeneration. Bavaria is comparatively healthy because it is not completely industrialized. However, all Germany, including Bavaria, is condemned to intensive industrialism by the smallness of our territory. If we wish to save Germany we must see to it that our farmers remain faithful to the land. To do so, they must have room to breathe and room to work."

"Where will you find the room to work?"

"We must retain our colonies and we must expand eastward. There was a time when we could have shared world dominion with England. Now we can stretch our cramped limbs only toward the east. The Baltic is necessarily a German lake."

"Is it not," I asked, "possible for Germany to reconquer the world economically without extending her territory?"

Hitler shook his head earnestly.

"Economic imperialism, like military imperialism, depends upon power. There can be no world trade on a large scale without world power. Our people have not learned to think in terms of world power and world trade. However, Germany cannot extend commercially or territorially until she regains what she has lost and until she finds herself.

"We are in the position of a man whose house has been burned down. He must have a roof over his head before he can indulge in more ambitious plans. We had succeeded in creating an emergency shelter that keeps out the rain. We were not prepared for hailstones. However, misfortunes hailed down upon us. Germany has been living in a veritable blizzard of national, moral, and economic catastrophes.

"Our demoralized party system is a symptom of our disaster. Parliamentary majorities fluctuate with the mood of the moment. Parliamentary government unbars the gate to Bolshevism."

"Unlike some German militarists, you do not favor an alliance with Soviet Russia?"

Hitler evaded a direct reply to this question. It may not suit Hitler to attack Bolshevism in Russia. He may even look upon an alliance with Bolshevism as his last card, if he is in danger of losing the game. If, he intimated on one occasion, capitalism refuses to recognize that the National Socialists are the last bulwark of private property, if capital impedes their struggle, Germany may be compelled to throw herself into the enticing arms of the siren Soviet Russia. But he is determined not to permit Bolshevism to take root in Germany.

He responded warily in the past to the advances of Chancellor Bruening and others who wished to form a united political front. It is unlikely that now, in view of the steady increase in the vote of the National Socialists, Hitler will be in the mood to compromise on any essential principle with other parties.

"The political combinations upon which a united front depend," Hitler remarked to me, "are too unstable. They render almost impossible a clearly defined policy. I see everywhere the zigzag course of compromise and concession. Our constructive forces are checked by the tyranny of numbers. We make the mistake of applying arithmetic and the mechanics of the economic world to the living state. We are threatened by ever increasing numbers and ever diminishing ideals. Mere numbers are unimportant."

"But suppose France retaliates against you by once more invading your soil? She invaded the Ruhr once before. She may invade it again."

"It does not matter," Hitler, thoroughly aroused, retorted, "how many square miles the enemy may occupy if the national spirit is aroused. *Ten million free Germans, ready to perish so that their country may live, are more potent than fifty million whose will power is paralyzed and whose race consciousness is infected by aliens.*

"We want a greater Germany uniting all German tribes. But *our salvation can start in the smallest corner. Even if we had only ten acres of land and were determined to defend them with our lives, the ten acres would become the focus of regeneration.* Our workers have two souls: one is German, the other is Marxian. We must arouse the German soul. We must uproot the canker of Marxism. Marxism and Germanism are antitheses.

"In my scheme of the German State, there will be no room for the alien, no use for the wastrel, for the usurer or speculator, or anyone incapable of productive work."

The cords on Hitler's forehead stood out threateningly. His voice filled the room. There was a noise at the door. His followers, who always remain within call, like a bodyguard, reminded the leader of his duty to address a meeting.

Hitler gulped down his tea and left.

Roman Fever
a story by Edith Wharton

A Distinguished Novelist Presents as Brilliant and Memorable a Love Story as We Venture You've Read This Year

FROM THE TABLE at which they had been lunching, two American ladies of ripe but well-cared-for middle age moved across the lofty terrace of the Roman restaurant and, leaning on its parapet, looked first at each other and then down on the outspread glories of the Palatine and the Forum with the same expression of vague and benevolent approval.

As they leaned there a girlish voice echoed up gayly from the stairs leading to the court below. "Well, come along, then," it cried—not to them but to an invisible companion—"and let's leave the young things to their knitting."

And a voice as fresh laughed back: "Oh, look here, Babs, not actually knitting!"

"Well, I mean figuratively," rejoined the first "After all, we haven't left the poor dears much else to do." And at that point the turn of the stairs engulfed the dialogue.

The smaller and paler lady shook her head and colored slightly. *"Barbara!"* she murmured, sending an unheard rebuke after the mocking voice in the stairway.

The other, who was fuller and higher in color, with a small determined nose supported by vigorous black eyebrows, gave a good-humored laugh. "That's what our daughters think of us!"

Her companion replied by a deprecating gesture. "Not of us individually. We must remember that. It's just the collective modern idea of mothers. And you see—" Half guiltily she drew from her handsomely mounted black-doeskin bag a twist of crimson silk run through by two fine knitting needles.

The dark lady laughed again, and they both relapsed upon the view, contemplating it in silence, with a sort of diffused serenity which might have been borrowed from the spring effulgence of the Roman skies. The luncheon hour was long past and the two had the end of the vast terrace to themselves.

"Well, I don't see why we shouldn't just stay here," said Mrs. Slade, the lady of the high color and energetic brows. Two derelict basket chairs stood near, and she pushed them into the angle of the parapet and settled herself in one, her gaze upon the Palatine. "After all, it's still the most beautiful view in the world."

"It always will be, to me," assented her friend Mrs. Ansley, with so slight a stress on the "me" that Mrs. Slade, though she noticed it, wondered if it were not merely accidental.

"When we first met here we were younger than our girls are now. You remember?"

"Oh, yes, I remember," murmured Mrs. Ansley, with the same undefinable stress. "There's that head waiter wondering," she interpolated.

"I'll cure him of wondering," said Mrs. Slade, stretching her hand toward a bag as discreetly opulent-looking as Mrs. Ansley's. Signing to the head waiter, she explained that she and her friend were old lovers of Rome, and would like to spend the end of the afternoon looking down on the view—that is, if it did not disturb the service? The head waiter, bowing over her gratuity, assured her that the ladies were most welcome, and would be still more so if they would condescend to remain for dinner. A full-moon night, they would remember.

Mrs. Slade's black brows drew together as though references to the moon were unwelcome. Then she smiled. "Well, why not? We might do worse. There's no knowing, I suppose, when the girls will be back. Do you even know back from where? I don't!"

Mrs. Ansley again colored slightly. "I think those young Italian aviators we met at the embassy invited them to fly to Tarquinia for tea. I suppose they'll want to wait and fly back by moonlight."

"Moonlight—moonlight. What a part it still plays! Do you suppose they're as sentimental as we were?"

Her friend gave her a shy glance. "I never should have supposed you were sentimental, Alida."

"Well, perhaps I wasn't." Mrs. Slade drew her lids together in retrospect; and for a few moments the two ladies, who had been intimate since childhood, reflected how little they knew each other, after all. Each one, of course, had a label ready to attach to the other's name. Mrs. Delphin Slade, for instance, would have told herself, or any one who asked her, that Mrs. Horace Ansley twenty-five years ago had been exquisitely lovely—no, you wouldn't believe it, would you?—though of course still charming, distinguished. Well, as a girl she had been exquisite; far more beautiful than her daughter Barbara, though certainly Babs, according to the new standards at any rate, was more effective—had more *edge,* as they say. Funny where she got it, with those two nullities as parents. Yes; Horace Ansley was—well, just the duplicate of his wife. Museum specimens of old New York. Good-looking, irreproachable, exemplary.

Not many months apart, both ladies lost their husbands. And now they had run across each other in Rome, at the same hotel, each of them the modest appendage of a salient daughter.

For Alida Slade it was a big drop from being the wife of Delphin Slade to being his widow. She had always regarded herself (within a certain conjugal pride) as his equal in social gifts, as contributing her full share to the making of the exceptional couple they were; and the difference after his death was irremediable. As the wife of the famous corporation lawyer, always with an international case or two on hand, every day brought its exciting and unexpected obligation: the impromptu entertaining of eminent colleagues from abroad; the hurried dashes to London, Paris, or Rome, where the entertaining was so handsomely reciprocated; the amusement of hearing in her wake: "What, that handsome woman with the good clothes and the eyes is Mrs. Slade—*the* Slade's wife? Really? Generally the wives of celebrities are such frumps."

Now she had only her daughter to live up to; for the son who seemed to have inherited his father's gifts had died suddenly in boyhood. She had fought through that agony because her husband was there, to be helped and to help; now, after his death, the thought of the boy became unbearable.

There was nothing left but to devote herself to her daughter; and dear Jenny was such a perfect daughter that she needed no excessive mothering. "Now, with Babs Ansley, I don't know that I *should* be so quiet," Mrs. Slade sometimes half-enviously reflected; but Jenny, who was younger than her brilliant friend, was that rare accident, an extremely young and pretty girl who made youth and prettiness seem as safe as their absence.

It was all perplexing—and to Mrs. Slade a little boring. She wished that Jenny would fall in love—with the wrong man, even; that she might have to be watched, outmaneuvered, rescued. And instead it was Jenny who watched her mother, kept her out of drafts, made sure that she had taken her tonic.

Mrs. Ansley was much less articulate than her friend, and her mental portrait of Mrs. Slade was briefer and drawn with fainter touches. "Alida Slade's awfully brilliant, but not as brilliant as she thinks," would have summed it up; though she would have added, for the enlightenment of strangers, that Mrs. Slade had been an extremely dashing girl—much more so than her daughter, who was pretty, of course, and clever in a way, but had none of her mother's—well, "vividness," some one had once called it. Sometimes Mrs. Ansley thought Alida Slade was disappointed. On the whole she had had a sad life, full of failures and mistakes. Mrs. Ansley had always been rather sorry for her.

So these two ladies visualized each other, each through the wrong end of her little telescope. . . .

For a long time Mrs. Slade sat quite still, her eyes still fixed on the golden slope of the palace of the Cæsars, and after a while Mrs. Ansley ceased to fidget with her bag and she too sank into meditation.

Suddenly the air was full of that deep clangor of bells which periodically covers Rome with a roof of silver. Mrs. Slade glanced at her wrist watch. "Four o'clock already," she said, as though surprised.

Mrs. Ansley suggested interrogatively: "There's bridge at the embassy at four."

For a long time Mrs. Slade did not answer. She appeared to be lost in contemplation and Mrs. Ansley thought the remark had escaped her. But after a while she said, as if speaking out of a dream: "Bridge, did you say? Not unless you want to. But I don't think I will, you know."

"Oh, no," Mrs. Ansley hastened to assure her. "I don't care to at all. It's so lovely here; and so full of old memories, as you say."

"I was just thinking," Mrs. Slade said slowly, "what different things Rome stands for to each generation of travelers. To our grandmothers, Roman fever. To our mothers, sentimental dangers—how we used to be guarded! To our daughters, no more dangers than the middle of Main Street. They don't know it—but how much they're missing!"

The long golden light was beginning to pale, and Mrs. Ansley lifted her knitting a little closer to her eyes. "Yes, how we were guarded!"

"I always used to think," Mrs. Slade continued, "that our mothers had a much more difficult job than our grandmothers. When Roman fever stalked the streets it must have been comparatively easy to gather in the girls at the danger hour. But when you and I were young, with such beauty calling us, and the spice of disobedience thrown in, and no worse risk than catching cold during the cool hour after sunset, the mothers used to be put to it to keep us in—didn't they?"

She turned again toward Mrs. Ansley, but the latter had reached a delicate point in her knitting. "One, two, three—slip two. Yes, they must have been," she assented without looking up.

Mrs. Slade's eyes rested on her with a deepened attention. "She can knit—in the face of this. How like her!"

Mrs. Slade leaned back, brooding, her eyes ranging from the ruins which faced her to the long green hollow of the Forum, the fading glow of the church fronts beyond it, and the outlying immensity of the Colosseum. Suddenly she thought: "It's all very well to say that our girls have done away with sentiment and moonlight. But if Babs Ansley isn't out to catch that young aviator—the one who's a marchese—then I don't know anything. And Jenny has no chance beside her. I know that too. I wonder if that's why Grace Ansley likes the two girls to go everywhere together. My poor Jenny as a foil!"

Mrs. Slade gave a hardly audible laugh, and at the sound Mrs. Ansley dropped her knitting.

"Yes?"

"I—oh, nothing. I was only thinking how your Babs carries everything before her. That Campolieri boy is one of the best matches in Rome. Don't look so innocent, my dear—you know he is. And I was wondering, ever so respectfully, you understand—wondering how two such exemplary characters as you and Horace had managed to produce anything quite so dynamic." Mrs. Slade laughed again, with a touch of asperity.

Mrs. Ansley's hands lay inert across her needles. She looked straight out at the great accumulated wreckage of passion and splendor at her feet. But her small profile was almost expressionless. At length she said: "I think you overrate Babs, my dear."

Mrs. Slade's tone grew easier. "No; I don't. I appreciate her. And perhaps envy you. Oh, my girl's perfect. If I were a chronic invalid I'd—well, I think I'd rather be in Jenny's hands. There must be times— But there! I always wanted a brilliant daughter, and never quite understood why I got an angel instead."

Mrs. Ansley echoed her laugh in a faint murmur. "Babs is an angel, too."

"Of course—of course! You mustn't misunderstand me. Well, they're wandering by the sea with their young men; and here we sit. And it all brings back the past a little too acutely."

Mrs. Ansley had resumed her knitting. One might almost have imagined (if one had known her less well, Mrs. Slade reflected) that for her also too many memories rose from the lengthening shadows of those august ruins. But no; she was simply absorbed in her work. What was there for her to worry about? She knew that Babs would almost certainly come back engaged to the extremely eligible Campolieri. "And she'll sell the New York house, and settle down near them in Rome, and never be in their way. She's much too tactful for that."

Mrs. Slade broke off this prophetic flight with a recoil of self-disgust. There was no one of whom she had less right to think unkindly than of Grace Ansley. Would she never cure herself of envying her? Perhaps she had begun too long ago.

She stood up and leaned against the parapet, filling her troubled eyes with the tranquillizing magic of the hour. But instead of tranquillizing her the sight seemed to increase her exasperation. Her gaze turned toward the Colosseum. Already its gold flank was drowned in purple shadow, and above it the sky curved crystal clear, without light or color. It was the moment when afternoon and evening hang balanced in mid-heaven.

At length Mrs. Slade turned back and laid her hand on her friend's arm. The gesture was so abrupt that Mrs. Ansley looked up, startled.

"The sun's set. You're not afraid, my dear?"

"Afraid?"

Of Roman fever—pneumonia? I remember how ill you were that winter. As a girl you had a very delicate throat, hadn't you?"

"Oh, we're all right up here. Down below, in the Forum, it does get deathly cold all of a sudden; but not here."

"Ah, of course you know, because you had to be so careful." Mrs. Slade turned back to the parapet. She thought: "I must make one more effort not to hate her." Aloud she said: "Whenever I look at the Forum from up here, I remember that story about a great-aunt of yours, wasn't she? A dreadfully wicked great-aunt?"

"Oh, yes; Great-aunt Harriet. The one who was supposed to have sent her young sister out to the Forum after sunset to gather some night-blooming flower for her album. All our great-aunts and grandmothers used to have albums of dried flowers."

Mrs. Slade nodded. "But she really sent her because they were in love with the same man—"

"Well, that was the family tradition. They said Aunt Harriet confessed it years afterward. At any rate, the poor little sister caught the fever and died. Mother used to frighten us with the story when we were children."

"And you frightened *me* with it, that winter when you and I were here as girls. The winter I was engaged to Delphin."

Mrs. Ansley gave a faint laugh. "Oh, did I? Really frightened you? I don't believe you're easily frightened."

"Not often; but I was then. I was easily frightened because I was too happy. I wonder if you know what that means?"

"I—yes," Mrs. Ansley faltered.

"Well, I suppose that was why the story of your wicked aunt made such an impression on me. And I thought: 'There's no more Roman fever, but the Forum is deathly cold after sunset—especially after a hot day. And the Colosseum's even colder and damper.'"

"The Colosseum?"

"Yes. It wasn't easy to get in after the gates were locked for the night. Far from easy. Still, in those days it could be managed; it *was* managed, often. Lovers met there who couldn't meet elsewhere. You knew that?"

"I—I dare say. I don't remember."

"You don't remember? You don't remember going to visit some ruins or other one evening, just after dark and catching a bad chill? You were supposed to have gone to see the moon rise. People always said that expedition was what caused your illness."

There was a moment's silence; then Mrs. Ansley rejoined: "Did they? It was all so long ago."

"Yes. And you got well again—so it didn't matter. But I suppose it struck your friends—the reason given for your illness, I mean—because everybody knew you were so prudent on account of your throat, and your mother took such care of you. You *had* been out late sight-seeing, hadn't you, that night?"

"Perhaps I had. The most prudent girls aren't always prudent. What made you think of it now?"

Mrs. Slade seemed to have no answer ready. But after a moment she broke out: "Because I simply can't bear it any longer!"

Mrs. Ansley lifted her head with a jerk. Her eyes were wide and very pale. "Can't bear what?"

"Why—your not knowing that I've always known why you went."

"Why I went?"

"Yes. You think I'm bluffing, don't you? Well, you went to meet the man I was engaged to—and I can repeat every word of the letter that took you there."

While Mrs. Slade spoke Mrs. Ansley had risen unsteadily to her feet. Her bag, her knitting and gloves slid in a panic-stricken heap to the ground. She looked at Mrs. Slade as though she were looking at a ghost.

"No, no—don't!" she faltered out.

"Why not? Listen, if you don't believe me: 'My One Darling: Things can't go on like this. I must see you alone. Come to the Colosseum immediately after dark tomorrow. There will be somebody to let you in. No one whom you need fear will suspect—' But perhaps you've forgotten what the letter said?"

Mrs. Ansley met the challenge with an unexpected composure. Steadying herself against the chair, she looked at her friend and replied: "No; I know it by heart too."

"And the signature? 'Only your D. S.' Was that it? I'm right, am I? That was the letter that took you out that evening after dark?"

Mrs. Ansley was still looking at her. It seemed to Mrs. Slade that a slow struggle was going on behind the voluntarily controlled mask of her small quiet face. "I shouldn't have thought she had herself so well in hand," Mrs. Slade reflected almost resentfully. But at this moment Mrs. Ansley spoke: "I don't know how you knew. I burnt that letter at once."

"Yes; you would, naturally—you're so prudent!" The sneer was open now. "And if you burnt the letter you're wondering how on earth I know what was in it. That's it, isn't it?"

Mrs. Slade waited, but Mrs. Ansley did not speak.

"Well, my dear, I know what was in that letter because I wrote it!"

"You wrote it?"

"Yes."

The two women stood for a minute staring at each other in the last golden light. Then Mrs. Ansley dropped back into her chair. "Oh!" she murmured, and covered her face with her hands.

Mrs. Slade waited nervously for another word or move. None came, and at length she broke out: "I horrify you."

Mrs. Ansley's hands dropped to her knee. The face they uncovered was streaked with tears. "I wasn't thinking of you. I was thinking—it was the only letter I ever had from him!"

"And I wrote it. Yes, I wrote it! But I was the girl he was engaged to. Did you happen to remember that?"

Mrs. Ansley's head dropped again. "I'm not trying to excuse myself. I remembered—"

"And still you went?"

"Still I went."

Mrs. Slade, leaning against the parapet, stood looking down on the small bowed figure at her side. The flame of her wrath had already sunk, and she wondered why she had ever thought there would be any satisfaction in inflicting so purposeless a wound. But she had to justify herself.

"You do understand? I'd found out, and I hated you—hated you. I knew you were in love with Delphin—and I was afraid: afraid of you, of your quiet ways, your sweetness; your— Well, I wanted you out of the way, that's all. Just for a few weeks; just till I was sure of him. So in a blind fury I wrote that letter— I don't know why I'm telling you now."

"I suppose," said Mrs. Ansley slowly, "it's because you've always gone on hating me."

"Perhaps. Or because I wanted to get the whole thing off my mind." She paused. "I'm glad you destroyed the letter. Of course I never thought you'd die."

Mrs. Ansley relapsed into silence, and Mrs. Slade, leaning above her, was conscious of a sense of isolation, of being cut off from the warm current of human communion. "You think me a monster!" she burst out.

"I don't know. It was the only letter I had. And you say he didn't write it?"

"Ah, how you care for him still!"

"I cared for that memory," said Mrs. Ansley.

Mrs. Slade continued to look down on her. She seemed physically reduced by the blow—as if, when she got up, the wind might scatter her like a puff of dust. Mrs. Slade's jealousy suddenly leaped up again at the sight. All these years the woman had been living on that letter. How she must have loved him, to treasure the mere memory of its ashes! The letter of the man her friend was engaged to. Wasn't it she who was the monster?

"You tried your best to get him away from me, didn't you? But you failed; and I kept him. That's all."

"Yes. That's all."

"I wish now I hadn't told you. I'd no idea you'd feel about it as you do; I thought you'd be amused. It all happened so long ago, as you say; and you must do me the justice to remember that I had no reason to think you'd ever taken it seriously. How could I, when you were married to Horace Ansley two months afterward? As soon as you could get out of bed your mother rushed you off to Florence and married you. People were rather surprised—they wondered at its being done so quickly. But I thought I knew. I had an idea you did it out of pique—to be able to say you'd got ahead of Delphin and me. Girls have such silly reasons for doing the most serious things. And your marrying so soon convinced me that you'd never really cared."

"Yes; I suppose it would," Mrs. Ansley said.

The clear heaven overhead was emptied of all its gold. Dusk spread over it, abruptly darkening the Seven Hills. Here and there lights began to twinkle through the foliage at their feet. Steps were coming and going on the deserted terrace—waiters looking out of the doorway at the head of the stairs, then reappearing with trays and napkins and flasks of wine. Tables were moved, chairs straightened. A feeble string of electric lights flickered out. Some vases of faded flowers were carried away and brought back replenished.

A stout lady in a dust coat suddenly appeared, asking in broken Italian if any one had seen the elastic band which held together her tattered Baedeker. She poked with her stock under the table at which she had lunched, the waiters assisting.

The corner where Mrs. Slade and Mrs. Ansley sat was still shadowy and deserted. For a long time neither of them spoke. At length Mrs. Slade began again: "I suppose I did it as a sort of joke—"

"A joke?"

"Well, girls are ferocious sometimes, you know. Girls in love especially. And I remember laughing to myself all that evening at the idea that you were waiting around there in the dark, dodging out of sight, listening for every sound, trying to get in. Of course I was upset when I heard you were so ill afterward."

Mrs. Ansley had not moved for a long time. But now she turned slowly toward her companion. "But I didn't wait. He'd arranged everything. He was there. We were let in at once," she said.

Mrs. Slade sprang up from her leaning position. "Delphin there? They let you in? Ah, now you're lying!" she burst out with violence.

Mrs. Ansley's voice grew clearer and full of surprise. "But of course he was there. Naturally he came—"

"Came? How did he know he'd find you there? You must be raving!"

Mrs. Ansley hesitated, as though reflecting. "But I answered the letter. I told him I'd be there. So he came."

Mrs. Slade flung her hands up to her face. "Oh, God—you answered! I never thought of your answering—"

"It's odd you never thought of it, if you wrote the letter."

"Yes. I was blind with rage."

Mrs. Ansley rose slowly and drew her fur scarf about her. "It's cold here. We'd better go. I'm sorry for you," she said as she clasped the fur about her throat.

The unexpected words sent a pang through Mrs. Slade. "Yes; we'd better go." She gathered up her bag and cloak. "I don't know why you should be sorry for me," she muttered.

Mrs. Ansley stood looking away from her toward the dusky secret mass of the Colosseum. "Well—because I didn't have to wait that night."

Mrs. Slade gave an unquiet laugh. "Yes; I was beaten there. But I oughtn't to begrudge it to you, I suppose. At the end of all these years. After all, I had everything; I had him for twenty-five years. And you had nothing but that letter that you didn't dare to keep."

Mrs. Ansley was again silent. Then she turned to move toward the door of the terrace. She took a step, and turned back, facing her companion.

"I had Barbara," she said—and began to move ahead of Mrs. Slade toward the stairway.

"So You Married an Aviator"

It's Thrill and Shock, Says One Who Did,
But the Glory You Find Is Worth It All!

"HOW DOES IT feel to be the wife of a pilot?" "Do you ever get used to having your husband up in the air most of the time?" "Does hearing about crashes frighten you?"

These—and many more like them—are the questions flung at every woman who is married to a flyer. And I must confess that it has taken five years of stiff mental and spiritual training for me to get even to first base in the game of not showing all I feel. For the life of a pilot's wife is a constant whirl of shocks, with the throttle of life kept at top speed.

When I met Peter I was afraid of aviation and all it stood for. But falling in love with a flyer, listening to him expound his dreams of what flying meant to him, soon transformed me into one of the greatest boosters for the air.

Perhaps I was carried away by a pair of wings, as so many others are, for when Peter and I married, I found the hazards and irregularities of a professional flyer's life pretty hard to take. It meant a complete readjustment of my ideas of living. Just when I thought I had a husband, he was yanked out from under my nose, shuttled here and there. But I argued myself out of my feeling of rebellion. Who was I, I reasoned, to stand in the way of a career Peter loved?

Of course I had my hours of worrying. What flyer's wife hasn't? One of these times came when Peter was flying the mail between Los Angeles and Salt Lake City, a run referred to as "the graveyard." I shudder now to think of the chances they took in those days. No instruments to guide them, nothing but dead reckoning and Lady Luck!

Peter and I were planning a wedding-anniversary celebration and we calculated that he would be back from his trip on the morning of the party.

But the morning came—and went—and no Peter.

I telephoned the dispatcher at Burbank. He told me that the ship was still at Salt Lake City, "holding for weather." I wasn't worried because I had heard similar reports many times. The spring sun shone brilliantly as

I went about my work, and such a thing as stormy weather elsewhere did not enter my mind.

A little after noon the dispatcher called to say the ship was on its way. At three he reported that it was fighting its way through severe storms.

I tried to stifle the fears tugging at my heart. But I was haunted by the thought of what news the next jingle of the telephone might bring.

When it came, I caught my breath. "They'll never make it," the dispatcher said. "Storms are growing more severe in those parts of the country they must fly through. . . . We believe—we hope—they have made a forced landing."

An agony of waiting, of pacing the floor as the hours dragged along. Then, at seven-thirty, the telephone rang again. I flew to answer it, my heart pounding, my hand shaking as I lifted the receiver.

One of our friends was on the wire. He had been in touch with the airport all afternoon, and now he was telling me, "They've landed! The ship is just touching the ground. I knew you'd want to know!"

Want to know! Want to know, after hours of anguished waiting, that my husband was safe!

Another shattering experience came to me over the radio when Peter was flying the night mail.

I had seen him off at the airport, watched him take off, alone in the open cockpit of a single-motored ship. With the stars so close, it seemed as if he could have reached up and gathered a handful. I felt a sense of exhilaration as the ship soared. I get the same feeling to this day when I watch a plane take to the air. It makes me understand a little what flying means to Peter.

I couldn't sleep that night, and at two-thirty in the morning I dropped my book and turned on the shortwave radio. I was startled to hear Pete's voice coming over the air waves: "Brinkerhoff calling Tucumcari. No report over my radio for forty minutes. Flying blind, running short of gas. I'll keep talking; perhaps some one will hear!"

A buzzing sound and then the voice again: "Brinkerhoff calling Tucumcari. I'm losing altitude. I'll give myself twenty minutes and then it's over the side."

After that, silence. I felt sobs tearing at my throat. Desperately I prayed for a miracle. A miracle was all that could save him now.

And the miracle happened. The voice came once more, this time eager, exultant: "I'm coming out of the fog. Pasture just below. Going to land."

Yes, a pilot's wife has her moments of suspense and anguish—many of them. That terrible night cured me of listening in on the shortwave radio. But nothing can cure me of the sickening sensation that comes when I hear the word "crack-up."

I remember the night the news came about Frank Perkins. Pete and I were at home, but five minutes after a telephone call had announced a crack-up on the line, we were bound for the airport.

I sat in the car while Pete went into the office. Only two nights ago Mrs. Perkins and I had waited in the same car to drive home with our husbands. And now Frank—

"Better go now, dear," Pete said when he came out. "Hard to say how long this will detain me. I may even take a train to Pittsburgh tonight. Anyway, I'll wire." And all the time I knew he was trying to tell me, "I'm going to fly a ship over myself. I'll fly through the same weather Frank did, but it's duty—duty—" A train? Never, with moments so precious!

So I drove home alone to the same bright living room where we had sat so peacefully scarcely two hours before. And I thought of Frank Perkins' wife, who would never see her husband again, never hear his gay infectious laughter. She would hold her head high, I knew; would carry on and think of the glory that was, and still *is,* if only she could see through the clouds.

And I thought, Shall we, the wives of these fortunate mortals, fret and nag them down from the clouds to some prosaic stuffy ground job, just because we may sometimes fear that Fate may snatch them from us?

For my part, I answer, No. For only those who have gone through dark hours can understand how danger can link two lives more closely, can understand the futility of pretending to be happy with a man whom you, his wife, forced to quit because you were a coward.

Did Edison Try to Talk with the Dead?

by Allan L. Benson

A Machine to Penetrate the Unknown! Here Is the Most Surprising Revelation Ever Made Concerning the Great Inventor

SOME YEARS before his death Thomas Alva Edison began to give thought to the possibility that a machine might be invented with which the dead could speak to us.

This is astonishing news, for America's greatest inventor, so far as the world knew, was all his life a confirmed agnostic. The mind that created the phonograph and the incandescent bulb refused to accept the belief in personal immortality or a personal God. Other great experimenters in the realm of science, like Sir Oliver Lodge and Sir William Crookes, embraced spiritualism. Edison never publicly avowed the slightest interest or the slightest faith in another world. Nevertheless, something must have happened to him to change his mind before he himself sailed down the River of the Dead.

I did not know Edison until 1909. He made it plain that while he disputed nothing that came under the head of religion, he remained unconvinced of the truth of any of it.

"The statement that the universe was made by a Creator does not help," he said, "because such a supposition immediately makes it necessary to explain what or who made the Creator."

The first time Edison talked to me in this strain, his secretary, Mr. Meadowcroft, whispered to me that the inventor's wife objected to seeing his views in print. Evidently other writers were similarly admonished. For twenty years he continued in his talks with me to set forth his beliefs on the origin and destiny of man. Nobody printed any of this matter for ten years. Then some writer, who apparently had not been asked to apply the soft pedal, wrote what Edison said to him. Then the cat was out of the bag. But no one even hinted that toward the end a change had come in Edison's convictions.

Edison's ideas on life, death, and religion were very definite. He believed that there was intelligence back of the universe but not personality. He did not believe that this intelligence had any interest in man.

Edison had a peculiar theory with regard to what he called the "life force" in back of every living thing. This theory is important, because it carried with it a train of conclusions that was completely overthrown if, toward the end, something came into his life that made him accept the possibility of the survival of personality after death.

"The life force itself," Edison said to me, "is immortal. It expresses itself in an endless succession of changing forms. This manifestation of energy came to the earth from some other part of the universe. It has the power to travel any distance instantaneously. But its quantity is limited. In other words, not more than a certain number of things can live on the earth at a time.

"Every form of life produces enough seeds or eggs to swamp the planet if each were to sprout or hatch and become a living thing. A single codfish could produce enough eggs to cover the earth several feet deep with his progeny if all the eggs were to hatch."

"Why, then, did it not happen?" I asked.

"Because," the great inventor thoughtfully replied, "there is not enough life force on the planet to convert all the eggs and seeds into living organisms."

Edison did not believe that every egg or seed contained a germ of life. "Seeds and eggs," he declared, "are the 'blue prints' which determine the form which the life force, when it flows, will make. Life force poured into a seed becomes a plant. Life force poured into an egg assumes the shape of an animal." He therefore believed in the underlying kinship of every living thing—the flower and the bird, the man and the tree, the nightingale and the tiger. "But," Edison emphatically declared, "the life force is at the bottom of each, irrespective of the design supplied by the blue print."

"What," I asked, "is your definition of life?"

"First of all," he replied, "energy. That is what I mean by life force. But there is another ingredient—intelligence. Every cell in every plant and animal possesses intelligence."

"Where does this intelligence come from?"

"It is drawn from some common source—a reservoir, to which it returns after each individual life ends, to be used again and again forever. Intelligence, like energy, is indestructible and immortal.

"Each cell is intelligent, but some are more intelligent than others and develop the ability to do some things that the others cannot do. Some of the cells of a tree, for instance, know how to pump water from the earth into its branches, while others conduct the intricate chemical processes involved in the metabolism of the leaf. My stomach," he added, "knows how to make hydrochloric acid. I don't."

Edison believed that each cell in the human body was made up of over a hundred million particles of intelligence, just as an atom is supposed to consist of electrons. He playfully called these particles "little peoples." Each of these mites, Edison believed, was an individual entity, having the power to form preferences and to act for itself.

"The widest differences," he reiterated, "exist among these ultra-microscopic men, some stupid, some bright, some good, some bad. Some have a social conscience and attempt to promote the general welfare, while a minority is antisocial. They are more or less a mirror of the world at large. The great majority are mixtures—leaning, perhaps, a little toward the good side."

This explains, perhaps, why human beings are what they are, and human nature is what it is. In Edison's opinion, like tends to attract like among the "little peoples" just as it does among us. If the ancestors of a given individual have long been more than ordinarily intelligent or well disposed, little peoples are attracted who have the same qualities. But the inferior or bad peoples also attract their kind. The individual is, therefore, the sum of all his ancestors, and a human skull is like a huge convention hall in which millions of people are assembled. Whoever is strong and agile enough to get hold of this crowd, organize it and discipline it, is the one who determines what kind of an assemblage it shall be. If there are plenty of good people present, and they are sitting up in front—in other words, if they represent the characteristics of recent generations—they may be expected to take charge.

"Occasionally," Edison continued, "a riot is raised by somebody far to the rear, the descendant of a bad relative, who has been kept in order by the decent ones since his ancestor was on earth, hundreds of years ago. When a bad man thus breaks out in a good family, neighbors wonder how it happened, and speak of a 'black sheep.' But nobody exists without such ancestors, and of these dangerous persons each of us has so many.

"So long as most of the little peoples in a human body are of one kind they are comfortable and wish to continue the association. When the little peoples feel this way, the man concerned is never tired of life. But when there is violent dissension inside and a strong group feels that further struggle is hopeless—then the man's spirits sink until he may kill himself.

"The death of my father," Edison added, "in his ninety-third year was plainly due to the fact that the 'little peoples' of whom he was composed became convinced that nothing desirable was to be gained by further association. Suddenly the old gentleman said he was going over to his daughter's and die, which he proceeded to do within three days, though he had not been ill."

Edison, I repeat, believed that the energy and intelligence that we call life are immortal but disbelieved in personal immortality. The individual, after closing his eyes here, would never know whether another life or another world awaited him. Edison, when I first met him, and maybe even until the end, had not the slightest belief that such a thing as a soul existed. He had no sort of belief in any existence beyond this life. Though not an atheist, he was a thoroughgoing agnostic. Whoever wrote a book setting forth such views was likely to receive a commendatory letter from the Edison laboratories, signed by the old wizard himself.

To the end of his days he honored the memory of Thomas Paine not because he was a patriot but because he rejected religion. What, then, made him busy his mind—a mind unclouded to the end—with thoughts of a contrivance by means of which the dead might talk to us? It may be that he still remained an agnostic but that, like a true scientist, he considered it his duty to investigate every reasonable hypothesis.

There is no doubt that fifteen years before he died and five years after I met him, Edison's mind turned toward the hereafter. This did not imply a sudden interest in spiritualism or spiritual matters.

"Benson," he told me about this time, "the older I grow the less I care whether there is a hereafter or not."

If this was the truth, and I have no doubt that Edison thought it was, his attempt to break down the wall between the living and the dead must have been due purely to a scientific interest. His business as an inventor had been first to find facts and then to use them. What were the facts about man? Had he an immortal soul? When earth life ceased, did it go out like a candle that is snuffed, or did it continue somewhere else? If it continued, could the dead speak to the living?

Edison wondered whether it might not be possible to make a machine that would enable the hereafter to prove itself without the aid of mediums or other living human agencies. If spirits could communicate directly with the earth, doubting would soon have to stop.

Edison was a scientist and, as such, had a profound respect for facts. He might be wrong about the soul, a

174

hereafter, and the possibility of conducting conversation between the two worlds. If so, he wanted to shift his course to fit the facts.

It may be that as the shadows grew longer, Edison, or some of the "little peoples" within him, began to hope that there was such a thing as survival after death. It may be that he was influenced by his friendship with Sir William Crookes. That great physicist believed in spiritualism as firmly as he believed in the existence of his own hands and feet. His familiarity with chemistry and physics had not destroyed his faith in the reality of a future life and the ability of the spirits of the dead to communicate with the living. Crookes had braved the skepticism of his colleagues by setting forth in print again and again, over his own signature, his extraordinary experiences.

Edison had a profound respect for Crookes. His friend's intelligence and honesty made it impossible to treat lightly anything that he said. He was indebted to Crookes scientifically. The filament of the incandescent electric light could function only in a bulb from which most of the air had been exhausted. Crooke's work on creating vacuums had helped Edison. Sir William's account of what he saw with his own eyes was enough to give pause to any one.

Perhaps the most astonishing story he told was that concerning the visits of the spirit of a dead woman to his home. She never came except when brought by a medium. The medium would lie down on a couch in a dark adjoining room, and in a little while the spirit would appear before Sir William and his friends. She appeared in what seemed to be flesh and bones, clad as any woman might be for an afternoon call. But she did not walk in. She came in instantaneously—how, nobody knew.

Suddenly she appeared before the company, standing where a moment before there had been no one. And she could talk as well as any other woman; could create sound waves that traveled to the ears of other persons. Some suggested that she herself was the medium and that the woman who had lain down on the couch was no longer there. But a visit to the adjoining room showed that the other woman—the medium—was there, lying in what appeared to be a profound stupor. Some were still unconvinced. The woman on the couch might be a dummy. A dummy would not have a pulse, so the medium's wrist was felt. Not only was there a pulse, but it was registering the fast tempo of ninety-five a minute. Then the pulse of the spirit was felt. Sure enough, she had one. It was beating seventy a minute.

These meetings in the library of Sir William continued all winter. They were held behind locked doors. There were present only his personal friends. By permission of the spirit woman, Sir William took forty-three pictures of her. Toward spring she said she could not come again, bade him an affectionate farewell, and—was gone. The next second she was just not there, though she had not made an audible sound or a perceptible movement.

Such was the substance of what Crookes wrote and Edison read. The American could not doubt the veracity of Crookes, or his intelligence. It was unlikely that anybody could dupe him. If he was hypnotized, so were all the guests.

But was the camera hypnotized too? What about the forty-three negatives of the spirit woman?

Edison was in the tough position of one who cannot doubt a statement that has been made to him by a friend —yet cannot believe. If there were only a machine by means of which spirits (if there were any and they were so inclined) could speak directly to earth beings! The camera, in this instance, still left upon those who might see the pictures the burden of believing that they were pictures of a spirit. The camera did not, in behalf of the spirit, speak out and say what she had to say. A machine was needed—

Unconvinced, Edison still had an open mind. It would do no harm to try. If nothing happened, it would be just what he expected. On the other hand, if the idea worked, there would be no more doubt about the hereafter.

The acceptance of the smallest part of Sir William Crooke's story would have been like the explosion of a charge of dynamite under the foundation of Edison's beliefs.

Yet five years before his death his attitude toward all of these questions underwent a decided change. The last utterance attributed to him was that there was "a fifty-fifty chance that there might be a hereafter with immortality for the individual."

Whether Edison, toward the end, swerved toward Crooke's views is not known to this writer. Whether Edison ever had any experiences of his own that might have had the same effect is also unknown. We cannot tell whether the master of electricity received some signal from the other world or talked to the dead before he himself entered the Great Beyond. We know only that his old views crumbled.

Edison always said that the easiest way was usually the wrong way. In seeking to invent a machine for spirits to use he would certainly choose the most difficult way. The details of Edison's ideas about a machine are not known to man. I do not know to what extent his conception resembled a phonograph or radio. It may be that he hoped that intelligent spirits, if they existed, would prefer to manifest themselves through mechanical means rather than through human beings. For the machine cannot lie.

At all events, Edison is gone, and with him the reason why he seemed upon the point of modifying views that required a lifetime to formulate, and the secret of his thoughts about a machine to enable the dead to talk to us.

The Eel-Snooper

by Robert Benchley

COME, COME! WHAT'S all this we hear about eels? Some Danish ichthyologist (look it up yourself— I had to) named Schmidt comes back from a scientific cruise and says that every single one of the eels on the eastern coast of the United States and the western coast of Europe came originally from the Sargasso Sea (the Sargasso Sea being that small area of the Atlantic Ocean down around the Antilles which is always full of tea leaves and old bits of grass). He says that whenever our eels get to feeling sappy and foolish and want to become parents, they pack up and leave the fresh waters of New England or Virginia or wherever they happen to be living at the time, and glide all the way south to the Sargasso Sea. Here the eggs are deposited and (pardon me) fertilized, and here the happy event takes place. Or perhaps it should be happy events, since they hatch out in litters of ten million per mother.

At this point, according to the Danish Dr. Schmidt, the parents die, evidently disgusted at the prospect of cutting up food and picking up toys for ten million babies. The offspring, finding themselves orphans, immediately turn tail and wriggle north, where they, too, stay until Joe feels that he is earning enough to have kiddies. Then the whole rather silly procedure takes place all over again.

At least, this is what the Danish Dr. Schmidt says. Just what anyone named Schmidt is doing in Denmark (unless his parents, like the eels, went somewhere else for the time being) is beside the point. What I want to know is how does he know that our eels all come from, and go back to, the Sargasso Sea? How do you keep track of an eel?

According to the story told by the ichthyologist (don't tell me you haven't looked that up *yet!*), he "banded" thousands of eels and then followed them all over the various seas. I take this to mean that he tied little markers on each eel, labeled "Georgie" and "Fred" or perhaps just "No. 113,539." While he was at it, it would have been just as easy to have the plate engraved "This is Rover, and belongs to Dr. Johannes Schmidt, 114 Nvjeltidg Boulevard, Copenhagen," or "Please put me off at Jacksonville, Fla." He might even have gone so far as to put little false mustaches on those eels which he particularly wanted to keep track of and to give them each seventy-five cents to spend for candy on the trip south. The whole thing sounds just a little bit fishy to me.

An eel must be an awful sap to let himself be caught just for the sake of being tagged and thrown back into the water again. My experience with eels is rather limited, having got hold of one for only a few seconds once and then decided that it wasn't worth the struggle. But I should think that any self-respecting eel would resent being caught and "banded" and then tossed back, making him a figure of fun among the other eels, and perhaps laying himself open to the charge of being a sissy. For a breed of fish (or are they fish?) which has gone proudly through the centuries without ornamentation of any kind, it must be very humiliating for one particular member to find himself wearing a shiny new band around his tail reading "Prince."

No wonder these eels who have been subjected to this indignity rush off to the Sargasso Sea. They probably can't bear to stay around the home town with all the kidding they must get. I shouldn't be surprised to find that it was *only* those eels who wore bands that fled to the south. The rest are probably still in the northern fresh waters, laughing their heads off and saying: "Whatever became of that pansy who used to wear a tin ring on his tail?"

And from then on, just what is Dr. Schmidt's course of action? Does he follow the eels down the coast, fishing them out every few days to see if their bands are on tight? Or does he rush right off by airplane to the Sargasso Sea in order to be there when his pets arrive? It must be rather confusing for a bunch, or covey, or flock of eels to leave New England after their distressing experience with Dr. Schmidt, and swim all the way down to Central America only to be fished out by the same Dr. Schmidt at the other end and made mock of all over again. If eels figure out anything at all, they must have evolved the theory that there are two Schmidt brothers who look exactly alike.

"For the love of Mike," they must say, "didn't we just *leave* this guy? What is this—a racket? Can't we *ever* shake him?" The twin brothers theory would be the only one that would satisfy a clear-headed eel, especially when he finds out that the name is Schmidt again. The wonder is that they have enough patience left to go ahead with the breeding.

The behavior of the young eels on the return trip is even more extraordinary, according to the Doc. They start out for the north just as soon as they are born (which is not surprising when you consider that the Sargasso Sea is full of pretty unpleasant stuff, even for an eel) and, if they don't swim fast enough, or, as Dr. Schmidt phrases it, "are dilatory," they outgrow their salt-water days and perish before they reach fresh water. I am not so sure that the ones who are "dilatory" are not the smart ones, for at least they have had the pleasure of being dilatory, than which there is no greater pleasure in the world.

The rest, who rush along to fresh water, have only just time to swim around once at their destination, be fished out and banded, and then rush right back again to die in the Sargasso Sea.

The little ones who are aggressive enough to make the grade northward sound very unattractive. They are "transparent, gelatinous creatures of which the only substantial parts are two disembodied eel eyes like mother-of-pearl." This presents a rather horrid picture, I am sure. I am just as glad that my bailiwick does not include the swarming grounds of these young eels, for coming home late at night and seeing a group of disembodied eyes with nothing to back them up must be a pretty trying experience. I still don't understand how a fish can have nothing but eyes, but there are a lot of things in this world that I don't understand.

When this unprepossessing-looking crowd of larvae reach a point about the latitude of Bermuda, they split up into eastbound and westbound parties, those who are more sober-minded going up to the New England territory and the gayer ones heading for the coast of France. I doubt if many of these who go to France ever bother about coming back to the Sargasso Sea to have children. They probably go up a river to some nice, rich, farming territory and settle down to salt away their money, or swim down the Seine to Paris and drink themselves to death.

Dr. Schmidt will only be wasting his time to band any of these.

In fact, I wonder if Dr. Schmidt isn't wasting his time anyway. Suppose it *is* proven that all eels come from, and go back to, the Sargasso Sea. What then?

To
the Ladies!

by Princess Alexandra Kropotkin

Linguist, Friend of the Famous in Europe,
and Descendant of the First Czar of Russia

THE RAIN CAME down soon after explorer Mitchell-Hedges and his assistant, Jane Houlson, had arrived at the little Maya-Kekchi village. In a native hut Jane Houlson was pounding her typewriter. Suddenly a crowd of Indians pushed in around her. With them they brought their sick—they even brought their dead.

Horrified, Miss Houlson would have fled the place, but Mitchell-Hedges stopped her.

"For God's sake, stay at your typewriter!" he whispered. "They think your machine is the magic that brought the rain and ended the drought that was killing them. Now they believe your typewriter can cure their sick and get their dead into heaven. Keep on hitting those keys!"

That's the kind of a time you may have if you spend your life blazing trails for archaeology. F. A. Mitchell-Hedges and Jane Harvey Houlson dig intrepidly into the ancient Maya ruins now lost among the jungles of Mexico and Central America. He sends his discoveries back to the Museum of the American Indian, to the British Museum, and other scientific institutions. He's English —a direct descendant of Oliver Cromwell. Miss Houlson is English too. She does the writing on their expeditions. Also she catches big fish. Her 4,600-pound sawfish is a record catch. She weighs ninety-seven pounds.

I was fascinated hearing Mitchell-Hedges tell about the white descendants of old Morgan, the buccaneer.

They live by themselves on some remote islands off the coast of Honduras.

"They live as primitively as the Indians," he told me, "yet they have never allowed their white blood to be mixed with the brown. The names of the men who served in old Morgan's pirate crew are still there—McNab, Cooper, Hayward, Kerconnell—a living generation sprung directly from the old freebooters who ravaged the Spanish Main."

For once in my life I have seen jealousy turned to good and useful account. The circumstances were rather pitiful in a way, but the cause was worthy.

It happened at a house party I attended not long ago. The other guests were all strangers to me. I noticed one of the men making a flirtatious fool of himself. Nothing outrageous—just whispering in the girls' ears, dancing à la burlesque—you know the antics of the *regular cut-up*.

"What a nuisance he is!" I heard several women say.

Then his wife gave me the real surprise. She became sternly vigilant, snatched him away from the girls, took him right straight home.

When they had gone I was let in on the secret. For years they have been the ardent lovers of the neighborhood. Always boasted about it. Now they are growing

Last year at this time I had a letter from a farmer's wife. Depression was then unchecked. The country-woman told me how her two boys, out of work in the city, had just come home to live. She told me how glad she was to have them with her; how thankful she was that the farm could at least keep them fed and sheltered. "We have a real reason for Thanksgiving," she said.

I can't help thinking of her again this year. I hope her boys are with her now—not seeking refuge, as before —just home from their own jobs for an old-fashioned Thanksgiving visit.

Thankful as we must be for the old resources of the land that keep us alive through adversity, we should be even more thankful this year, I believe, for the strong and resourceful men now leading us out of adversity.

Escape, by F. Yeats-Brown, is the best thriller I have read this season—and all the hairbreadth escapes it tells about were real. (Published by Macmillan.)

old. He pretends to flirt so that she can pretend to be jealous. Just to keep up their sentimental reputation. Touching, isn't it?

With a party of friends I had dinner in a Hindu restaurant one evening recently. We were told it was correct to eat our curry, rice, fried bananas, etc., with a spoon. One of the men in our party exclaimed with joy.

Other men at our table seemed to feel the same way. They said they wished that spoons were more generally sanctioned by our own rules of etiquette. How silly it is, they said, to fork fussily at a stew, a casserole, or any juicy dish of that kind. Also fried and poached eggs.

The men want spoons. They asked me to start a pro-spoon movement right here and now. I said I would write this little piece, putting it up to my women readers. What do you say, girls? Are you *for* spoons or *agin* 'em?

"Women may slip," says Mme. Julienne of Paris, "but women must never wabble."

Right away I want you to know that Mme. Julienne is talking about our shoes—not our morals. She's the big shoe designer of France today. She says every shoe you wear should grip your instep firmly to prevent wabbling. Low squarish heels for street wear. Any shoe, she warns, that does not place your foot solidly and comfortably on the ground will certainly throw your figure out of balance, eventually disturbing your insides.

Paris has been listening to this advice. Low heels are now the fad over there. For daytime the smart Parisiennes are wearing patent-leather slippers, almost heel-less— little-girl style. For evening they wear Directoire slippers with crisscross ribbons to tie them on. These Directoire slippers have no heels at all.

What Being Kidnaped Has Done to Me

by Mary McElroy, as told to Corinne Reid Frazier

A Vivid Account of the Aftermath of a Terrifying Experience

EDITOR'S NOTE: Two years ago, Miss McElroy, daughter of Judge H. F. McElroy, city manager of Kansas City Missouri, was the victim in a kidnaping which was front-page news everywhere. On May 27, 1933, she was surprised by intruders as she was taking a bath and was "snatched" from her home and carried across the state line, to be held for ransom in a dungeonlike basement by four men and a woman. Of these, Walter H. McGee, the ringleader, is now to be hanged for the crime on May 10—within two days after this issue of Liberty appears on the newsstands. If his execution is carried out as scheduled it will be the first in the United States for kidnaping. His brother George is in prison for life, and a third kidnaper, Clarence Click, for eight years.

THE ACTUAL PHYSICAL experience of being held captive is nothing compared to the mental torment that lingers after release. *This is the real crime of kidnaping!*

To awaken at night months later, cold from a dream in which you are being killed or tortured; to be unable to walk down a quiet street after dark or to go into an empty room without the heart leaping in fear and the hands trembling—this is the phase of the crime which I believe few people who have not been its victims are capable of grasping—least of all, the kidnapers themselves.

Kidnaping is a *mental inquisition*. I am haunted today not only by my own memories but by two great fears —that someone else may be in danger of experiencing at any moment what I experienced, and that somewhere other men are planning such another crime, with the certainty of death or imprisonment for it awaiting them.

The physical aspects of kidnaping are bad enough. No one enjoys being snatched rudely from the privacy of one's own bedchamber; ordered to "get a move on," with the threat of death for disobedience; and forced to plead for permission even to clothe oneself first! It is

frightening, to say the least, to be hustled into a motor and thrust rudely on to the floor, to ride unnumbered miles with unknown captors, and finally to be chained to the wall of a damp basement room.

When the men first came into my room my mind was painfully clear on the minutest details. I dressed with the most meticulous care while one of the kidnapers stood outside my door threatening to shoot me if I didn't hurry. And on that long ride, while my nerves were still numbed by the shock, my most conscious thought came when I looked down at my hands and noticed my white gloves, and thought how foolish I had been to wear them.

"You're certainly not going to need a white hat and gloves where you're going, Mary!" I told myself. And the thought somehow amused me tremendously. I kept as quiet as I could. I felt I would rather die than let those men guess I was afraid.

Strangely, my first vivid feeling at the cabin where I was taken was the fear I had spelled "counterfeit" wrong in the ransom note the kidnapers forced me to write my father. And I wasn't sure about the number of p's in "kidnaped."

But, once I began to realize the seriousness of my plight, a sort of dead calm settled down upon me—the calm of utter hopelessness. One does not worry when there is no hope. Through no fault of my own I was in this predicament. There was nothing I could have done to prevent it—nothing I could do now.

I had heard so much of kidnapers killing their victims that I thought this was to be my fate ultimately. My one hope was that they would not torture me first. The man who guarded me throughout the night seemed friendly when we talked. I told him of two books in which I thought he might be interested: Victor F. Nelson's

Prison Nights and Days and Warden Lawes's *Twenty Thousand Years in Sing Sing.* I recalled that Warden Lawes had said: "If you want to make a dangerous man your friend, let him do you a favor." So I followed that advice.

While I was not conscious of worry, I knew fear. A fear that I tried with all my strength to hide. This strain told on me. It was a fear bred of the unknown, of what *might* happen. To pass through a night of such fear—perhaps many of them—is to experience a nerve shock which impresses indelibly upon the subconscious mind horrors that not even the joy of unexpected release can wipe out.

My anxiety for my family's mental suffering was acute. No jury should overlook this angle of the crime—the mental anguish of the victim's family and friends, with its sometimes fatal results.

In the morning, that black morning when I was almost too weary and bewildered to think, I was permitted to have a mirror, and it took me nearly an hour to make up my mind to look into it—so sure was I that my hair had turned white!

That afternoon I was told to prepare for a journey. It proved to be my journey of release.

The real effect of those hours of captivity only began to make itself felt weeks afterward. Only then, when the strain was over, when there was no longer any stimulating excitement, did I begin to experience the reactions so difficult to describe. These seem almost too terrible to put into words. They involve the things that *might have happened.* How can I explain them? The torture I mercifully escaped; the personal attacks I thought inevitable; the death I felt to be a certainty. Can't you imagine for yourself what shape these dreams would take?

I cannot believe my kidnapers (one now sentenced to be hanged; two, to long terms of imprisonment) could

have brought themselves to commit such a crime had they given a moment's thought to the almost unimaginable cruelty of its results. Had they considered, even, the mental torment of my father, who for all I know may suffer still as I do from the effects of those agonizing hours of waiting for my return.

To most kidnapers plotting the crime I am sure it never occurs that with the physical presence of their victim must go, also, the mental and spiritual being—a being they will injure inevitably, beyond complete restoration. Nor, I believe, does it occur to many of the citizens whose indignation is aroused by the physical aspects of the crime.

In my own case I could not help noticing at the trial of the kidnapers that the jury was much more affected by the evidence of a threatened attack upon my person than by the far more terrible evidence of an actual attack upon my mental and nerve centers!

The point I am trying to make clear is that the world should be made to recognize kidnaping as a crime of mental destructiveness, to be punished with equal severity whether the victim is returned physically "safe and unharmed" (this is ironical to me), or whether his battered body is found in some isolated wasteland.

I am quite as much concerned with ways and means of preventing men like my kidnapers from committing such crimes as in the protection of people from being kidnaped.

I believe that I have a peculiar right to express certain opinions on kidnaping, for I have never felt any personal bitterness toward my kidnapers. I feel exactly the same toward them today as I did while they held me captive and just after I was released. When I testified against them in court, it was their crime I was fighting. I don't know why it is so hard to make people understand that it is possible to believe a man must pay the penalty for his crime and at the same time to wish that he didn't have to.

And one way of staying them, I believe, is to bring to them a realization of the hideousness of crime. Let the law, the people, and the potential kidnaper himself remember this: It takes but a few hours to "restore" a kidnap victim to his loved ones. *It may take a lifetime to restore him to himself.*

Bonnie and Clyde

by Will Irwin

CLYDE AND BUCK Barrow, together with Bonnie Parker, Clyde's lurid light-o'-love, were the first to shoot their way into national notoriety. Let us look at them as they were—we have of late hung too many romantic trimmings upon thugs and morons of this sort. The Barrows were mental, moral, and physical scrubs. Buck measured five feet five inches in height; Clyde, the worse of the pair, five feet three. Neither weighed much more than 100 pounds.

Parenthetically, most of the really dangerous characters whose Bertillon measurements decorate the criminal archives at Washington rate in the flyweight class. Any modern psychologist will tell you that this is no accident. The scrubby little boy with criminal tendencies has in his childhood stood for bullying and persecution by other little boys. When he grows up and goes on the loose, he has a complex of physical inferiority; and he compensates for it by brutality with those instruments which made dwarfs stand equal to giants—guns.

The bodies of the Barrows were colossal compared to their souls. I need cite only one instance. Getting away from a robbery, they needed a car. They found one in possession of a farmer's wife. Even when she faced a gun, she objected to handing over the keys. Whereupon they knocked her out with a chain and assaulted her criminally before they went their way.

From small holdups at filling stations they passed on to bank robberies. Rather early in the game, a posse shot at Buck. He died miserably a few weeks later from infection in his wounds. Clyde and Bonnie Parker carried on. She was a blonde with a hard mouth who smoked black cigars, had herself photographed guns in hand, and shot as well as her man. When hiding out in the wilds they practiced their shooting constantly—and photographed each other standing beside their targets. Except for a sentimental streak in Bonnie which moved her to write atrocious poetry, vanity was the only human trait they possessed.

Gradually the posses hunting them grew larger and larger. Once Governor Murray of Oklahoma called out four companies of militia and all the deputies in four or five counties. Sometimes they sneaked through the cordons; just as often, they got away by accurate fast shooting with machine guns or automatics. Before they died they had at least a dozen murders on their souls. Most of the victims were police officers doing their duty. One murder reveals again what kind of people these Barrows were. They had held up a grocer in the presence of his wife. He hoisted his hands and made no resistance while they stripped his till. Then, as they turned away, one of them shot him dead—"just for luck."

Both Clyde Barrow and Bonnie Parker took several wounds in their brushes with the law. They sneaked at last into the remote bayou country of Louisiana. Sheriff Henderson Jordon of Bienville Parish, learning of their presence from federal agents, formed a posse, laid a clever trap, annihilated them with automatic rifles and machine guns. He said afterward that he loathed the thought of killing a woman; but what else could a responsible officer of the law do with a Bonnie Parker?

Why Dillinger's Gang Is Doomed

by Al Dunlap

Poor Teamwork, Not Criminal Cunning, Delayed Their Leader's Grim Capture—But the Police Were Always on the Trail. Here at Last Is the Inside Story

DILLINGER HAD A lot of people fooled—including most of the newspaper readers and audiences who saw newsreels of his Little Bohemia adventures.

These people thought he was the cleverest crook that ever lived, the most daring, the most elusive. "Woodengun Dillinger" they called him. "The modern Raffles." "The new Jesse James." As such, they were "for him."

Yet Dillinger was as big a fool as any criminal at large today. The fact that he spent almost nine of his thirty years in jail, and was twice shot and twice captured in his little year of freedom following his parole, adequately demonstrates the truth of that statement.

What made him look so brilliant and dashing was the bad teamwork of the police. Never have the various police agencies of the United States worked in such utter disharmony as they did on the Dillinger case. Yet, even working against each other, they caught up with their quarry in a very short time and pumped him full of lead.

There is a semblance of coöperation now—since Dillinger is out of the way. A more or less united front is opposed to criminals of all kinds. There will be no mercy shown Dillinger's pals. And they will be found, soon or later, dead or alive.

It will not do any harm, therefore, to point out to the police the mistakes made while Dillinger was alive—since, no matter how often or how woefully the cops blundered, they finally erased all errors with their guns.

Dillinger's end should be a warning to other criminals. The chase of Dillinger should be a warning to all police officers that coöperation is essential in the war on crime.

Even the veriest fool can get away—and make himself look important—when police cross each other.

Dillinger had always been a fool. He never finished school. He never held a steady job. He thought he could live by easy money; and he was caught in his first attempt to get it. He cracked an old man, B. F. Morgan, a grocer, over the head with an iron bolt wrapped in a handkerchief, and took a few dollars from him. The victim recognized his assailant. He had known him most of his life. He caused Dillinger's arrest. And for his stupid and brutal crime Dillinger was sentenced to prison, to serve from ten to twenty-one years.

Released on parole in May, 1933, he involved himself immediately with ex-convict friends and loose women. With William Shaw he went out to Monticello, Indiana, to rob a payroll. The watchman frustrated the attempt, and Dillinger shot and wounded him—then wanted to go back and kill him. Shaw prevented that. Dillinger next proposed that Shaw help him rob a bank in Lebanon, Indiana. Shaw refused.

Dillinger thereupon rubbed Shaw off his list of friends, and allied himself with others who had no scruples about robbing banks and killing anybody.

By August, 1933, two good detectives knew all about him and his friends. They were Forrest C. Huntington, who was employed by surety companies that had bonded several banks Dillinger had looted; and Matt Leach, captain and head of the Indiana State Police.

Huntington and Leach, working in harmony for a time, talked to Shaw and got from him valuable clues to Dillinger's whereabouts. Then they brought about the arrest of "Whitey" Mohler, and Frank and George Whitehouse. Dillinger had spent money lavishly on these three men. He had taken Frank Whitehouse and his wife to the Century of Progress Exposition in Chicago.

Through them Leach learned that Dillinger, Sam Goldstein, Harry Copeland, and Homer Van Meter had rented a flat in Gary, Indiana, and housed their cars in a garage a block away. The Gary police gave Leach a few men to surround the apartment house—but they couldn't spare any to watch the garage. Leach went bumping over the roads at sixty miles an hour to the state police barracks eighteen miles away, and rounded up all the available men. When he returned he found the Gary police had arrested Goldstein. But Dillinger, Copeland, and Van Meter hadn't come near the apartment building.

Leach hurried to the garage. He had left instructions with the boy in charge there to phone the police immediately if any of Dillinger's band showed up. He had had to trust the boy; there was no one else to do the work. Dillinger, Copeland, and Van Meter had come to the garage during Leach's absence. They had left word for Goldstein to pick them up at a roadhouse about nine miles out of Gary.

The boy had phoned the police, he said, but some one at the police station had stated he didn't know anything about the matter, and had hung up.

Leach and his men went immediately to the roadhouse, but Dillinger and the other two had flown. Leach learned later that he had lost them by only a few minutes.

Whitey Mohler, however, gave the police another valuable lead: "Dillinger's got a girl in Dayton, Ohio—a Mrs. Mary Longnaker. She's got a husband—though she's not living with him. She can't run around with Dillinger on account of her two kids. So he goes to see her. Watch her house and you'll get him."

Leach and Huntington notified the Dayton police. And in September Dillinger was found in Mary Longnaker's room, and handcuffed before he could make a fight.

Chief of Detectives S. E. Yendes, who made the arrest, did not notify either Leach or Huntington. They read it in a newspaper. Leach felt bitter. He went to Dayton with a warrant for Dillinger, and demanded his custody and all his effects.

Yendes defied Leach and kept the prisoner in Dayton with all his papers for several weeks. He intended to turn him over to Chief of Police Mike Morrissey of Indianapolis—but not right away. Before he turned him over to anybody he wanted to know about the reward. He wanted the reward, he told Huntington, for the landlady who had notified him when Dillinger arrived. The surety companies had offered a reward of $100 for Dillinger's arrest in sixty days. The time limit had expired. There was no reward; but the surety companies promised to give Yendes something for the automobile and the $2,604 that Dillinger had with him when arrested.

Before anything could be done about this a smart Cincinnati lawyer advised Dillinger to plead guilty to robbing an Ohio bank, and stay in Ohio. Then he would be sent to a little jail at Lima. If he were sent back to Indiana, rescue might be difficult.

Dillinger pleaded guilty; but before he was sent to Lima, ten of his friends, armed with automatics, walked out of the Indiana state penitentiary at Michigan City. Among them were Harry Pierpont and Jimmy Jenkins, Mary Longnaker's brother, a lifer in for murder.

Dillinger, acting under Pierpont's orders, had bought the guns in Chicago, hidden them in a box containing thread, and shipped the box to the shirt factory in the prison. The box got there with scarcely any examination. At that time, convicts said, you could have smuggled machine guns into the prison.

Leach said this jail break could have been prevented had he seen the papers Yendes took from Dillinger. Yendes retorted that he had given Leach full permission to copy every word contained in those papers.

At any rate, because of a police quarrel ten men had broken jail, and Dillinger stayed in Ohio. Shortly after he was shut up in the jail at Lima, five of the ten rescued him, brutally killing Jesse Sarber, the sheriff.

Huntington had sent warning to the Pinkerton Agency, which guarded Ohio banks, that a rescue would be attempted; and the Pinkertons had warned Sarber.

Leach went to Lima at once. He was present when Pierpont's brother Fred was questioned. Fred admitted his brother was the ringleader of the gang that had liberated Dillinger. He identified—by their rogues' gallery pictures—every man in the mob. He swore they were living at a certain house in Hamilton, Ohio, or in a river camp operated by the couple who ran the house.

Leach remembered Gary. He phoned Al Feeny, Indiana's Commissioner of Public Safety, at Indianapolis, and asked for eighteen men. Then he went to see Chief Calhoun of Hamilton. "Let's surround the house at once," he said. "If the men are not there, we'll go immediately to the river camp."

"No," Calhoun said; "we'll investigate first."

He slipped away from Leach and his men. He was gone for three hours. He returned to say he had investigated the camp and found no one there. He was ready to rush the house.

Approximately thirty men were thrown about the house. Chief Calhoun knocked on the door, went inside, stayed a little while, and came out, saying the men had gone.

Leach, maddened to the point of fury, rushed his eighteen men to the river camp. He says the stove was still warm when he got there. He returned to Hamilton and made inquiries in the neighborhood of the raided house. Dillinger, Pierpont, and the others, he says he was told, had quietly slipped out the night before—while he was urging Calhoun to "do something immediately."

After the escape from Hamilton the gang raided the police stations at Auburn and Peru, Indiana, and stole machine guns, riot guns, and bullet-proof vests. Homer Van Meter, posing as the staff writer of a detective magazine, had been told by police themselves exactly what arms they had and where they were kept.

Thus armed and equipped they held up the Central National Bank at Greencastle, Ohio, and left with $20,000 in cash and $56,000 in bonds. They were in the bank ten minutes. A bank employee called the police.

The police had ample time to respond; but they went first to the sheriff's office—going a long way around the bank—and when they arrived the bandits had gone. The sheriff's office is directly across the street from the bank. There were a deputy sheriff and a state policeman in the office. Had they known of the robbery in time, they could have stood at their windows and picked off Dillinger and his pals as they came out.

The Dillinger-Pierpont mob went to Chicago. Dillinger was but second in command. Pierpont was boss.

Women Dillinger had known, men he had trusted, and stool pigeons he did not suspect soon made him and his whereabouts known to the Chicago police. One stool pigeon even paraded Dillinger in front of a police official to show that he, the stool, was on the level.

The Chicago police, through the work of Lieutenant John Howe and his undercover men and the coöperation of Huntington and two stool pigeons—one furnished by Huntington and the other by Emory Smith, assistant attorney-general of Illinois and counsel for the Illinois Bankers Association—learned where Dillinger kept his guns, who stole the automobiles for him and the gang, who was trying to sell the Greencastle bonds, and the addresses of his two flats.

They learned also that he was visiting a doctor on Irving Park Boulevard every day at certain hours. The doctor was treating him for ringworm.

They wanted him; but they wanted Pierpont more, and Makley and Clark and the others who had helped to murder the sheriff of Lima, Ohio. They could have picked Dillinger up at any time. But they wanted him to contact the others first. He was only a "punk" to Chicago.

Chicago coöperated with Indiana and Ohio at this time. Indiana demanded action. Three squad cars and one driven by Huntington went out to pick up Dillinger as he left the doctor's office.

They saw Dillinger arrive and park his car, saw him go across the street and up the stairs, leaving his girl, the half-Indian Evelyn Frechette, in the driver's seat. And now some of the thirty hunters got cold feet. They were afraid of missing Dillinger when he came out. They

conferred with Huntington—because his stool pigeon was involved. They wanted to take Dillinger as soon as he reappeared—but that might mean the murder of the informant. Huntington reluctantly agreed. The three squad cars moved into better strategic positions.

Dillinger's machine was bracketed by two police cars. Another was across the street. Thirty armed men waited tensely. Dillinger came out, got into his car, backed it into Irving Park Boulevard, and started away. Only one car had seen him. Only one car followed.

They fired at ten feet with riot guns and automatics. They shot into his windshield, his front window, his front tires. Dillinger stepped on the gas. So did Huntington. Dillinger went seventy-five miles an hour. Huntington followed him for miles. Dillinger put out his lights, slowed down, and darted into an alley. Huntington's car went past it. Before he could turn and come back, Dillinger and the girl had gone.

The police with Huntington told their superiors that Dillinger's girl and a companion with a machine gun had fired on them. They pointed to holes in the windshield and the side windows. But there was no machine gun in Dillinger's car. And neither Dillinger nor the girl nor anybody else fired on the cops. The holes in question had been made by the cops themselves.

After that, Dillinger cleared out of Chicago for a time. He made several trips to Mooresville, Indiana, to eat dinner at the home of his father or his sister. Once he went to kill a lawyer who had "vanished" with $3,200 of his money. Several times he went to Indianapolis with Pierpont to kill Matt Leach. Pierpont believed Leach had arrested his brother and his mother. Dillinger's reason was that Leach knew too much.

Running down an Indiana road at a great speed, Dillinger's car hit another machine and went into a cornfield. It was abandoned there, and curious farmers found an automatic cartridge clip in it.

Leach went out to investigate. "It must be Dillinger's car," he thought. "He's a fool for luck. Nobody else on the face of the earth could have gone into that cornfield in the dark without killing himself. If it was Dillinger, he probably went on to Indianapolis, and he'll probably buy a car and drive away. He'll have to buy it for cash— or have some woman buy it. If I call up every automobile dealer in the city, I'll get him."

But it might be a better idea, he thought, to have the Indianapolis police contact the dealers. The man on post could see every dealer within the city limits in a short time. Therefore he stopped at the police station, made his request, and busied himself in other ways.

It was not until three o'clock the next afternoon that he heard from the police. They had found a dealer who had sold a car to a woman for cash. Leach investigated immediately, found out beyond doubt that the purchaser was Evelyn Frechette, and tried to pick her up. But by that time she and Dillinger had been gone for hours.

In Racine, Wisconsin, the gang raided the American Bank and Trust Co. A bank employee stepped on an alarm button which not only notified the police but rang a gong in front of the bank. A great crowd, attracted by the gong, looked in through a window and saw the bandits at work. Leslie Homer, later arrested, pasted up a Red Cross banner and shut out their view.

The cops arrived in no time. Three dashed into the bank, one with a machine gun in his hands. A bandit standing near the door hit the machine gunner, Policeman Cyril Boyard, over the head from behind. Boyard dropped. The second policeman, Sergeant Wilbur Hansen, was shot and badly wounded. The third, Frank Worsley, wisely retreated.

The bandits emerged from the bank holding Boyard, President Grover Weyland, and Mrs. Ursula Patzke, an employee, in front of them as screens. They dropped Boyard a mile from the bank, and released the other two hostages thirty-five miles farther on.

Dillinger frequently used women to screen himself from police bullets—but he got a reputation for gallantry and chivalry just the same.

In January of this year the mob went back to Indiana, robbing a bank in East Chicago. Dillinger and Hamilton walked into the bank, the former carrying a machine gun in a trombone case. Again the police arrived in a few moments. Patrolman Hobard Wilgus walked in, pistol extended. He was disarmed and made to line up with the employees. Dillinger, machine gun ready, looked outside.

"Get all the dough!" he cried to Hamilton. "There's cops out there, but we'll kill them and get away!"

When all the cages had been cleaned out and some $20,000 had been bagged, Dillinger forced Vice President Walter Spencer to accompany him outside.

At the entrance of the bank stood Policeman William P. O'Malley. He wouldn't endanger Spencer by firing. While he hesitated, Dillinger sprayed him with machine-gun bullets. Dillinger and Hamilton then rushed to their car, still using Spencer to protect them. At the car Spencer fell, and the police opened fire, wounding Hamilton. But he and Dillinger got away.

Leach and Huntington learned that Evelyn Cherrington, alias Fay Miller, Mary Johnson, Ann Johnson, and Ann Jackson, formerly Harry Copeland's sweetheart, was nursing Hamilton. They started looking for her. Meanwhile Dillinger, Pierpont, Makley, and Clark went West with their molls. They were arrested in Tucson, Arizona.

The Wisconsin police wanted them for the Racine bank job. Leach, representing Indiana and Ohio, wanted them for bank robberies and for murder. Wisconsin offered a $2,500 reward. Dillinger offered to pay that and $5,000 more to the Arizona police if they'd turn him over to Wisconsin. Leach called the Governor of Indiana, who called the Governor of Wisconsin. Wisconsin withdrew.

Ohio was awarded Pierpont, Makley, and Clark, wanted for the murder of Sarber. Lake County, Indiana, got Dillinger. Leach had to be content with the other three.

Leach quarreled with two Tucson officers who wanted to accompany him East—at Indiana's expense.

"They came to me at the train as I was putting the prisoners aboard," he says. "They called me such names that I almost pulled my gun on them. No man ever called me such things in all my life. It was more than any man could endure. The chief of police of Tucson was appalled. He wrote me that he was sending those two men to me to make their apologies in person. They did come to Indianapolis. But they never came near me. They came East in an effort to get a vaudeville engagement. And that's a statement I can prove."

Dillinger was placed in the "escape-proof" jail at Crown Point, Indiana, and the lady sheriff, Mrs. Lillian Holley, nervously swore he would never escape. She wasn't so sure of that, however, for she asked to have him removed to the state penitentiary. Lake County officials, who wanted the glory of convicting Dillinger, made her change her mind. Dillinger escaped soon afterward, and the world was told he did it with a wooden gun.

This is untrue. It cost him $20,000 to escape. For that sum two loaded guns were smuggled in to the Crown Point jail, one for Dillinger and one for his colored cell mate, Herbert Youngblood. The money was paid by Evelyn Frechette.

The guns were hidden in the false bottom of a garbage can that was placed in the cell block. Mrs. Anna Sage, a notorious woman, had been allowed to visit Dillinger in prison and warn him to be ready.

With these guns Dillinger disarmed his jailers and got away. He rode off in the sheriff's car to Chicago. He passed hundreds of cops looking for him. In her excitement Sheriff Holley had broadcast the wrong license number of her car. Only Dillinger, a fool for luck, could have that "break."

Incidentally, the garage in which Sheriff Holley kept her car was owned by Clyde Rothermel, whose sister married John Hamilton's brother.

These facts were related to Edward Barce, assistant attorney-general of Indiana, by prisoners in the jail at the time, and were confirmed by George Hargrave, head of the Hargrave Secret Service of Chicago. He was employed by the State of Indiana, after the escape, to make a thorough, independent, and impartial investigation into the "wooden gun" story.

"We'll get Dillinger through Hamilton," Leach said. "And we'll get Hamilton through his nurse."

The nurse prepared a home at 75 Windermere, Highland Park, Detroit. Leach's men holed up in a house across the street. They watched the place night and day with spyglasses. Presently Evelyn Frechette appeared. It would be but a day or two before Dillinger arrived—and, perhaps, Hamilton and others.

But Youngblood ran amuck in Port Huron, Michigan, killed an officer, and was himself shot. On his deathbed he said he had been with Dillinger the night before.

Leach hurried to Port Huron, believing Dillinger might be there. Newspapermen recognized him. Was Dillinger in Detroit? He answered as best he could. The newspapers printed what they believed. They had been on the street an hour when Evelyn Frechette and Evelyn Cherrington packed up and disappeared, going to New York with Dillinger and Hamilton.

Dillinger was next found in St. Paul.

Mrs. D. S. Coffey, owner and caretaker of an apartment building, became suspicious of people visiting one of her flats, and called up a federal agent. An investigation showed that the occupant of the flat had bought a car which was registered under a fictitious name and address. He called himself Carl Hellman.

Department of Justice Agent R. C. Coulter went to talk to the suspect. He took with him Henry Cummings of the St. Paul detective bureau, a man of about sixty.

Cummings and Coulter went up to the third floor and knocked. Evelyn Frechette stuck out her head, said Hellman was out, and locked and bolted the door.

"There's going to be trouble here," Cummings said. "Go phone the police for more men."

On the way downstairs Coulter met Homer Van Meter, who fired at him. Coulter ran into the street.

Dillinger, alias Hellman, opened the window and fired at Coulter with a tommy gun. It was only a few feet, but he missed. Coulter saw a car at the curb. He shot holes in the rear tires, then got to a telephone.

Dillinger moved into the hallway and tried to pot Cummings through the door. The tommy gun tore great holes in the wood—but Cummings was standing to one side.

Those holes, incidentally, prove Dillinger never knew how to use a tommy gun—how to allow for its tendency to throw the barrel up and overshoot.

Cummings sped down the hall and stood behind a projection. Dillinger opened the door and riddled the door of another apartment. Cummings fired and drilled Dillinger through the right leg; whereupon Dillinger closed and locked the door, and began to pack.

He went down the back way, carrying the gun. Evelyn carried all the luggage he had time to put in her arms.

Cummings waited for reënforcements. But they were long in coming; for Coulter hadn't called the police. He had called his chief, J. M. Ladd, in charge of the St. Paul office. There were police radio cars all around the flat building at the time. Ladd had only to call the police —and Dillinger would be captured or killed. But instead Ladd sent two men a considerable distance to the office of the chief of police, to tell him what had happened. By that time it was too late.

After his wound healed Dillinger went back to Mooresville, Indiana, for a good old home-cooked meal. He took Hamilton and Evelyn Frechette with him. The Department of Justice men who were supposed to be watching the house were nowhere around.

After satisfying his appetite he drove to Warsaw, Indiana, where he met others of the mob. They raided the police station and took a few machine guns, a few riot guns, and a few bullet-proof vests, and then Dillinger and Hamilton started in a leisurely way for the home of Hamilton's sister in Sault Ste. Marie.

Huntington and Leach had known of Hamilton's sister and had informed Oscar Olander, Commissioner of Public Safety for Michigan, and head of the state police. They had also informed the Department of Justice.

The federal men got a tip that Dillinger and Hamilton were headed north, going through northern Michigan. They said no word to any one. Two of them hopped in a plane and started for "the Soo." At Green Bay, Wisconsin, they had to make a forced landing because of fog; but they didn't continue by train or auto. They lay over a day, and resumed their flight the following noon. They arrived too late. The birds had flown a few hours before. Even then, if they had notified the Michigan State Police, the pair could have been apprehended, for there are only two roads they could have taken out of Sault Ste. Marie.

After this escape, if such it can be called, Dillinger arranged for a few days of peace and quietness at Emil Wanatka's roadhouse, Little Bohemia, near Mercer, Wisconsin. He had with him John Hamilton, "Baby Face" Nelson, Tommy Carroll, Homer Van Meter, and Pete Reilly, former mascot for the St. Paul baseball team, who joined the mob in St. Paul. These and their women made ten in all. They came in three autos. They played cards with Wanatka. They stayed awake nights talking. They shot at targets in competition with Wanatka—who could beat them all, though he was not especially good.

Their laundry was taken to Julia Brown, who lived about a quarter mile away. It was a large package. It contained seventeen shirts, eighteen suits of underwear, nine pairs of socks, fifty-one handkerchiefs, three gingham dresses, and a silk slip.

Mrs. Brown, an intelligent and observing woman, noticed that fifteen of the shirts were new and had been worn only once, and that all the other things were new. One of the two old shirts had a label showing it had been bought in Nashville, Tennessee. The other had a laundry mark, "J.H.D." Mrs. Brown thought J.H.D. had been doing a lot of traveling. He must have been in a hurry though—to keep buying a new shirt every day—too much of a hurry to have them laundered. And Mrs. Brown must have these done by Sunday morning. Mr. D. had to move. Who was Mr. D.? Mr. Dillinger?

She talked. She told Wanatka she knew who his guests were. Wanatka told her he didn't know; but he brought

Van Meter to her, and Van Meter jokingly said, "Sure, I'm Dillinger." Mrs. Brown had seen Dillinger's picture, and knew he lied. She kept on talking.

Mrs. Wanatka learned who the guests were—from Mrs. Brown's talk. She called a meeting of her brothers and sisters, and decided on action. She made Emil write a letter to the Department of Justice. He sent it to the Chicago office. Mrs. Wanatka sent a relative to call Chicago on the phone. The call was received at one o'clock Sunday morning, April 22.

Melvin H. Purvis, in charge of the Chicago division, immediately arranged to have twenty-four men from Chicago and St. Paul meet at Rhinelander. He arranged for autos to take them to Manitowish and Little Bohemia, a distance of about fifty miles from Rhinelander.

They arrived at Rhinelander by airplane late Sunday afternoon. But the cars were not ready, and there was an hour's delay. The Dillinger mob, however, was still at the inn. They had intended to leave Sunday morning, but Reilly and one of the women had gone to St. Paul and had not returned. So the federal men had time to complete their plans. They arrived at Little Bohemia about eight o'clock. It was dark. They approached the inn on foot, each with a machine gun and a bullet-proof vest. They scattered and moved up in a semicircle. No one guarded the rear of the house.

Three men came out of the lodge and got into a car. One was an elderly man. Two wore denim clothes, the third a mackinaw. The lights were bright. It seems impossible these men could be mistaken for any of the Dillinger crowd. Their car started. The federals ordered them to stop, then fired. One man was killed, two were wounded. All three were innocent victims.

The federals charged the inn then. Dillinger's mob blasted them with machine guns. The attackers came on until they reached a barbed-wire fence they didn't know was there. Meanwhile the "Dillingers" got away at the unguarded rear of the house.

The gang split up and went in various directions. "Baby Face" Nelson killed W. Carter Baum, federal agent, wounded J. C. Newman and Carl Christensen, and drove away in a federal car.

Later it became evident that had Purvis taken the local authorities into his confidence he could have got each and every one of the Dillinger gang, dead or alive, by blocking two bridges and a sixty-foot pass.

At two o'clock Monday morning a federal agent called the sheriff of Hastings, Minnesota, and asked him to be on the lookout for three cars. "Guard the spiral bridge at Hastings," he said. "The other bridges will be taken care of."

It later developed the other bridges were not taken care of. Deputies guarded the spiral bridge until 10 A. M., when they saw a Ford coupé coming from the south and on the Minnesota side of the bridge—distinctly not the Wisconsin side. But the first two figures of the license plates were the same as those on one of the cars they were hoping to see. They gave chase to get the rest of the number.

It was the right one but was on another car than the one described to them.

The deputies closed in on the car, which contained three men. Just as they were about to overtake it a cattle truck got in their way. The bridge is narrow, and by the time they got around the truck the bandits were two miles ahead. A thirty-mile chase followed, the deputies getting close enough in St. Paul Park, South St. Paul, to shoot at the tires.

One of the bandits knocked a hole out of the back window of his car and returned the fire. A hundred bullets were exchanged. The bandits got away in the hills, abandoned their car, stole another, and escaped. Their car was thoroughly soaked with blood.

Who had been hit? It proved to be Dillinger.

He went to Chicago and was nursed back to health. He had his face lifted. He had some identifying marks removed. He walked openly about the city, disguised only with glasses. He picked up Polly Hamilton, a waitress.

He took her to movies, baseball games, dances. He took her occasionally to the home of Anna Sage, who had notified him in the Crown Point jail about the guns.

He trusted Anna Sage. He trusted Polly Hamilton. He was a fool. The federal government had offered $15,000 for his capture, dead or alive. Anna Sage wanted that money. A policeman who had been her sweetheart for fifteen years, wanted it too. When Dillinger's bank roll dwindled, the policeman went to Melvin Purvis and arranged to put Dillinger "on the spot."

He kept his word. He sent him to a movie with Polly Hamilton and Anna Sage. The federals waited outside and blew the life out of him. It was the copper friend of Anna Sage who shot him from behind.

Dillinger's dead. Makley is dead and Pierpont wounded—both shot in an attempt to escape from the Ohio penitentiary by the use of pistols made of soap, after having been condemned to die in the chair for the murder of Sheriff Sarber. Clark was sentenced to life. Copeland, Crouch, Shouse, and other members of the "Dillinger crowd" are in jail. Tommy Carroll is dead—killed by policemen.

They were all fools. For that matter, all crooks are fools. The cops may be dumb at times. They may fight and double-cross each other. But, no matter what they do, they get the crook in the end.

Dillinger Dies!

by Will Irwin

THIS IS HOW Uncle Sam's police—whom the under-world calls the "G-men"—cornered and killed that poisonous little rat John Dillinger, to the satisfaction of all.

On the afternoon of Sunday, July 22, J. Edgar Hoover, who directs the Division of Criminal Investigation, Department of Justice, sat in his Washington home, reading a frivolous novel and taking his rest after a hard week. The telephone rang. He had given instructions that he was to be disturbed only in case of really important business; and even before he lifted the receiver his mind said, "Dillinger." For three months the little force of federal agents had been pursuing that elusive killer through a maze of hard luck. Four times they had almost cornered him; and each time fate had played on his side. His hairbreadth escapes, his weird luck, had made him a symbol of defiance for law.

And Dillinger's name, disguised in a rough-and-ready code, was the first word to come over the wire. Agent M. H. Purvis was speaking from Chicago. "He is going to the movies tonight," said Purvis in code. "Either the Marboro Theater or the Biograph. He'll have two women with him. The boys are looking over the land right now. We'll get him when he goes in or when he comes out. Wish us luck, and good-bye!" And Hoover settled down to the most anxious six hours of his life.

Purvis had to cover both theaters, but the Biograph more closely than the Marboro. For it was showing a gangster film, and they knew Dillinger's tastes. The human instinct was to fill the environs with plain-clothes men. But Dillinger, that creature of instincts, would take alarm if he saw an unusual number of men loafing about the theater. Moreover, shooting by a large posse might turn into a fusillade; and Purvis found himself more concerned with the lives of women and children crowding in and out of the theater than with his own life and that of his agents. Three or four men at each theater, dead shots all, would be enough. The police of East Chicago, Indiana, bent on avenging a comrade whom Dillinger had murdered in cold blood, were following his trail almost as closely as the federal men and had given invaluable help. They deserved a place in this operation. If Dillinger showed signs of resisting arrest, each man was to shoot only once—and to the spot.

So, when the crowds began entering the Biograph and the Marboro, four men loafed inconspicuously about each entrance. Purvis himself was at the Biograph. Neither he nor his associates had ever seen the enemy in the flesh. But Purvis had studied Dillinger's face in photographs and newsreels until he felt that he knew him like a brother.

A little man escorting two women stepped to the box office. He was in his shirt sleeves, for it was a hot night; but he wore a straw hat. Dillinger! Or was it? He was wearing spectacles, and the face seemed oddly changed. Then he spoke, and Purvis caught a characteristic expression which he had noted in the newsreels—caught it a tenth of a second too late. The Sunday night crowd pushed in close. Shooting would mean a massacre. Before an opening appeared, Dillinger and his two girls had entered the theater. A delay. (In Washington, Mr. Hoover was walking the floor, consulting his watch every five minutes.) They would get him when he came out.

A messenger brought over the force from the Marboro. Quietly Purvis deployed his troops; at the entrance, he and two other federal agents; at the curb, one federal agent and the East Chicago policemen. After an interminable wait the audience began to emerge. Purvis lighted a cigar. Here he was—Dillinger! Purvis dropped his cigar.

That was the signal. Dillinger's animal intuition stayed with him to the end. The motion had occurred behind him—but he glanced nervously over his shoulder and his right hand shot to the automatic pistol in the pocket of his trousers. It caught in the vent of the pocket. He jammed it down to get it free—and three shots exploded almost as one. Staggering, glassy-eyed, bleeding, he ran down the street toward an alley. The squad at the curb closed in. But it would not be necessary to fire again. At the entrance of the alley he pitched forward on his face. In twenty minutes he was dead.

He had been hit three times in different spots. The federal men had thought out even that detail before hand. Traditionally, the safest plan for a man in a life-and-death gun fight is to aim at the heart. Even if you miss a trifle, you've probably inflicted a fatal or disabling wound. The bulletproof vest has somewhat altered that rule. Dillinger might be wearing armor under his shirt. So one marksman had fired at his torso, one at his head, and one at his leg, so that he could not run away. All hit the mark. The woman bystander wounded in the fracas took a bullet which went clean through Dillinger. As for the men behind the guns—"Never mind," said Director Hoover at the time. "They have families." However, we know now that agents Hollis and Cowley, who four months later died heroically while ridding us of "Baby Face" Nelson, were in the federal squad.

At half past ten Hoover's telephone rang again. Chicago was speaking: "We've got him—he's dead!"

"Any of our boys killed?"

"Not one! A woman in the crowd wounded, but not badly, we think."

"Thank God!"

The Gay Life of a Prima Donna Is the Bunk

by Lily Pons, as told to Gladys Heylbut

Says One of Opera's Most Sensational Stars

WHEN I WAS a girl at home in France I used to delight in reading stories about stage stars. What thrilled me especially was the pictures they painted of the star's life. Satin-damask dressing rooms filled with flowers. Ermine robes. Whole squadrons of gallant gentlemen, all rich, handsome, and devoted. Luxury. Temperament! Parties, midnight suppers, champagne every day, night after night of after-theater gayeties. *Life!* Oh, how I yearned, somehow, some day, to be able to lead a star's life myself!

Then, three years ago, all unknown and unheralded, I stepped upon the great stage of the Metropolitan Opera House. The next day I found myself an operatic star!

Well, for three years now I, too, have been living a star's life. And how does the real thing compare with those glowing stories I used to devour? About as a good solid kitchen stove compares with a penthouse set in the movies.

No, I'm not the least bit disillusioned. I love my work—my *work,* mind you—more than anything else. I love my public. But a career of singing has very little in common with the popular idea of a prima donna's life.

Certainly there is glamour in successful stage work. But it doesn't show much. It has to do with slaving six days a week, so that on the seventh you may know the satisfaction of a job well done. It has to do with living up to responsibilities, with knowing that you are keeping true to the best that's in you. Every worker who takes his job seriously knows that sort of glamour, and *that is the biggest glamour of a star's life.*

As for the rosy pictures made by those beautiful stories, let us begin with the great roomy satin-damask dressing rooms. The dressing rooms of a repertory company, where bills and casts are changed every night, are not privately owned. They are used according to rank. All the first sopranos, for instance, use the same room on the nights they sing. These rooms measure something like ten by ten, and are painted glossless gray. There are a dressing table, two chairs, and a couch, all plain and impersonal.

It is seldom that flowers are unpacked in the dressing room. There isn't time to do more than glance at the cards and project a grateful thought to the senders until one gets back home.

The ermine robes give way in reality to the plainest sort of washable kimono, which you wear to keep yourself free of grease paint and powder while you're making up. Then you cover your hair with something that looks like a bathing cap and the wig goes on. Then you put on your first-act costume, and the call boy taps on your door and says:

"Madame, we are beginning in half a minute!"

Nobody ever comes to your dressing room before or during a performance. After the opera is over, near midnight, a few friends rap on your door. What they see is a small person taking deep breaths on the couch and wiping away what would be beads of perspiration if they could get through the grease paint. They seldom stay very long.

So much for the squadrons of rich, handsome, and devoted gentlemen!

The next charming myth that needs exploding is the one about "operatic temperament." I often used to wonder just what about a musical career made you "temperamental"—that is, mean, contrary, sulky, bad-tempered. In my three years' experience with the ranking stars of the musical world I have never witnessed one outburst of temper or lack of consideration. On the other hand, I have seen displays of patience and perseverance that could give pointers to a professor of pedagogy. I remember one rehearsal in particular, where the stellar rôle of one of my colleagues was being completely "muffed" by the slipshod performance of one of the minors in the cast. The stage manager was beginning to pass his hands through his hair. The conductor was making sounds in his throat. The rehearsal was dragging. And then the star held up her hand and said, "If we've spent this much time on this scene, possibly we can have just ten minutes more?"

And she went off into a corner of the wings with the miscreant minor and coached that girl in word, tone, and gesture with greater patience and thoroughness than the average vocal coach would have displayed. To picture Miss Lucrezia Bori, for instance, in a fit of jittering "temperament" is as ludicrous as to picture Queen Mary of England similarly distressed.

I am proud to think that no one has ever seen me lose control of myself. Do I get nervous? Of course I do! Any one feels a certain indescribable trembling as the zero hour draws near. It's a feeling one never quite gets over.

But it's a point of honor with me not to give in. I don't like people to see my weaker moments! Besides, if I were to "get temperamental," I should accomplish nothing more than to spread an infection of nerves among a dozen singers, stage managers, conductors, and assistant conductors who are probably conquering zero-hour quivers of their own.

And now for the parties! When my performance is over and I have been thoroughly rubbed down and have changed my clothes, I rush for a taxi (no, not my private limousine), drive a weary mile to my apartment, have a bath, and creep into bed, after a very light supper. And that is all I am fit for. Not only are parties impossible after singing, but one avoids them altogether. Unsociable? Not a bit. You avoid them because you are a star and must guard your health, your endurance, your throat. My cook goes to more parties a winter than I. This season I've been out exactly twice—and I like a jolly time as well as any one!

Here is a typical day for me in midseason. I rise before eight, have a light breakfast of coffee and rolls, and set to work practicing. It is best for the voice to work early. At eleven I have my English lesson. From twelve to one my manager comes, or representatives from the press, or a photographer. After a one-o'clock lunch, I rest an hour. This rest is my one regular luxury.

Stage rehearsals may be called at any hour of the day, and when that happens my entire routine is thrown out of gear. But let us suppose that we have an afternoon rehearsal today. It is called for three, and, since there is no knowing how long it will last, I can make no advance plans for the later hours. If I have time after it, I visit shops—I'm very fond of shopping—or I take a walk in the park with Ita, my tiny Brazilian jaguar. Then I come in for dinner.

In the evening I may practice a bit more if I'm not too tired, and go through the day's mail. I'm usually in bed before eleven, because my constitution is one that happens to need much sleep. On the day of a performance I remain perfectly quiet all day, to keep fresh for the evening. Up to now I have not found time in this routine for much carousing! Vacations? Well, I really don't know. In the three years I've been a star I haven't had any!

You must remember that the position of star is still something of a novelty for me. I was trained to be a pianist, and a severe illness cut me off from that career. Later, when it came time for me to earn my own living, I got a job on the stage in Paris, playing small parts. My voice was discovered by the merest accident when I was twenty-one. For two years I studied, and made my operatic début when I was twenty-three. An odd thing about my career is that before I was engaged for the Metropolitan Opera, I was never a regular member of any opera company.

After two years of singing abroad, I was engaged for the "Met" and I've been there three years.

You can easily imagine that when a generous public flings the mantle of approval upon a girl who is unused to glamour, the sensation is startling. Sometimes I stand before the mirror and tell the girl I see there:

"That isn't *you*—that's Lily Pons!"

The *me* I know best is a provincial French girl who never had more than moderate comforts. I was born in Cannes, one of the Riviera cities in the south of France. We are a family of three girls. I'm the oldest, and my youngest sister is seventeen. My mother has always been a good pal to us. We spent much of our time outdoors, gardening, hiking, swimming, riding horseback. A great deal of time went into household tasks and studies, of course.

Treats were rare in our household—something to be looked forward to. I can vividly recall the thrill of walking to an old bakery once a week, as a reward for good behavior, and selecting one cake. I used to try to do my tasks and my duties so that I might try a different cake each week.

And now I am a star! But surely, you will say, I have time enough and money enough today to live better. To which I might reply, Is that so? First of all, I am separated from my family, which is really a great deprivation. Next year perhaps, when my youngest sister's schooling is finished, I hope to have them come to America with me.

True, I am able to live better now than I ever have. I have an apartment overlooking Central Park, and a maid to cook for me. Best of all, I am able to provide for mother and the girls at home.

But as to the rest of my present mode of life, I thank fortune for the discipline I was given as a girl!

Practically none of the things I would normally seek as recreation enter into my program. I have little time to read. I daren't go in for the accustomed sports lest I take cold, or strain myself, or lose weight. My contacts with people—plain everyday people—are necessarily limited. My work happens to be the sort that the world calls glamorous, but the conscientious pursuit of it keeps me as routined, as confined, as any research chemist in a laboratory.

That is what I have found the gay life of the prima donna to be.

Then why do I stick to it? Why don't I break loose and have fun? Because I happen to be born with an unconquerable love for music. To work at music, to serve it in my own small way, means more to me than the most thrilling list of individual pleasures.

Life Begins at Four

by Sidney Skolsky

And Wisdom Arrives at Five! What the Business of Being a $1,250-a-Week Star Has Done to Shirley Temple

WALTER B. PITKIN IS wrong. Life Begins at Four. He knew nothing about the movies. He didn't take into consideration the sensational career of the kid star, Shirley Temple.

Shirley, the only actress in pictures whose weight is the same numeral as her height—43 pounds and 43 inches tall—is a box-office sensation at the age of five. It was not an overnight hop, skip, and jump for kid Shirley. There were long years of struggle and preparation for stardom. She only started to get into her stride at four. Yes, Mr. Pitkin, Life Begins at Four.

We will follow the career of Shirley Jane Temple from the cradle to the present day. To start we have to take the road back, way back to 1929. It is Monday evening, April 23, nine o'clock. A third child is born to the sedate bank manager George Temple and his wife Gertrude, a typical housewife.

We see Shirley in her cradle and stand guard over her for eight months, waiting. At eight months she stands up in her cradle, hears music, and wiggles her toes trying to dance. This is the first sign.

There are patient years of waiting. Other parents might have given up hope; other youngsters might have despaired of trying to be a child star. Not the Temples! For three years Shirley stays at home, and whenever she hears music she breaks into a dance.

Next, at three, little Shirley Temple is sent to dancing school. This is similar to Lynn Fontanne going to a dramatic academy to take a course in acting.

Four months later at this dancing school Shirley is noticed by Charles Lamont, a director for Educational Pictures. Mr. Lamont is a depositor at the bank where Mr. Temple is manager. It is Mr. Temple who has asked Lamont to notice his daughter.

Shirley starts acting in motion pictures, baby burlesque comedies. She is a leading lady at the beginning. Her leading man is a baby boy named George Smith. Her salary is a mere ten dollars a day. Those are the hardships and hard knocks that a baby star must expect.

It wasn't all a joy ride to fame for Shirley. There might have been a scene at home in which mama and papa scolded Shirley for being a failure. They probably pointed to Baby LeRoy and said: "Look at him, not half your age yet, and he's starring with Chevalier and making a hundred and fifty dollars a week!"

Perhaps this was what spurred Shirley. Soon she was graduated into a series of shorts called *Frolics of Youth*. Her salary was fifteen dollars a day. She was also hired out to play small rôles in features.

A feature she played in was the Western, *To the Last Man*, at Paramount. It was this studio that later paid big money to borrow her to star in *Little Miss Marker*, and *Now and Forever*. While making *To the Last Man*, Harpo Marx—busy on the same lot in *Duck Soup*—noticed Shirley and fell in love with her. He wanted to adopt her. He went to Mrs. Temple and offered her $50,000 for Shirley. Mrs. Temple refused to sell.

Until Shirley appeared in *Stand Up and Cheer* she never received much attention or big money. Since then a number of people have been pinning medals on themselves for getting Shirley that job. This is the true story:

Lew Brown was looking for a cute youngster for that picture to sing *Baby, Take a Bow*. Jay Gorney, who wrote the music for Brown's words, went to a movie to pass a

Hollywood evening. On the program was a preview of *Pardon My Puff,* one of those kid shorts with Shirley. Jay was introduced to Mrs. Temple that evening and arranged an appointment for her and her daughter to meet Lew Brown.

One rehearsal, and the search for the kid for *Stand Up and Cheer* was over. The first number shot for that picture was *Baby, Take a Bow.* Winnie Sheehan looked at the rushes and realized he had a screen personality. He never dreamed he had the screen sensation of the year. She was signed for seven years at $150 a week. Still short of her fifth birthday, she was making more money than her father.

We will not peep behind the scenes at Shirley Temple at work. She is a natural. She doesn't know anything about the technique of acting and therefore she is herself. The public, delighted to see something genuine on the screen, takes her to its bosom; and Shirley Temple with her dimples becomes America's newest sweetheart.

Until now, Shirley has seen only one motion picture: Jackie Cooper in *Skippy.* She is the only actress who can't read her press clippings. All these are strong points in her favor.

Also she can't read the lines of the scene she is to play before the camera. Every night before she is put to bed —bedtime is usually about eight—Mrs. Temple reads to her the scene she is to make the next day. Shirley repeats line after line as she hears it. She has a remarkable memory and knows the dialogue after two rehearsals.

The next morning at breakfast time Shirley must recite the lines she learned the night before. Her memory is much keener in the morning. Then to the studio. Her best scenes are generally shot early in the day. Seldom while the camera is turning does she forget a line. No matter how many times a particular scene must be played, Shirley Temple will always play it the same way, right down to the gesture and the intonation of the voice. Unless, of course, she is instructed otherwise by the director.

She is eager to work. It is a game to her. She doesn't know what it is all about.

Shirley's mother sits in a chair on the set watching, like a football coach who has just sent in the star player. Before a scene is taken Mrs. Temple will give the final instructions to her player. She says: "Now sparkle, Shirley, sparkle!" So far, this is Shirley Temple at the hitching post, hitching her wagon to a star. Later we will take another peep behind the scenes to look at Shirley Temple the star.

An odd thing about Shirley is that she is not emotional. It is difficult to get her to laugh outright for a scene; she smiles readily. It is even more difficult to get her to cry. A director has to resort to tricks. In *Little Miss Marker* they got her to cry by not letting her mother on the set. Then they told Shirley that her mother had rushed away to see about their new car, purchased that week, which had just been wrecked. Hearing that her new bright-colored auto was ruined, little Shirley Temple cried like a baby.

Shirley uses no make-up. Her golden hair, naturally curly, her hazel eyes, her two dimples, and her cute smile are make-up enough. There are no wrinkles, bad skin, or blemishes to hide. Mrs. Temple may take out her powder puff and dab the tip of Shirley's nose to keep it from shining, but that's all the make-up she uses.

It is useless to deny that success changes people, even kid stars. It also affects the lives of their parents.

It starts with the reviews of *Little Miss Marker* being read to Shirley. Fan mail is also read to her. Shirley is taken into a projection room to see the picture. It is the first time she has seen herself on the screen. She likes herself very much and applauds often.

Now Shirley Temple begins to know what it is all about.

The little youngster's fame has affected the routine of the entire family. Her mother has to be a mother, a guardian, a dramatic coach, and a nursemaid.

She takes Shirley to work. She sits on the set all day under hot arc lights and watches the child. She teaches Shirley her lines at night.

Father Temple stays in the bank, his chest swelling with the usual pride. He calls for his wife and daughter at the studio every day at five. He points proudly to the fact that business has increased at the bank because people want to gaze at Shirley Temple's father. At home he has to wait an extra hour for dinner. Shirley gets first attention. Her wants are satisfied first. She is the head of the family.

Shirley's two brothers—Jack, age eighteen, and George, fourteen—are amazed by their tiny sister. At first it is unbelievable, and they go to the movies again to see the picture and try to get used to it. Then they also become a part of it. Now Jack and George sit at home and answer Shirley's fan mail, send out her photographs, and paste her clippings into the special press book.

The Temples, just everyday folks, have suddenly been pushed into the spotlight. They suddenly have to deal with agents, business managers, executives, and movie stars. They are now in close contact with people they have looked upon with awe from a distance. They are bewildered.

Shirley Temple is offered $10,000 for a week of personal appearances at the Paramount Theater. . . . Shirley Temple is offered a young fortune to go on the radio. . . . Shirley Temple is offered money to indorse this and Shirley Temple is offered money to do that. . . . Another picture company offers Shirley Temple $80,000 to make one picture. . . .

And all the while Shirley Temple is under contract to Fox for seven years at $150 a week.

The Temples are bewildered, puzzled, annoyed, and angry. They have the magic password to a fortune and are not permitted to utter the word. They know the history of the screen's kid stars. They must do the collecting now. Jane and Katherine Lee, Clara Horton, Baby Peggy, Davey (Sonny Boy) Lee, and Jackie Coogan are merely a few of the kids who outgrew fame.

The story is made forceful to them, for on the very set on which Shirley is making *Now and Forever* there is working the first baby star of pictures.

This baby star was the Shirley Temple of her day. And today, at the age of twenty-four, she is trying to make a comeback. Her name is Ynez Seabury. She has been in pictures longer than Cecil B. De Mille, Charles Chaplin, Lillian Gish, and other pioneers of the industry. She was a star back when screen players didn't get their names in the billing. Ynez Seabury was known and billed as "The Biograph Baby," a trademark second only to "The Biograph Girl," who later became famous as Mary Pickford.

There is only one former kid movie star who grew up and amounted to something in pictures, and that is Madge Evans. The odds are too great against Shirley Temple. They don't pay off on past performances at the race track or at the picture studios.

After many weeks of wrangling, the Fox studio finally consented to give America's doll friend a new contract,

Shirley Temple's new contract calls for Miss Temple to receive $1,000 every week and for Mrs. Temple to receive $250 every week for her services on the set. The most unusual thing about Shirley Temple's contract is that it is the only one issued in Hollywood that doesn't contain a morality clause.

Shirley Temple is having her day. She should be allowed to rule it supreme. We will now take that peep behind the scenes and watch Queen Shirley at work.

She has learned something of the technique of acting. She has learned enough to try to be the nearest player to the camera. She knows how to steal scenes. Now that she is a star, the actors and actresses who previously thought her cute, and did everything to help her, are on the lookout. They don't want her to strut away with their scenes. She has learned tricks to fight their tricks.

Shirley acts like a grown star. She goes to the projection room to see the daily rushes now. All reviews are read to her. She is interviewed at least once a week. She has become too smart for her age. Her mother asks: "You don't believe Shirley has become spoiled, do you?" It's something that can't be guarded against. It happens to all kid stars.

She believes all interviews are foolish. "They all ask you the same questions," says Shirley. They all ask: "And what is your favorite color? What's your ambition?" One interviewer, once a noted actress, was annoyed because Shirley Temple wasn't aware who she was.

Shirley now has a stand-in. The stand-in, Marilyn Grannas, is a girl of her own age. While other performers are doing a scene, Shirley and Marilyn play on the rear of the stage. Marilyn is Shirley's only playmate.

Shirley Temple the picture star doesn't get much time to play. It's home to eat, to learn lines, and to sleep. It's to the studio to pose for pictures, to be interviewed, to work before the camera. Shirley has to be careful of her companions. She can't wander about the neighborhood and play with any one. She is now a curiosity and there are the cranks and kidnapers.

The only time Shirley plays with a doll is when she is posing for a still photograph which will be published in a fan magazine to show the public how Shirley plays at home with her dolls.

Shirley realizes she is a movie star. One day on the set the still photographer wanted to take some pictures and asked her to wait for him. He was delayed a little longer than he had expected. Shirley loudly said:

"Make the pictures now or not at all. I can't wait for you!"

A child has been transformed into a movie star, a kid movie star. There ought to be a law.

Before, when Shirley's mother sent her in to play a scene, she'd say: "Sparkle, Shirley, sparkle!" Now, after watching Shirley make a scene that has to be done again, the child star is told: "Come on, now. Play it like Shirley Temple would play it."

Shirley Temple has a bank account in her name and she has electric lights spelling out her name throughout the nation, and she is still trying to learn how to write that name.

Yes, Mr. Pitkin. Life Begins at Four. Yet there is Baby LeRoy, age two, who doesn't want to be all washed up when he is four.

My
New Year's
Resolutions
by Shirley Temple

America's Youngest Sweetheart Means to Lead a Better Life—
but She Needs a Number of Things to Help Her Do It!

RESOLUTIONS IS A big word and I did not know what it meant until Mother told me. I think there must be a smaller word for what it means. My teacher says she is going to try and think of one for me.

I don't know what my resolutions are going to be for the New Year, but Mother says I have to think some up and that I have to do it right away. So I guess I'll have to, because she checks up every night to see that I do the things she asks me.

The next year I am going to make my father give me a small automobile that runs itself, because I am tired of walking at the studio. This studio is big and the stages are very far apart and sometimes walking hurts my feet.

My father says he thinks I am too young for an automobile, but that isn't so. Once Will Rogers let me turn the wheel on his automobile, and I didn't hit any one or run into anything. The kind of automobile I want has a small motor in it that makes a nice chugging noise, and it has brakes and a horn, and goes real fast when you want it to. I think I'll get it if I ask enough.

The next year, I am going to say "please" every time I ask for something, and Mother says that is very important for a little girl. If it is so important for a little girl, I wonder why so many grown-up people don't say "please" when they ask me to do something. Anyway, I guess I'll have to do what she wants. I am going to ask Mr. Dave Butler to say "please" when he asks me to make a scene.

I like Mr. Butler. He directed me in *The Littlest Rebel*, and he is nice to get along with because he calls me "One-Take Temple," and he lets me off every night at five so I can go home and play with the kids on the block. But I wish Mother would speak to him and make him say "please." I would like him a lot better then, and then I wouldn't mind saying "please" myself.

Then, I am going to ask Mr. Zanuck to make the print larger on my scripts. I don't like small type because it is hard to read and I can't read very well yet. I have just finished the Fourth Reader, and the letters are so big in that that I don't have to squint. I would like to have glasses to read the scripts Mr. Zanuck gives me, but Mother says glasses wouldn't look good on me. I don't know why, because other people wear glasses to read small print—and I'm smaller than they are.

But sometimes I fool Mother and don't read the script at all. I say, "Mother, I can't read that big word," or I say that I am very tired and can't learn any more. Then Mother takes the script and reads it to me. I can learn faster doing it that way. She reads my speech and I remember it pretty well, and Mr. Butler says I make few mistakes, which is why he calls me "One-Take Temple."

I am going to ask Mother to make my allowance five dollars next year instead of four dollars like I get now every week. Mother says all my money must go into the bank except the four dollars. But I don't see how I can get along on that. This money isn't enough for all the candy, chewing gum, and coca-cola I need when I work. And besides I have to treat other children who work with me, and that leaves very little for the other things I want. I want to buy a lot of animals, but I don't see how I can on four dollars. I must have at least five dollars.

The next year I am going to get Mother to buy me some foxes and bantam chickens for my play yard at the studio. I already have twenty-four rabbits, and that is very funny. I started with four that the studio gave me. Then Mother, Dad, and I went to Honolulu, and when I came back there were twenty little ones. I guess I will have to make the coop very much larger. If I go to Honolulu again there wouldn't be room for any more.

I like foxes and bantam chickens best of all and I will have some next year in coops next to the rabbits. There is a lot of money in raising foxes, which is why I want to get some. When they are old enough I will have them made into furs which I am going to sell. That is one way I am thinking of making more money if Mother doesn't raise my allowance to five dollars.

I don't think I would be able to make money right away with the bantam chickens, because their eggs are very small and there is very little meat on them. But I want to raise big chickens when I am older, and I think I will learn a lot practicing on small ones.

My mother says I will have to learn how to ride a horse next year. So I suppose I will have to make up my mind about that. I like horses, but they are so big that I am afraid of them. I like ponies, though; but I guess there wouldn't be much use of my learning to ride on a pony, because they don't use them in pictures.

Later on in the year I am going to go on the radio. I couldn't before because the studio thought I was too little. Microphones in radio stations are made for old people, but I don't see why that should keep me from going on the air. I could use a chair to reach the microphone. I wonder why no one thought of that before?

I guess that is all that I can make up at this time.

How It Feels To Be a Has-Been

by Babe Ruth

The Retired Sultan of Swat Looks Wistfully Over
His Record, and Reflects that, Anyway, He
Does Mean Something to a Few Million Kids

THEY CALLED ME the King of Swat. It was great while it lasted. And it lasted quite a while, at that.

But these seem to be bad days for kings. Like that Alfonso of Spain, I'm out of a job now. He's playing polo over in Cannes or one of those other places on the Riviera. I've got my golf—in Florida in the winter, on Long Island in the summer.

His public quit on him. My legs went back on me. But it all comes to the same thing. We're both out of jobs and having a little trouble convincing ourselves that we're getting the kick out of life that we used to get.

I'm not complaining. Coming out of that orphange down in Baltimore, where twenty-five cents of spending money was the week's reward for good behavior, I had a full twenty years in the great game that I gave a lot to but which also gave me more money, more fun, more comfort than the rough-and-tumble kid I was had any right to expect. Now maybe I'm through with baseball, maybe not. Sometimes I hope not, although it would take a swell job to bring me back.

But I'll admit that it gave me a funny feeling earlier this spring, playing golf down at St. Petersburg and around in Florida, not to be trying out the old legs and then jumping into the workouts with the gang, getting ready for the American League grind with the Yankees. Remember how everybody used to worry about whether I could get that waistline down and what my weight would be when the bell rang? Those tourists from the Middle West used to worry more about my legs than I did. I'm being honest now. I miss that stuff. This year's was the first training season since 1915 that I didn't go South with a major-league ball club.

That opening day in New York always brought a tingle. And I don't mean only because they had bands there and the mayor threw out the first ball. I got a real kick even last year when for the first time I wore a National League uniform. I didn't feel very much at home up there in Boston's Braves' field, and it was colder than an umpire's heart. But I busted one that day just the same, just to make the opener official for the Boston fans. Funny how you can rise to the occasion when the crowd that has faith in you expects you to. Even a king who is on the way out manages to do that once in a while.

Even an old ex-king is entitled to his memories. I've got mine. Of all the 723 homers I hit during my twenty years in the American League with the Boston Red Sox and the Yankees, that homer off Charles Root of the Cubs in the 1932 World Series at Wrigley Field in Chicago stands out as the most satisfactory. Remember how I pointed to the outfield stands, showing the fans where I was going to put the ball and, on the third strike, did park it there? I've often thought since how bad I would have looked if I hadn't connected. By that time I was old enough to know better than to gamble that way. But that's the chance you take in the pinch.

I suppose you think I am proud of my home-run records. You know I have played in ten World Series and have hit fifteen home runs in World Series contests— three in a single game on two occasions. But, now that I'm reminiscing, I'll admit I'm prouder of the fact that I was a pretty fair pitcher as a youngster and that I have a record of having pitched twenty-nine consecutive scoreless innings in World Series games.

Back in 1916 I pitched a fourteen-inning battle for the Red Sox against the Brooklyn Dodgers and held them scoreless after the first inning. Then in 1918, still with the Red Sox, I shut out the Cubs to win a nine-inning game, and blanked them again to the seventh inning of a later game before they scored. Twenty-nine consecutive innings out there on the mound under World Series pressure. Yes, I'm a little proud of that.

But I get a little tired of talking about nothing but records. Mine have meant a tidy bit of money to me, of course. And after I outgrew the boyish stuff, I managed to put a good bit of it away, too.

However, when you get to be an "ex," you start counting things up aside from records and money. We were doing that the other evening at the dinner table. A writer with whom I had been out playing golf said: "Babe, you've played a lot of baseball. You've been seen and cheered by millions. Your name is about as well known as any one's in the world. What does it all add up to? What do you think you have accomplished?" That stopped me. I had never thought about that before. Maybe it doesn't seem as if I have exerted any vital influence on the country. At any rate, I haven't made the grade in *Who's Who in America,* although among the names in it that begin with RU there are some college professors that I never heard of before and I'll bet you never did either.

That's O.K. with me. I was hitting home runs while they were hitting the books. But I'm wondering, at that— and I'm serious now—whether those academic gentlemen have had a much more definite or constructive influence on the life and thought of this country in the past twenty years than I have. Please don't get me wrong. I'm not trying to go intellectual. And no one has ever accused me of being swelled-headed.

I'll try to explain what I mean.

Remember those kids in that Passaic orphan asylum over in New Jersey three years ago? Looking out of their windows early on that May evening, the flashes of lightning showed them that, with rain falling in torrents, the railroad was washing away. Then one of them remembered that the express out of Jersey City was due any minute. It didn't take Johnny Murdock and his pals more than a second to figure out that there would be a real wreck if that express came through. But there was no trackwalker around and there wasn't time to phone ahead to stop the train. And there was the roadbed washed away from underneath the rails.

You remember the story. While the lady in charge telephoned for help, the six kids—Johnny Murdock, Jacob Melnizek, Rudolph Borsche, Douglas Fleming, Frank Mazzola and his brother Michael—ran down the track a quarter mile waving their raincoats, refusing to budge from the track, risking their lives to convince the engineer that he either had to stop or run over them.

It was a real act of quick-thinking heroism. Without question, they saved lives. Remember what Johnny Murdock and his pals said that night when the railroad officials told them they could have almost anything they wanted as a reward?

They said, "We don't want anything special as a reward. But could you please let Babe Ruth know what we did? That's what we'd rather have than anything. We have a ball team here and we'd like him to know that we did something worthwhile, even if we're not great ballplayers. Perhaps we could even meet him."

The Yankees, as I recall it, were out in Cleveland. A telegram telling me about the boys and their great stunt woke me up early in the morning out there. I sent them a telegram and wrote them letters, and when we got back into New York, they came over to the Yankee Stadium. I posed for pictures with them and autographed balls and we became real friends. If you could have seen what that meant to them, you'd have a little idea of what I mean. And don't forget that kids all over the country read that story in the newspapers.

During my last couple of years with the Yankees, my legs were giving me some bother. In 1934 I couldn't get in there every day. I used to sit on the bench and hear the kids out in the left-field stands, where they were admitted free a couple of afternoons a week, yell, "We want Ruth! We want Ruth!" Maybe you think it doesn't mean much to an old guy to hear a couple of thousand kids proving in that way what they think of him! If you don't think it means a whole lot, you're crazier than any left-handed pitcher I ever knew.

On trains, in hotels, everywhere I went, I saw evidence during those years of what the American boy thought of the Babe. I'm not going to tell you now about some of those trips I made to hospitals. I didn't use to publicize them unless it was for some good cause, and I'm not going to start now. And, as the kids themselves know, I never put myself away with them as a lecturer.

But I am beginning to realize that I accomplished something during those twenty years beyond hitting into the outfield stands, throwing to the right base, and giving the best I could as a team competitor.

I have shown a lot of American boys in my time how to bear down when the count is three and two and there are a couple on the bags, with two out. I've shown them that a real man stands up under competition and comes through when the going is tough. I think they have liked me, thousands of them, maybe millions of them, and have taken hints from me that they might not take from a teacher or a scoutmaster or someone like that. The lessons of competition, which a boy will take from one who has been through that competition, won't do him any harm in later life, if you ask me.

Swat the Tsk-Tsk Midge!

by Robert Benchley

AMONG THE LEAST flashy, and least interesting, of the movements looking toward the betterment of the human race comes our intensive campaign in the Uganda for the elimination of the tsk-tsk midge, or Hassenway's crab-fly. The tsk-tsk midge (or Hassenway's crab-fly) is something like the tsetse fly, except that it uses the hyphen. It is a very tiny fly, with plain features and was first discovered by Dr. Ambercus Hassenway while he was looking for something else.

For a long time the residents of the Uganda had been conscious of the fact that *some*thing was wrong with them, but couldn't quite decide what it was. They were nervous and fidgety and likely to break down and cry if you pointed a finger at them, until it finally got so that they would just walk about all day rubbing two sticks together and looking out of the corners of their eyes at people. This was bad for business.

It was not until Dr. Hassenway isolated the tsk-tsk midge and had a good talk with it, that the Ugandans realized what the trouble was. They had been accepting the tsk-tsk midges all along, thinking that they were cara-way seeds and rather liking them. Dr. Hassenway pointed out their error and showed them that this little animal was probably the cause of all their *malaise,* and, in recognition of his services to them, they insisted on renaming the tsk-tsk midge Hassenway's crab-fly. Dr. Hassenway protested that he really had done nothing to deserve this honor, that he already had had an oak tree blight named after him ("Hassenway's leaf-itch"), and that he was going home in a couple of days anyway. But the natives insisted, and Hassenway's crab-fly it was.

Then began the campaign to eliminate it. Dr. Hassenway is said to have remarked, a little bitterly: "Why bother to change its name if you are going to eliminate it right away?" But he took the thing in good part and entered into the game with a will. In fact, it was he who threw the first midge in the opening battle.

The first thing to do was, obviously, to discover the personal habits of the tsk-tsk and try to upset them. It was discovered (probably by Dr. Hassenway, as he was the only one in the Uganda at the time who knew how to read and write or even part his hair) that the tsk-tsk midge was dependent on a certain set of antennæ, cleverly concealed under a sort of raglan-like coat, for its pleasure in biting people. The bite of the tsk-tsk midge, by the way, is barely noticeable at the time of biting. The victim merely feels that he has forgotten something. It is not until later that he begins to rub two sticks together and look out of the corners of his eyes. And, by then, it is too late.

Now, in order to remove these antennæ, or "antlers," it is necessary to get the tsk-tsk midge into an awkward position, such as a big bonfire or a printing press. He must be convinced that he is among friends, and then set upon; a rather nasty trick, if you ask me. The difficulty comes in locating the midge, for he is (I don't know why I keep referring to the midge as "he." "Midge" is certainly a girl's name.)—it is—able to change its color, and even its shape, at the drop of a hat. This completely confused Dr. Hassenway.

The next complication to arise in this mammoth battle of man against midge was the discovery of the fact that the female midge did not lay eggs but *bought* them from a sort of common egg supply. (If I am not making myself clear to you, you have nothing on me. I am, frankly, in a panic about the thing.) All that we know *is,* that the female midge, when she wants to hatch a couple of million eggs, goes to the corner egg place and, in exchange for some bits of old moss and acorn ends, gets the required number of larvæ. These she takes home, and puts into a quick oven, and, in fifteen or twenty minutes, there are you, bitten by a whole new set of tsk-tsk midges. The way to fight this sort of thing was, obviously, to close up the egg supply station. Try and do it, however.

The problem called for outside help. Dr. Hassenway cabled to America, imploring the authorities to start a drive in behalf of this humanitarian campaign, and, as a result of a whirlwind publicity avalanche, the good people of that country sent an expedition of five scientists to the Uganda with instructions to stay there. These scientists, under leadership of Dr. Joe Glatz, set out October 12, 1929, and, so far as anyone has ever found out, never arrived.

So far, so good. The tsk-tsk midges had, by this time, so firmly intrenched themselves in the more tender sections of the Uganda that the natives were looking up time-tables and planning business trips into the interior. It was a young Ugandan, Tanganyika Tangan (yika) by name, who finally came forward with a plan which was destined at least to postpone this hegira and to give his countrymen a good night's sleep.

Tanganyika was a college man (Harvard, 1915) who had returned to his native land on a visit after graduation and had never got around to putting on his collar again. He saw the crisis and he decided that it was up to him to meet it. So he called a council of chiefs and told them that, unless they worked up some way to get rid of this devastating pest (pointing, by mistake, to his father), the country would be the laughingstock of the civilized world. "A people of our caliber," he said, "a people of our traditions, do not go on forever being bitten by tsk-tsk midges." (There were cries of "Hassenway's crab-flies!" from the Extreme Left, but he frowned them down.)

He then brought out some maps and charts which he had had left over from his botany course at Harvard and showed them that, for every tsk-tsk midge which was born, 300,000 Ugandan babies woke up in the night and asked for a drink of water. He showed them that Dr. Hassenway had been doing all the work and that nothing

had come of it (Dr. Hassenway was on his sabbatical at the time, a fact which was noticed only when Tanganyika mentioned it), and that if the Uganda was to have any national pride left, the tsk-tsk midge must go. Then he threw himself on the ground in a tribal doze.

It was, at this time, what is known as "the rainy season" in the Uganda, which means that everybody had lost interest. Everybody, that is, except the midges, and they were working in three shifts. Tanganyika tried to start grass fires, with a view to burning the midge nests, but succeeded only in burning his fingers badly. He instituted a spraying contest, in which the youths on the left side of the village street tried to spray more poison around than the youths on the right side of the street, with the result that the youths on both sides of the street were made violently ill. In fact, he tried everything known to science, but the only thing that happened was that the next litter of tsk-tsk midges was larger and had better color.

This is where the matter stands now. Dr. Hassenway and Tanganyika are both at French Lick Springs and don't seem to care any more. The natives of the Uganda are getting used to being made nervous and jumpy, and *they* don't seem to care any more. The tsk-tsk midges are having the time of their lives. The only ones who are concerned in the elimination of this little animal are the scientists, and I don't know how much longer their interest can be held. I am issuing this as a sort of appeal that Something Be Done!

———

Mr. Benchley will publish another paper on things that matter in an early issue of Liberty.

III

Honeymoon with FDR

(1936-1940)

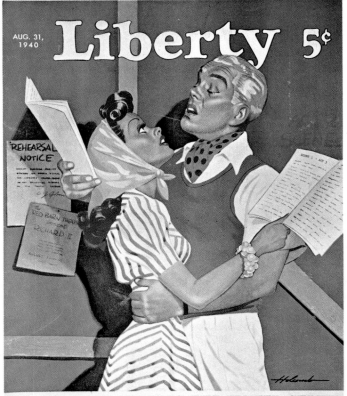

AUG. 31, 1940

Liberty

5¢

REHEARSAL NOTICE

WHEN HITLER INVADES THE UNITED STATES
Start Now LIGHTNING IN THE NIGHT — The Startling Modern Successor to THE RED NAPOLEON
YOUTH CONGRESS and the COMMUNISTIC BLIGHT by GENE TUNNEY

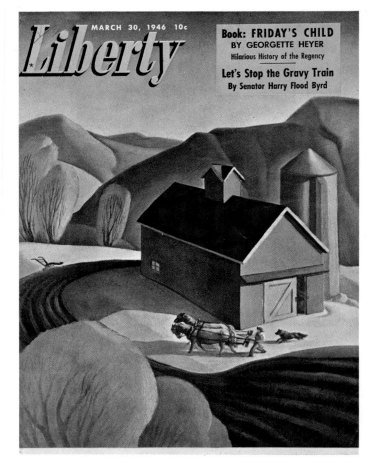

MARCH 30, 1946 10c

Liberty

Book: FRIDAY'S CHILD
BY GEORGETTE HEYER
Hilarious History of the Regency

Let's Stop the Gravy Train
By Senator Harry Flood Byrd

THE YEAR 1935 may well have been the greatest in *Liberty*'s history. Here, for the first time, its ledgers displayed a profit, with single issues carrying enough advertisements to give a pleasant aura of prosperity.

Several reasons can be advanced for this belated financial success. To begin with, the nation had begun emerging from the worst of the Depression, giving its citizens ample reason to be grateful to President Franklin D. Roosevelt. Yet major newspapers and magazines of the land still opposed the President, printing hostile editorials and news accounts lukewarm to the New Deal. *Liberty* was one of the few American publications which wholly supported the President; the fulsome editorials from the pen of Bernarr Macfadden were just the sort people wished to read. Sensing this public approval, advertisers took space in *Liberty* columns—or, better still, on full *Liberty* pages.

Secondly, *Liberty*'s extra-strong coverage of the Dillinger-style crime sprees in the middle west helped push the magazine forward. Thirdly, *Liberty* gave lavish treatment to Hollywood, where the opulent star system was in its full glory. The nation worshipped such stars as Garbo, Crawford, Shearer, Cagney, and Gable. *Liberty*'s articles about them were always lively, informative, and realistic.

Despite these advantages, however, the magazine's main claim to fame lay in the Roosevelt family. *Liberty* was so close to these occupants of the White House that the magazine often seemed to be the administration's unofficial house organ—or if not quite that, at least the Roosevelt family favorite. Beginning with Governor Roosevelt's Depression-time declarations, *Liberty* appeared to have an inside track to everything written by the first family. In promotion brochures of the time, it even claimed that FDR officiated as an associate editor of *Liberty* in the months before his nomination.

After the Inauguration, publisher Macfadden embraced the New Deal as fervently as he did the President. At the same time *Liberty* published articles which gave every indication of stemming directly from the White House.

Among them were excerpts from Presidential press conferences, with introductory comments by the Chief Executive himself.

However, the President was only one of the reigning contributors. Eleanor Roosevelt wrote for *Liberty* before becoming First Lady, and once in the White House, she stepped up the number of her contributions. And her daughter, Anna Roosevelt Dall, wrote a weekly column for the magazine.

Actually, Mrs. Roosevelt and Bernarr Macfadden were closely joined in a special publishing venture. Shortly before her husband's nomination, she had agreed to become editor of the new Macfadden publication, *Babies, Just Babies*. Her working assistant was daughter Anna. *Babies, Just Babies* ran through the chill winter of 1932-33, when Roosevelt was President-elect. When Mrs. Roosevelt became First Lady she was still editor of *Babies, Just Babies,* and much argument followed over the propriety of her position. The controversy ended abruptly as Macfadden shut down what had been a costly and unremunerative project—a decision which, with hindsight, has been branded a mistake. But if nothing else, *Babies, Just Babies* served to bring the names Roosevelt and Macfadden closer together in the public mind.

But the happy state of *Liberty* affairs went on. In the late summer of 1936, the Republicans nominated Alfred E. Landon of Kansas to run against Roosevelt in the Presidential election. Macfadden instantly reacted by printing one of *Liberty*'s better "surprise" pieces—"My Son Is Not So Great," by Alf Landon's father.

Then, just before the election, Macfadden suddenly turned to bite the administration that had pleased him. This stunning reversal was signaled by a flaming editorial, "Why I Have Been Forced to Abandon the New Deal!" Macfadden's venom continued to spill even through the election, which Roosevelt won by a landslide. *Liberty,* it must be noted, failed to show a financial profit in 1936.

Macfadden always claimed he had soured on the New Deal because its bright promises had turned out to be a confining form of socialism. This may well be the true reason. Over a period of sixty-eight years, Macfadden had risen from a barefoot country boy to a multimillionaire who still advocated bare feet for reasons of health. His life story was one of the true success sagas of the era, and contemporary newspapers were full of his manifold accomplishments and eccentricities. He was especially favored by *Time,* which invariably referred to him as Bernarr "Body Love" Macfadden. Such a relentless egoist might easily have decided that the restrictions of the NRA and other New Deal measures were aimed at stamping out his breed of man.

Yet a devil-theory also exists concerning Macfadden's reversal. No man could be as opinionated as he was without attracting enemies, and certainly he had his share. Some of them claimed the fiery publisher's dedication to physical culture had convinced him that the President's Cabinet ought to be expanded to include a Secretary of Health. In their view, his early espousal of Roosevelt had arisen from a daydream that the President would follow his advice and, moreover, appoint Macfadden himself to the newly-created post. The story cites that in 1935, Macfadden was finally summoned to Washington, and entrained intoxicated with hope. At the White House, however, he was appointed Chairman of the Fishery Advisory Commission. His disappointment was deep, and within a year he had turned against the President.

The devil-theory can be made more devilish. Others viewed Macfadden as a man who actually dreamed of the Presidency itself. Accordingly, his early support of Roosevelt had somewhat sinister motives. Macfadden, the eternal body worshiper, had an inherent contempt for all invalids and cripples, and saw them as inferior beings. Thus he did not subscribe to his own magazine's glowing accounts of FDR's physical and mental powers; instead, he expected the President to die after a year or so in office. Then—he reasoned—a shaken nation would insist on a man of overpowering health as President. Bernarr "Body Love" Macfadden expected to be that man.

So run the devil-theories. Whatever the truth, Macfadden continued to oppose the New Deal, at the same time verifying his own political ambitions by running for Senator from the state of Florida, the location of one of his physical culture resorts.

Still, it is amazing to report that Roosevelt kept writing for *Liberty*. In 1938 the President allowed the magazine to use his introduction to a book of state papers on the New Deal. *Liberty* gave this the catchy title "Roosevelt's Own Story" and billed it as an article from the pen of the President—as, in a sense, it was. Mrs. Roosevelt also remained on the roster of steady contributors, and even did a piece of fiction. In time, the Roosevelt sons also got around to writing for *Liberty*.

Even apart from the Roosevelts' contributions, these were good editorial years for the magazine. As if to compensate for grim Depression, the public was now clamoring for a series of romantic and sentimental sensations. Soon afterwards, war clouds would break in Europe.

Liberty was ready on both counts. . . .

The greatest romantic story of all time came as Edward VIII abdicated his throne for love of an American divorcée. *Liberty* had been ever-partial to Edward in his halcyon days as Prince of Wales. Among the many stories on him was one which told "Why the Prince of Wales Will Never Marry."

Edward was still Prince of Wales when behind-the-scenes whispers indicated he had fallen in love with Mrs. Wallis Warfield Simpson. This was *Liberty's* cue to offer a nostalgic re-cap of his past romances called "Ladies Who Have Charmed the Prince of Wales," making neat mention of Mrs. Simpson as the latest and perhaps most formidable of the charmers.

When the King renounced his throne to become the wedded Duke of Windsor, *Liberty* invited Upton Sinclair, John Erskine, and Cornelius Vanderbilt to join with editor Fulton Oursler in a series of articles advising Duke and Duchess how to face a unique future. As King, Edward had manifested interest in the plight of Welsh coal miners and other downtrodden groups. The *Liberty* writers urged him to continue such humanitarian interests, to become a link betwixt the mighty and the lowly of the world. The passage of years has brought unhappy proof that the Duke of Windsor paid absolutely no attention to *Liberty's* counsel.

The birth of the Dionne Quintuplets brought the magazine its ideal source of copy. Bernarr Macfadden, the man who once called a mother's tears the perfect feature, had to admit that five tiny tots were better. In *Liberty*, Marguerite Mooers Marshall covered the story of the Quints in glowing detail, and seemed to make their continuing saga the magazine's exclusive own.

Liberty also published "Why My Wife and I are Unhappy," by Papa Dionne, which was not about marital discord but the fact that his five daughters had been snatched away from home by higher authority. Eventually, and with great reluctance, *Liberty* dropped its stories on the Quints, for the girls were growing up. The last one was called "Bright Sayings of the Quints."

In 1937 *Liberty* published the short story which in retrospect becomes its most famous bit of fiction. The issue of October 30th ran, "What Makes Sammy Run?" by a young man who then signed himself Budd Wilson Schulberg. Using the *Liberty* story as a base, Budd Schulberg then wrote the novel whose Sammy Glick became our first non-hero. Today the phrase, *What Makes Sammy Run?* is part of the language.

As war clouds darkened, *Liberty* featured articles by Neville Chamberlain and Charles de Gaulle, together with "Must Japan and the United States Go to War?" by the Japanese Ambassador to the United States. Yet its early war coverage was not altogether glorious. Bernarr Macfadden and editor Oursler manifested a curious tolerance for writer George Sylvester Viereck, who had been a German apologist during World War I and stood prepared to enact the same role once again.

According to Viereck's *Liberty* pieces (and others which he may have been instrumental in planting) Hitler was really a nice guy who made warlike gestures he did not really mean. Or, in the words of a Viereck opponent, "He pictured Nazi Germany as superficially harmless, legal, even praiseworthy." Viereck himself swore he was only trying to improve relations between Germany and the United States. For a time Macfadden and Oursler went along with him, but other members of the staff assisted the FBI in cutting Viereck down. This bit of American magazine curiosa may perhaps be explained by the fact that Viereck's material fell under the heading "sensational."

Aside from this unhappy episode, *Liberty* continued picturing the world in its own lively way. It was a period between wars—the one on the home front, against Depression, was just ending; the one overseas, just beginning.

As usual in such times, Americans looked for the saving frivolity amidst reality. Look back now on such attractions of the time as Father Divine, the Quints, young Joe Di Maggio, Snow White and the Seven Dwarfs, the Big Apple, and Benny Goodman's Swing, Swing, Swing . . .

Why Civilization Will Not Crash

by Albert Einstein

The Foremost Living Scientific Thinker Declares
His Reasons for a Belief in a "Finer Future"

THE OPTIMIST AFFIRMS, the pessimist denies life. The pessimist, for all his denial, clings as a rule to the sweet habit of living. Every man at one time or another asks himself Hamlet's immortal question, "To be, or not to be?" If he decides that being is on the whole preferable to not being, he is an optimist, even if he quotes Schopenhauer or the Biblical adage that all is vanity.

I am an optimist.

I affirm life because, whatever may be the destiny of dissolving suns and dissolving universes, there is such a thing as progress and evolution in the cycle of the human species, however brief its existence may be, measured in astronomical terms.

I am an optimist in spite of Depression, Famine, Dissatisfaction, and the Rebirth of Militarism—the Four Riders of the New Apocalypse riding in the blood train of the World War.

I am an optimist in spite of the worldwide suppression of the rights of the individual which has followed the ambitious attempt to make the world safe for democracy. It is the battle of the individual soul to reassert itself which characterizes the epoch in which we live. No man can find his own soul until he strikes a balance in the account between himself and society at large.

If we meditate over our life and our hopes we are almost invariably faced by the discovery that nearly all our achievements and endeavors are closely intertwined with the existence of others. We notice to what extent we resemble other animals living in collective communities. The food we eat is garnered and prepared for our table by our fellows. The very clothes we wear are woven and patterned by others. Hands other than ours rear the shelter we call our home or our workshop.

Our knowledge and beliefs are mostly a heritage. They are almost entirely transmitted to us by others. Others long since gathered to their fathers have created the means by which understanding comes to our brains. Without speech our mental coffers would be empty indeed! Our intellectual horizon would hardly extend beyond that of the elephant and the ape. Language creates the brotherhood of man. It is this gift, the ability to convey complex ideas and emotions to others, that differentiates the human biped from his zoölogical kinsmen.

Left entirely to himself man is more helpless than the animals. Try to picture a baby left to grow up absolutely alone from birth! The abysmal primitiveness of such a creature is beyond the scope of our imagination.

What does all this mean?

It demonstrates our dependence upon our fellows.

No matter how great or distinguished a man's gift or potentialities may be, he is distinguished or great only in reference to his group. The individual is significant not so much as an individual but as a member of the human family. Society is the force which directs his material and spiritual ends from birth to death.

That gives us a rod by which we can measure the merits of any man. His value depends primarily upon the degree in which his emotions, his thoughts, and his actions are directed toward enriching the life of his fellowmen. Good and bad are not absolute terms; as applied

209

to a man's worth or his character they depend on his position or his attitude in his relationship to his group. Thus it would seem as if the social attributes of a man were the sole factors upon which his relative position in the scale of humanity rests.

Yet this conclusion is erroneous.

It is not consistent with the history of the human race. For if the individual depends upon society, society itself is nurtured by the riches in the individual soul. Patently all material, spiritual, and moral possessions which we receive from society at large have come to society from individual forces. Ever accumulating, ever growing, through innumerable generations, all civilization and all culture rise from the roots of creative individualism.

It was not society at large but an individual that first struck fire from flint. Some individual first conceived the thought of wresting food from the soil by growing plants. Still other individuals first envisaged the steam engine and the filament that brings us light.

Only the individual can think and, thinking, create new values for the world. Only the individual can set up new moral standards which point the way for generations to follow. Without decisive personalities thinking and creating independently, human progress is inconceivable.

The health of society depends no less on the integrity of the individual than upon the social bond which unites the individual with his group. But the individual cannot grow without the background of a coöperative community. Greco-European and American culture blossomed from the seed of individual achievement. In particular the cultural flowering of the Renaissance drew its strength almost entirely from the literation and relative isolation of individual souls.

What does all this signify for us?

Let us look at the time in which we live. What is the condition of the group? What of the individual?

The population of the areas where our peculiar type of civilization prevails has increased enormously. The population of Europe alone has increased threefold in a century. In America the rate of increase has been even more prodigious. But the number of independent leaders, creators, and thinkers has decreased in inverse proportion. There are few individuals today who tower above the crowd. The few who stand out owe their distinction chiefly to some productive achievement. In the world at large organization has taken the place of individual leadership. This holds true particularly in the realm of technical achievement. It is also true in a striking degree in the domain of science.

The lack of great individualities in the world of the arts stands out with painful clearness. Painting and music especially have degenerated. Politics, too, is bankrupt. Not only are there no great political leaders but the individual citizen has suffered almost universally a decline in spiritual self-reliance and in his sense of justice. Yet spiritual self-reliance and a keen sense of justice on the part of the individual citizen are the two pillars on which the structure of democracy rests. Without them parliamentary systems are barren. Because the individual has lost these two prime civic virtues, democracy and its parliaments are tottering in many countries. Everywhere dictatorships arise and are tolerated because the sense of dignity and individual rights is no longer sufficiently and vibrantly alive.

The masses everywhere lack independent political judgment. The public of every country can be egged within two weeks into such a degree of hate and hysteria that its individual members are ready to kill or be killed in military trappings for any special interests without regard to its merit. Propaganda creates compulsory military service, or rather compulsory military servitude. In my opinion the most shameful symptom of the lack of personal dignity from which our civilized world suffers today is its acceptance of the shackles of compulsory military service in any form. In view of these disturbing phenomena there is no dearth of prophets who proclaim the imminent collapse of Western civilization. I do not align myself with these pessimists. All signs to the contrary, I believe in a finer future. I may be permitted to substantiate briefly the reasons for my conviction.

Mankind suffers not because it has failed to advance but because it has advanced too fast.

I attribute the present manifestations of disintegration to the fact that the growth of industry and machinery has sharpened the battle of existence to a point where it impairs the free development of the individual. Potential leaders lack the leisure which they need for their growth. The development of the machine should have produced the opposite effect. It should have diminished the demands on the individual for labor to supply the wants of the community. But the world has not adjusted itself to these changes. As a result unemployment and restlessness stalk feverishly through an unstable world. Mankind is beginning to realize that its most imperative task is a carefully planned reapportionment of labor.

Once we have accomplished this redistribution we can readjust our lives with material security and leisure for each individual. Enlivened by a new sense of security and freedom, energies now harnessed and repressed will liberate themselves in the individual soul. We shall evolve once more great personalities, able to enrich our cultural life. Drawing new strength from individualities, thus mankind will regain its economic balance and its spiritual health. The very intensity of our trouble indicates the determination of the social organism and of the individual to throw off the ailment.

Further historians will construe the crisis that grips the world today as a symptom of a social malady brought about solely by the too rapid tempo of civilization. Humanity, conquering its infantile disease, will strive upward and on to attain its appointed goal.

Ladies Who Charmed the Prince of Wales

by Frederick L. Collins

The Story of What Dame Rumor Has Done to Some Royal Friendships—Is Another of Them Now on the Rocks of Gossip?

O F COURSE THERE have been ladies. Why shouldn't there be?

The fact that a man happens to be Edward Albert Christian George Andrew Patrick David, Prince of Wales and Earl of Chester, Duke of Cornwall, Duke of Rothesay, Earl of Carrick and Baron of Renfrew, Lord of the Isles and Prince and Great Steward of Scotland, doesn't make him any different as a man from other normal, healthy, attractive masculine individuals.

In fact, the finest of the many fine things about the Prince of Wales is that he is *not* different.

And who could begrudge the Prince his good times with pretty girls here, there, and yon? They are about the only deviations he allows himself from a life which is about as exacting as ever fell to the lot of human male. And it isn't his fault that he has to have his good times in front of cameras and microphones.

By the same token, nobody can fail to agree with the late Will Rogers that "for a young man who has had the world's attention showered on him like he has, and come through the way he has, it is really remarkable."

The world's attention is right, but the feminine world's attention is righter. Think of all the princesses, society matrons, debutantes, and actresses whose names have been coupled in the press with that of the Bachelor Prince!

Take the princesses of royal and near-royal blood. There are said to be fifteen hundred trying to get themselves married to about seventy-five princes, of whom only Edward of England has even a Chinese laundryman's chance of sitting *and staying* on a working throne. H. R. H. has done his duty by a good many of them: Ingrid and Astrid and Marthe of Sweden, Marguerite of Denmark, Juliana of Holland, Marie-José of Belgium, Beatriz of Spain, Yolanda and Mafalda of Italy, Ileana of Rumania, Marina of Greece; and has had the satisfaction of seeing most of them married off, one to one of his brothers, the others to his friends.

When it became obvious that he did not have the slightest intention of marrying any of these Continental young ladies, the rumormongers switched their attention to home-grown daughters of the local nobility. The change was greatly appreciated by H.R.H. Some of these English and Scottish girls were, as he expressed it, "good kids" and "good sports." One or two even brought forth the adjective which he habitually applies to his favorite women friends: they were "snappy."

Lady Elizabeth Bowes-Lyon, who afterward married the Duke of York, and Lady Mary Cambridge, one of her bridesmaids, and Lady Alexandra Curzon came definitely in the first two categories; whereas Edwina Ashley, thirty-million dollar heiress of Sir Ernest Cassel, was indubitably snappy. But, so far as marriage was concerned, the nobility didn't take with Edward of Wales any better than royalty had done.

"Mother," he laughed, in that affectionate manner he always maintains toward the Queen, "would like me to 'buy British.'"

But he didn't.

There is nothing in his history to show that he is unduly intrigued by women of the theater. Gertrude Lawrence, who was recently on the verge of marrying into the royal family of the Cinema, is a favorite of H.R.H.'s both on and off the stage. He sees everything in which she appears. Beatrice Lillie is another. He went to see her fifteen times in that show where she dressed up as Britannia and sang that absurd "March, March" number. The gossips made a lot of it; but that didn't bother the Prince.

"Love her?" he said. "Of course I love her."

And then, as the boys were about to break for Fleet Street with the biggest news story of the year, he added, with his famous crooked smile working overtime:

"She reminds me so much of my grandmother, Queen Alexandra!"

ELEANOR NICHOLS

VIRGINIA BRISCOE

After the theater the Prince likes to go somewhere to dance. In London it is usually the Embassy. In Paris it was Jed Kiley's. In New York it was the Lido. But his behavior in all these places has, at all times, been unexceptionable.

Naturally "Digger," as he is known to his intimates, has met a good many society girls—mostly Americans—who were not on either the royalty or nobility list at Buckingham Palace. But there was nothing unusual, certainly nothing to be criticized, in these meetings. They were the same girls he might have met, and often did, at private parties both in London and New York.

Black-tressed Beth Leary taught him backgammon. Smiling Beatrice Gottlieb taught him golf—at least she taught him that a good woman golfer can beat a fair-to-middling man golfer. Mrs. Freddy Cruger would have taught him, if he had needed teaching, to dance; for he said her footwork was "divine."

None of these casual acquaintances, however, tried to teach the Prince of Wales to marry!

Neither did Tallulah Bankhead, once of the London stage, nor Corinne Griffith, once of the American screen. And the same thing is undoubtedly true of Miss Peggy Simmonds, daughter of Mrs. Clarence Crittenden Calhoun of Washington, who was touted in the press as the object of the Prince's "serious intentions."

The Prince always has liked American girls. As for the English girls with whom his position at home permits him to associate, they often pass his standards of good-sportiness and snappiness, but they are seldom at their best with him. To them, although he insists on their calling him David or Digger, he is always His Royal Highness, the heir to the throne, the son of their king.

The Prince is more American than many Americans. He is probably the only man who has been born on either side of the Atlantic since the Boston Tea Party who might conceivably stand an outside chance of uniting the old country and the new.

It is this kinship with American ideals that leads him to seek and enjoy the companionship of the American girl. But that doesn't mean that he is in love with every specimen he meets, or that he intends—or would be permitted—to marry any one of them.

There is still no American princess at the Court of St. James's, and in all probability, within the lifetime of any one now alive, there never will be.

The misunderstanding on this point—and that there has been a misunderstanding in some maternal quarters cannot be denied—is due not to the Prince but to the press. The girls who have been so highly publicized as dancing partners of the Prince of Wales have been just that—and nothing more.

He is an exceptional dancer. He has perfected himself in the thing which he loves to do. Before his South American trip, he danced mostly fox trots; after it he preferred to tango. He has always been a devotee of jazz. Among his favorite Americans are Paul Whiteman and Fred Astaire. And he has become a partner whose skill is far beyond that of the average woman he meets.

Naturally, when he finds a girl whose step fits his, he dances with her all evening. Then—although their pleasure has been of the most open and obviously casual sort—he and she wake up late the next day to find that he has made her famous. She is not only the girl who danced with the Prince of Wales but she is hailed as the future mistress of Buckingham Palace.

Lenore Cahill of St. Louis was the first American girl to achieve fleeting prominence in this simple way. Miss Cahill and the Prince met on the boat coming to New York, and he danced with her several times on the voyage. That was all there was to it—but the news of his supposed "infatuation" was promptly wirelessed around the waiting world.

Then there was little Valerie Jones, a Canadian girl who danced so well with him at the Ottawa Country Club that his hostess invited her on a yachting cruise through the Thousand Islands; and there was Eleanor Nichols, the blue-eyed, chestnut-haired daughter of Commander Nichols, U. S. N., with whom he danced under a tropical

212

moon at Panama; and Virginia Briscoe, seventeen-year-old daughter of the Oklahoma oil man, with whom he danced in Budapest; and Veronica Purviance, formerly of Kansas City and now of Montevideo; and Blanche Warwick of Paw Paw, Michigan; and—but what's the use?

That there were, and still are, so many of these supposedly favored young women should indicate to fair-minded observers that no one of them could be very important in the life of the Prince. In the few instances where he has permitted his attentions to a pretty woman to go beyond the occasional casual meeting, the flaming tongues of even uglier and more unfounded gossip have quickly assailed both him and her.

In each case this deplorable result has meant the end of an often delightful friendship—and that is just what happened in the case of Mrs. Dudley Ward.

In Mrs. Ward the Prince seemed to have found his ideal dancing partner. She was not only "snappy," she was clever. She made him laugh. Moreover, she had the physical stamina to keep up with him.

Now, as it happened, Dudley Ward was one of the Prince's very best friends, and still is. H. R. H. went to prize fights with Dudley with just as much gusto as he did to night clubs with Mrs. Dudley.

The arrangement worked beautifully for years. Then the Mrs. Ward part suddenly stopped—because London busybodies would "talk." That was the real reason why the night-club table which used to be reserved for the Prince and his erstwhile favorite partner remained eloquently vacant.

Another friendship broken up in the same way was that with Thelma, Lady Furness. In America, Lady Furness is known chiefly as the "other Morgan twin"—the twin sister of Gloria Morgan, who married Reggie Vanderbilt and gave birth to that much litigated poor little rich girl, Gloria Vanderbilt. In Europe Thelma stands—and also dances—on her own shapely feet.

It was her skill in dancing which led H. R. H. to be seen frequently with the lovely Thelma. She was seen quite as frequently dancing with the son of the Aga Khan, the Indian potentate who is much richer than his sovereign.

As for Mrs. Simpson, widely heralded in the sensational press as Lady Furness's "successor," the great gossip-loving public first became conscious of her existence in the late summer of 1934, after Riviera dispatches had stated that the Prince of Wales, on vacation at Cannes, was having "such fun" that he had sent back an airplane which he had ordered to take him to Paris; and then solemnly added: "To the delight of hundreds of onlookers last night, the Prince danced the rhumba with an American woman identified as a Mrs. Simpson."

That same year, at Biarritz, when Mrs. Simpson and her aunt stepped off the Sud Express, H. R. H. was on the platform to greet them and insisted on seeing personally to their luggage. To our American minds this would seem to be a simple act of courtesy, but to certain sections of the British press it was epochal. As one observer well expressed it:

"A Mrs. Simpson had become *the* Mrs. Simpson."

Worried British dowagers hustled to look up her ancestry, and found it disconcertingly good. She was born Wallis Warfield of Baltimore. Her mother was a Montague. Her father, after whom she was named, was a brother of S. Davies Warfield, for many years president of the Seaboard Air Line Railway, and she was related more distantly to former Governor Warfield of Maryland.

As a young girl, Wallis Warfield married Lieutenant, now Commander, E. Winfield Spencer, U. S. N. The marriage ended in divorce in Warrenton, Virginia, in the early '20s. In 1926 she married her present husband, Ernest A. Simpson, who was graduated from Harvard in the year 1919.

Until comparatively recently the Simpsons made their home in New York. Latterly they have been living in London at 5, Bryanston Court, Bryanston Square.

A lot of rot has been printed about the enmity between Lady Furness and Mrs. Simpson. As a matter of fact, the two girls have long been close friends—and it was through the former that the Prince met the latter. In fact, until Lady Furness came to America, the trio was frequently seen in dancing places both in London and on the Continent. It was entirely natural that when Lady Furness went away the Prince should continue to go dancing with Mrs. Simpson. It was natural, too, that if she was to be in Biarritz during the season and H. R. H. was to be there too—as he so often is—they should see a good deal of each other in the busy life of the gay resort.

But reporters with space to fill wrote at length of motor trips to St. Tropez to dance to the music of Ted Delmuth's band—harmless diversions, surely—and of the equally harmless reception at which Mrs. Simpson and her aunt hostessed for the heir to the throne, and to which straight-laced British notables were invited.

As a result, gossiping tongues were soon wagging and rolling. The Prince's old nemesis, publicity, was pursuing him again—and is still pursuing him.

Returning once more to Cannes last fall, H. R. H. decided one sunny morning to visit his cousin, Lord Mountbatten, commander of H. M. S. *Wishart.* He was wearing a typical Riviera costume of gray linen trousers, rope-soled sandals, and brick-red shirt. Not until he stepped aboard the *Wishart* did he remember that he would be expected to salute the quarterdeck, and to do so he should wear a hat.

The situation seems silly enough to us, and it evidently did to the Prince, for when some one produced a white linen hat he pushed it aside. Mrs. Simpson, who was in Cannes at the time and was accompanying him on the visit, fully realized the possible offense to British naval tradition, and even went so far as to remonstrate with her host. But the Prince stood his ground.

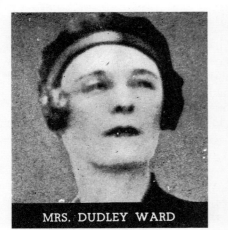

MRS. DUDLEY WARD

LADY FURNESS

MRS. SIMPSON

BEATRICE GOTTLIEB

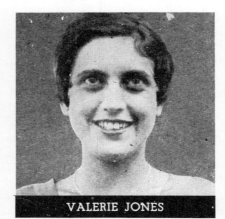

VALERIE JONES

BEATRICE LILLIE

So the news cameras clicked on a hatless salute—and one more black mark was scored, apparently undeservedly, against beautiful Wallis Simpson as an "influence" on the future King of England.

And now comes what is probably the most unfair of all the unfair publicity which has attended this perfectly open and natural friendship.

London gossips are all in a dither over a little pamphlet —alleged to be autobiographical—entitled "What Charmed the Prince."

The pamphlet has had a brisk sale. Jealous beauties and their mamas read that one "should ask questions hesitatingly, girlishly, charmingly," and that throughout most of the day one should "languidly take it easy, saving up strength for the 'concentration moments' when the man is around." Above all, one should acquire "a honey-ish Baltimore drawl."

It was this last advice which sent news hawks scurrying to the home of the Baltimore-born Mrs. Simpson, where her husband said indignantly:

"Of course my wife didn't write it!"

Of course she didn't. Nobody who knows Mrs. Simpson thinks she did. But since *somebody* did, it begins to look as if still another charming friendship is going on the rocks of gossip.

At first glance these recurring troubles of the Prince and the ladies with whom he chooses to dance may seem to harm no one, except, of course, him and them. They probably aren't important enough to affect the peace of nations. But it is not too much to say that if the misrepresentation of his conduct and mode of life is allowed to continue, it might conceivably affect the social deportment of a good many of the world's sons and daughters.

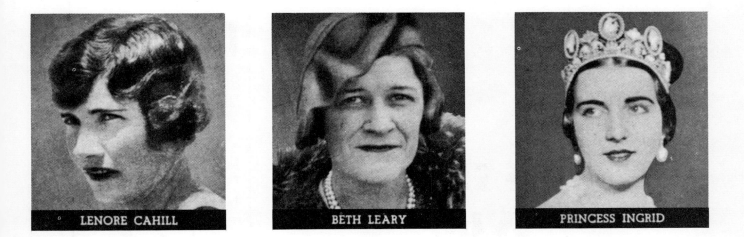

LENORE CAHILL — BETH LEARY — PRINCESS INGRID

GERTRUDE LAWRENCE — PRINCESS ILEANA — TALLULAH BANKHEAD

In England the Prince is much more than the son of the King.

He is the national idol—and properly so, for no man alive today has worked so hard or so successfully to sell the British Empire to the world and to itself. As the national idol, he is naturally the national model. Everything he does, everything he says, even everything he wears, is taken up and done, said, or worn again by Englishmen throughout the world.

And this slavish copying of the Prince is not confined to Englishmen.

Although now in his early forties, Edward of Wales is still the idol, and therefore the model, not only of the men of his own decade, but of the younger men of the two decades which follow—quite regardless of geography, nationality, or race.

When he was in this country the last time, the picture papers caught him walking on Long Island wearing a favorite old hat with the brim turned down all around. At the polo game next day, one observer estimated that ten thousand young men appeared with their hatbrims worn the same way.

Most of the brims on those American hats were too broad to be turned down. Their owners would probably never have seen the game at all if the Prince himself had not come to their rescue by arriving in a neat new fedora with the brim *turned up*.

Silly? Yes, but significant.

In common fairness, therefore, to the Prince, and with due consideration to the influence which he wields, isn't it about time for him to be held up to view not as an irresponsible philanderer—which he isn't—but as a sincere, hard-working, public-spirited citizen who is doing a big job and doing it well?

215

The King Who Might Have Been

a short short story
by Dorothy Sherrill

KING EDWARD VIII

NICKNAMED "SARDINE" BY HIS CLASSMATES, IS THE WORLD'S MOST TRAVELED RULER. ON A SINGLE TOUR HE GAVE, AS TIPS, 600 TIE PINS, COSTING $20,000! MOST DEMOCRATIC OF KINGS,

HE RULES ¼ THE ENTIRE POPULATION OF THE GLOBE!

THIS IS THE story of a man who might have been King of England if it hadn't been for a woman.

No man had ever been more greatly loved. Ever since his birth he had been the Prince Charming of the world. But for years now he had not set foot on British soil. The English ministers had forbidden his return.

The woman wasn't well-born. In fact, she was a commoner with no title or wealth. The only thing she had was charm, and she had always treated him as if she were his equal. That is why he had fallen in love with her.

The first few years of living in foreign exile had been fun. Austria, Italy, Switzerland, France—he visited them all. But mainly France.

He lived first in magnificent castles of friends and well-wishers. His story was on every one's lips. Servant girls and great ladies of three continents went to sleep to dream of him.

But eventually he wore out his welcome in castles of friends. Even the warmth of well-wishers cooled as his kingly qualities paled and his playboy habits became increasingly apparent. Besides, King George, who sat on the throne of England, frowned whenever he heard that foreign countries were paying what he considered undue honor and attention to this royal wanderer.

And no longer did women of three continents dream very often of him. For they were a trifle weary of his publicized devotion to one woman.

The royal exile, however, didn't mind too much at first. His companion was gay. She amused him. They flitted about, like two butterflies, from parties to gambling casinos, to hunt clubs, to race meets. And they were happy enough—for a few years.

But the woman didn't have it in her to hold him forever. And he had it in him to remember what might have been. A throne is a weighty thing to forget!

Therefore they began to get terribly on each other's nerves. They taunted each other with their pasts. He was ashamed of her because she wasn't as fine as some of the duchesses at whose homes he was still welcome. She was ashamed of him because he seemed willing to drift about and do nothing to regain the throne that was his by right of birth. They quarreled continuously.

Finally, on a particular morning in a villa on the outskirts of Paris, matters came to a climax. He told her he was through. He was bored to death. He could stand no more of this kind of life!

"Then why aren't you man enough to go back to England and seize what's yours?" she taunted him.

"Taking you with me, I suppose! What relief would that be?"

Her eyes blazed. "You needn't bother about me!" she cried. "I'm leaving you now! If you think taking care of a drunken no-good for years has been fun, you're crazy! I'm as bored as you are! I'll pack my things at once and you'll never see me again!"

As soon as she had stormed out of the room, he leaped to his feet. Free! Free at last! He felt like a new man!

And then a knock came at the outer door.

His servant ushered in a delegation—of lords and ministers from England! Weighty gentlemen who had been his secret friends for years.

"Your Majesty," the spokesman said, bending his knee, "we come beseeching you to return to the throne of your fathers."

A second minister stepped swiftly forward. He bore a parchment scroll.

"We have here, sire, a petition from thousands of your loyal subjects."

A third minister bowed low.

"Subjects who have always looked upon you as their rightful king, even though George now sits on your throne!"

The man whose life—up till a month ago—had been so empty drew himself up, filled with refreshed pride and hope. He suddenly looked, in spite of his years of dissipation, every inch a king.

"Gentlemen, I have been waiting for this for a long time! I will come back," he said.

Tears of joy filled their eyes. They kissed his hand. It was a touching and impressive scene.

Then the spokesman cleared his throat.

"There is, of course, Your Majesty, one condition on which we are all agreed—the woman may not come with you!"

The king's brow darkened. Lightning flashed from his imperious eyes.

"Condition!" he shouted. "You *dare* impose conditions on *me,* your lord by the grace of God!"

He strode across the room, threw open a door. "My sweet!" he called.

The woman came and stood on the threshold—not so young as she once had been, nor so attractive. Yet with a light suddenly radiant in her eyes.

He took her hand and turned to the aghast delegation.

"Gentleman, this is the woman of my choice! Where I go, she goes! That is final!"

The loyal old men, trembling with bitter disappointment, saw their long-cherished hopes dashed to dust. There was only one thing that they could say.

"We are broken-hearted, sire! But England will never accept her! We must go back without you!"

"Go, then! And George can keep the throne! But always remember this—I am your rightful king wherever I am, and I'll not be dictated to about the woman I love!"

Thus spoke Charles Edward Stuart, "Bonnie Prince Charlie," about Clementina Walkinshaw in Paris, in the year 1764, while George III reigned in England.

The Private Life of the Dionne Quintuplets

by Marguerite Mooers Marshall

An Intimate Chronicle of the First Year . . . Here, in a Revealing Close-up, Are All the Things the World Has Wanted to Know About Its Most Famous Babies

THOSE FIVE DARLINGS of the world, the Dionne quintuplets—Yvonne, Annette, Cécile, Emilie, Marie —are at this moment trying to break the brand-new toys presented to them at their first birthday party. I know that is what the scamps are up to, because I have watched for six months the heavy toy mortality in the quintuplet set. Yvonne probably is grabbing Annette's doll, while Annette is tugging at Yvonne's hair. Cécile and Emilie doubtless are making passes at each other with the beautiful metal mugs which the babies use as musical instruments—drums for choice. Sober little Marie is hugging with both hands her most beloved plaything—Dobbin, the wooden horse with the long fierce gray tail. All five babies are doing their best to kick off their knitted booties —or at least to kick holes in them.

Over the group, at play like so many kittens on a wide soft pink blanket, the sunshine floods through the glassed-in walls of the nursery. It's exactly the sort of place where you'd like your own baby to be.

For the past half-year I have been paying them monthly visits. Masked and gowned as a protection against germ-carrying, I have watched them take their baths, eat their breakfast, wave their rattles, kick their nurses, go to bed. I can report as follows:

They are even better-looking than their pictures.

They are a gold-medal exhibit for child hygiene, with a greater chance to live and develop than the average little girl or boy.

They are mentally as well as physically vigorous

In every way they are wholesome, normal, lovely and lovable babies, who have an ideal existence.

Their triumphant survival proves that babies handicapped at birth can live and grow strong if they are given intelligent, indefatigable attention.

Of such multiple births—only thirty-two cases are recorded in medical history—there is no single instance until this one when all the babies lived for more than a few minutes or hours. In addition, the little Dionne girls were premature; the "seventh-months" children always so difficult to raise. Finally, their surroundings not only at birth but for months thereafter were primitive and fraught with peril.

Dr. Allan Roy Dafoe, wise and gentle country doctor who brought the Dionne daughters into the world, hardly dared hope they would all remain in it. When an American city editor with two children of his own, an unashamed fondness for all babies, and a liking for long shots, called Callander, Canada, from the telephone on his desk and offered an incubator, Dr. Dafoe could only reply that it would help. The doctor was taking no bets.

Their birthplace, miles from an electric plant, functioned on a kerosene and cordwood basis. To be of any service to them an incubator had to be an obsolete affair, its heating dependent upon a hookup with the kitchen stove.

Such a model, long since retired from active duty at Coney Island, New York, finally was unearthed in Chicago and rushed by plane, train, and road-burning motorcar to the quintuplets' aid. Meanwhile, for the first hours of their lives, they whimpered faintly and wriggled even more faintly in a homemade hotframe devised by their first plucky and ingenious little nurse. She was a youngster only six months out of a training school, a girl of the community in which the babies were born. She lined a market basket with blankets between which she slipped hot-water bottles, and nested the minute-size midgets in the center, wrapped in pieces of old sheeting.

There were no baby clothes in that home for even one infant, to say nothing of five. There was no hot-water bottle—the nurse had to send for her own, and for any that could be collected from neighbors.

During the first four days of the babies' lives she managed to obtain about four hours' sleep for herself. All the rest of the time she was working to keep her precious infinitesimal bits of babyhood warm and protected and fed from a medicine dropper.

They had their first baths in a saucer of olive oil while their nurse sat in front of a wide-open oven door. They were dressed in jackets of absorbent cotton as soon as these could be made by interested women.

What literally gave the breath of life to the babies might be called an oxygen cocktail. It consisted of inhalation of 95 percent oxygen and 5 percent carbon dioxide according to a technique perfected for the treatment of soldiers during the World War. Dr. William A. Dafoe, brilliant Toronto gynecologist and a brother of the famous "country doctor," rushed this special treatment to the aid of the gasping little girls within twenty-four hours of their birth.

Their first food was a combination of milk, water, corn syrup, with a drop of rum added as a needed stimulant. As premature babies, they would not have stood a chance without the natural nourishment of mother's milk. Nursing women in the neighborhood gave what they could spare, but the quantity proved insufficient. Members of the Junior League in Toronto, two hundred and fifty miles away, scoured the city for breast milk. The precious fluid was packed in ice and sent daily to the babies. They were drinking a gallon a day at the end of five months, although they had started on a pint.

At one time the quintuplets weighed less than ten pounds altogether. They were typical premature children —their skin a purplish blue, their stomachs bulging, their faces and limbs pitifully thin. They gained and lost—lost and gained—during the critical early weeks; now one, now another in the lead. At the end of six months, Yvonne and Annette had surpassed by 400 percent their birth weight.

The doctor and his devoted nurses, furnished by the Canadian Red Cross, waged a never-ending struggle to maintain proper standards of child hygiene in a house without modern sanitation and in a small makeshift nursery seldom visited by the sun, and minus even a door to separate it from the family living room.

The elder Dionnes had been induced to sign a contract for the public exhibition of their offspring—a contract which, in the case of such frail little beings, was nothing less than a death warrant. The parents did not realize this, and therefore the Canadian government found it necessary to appoint a board of guardians and build a special, separate nursery-hospital—the Dafoe Hospital for the Dionne Quintuplets.

It stands just across the road from the Dionne homestead. The babies were moved into it at the end of their first summer. The nursery—for the babies' second summer it will be remodeled to twice its original size—is a spacious room, its three outer walls practically all windows so that the place is awash with sunshine. The decorations are ivory and green, the floor is spotless hardwood. Five ivory cribs with pink wreaths painted on them are hung with badges and medals blessed by the great church of which the babies' parents are members and in which they have been christened.

A fascinating toy is clamped to the bars of each crib— a wooden bunny and wooden rooster which can be drawn out on a pulley of elastic and snapped back with a gratifying zip by busy little fingers. Each baby also has a tiny wooden "pet" tied to the crib bars. Yvonne's is a puppy, Annette's a squirrel, Cécile's a rooster, Emilie's a rabbit, and Marie's a goose.

There are ivory enamel high chairs and nursery chairs and play pens. Each quin has her own yellow porridge bowl with her name on it, her own brightly colored hot-water bottle with her name written across it in script.

Though immaculately clean, this nursery is gay with color. Bright patchwork quilts are folded across the foot of the cribs. The babies' blankets are pink and blue and yellow and green, with bunnies stamped on them. The winter sleeping-bags, worn in the carriages for four-hour naps on the sun porch, are pink.

I have seen them snoozing peacefully outdoors in morning sunlight at eight below zero. The one cold from which they have ever suffered was an outside infection brought them in the spring. The cheeks of the five are a lovely glowing hue between pink and red—the exact shade of the old-fashioned cinnamon rose. Their finger tips and their tiny toes are as pink as if they had been rouged. Thanks to four-minute sun-ray treatments every other day, the plump, amazingly vigorous little bodies have turned a light biscuit-tan.

Their hair is dark and is so long that it can be curled in cockatoo crests on top of their heads, while it straggles in drakes' tails at the back of their soft necks. Their eyes are blue-black, and they have curling eyelashes of an incredible length.

The twice-a-day bath is always a high moment. When I first was admitted to the intimate performance, each little six-months-old girl went into a small white enamel tub by herself. Two months later they had splashed themselves out of the tiny tub into a bathtub full size, where they sported in couples. At ten months they fearlessly spread-eagled on their chests in several inches of water, sometimes without even a nurse's supporting hand beneath them. Yvonne and Cécile at this age were all but swimming. All five children are perfectly fearless. The nurses squeeze a facecloth so that it drips over dark heads and into dark-blue eyes; the babies just blink and that is that. Once when a few drops ran into Emilie's mouth, she started a small wail.

"Must keep your mouth shut in the water, Emilie," said a nurse cheerily. Emilie not only shut the mouth but shut off the cry.

They cry so little, these youngsters! At night there's hardly a peep out of them. When an occasional chirp sounds from a crib, the night nurse, whose bed is in the nursery, says "sh-sh," and baby obediently "shushes."

Awake or asleep, each baby has an unmistakable individuality, "identical" quins though they be.

Yvonne is now the largest and strongest physically, although in the beginning she seemed to have the feeblest grip on life. She could sit up without a pillow or other assistance for many minutes at a time when she was little more than ten months old.

Annette is a shade the most beautiful of the five. Mentally, she is the venturesome one who "starts things." She was first to creep, first to bear her weight on her feet while a nurse held her erect, first to evolve a one-woman pillow fight in her own crib, first to know her name and hold out her arms to be taken up. She cut the first tooth.

Emilie is the temperamental prima donna with the impish expression. She "tried on" a trick of crying for attention when she was only six months old. She would wait at bedtime until the lights were snapped off and the door shut, then utter a piercing dramatic wail. If she heard a nurse tiptoe back to the closed door she would pause, in the patent hope that some one would enter pick her up, and call her a poor, dear child. It never happened! After experimenting for several evenings Emilie abandoned this bid for the limelight.

Round-faced Cécile is the family flirt. She makes shameless eyes at the big broad-shouldered pink-cheeked Welshman, one of two constables from the district police who act as a pair of watchdogs for the nursery. She likes to bootleg her thumb—suck it on the sly against nursery rules—and she has an unassuagable passion for the color red. She wore out a scarlet Mickey Mouse rattle through never being willing to let it out of her hand. One day I saw her weep bitterly. She tried to pick the red poppies printed on her crib quilt, and they wouldn't come off!

In a litter of puppies Marie would have been called the "runt." She always has been the tiniest quin. She is the only one with a skin blemish; a small innocent tumor on her leg which is disappearing under radium treatment.

Marie, during the first months of her life, seemed just a bit slower on the uptake than her sisters. Now, however, for some time she has gained more, proportionately, in weight than any of the others.

After being weaned from mother's milk the children were put on a milk formula. They have received, from a very early age, rations of orange juice, tomato juice and cod-liver oil, in the successful attempt to ward off rickets. They have been given all the boiled and strained water they would drink. Each baby had first her individual water bottle and now her own tall water glass.

Dr. Dafoe decided when his little charges were about eight months old to introduce them gradually to cooked vegetables and pulped fruits, porridge, and egg. When they were a year old they ate nearly everything except meat, pie, ice cream, candy, and they liked whatever was served them—even spinach. Some time before their first birthday their meal schedule was arranged on an almost adult basis, with night feedings eliminated. These well-brought-up little persons now sleep twelve hours without giving a moment's trouble.

They wake up with a smile, stretching out their arms to the nurses who bring them a morning pick-me-up of cod-liver oil and orange juice. Then they have an arrowroot biscuit to munch, and you'd be surprised at the amount of chewing which can be done with one or two teeth, the quintuplet average, although more are looked for at any minute. Teething is, for them, a natural and comfortable process.

Seven A. M. brings a bath for each baby, with hair brushing and clean clothes—a shirt, diaper, dress, sweater, booties, but no slips, bands, or stockings. Breakfast is at seven thirty. Each sits up in her little high chair and eats a coddled egg with arrowroot biscuit crumbed in it.

She drinks milk from a glass, and is learning to hold the glass.

The outdoor nap in the carriage on the sun porch lasts all the morning. At eleven, each baby has a glass of milk; at twelve thirty, dinner, consisting of peas, beans, asparagus, spinach, beets, squash, or some other one vegetable, often mixed with beef broth and followed by a dessert of pudding or pulped fruit, with more milk to drink.

Afternoon is mixing time, in play pens or on the big blanket spread over the floor. The tiny squabbles over toys are matched by tiny peacemakings, even Annette and Yvonne pat each other's dimpled hands and smile affectionately.

Another cod-liver-oil-and-orange-juice cocktail is downed at three, and for the later hours of the afternoon each infant goes to her crib. The day's second bath is scheduled for 5 P. M., with a clean nightie and supper of porridge and milk to follow. Taps sounds promptly at six; the light goes out and the door is shut.

To me, the most inspiring and constructive aspect of this great adventure is its dramatizing and publicizing of practical child hygiene—the things every mother and father ought to know and do for every child.

And does the system mean that the quintuplets are deprived of a baby's right to be loved? You'd never think so, if you could see nurses and quins together. No rosy face may be kissed for fear of transmitting a germ, but I should say there are few other unkissed square inches on the five little bodies. That the babies recognize and care for their nurses is equally obvious from the way in which five pairs of eyes follow the white-robed figures and five small folk snuggle contentedly in the safe, sure embrace.

Oliva and Elzire Dionne, father and mother of the babies, have been urged to come to the nursery daily and share in the happy play hours. For reasons best known to themselves they choose, day after day, not to walk across the narrow strip of road which separates nursery and farmhouse. That the parents do not see more of the quintuplets is no fault of the guardians appointed by the government of Ontario to protect the babies as wards of King George until they are eighteen. Oliva Dionne himself is one of these guardians, Dr. Dafoe is another, the third is Judge J. A. Valin, a French-Canadian Catholic jurist of distinction in the community.

The large sums paid for photograph rights and all gifts to the quintuplets are set aside in a trust for them, which now amounts to over $150,000. These babies, it has been pointed out, in one year earned more than the President of the United States just by staying alive. While the principal of the trust will be held intact, the income is being used not only for Yvonne, Annette, Cécile, Emilie, Marie but for the benefit of their father, mother, and older brothers and sisters.

Dr. Allan Roy Dafoe, who warded off death a thousand times from these helpless little ones, now carries on his tireless selfless efforts for their welfare under a mud barrage of mendacious propaganda dictated by greed, ignorance, ingratitude, and baseless suspicion. But the private life of the quintuplets—the whole program of their perfect care—has been endorsed warmly by leading child specialists and by every intelligent observer, including physicians who visited the hospital at the request of the father.

The babies grow bigger, better, bonnier. Their future promises even more than their present performance—if in it they continue to be guarded as safely as they are in the nursery in the tiny village of Callander, toward which the eyes and the hearts of America turn today.

Quintuplets?
Shucks!
by Walter Winchell

A Close-up of the World's Most Modest Man—Who
Staged the World's Most Celebrated Blessed Event

THIS IS SUPPOSED to be a portrait of Dr. Allan Roy Dafoe. Acres of type have been set in praise of this engaging little surgeon from the Canadian provinces, but I think he can be "painted" in this line:

All the ballyhoo and acclaim that the world gave him couldn't spoil him.

That, to me, is the top. The Big Town poisons people with kindness when they've clicked. Too many celebrities have been turned into swelled-heads. Dr. Dafoe went home more beloved than when he arrived.

It was my good luck to meet Dr. Dafoe for the first time in a Broadway night club, and to tour other hot spots with him during his stay in town.

It was his first night club. If you are easily upset, take hold of something while I tell you that the headliner was Sally Rand. And Dr. Dafoe found nothing at all shocking in Sally's bareskin hoofing, and praised her attractive figure to boot.

At the time of our first meeting, Dr. Dafoe was the most-talked-about guest New York had had since Lindbergh's triumphant return from his Atlantic flight. He was round-shouldered from honors, and the toast of every drink in the club; but you knew in a minute he'd like it if you got chummy and called him Doc.

Along with forty million more Americans, I had a tremendous admiration for this country surgeon who staged the world's most celebrated blessed event—the Dionne-event. It was dramatic and mighty exciting, the way he carried the Dionne quintuplets through the most perilous period of infancy. It was more than all the big-time baby specialists in the world had ever done; and he didn't have all the equipment money can buy, as they did. His entire paraphernalia is in the little kit he lugs on his country rounds.

Doc Dafoe looks like what you expect from reading about him. Short, stocky, graying. The eyes behind his spectacles are kind and understanding, and sometimes very knowing. His graying mustache is close-clipped, just a wisp of a thing which makes him look, as somebody has said, puckish. The dancing girls called him "cute."

He wore a new blue sack suit, purchased for the visit. Also a new green felt hat, which perched uncertainly on his head, its brim rolled up all around. Back in his small town he wears a cap, yanked down over his ears to keep out the Ontario chill.

Doc Dafoe enjoyed the gaiety of New York's night life. In a phrase he popularized himself, "Sure; why not?" For twenty-six years he had been hidden away in the back country, with only his radio and the movies for amusement—he saw two in twenty-six years. And when his day was over with tall-browed medicos and learned statesmen, he liked to go out and have fun.

I hope, however, that readers won't get the same idea of Doc Dafoe's pleasure cruises that seems to have penetrated the conks (noodles to you!) of editorial writers on the Calgary *Herald* and the Salt Lake City *Telegram*. They deplored Doc's willingness to be "dragged off" to night clubs by hysterical New Yorkers, and counseled him to conduct himself with dignity and aloofness.

What hooey! To their minds Doc had no sooner hit the wicked city than he started tearing it wide open. Nothing sillier or more unfair could have been written. Like many other men, Dr. Dafoe took advantage of the good time New York provides and behaved as he might have been expected to behave—like the gentleman he is.

What won me to Doc Dafoe at once was that he had dusted off the shysters and phonies who fasten on to everybody who makes the front pages. His companions that first night were Fred Davis and Charlie Blake, two newspapermen who had come down from Canada with him. During the day he always delegated the formal chores to his brother, Dr. William Dafoe of Toronto, who, being a city feller, knew more about ceremonies than he did. But when he played he was on his own.

The first thing Doc said to me was that all this fuss over him was a bit bewildering. He seemed genuinely amazed when I assured him that he had the affection of all Americans. I had a proof of my next day's column with me, in it a paragraph of nice things about him. That astonished him, too—him with columns and columns in the other sheets!

"My, my!" he said, pleased, when I told him to keep it. "My, my!" "Well, well!" "Oh, dear!" and "My goodness!" were his favorite expletives.

The chorus girls came out flipping their shapely thighs and revealing oodles of nakedness. "Ooooh!" he said, "this is going to be fun." He watched them writhe through their paces. "This is peppy," he commented.

He wanted to know what wages the girls received "a month." It was almost cruel to tell him they collected more than twice the pay the Canadian government gives him—$100 a month—for toiling in blizzards. But he said they worked hard and deserved good pay.

Doc's stamina was amazing. At fifty-two, his energy is boundless. He was always ready to gallop, with his "Sure; why not?" when another excursion was suggested. Maybe the job of bringing 1,400 babies into the world (and he has never lost one) is a good way to keep in condition. For whenever Blake or Davis or your deponent wanted to hurl in the towel, Doc would put on his new green lid and look around for another spot.

His days were pretty full, too, as you have read. There was a lecture at Carnegie Hall, a plane flight to Washington to meet President Roosevelt, a call at Johns Hopkins University in Baltimore, and so on. But at sundown he was off to a musical show, then a supper place or four, always protesting that four hours was all the sleep he needed. We found that out.

Doc took some abuse from the papers, though it wasn't intentional. They put speeches into his mouth that didn't fit there. But he was considerate enough to overlook those things. He even overlooked the newspapers' hint that he was under the thumb of brother Bill.

That wasn't true. He had the same admiration for brother Bill—and maybe awe, too—that a country doctor always has for a successful city practitioner. He is a miracle of unpretentiousness. At a reception given by Arthur Brisbane he was no less than a wahfff, which is several points above a wow. He tore canapés with dowagers and won them over with his simple good nature. And if you think he had no mind of his own, hear this:

When he met former Governor Al Smith, Al wanted to know what the Dionne babies looked like at birth.

"Like rats," Doc told him.

Brother Bill, aghast, corrected him. "Like kittens."

But Doc knew what he saw, and the world knows the affection he has for his five little charges. No need to be prissy about them. "Rats," he repeated firmly. The press next morning made it "puppies."

He rebelled another time. He wearied of a musical show and, like a critic, walked out. His bodyguard, Detective Devine, found him strolling Broadway.

On his last night in town Doc went sleepless for twenty-five hours. At two-thirty, when Davis and Blake were hanging on the ropes, he invited me to join him. We went to the Casino de Paree, which is hotter than Singapore in midsummer. It was a tall thrill to him, and at four o'clock he began to sight about for another stop.

Downtown we went to a place where the whoopeeeee is spelled like that—five e's. He loved it. Next day he was off to the wilderness, and he wanted the night noisy and hilarious. He got it. The comics and hoofers and lovely gals lifted the roof in his honor.

"How often," he whispered, excitement in his burred tone, "do they have these parties?"

I told him this was the regular night show.

"Every night? You don't say. My goodness!"

This gladsome mischief held us till eight o'clock, when, reeling from fatigue, I persuaded him to catch a couple hours sleep. Regretfully he agreed to turn in.

"Tomorrow night I'll be home and I'll light my pipe and pull up to the radio. It'll be more fun listening to you all, now that I've met some of you."

New York should erect a plaque to remember the man who brought his naïve and simple lovableness into an arena too crowded with stuffed shirts. His presence was as stimulating as a hike through his own balsam woods.

If Doc Dafoe is a hick, that is a term to describe a man who enjoys and deserves the admiration and affection of everybody who has met him.

1936: Looking Backward
The Year in Movies
by Beverly Hills

Ten Best Pictures, Twelve Best Performances, Highlights Here and There; Liberty's Critic Reviews the Verdicts and Adds Some Personal Opinions

YOUR BEVERLY HILLS allotted four stars to exactly ten pictures during 1936. They were: *Captain Blood, Trail of the Lonesome Pine, These Three, The Country Doctor, Show Boat, Green Pastures, Nine Days a Queen, Romeo and Juliet, The Texas Rangers,* and *Winterset.*

In retrospect, some other pictures stand out as real achievements—*Mr. Deeds Goes to Town,* for a notable example. Others were *Piccadilly Jim, My Man Godfrey, Libeled Lady, Petrified Forest, Fury, Anthony Adverse,* and *Swing Time.*

The year had a marked trend toward sophisticated, biting modern comedy with sharp, pungent observation of life. *My Man Godfrey* and *Piccadilly Jim,* along with *Libeled Lady,* were stunning examples of what the screen can do in an intelligent way with comedy when it really tries.

Any summary of the year would not be complete without a list of best performances. Here are our own chosen twelve:

Adolphe Menjou's mad Barrymore in *Sing, Baby, Sing;* the earthquake in *San Francisco;* Norma Shearer's exquisite Juliet in *Romeo and Juliet;* Leslie Howard's introspective wanderer in *Petrified Forest;* Gary Cooper's altruistic millionaire in *Mr. Deeds;* the blood-crazed crowd in *Fury;* William Powell's forgotten man in *My Man Godfrey;* the two pixilated sisters in *Mr. Deeds;* Mickey Rooney's gutter dreamer in *The Devil Is a Sissy;* Eric Blore's man's

man in *Piccadilly Jim;* and Ronald Colman's heroic Sydney Carton in *A Tale of Two Cities.*

The best two scoundrels of the year were the tough hard-riding hombre of Humphrey Bogart in *Petrified Forest* and the savage tubercular slum killer of Eduardo Ciannelli in *Winterset.*

We are thinking of signing up the two for a championship battle in Madison Square Garden.

Want to recall some more interesting performances of the year? Here are a few: Gladys George as the generous magdalen in *Valiant Is the Word for Carrie;* Walter Huston as the tired business man of *Dodsworth;* Sir Cedric Hardwicke as the crafty Earl of Warwick in *Nine Days a Queen;* Leopold Stokowski's hands in *The Big Broadcast of 1937;* Spencer Tracy as the victim of mob lust in *Fury* and as the fighting priest in *San Francisco;* Akim Tamiroff as the Mongolian war lord in *The General Died at Dawn;* Paul Muni as the nineteenth-century chemist *Louis Pasteur;* and Carole Lombard as the dizzy debutante in *My Man Godfrey.*

The outstanding box-office stars as the curtain falls on 1936: Fred Astaire, Robert Taylor, William Powell, Clark Gable, Nelson Eddy, the Dionne Quints. Probably Greta Garbo still rates up there, too. And, of course, Shirley Temple.

Color still is having a hard time of it on the screen. Its loveliest use was in *The Garden of Allah,* but somehow

Ten of the best performances of the year. 1—Adolphe Menjou in Sing, Baby, Sing. 2—Norma Shearer in Romeo and Juliet. 3—Leslie Howard in Petrified Forest. 4—Gary Cooper in Mr. Deeds Goes to Town. 5—William Powell in My Man Godfrey. 6—Mickey Rooney in The Devil Is a Sissy. 7—Eric Blore in Piccadilly Jim. 8—Ronald Colman in A Tale of Two Cities. 9—The earthquake scene in San Francisco. 10—The blood-crazed crowd scene in Fury.

by
BEVERLY HILLS

or other it seems to get in the way of the drama. Sooner or later, of course, it will be with us.

The screen oddity of the year was the success of radio's Bob Burns, the bazooka mæstro.

The comedians had a not so good year. *Modern Times* seemed slow and dated, for all the vaunted silent comic genius of Charlie Chaplin. *The Milky Way* was funny, but it was not Harold Lloyd at his best.

Our individual award for best comedy performance goes to Adolphe Menjou for his hilarious work in *Sing, Baby, Sing.*

The biggest wallop of 1936 came in *Winterset* when the gangster, drilled three times and thrown into the East River, returned, bloody and mucky, to get his man.

The screen went historical often and hard. History was at its best in the French-made *La Kermesse Héroïque* and the English filming of *Nine Days a Queen.* It was at

its worst in Hollywood's version of Andrew Jackson in *The Gorgeous Hussy.*

The big box-office pictures of 1936 were *The Great Ziegfeld, Mr. Deeds, San Francisco, Follow the Fleet, Swing Time.* A fortune in each and every one of 'em.

The best directorial performance of 1936 was turned in by Frank Capra with *Mr. Deeds.* A few laurels, please, for Mervyn Le Roy and his *Anthony Adverse* and for Fritz Lang and his *Fury.*

The most tragic event of the year was the death of young Irving Thalberg, the best mind in the creation of pictures, at the very top of his career.

The films will be a long time recovering from this blow.

The year's meteor is Robert Taylor, who came from nowhere to be the talk of moviedom. Every one of the Taylor films has had the gals palpitating at the box office.

The nearest approach to Taylor is Errol Flynn, handsome and easy in his roles. Errol is a little too sure of himself. America likes its heroes just a little gauche right now.

Another boy coming along fast is Tyrone Power, Jr., who does splendid work in *Lloyds of London*. And Burgess Meredith reveals high promise, too, in *Winterset*.

Simone Simone is the heavily touted feminine find of the year. Your Beverly Hills is skeptical about this young woman. Luise Rainer was a glittering Anna Held in *The Great Ziegfeld*. Watch her coming film, *Good Earth*. That will give you an accurate measure of Miss Rainer's histrionic stature. Frances Farmer, who did double roles in *Come and Get It*, has high promise. The two loveliest newcomers are Madeleine Carroll and Olivia de Havilland.

Litigation and quarrels with studios have held up the careers of Bette Davis and James Cagney. Beverly Hills is sorry in the case of Bette. She's as promising and interesting a young actress as Hollywood possesses.

What actress made the most progress in 1936? Irene Dunne, possibly. Your guess is as good as ours.

Our favorites in musical entertainment were the Astaire dancing films, along with *The Great Ziegfeld* and *Sing, Baby, Sing*. Prize for the biggest set of the year (and 1936 had some hefty ones) goes to the big revue tableau in *The Great Ziegfeld*.

The best staged musical number? Oddly enough, it was a simple affair; Fred Astaire's dance with the three shadows in *Swing Time*.

The best camera work was done in *Romeo and Juliet*. Credit William Daniels for a job well done.

The most fantastic comedy interlude was the sequence in *Love on the Run* where Clark Gable and Joan Crawford, seeking refuge in Fontainebleau Palace, are discovered by the mad old night watchman.

The smartest screen treatment of 1936 was that of Maurine Watkins, H. E. Brown, and George Oppenheimer for *Libeled Lady*. We greatly admired Anthony Veiller's expert film adapting of Maxwell Anderson's *Winterset*.

The oddest heroine of the year: Calamity Jane (Jean Arthur) in Cecil De Mille's *The Plainsman*.

The worst publicity of 1936? "Caliban" John Barrymore's romance with "Ariel" Elaine Barrie.

Of the established male stars, Gable, Powell, Cooper, and Eddy more than held their own. No slipping anywhere in that distinguished quartet. Of the ladies, Norma Shearer, Marlene Dietrich, Carole Lombard, and Jeanette MacDonald stepped right along.

But Donald Duck still remains our favorite Hollywood player.

My Wife Left Me to Join Father Divine, A White Man's Story

by Edward Doherty

Time, 1936; Place, America! The Amazing Experience of a Hard-Fisted, Two-Gun Southerner Who Worshipped a Negro as God

HE WAS BIG and lean and dangerous as one viewed him from the doorway. "I'm Griggers," he said as I entered; "Charles J. Griggers. I'm a Texan."

On his olive-gray shirt, on the left, were three loops of black thread. The pin of a shield or star should go through those. But he had no badge. As for cartridge belt and revolvers, he looked half-dressed without them—until I glanced into his eyes. They were a washed-out blue, and mild as milk. His hair was growing white.

"I came here to find my wife and bring her back," he said. "But I guess that ain't to be."

He took out of his pocket a picture. "That's Eva. They call her Enoch Light now. She is a disciple of M. J. Divine."

"Is that Father Divine?" I said.

"Don't call him Father Divine. That means the divine Father—God. He ain't God. I know that now, though once I admitted that he was."

"You're a Texan, and you worshipped a Negro as God?"

"I'm a Californian now," Griggers said. "I was a policeman in Compton, near Los Angeles. I was a bank guard too. But I was born in Texas, in Grand Saline, a town where they don't allow any colored people. There were a lot of them there at one time, but the white men killed some and drove the rest out. So colored people were little more to me than animals. I was raised that way.

"That's why I was such a sensation in the M. J. Divine movement. A Texan. And I was one of the sincerest believers of them all. It cost me my house, my furniture, my wife, the love and respect of my children. I'm broke. Haven't got a dime."

"How did you get into it?"

"Curiosity, at first. My wife and me went every place together. Sometimes we went to the Mormon church. Oh,

I wasn't much of a churchman. I took a drink when I wanted one. And the girls—I'd been wild in my day. And I've been shot at lots of times, and I've done plenty shooting. And there have been times in this M. J. Divine business when I felt like selling out."

"Selling out?"

"In Texas when we sell out we stand with our back against a bar or a wall and we mow down everybody in front of us until they get us. That's selling out.

"Eva was a widow when I married her. She had a daughter. I had eight kids; some of them are pretty young yet. I'm only fifty-four. One night we decided, Eva and me, to go to one of those M. J. Divine extension meetings in Los Angeles. They are mostly all white people there. Well, it was fun. We went again. And again. The first thing I noticed was that my right foot was keeping time to the hymns. The next thing, I was clapping my hands.

"Then one night my arms and legs kept jerking and I couldn't stop them. When I got home I threw myself on the floor and kicked and jerked and screamed and hollered until four o'clock in the morning. It had me. I couldn't get away. I didn't want to. And it had Eva, too.

"A woman named Rebecca gave her transportation to New York. She went. That was in July 1934. She took the name of Enoch Light. And I went sort of crazy while she was gone. Her mother was living with us, and she grieved so over Eva's leaving that she got dangerously ill. I wired Eva that she was dying. I got no answer from her. I wired M. J. Divine. I got no answer from him.

"So I sold the house, took Eva's mother to the Divine extension in Long Beach and cared for her there until she died. Finally I started for New York. I had nothing but an automobile, and I gave it to Ross Humble, who

227

drives one of M. J. Divine's buses. I gave it to him for transportation to New York and transportation back for myself and Eva.

"In New York everyone made a beeline to the heaven at 20 West 115th Street. The room there was full when I went in. Someone mentioned my name, and M. J. Divine turned to look at me, smiling a little. I was so overcome I went right up to him, put my two hands around his, and said, 'Father Divine, I'm happy and proud to meet you.' He just kept smiling. Pretty soon there was a silence. Everybody was staring. He opened his mouth wide, closed it, and then said, 'Boom!'

"It was startling—so loud and unexpected. Some fell down on their faces. Some fainted. He smiled at me again, and I fell on my knees and admitted he was God.

"After a while I started out looking for my wife. I got lodging at the mission house where she worked. You sleep two or three in a bed, and you pay a dollar and a half a night. The men and the women are housed apart. But white and colored sleep in the same beds. Eva slept with colored women, and they made her do all the dirty work. Why? Because God was a colored man.

"She wouldn't speak to me. At the time, it didn't matter much, for I had found God, I thought, and God didn't want a man to have any wife. One night I was so carried away with the love of God that I shoved aside everybody and went directly to Divine. I threw my arms around him and kissed him all over his face and neck. How those people shouted! A Texan come to lay himself at the feet of a colored Jehovah!

"One morning I found a note from my wife. It asked me to meet her at noon. I did. She was weeping and in rags. 'I'm sick of all this,' she said. 'I'm ashamed. I've had enough. I want to go home or kill myself.'

"I bought her shoes, rented a comfortable room for her, and put her to bed. Then I went and told Divine what I had done. 'It's wonderful,' he said. 'Peace!'

"I sent a friend to get her things. A woman, Faithful Mary, said Eva would have to come for them herself, and called me a thief who had stolen Enoch Light from God.

"Eva and I were called to attend a meeting, and Divine stood up and accused us both in the worst word-whipping either of us ever experienced. Eva wilted at his words and then he turned on me. It was all I could do to control myself. I looked at Eva. She had fallen down. And now, standing where she had stood, I saw Jesus."

"You saw what?" I asked.

Mr. Griggers smiled his mild dead smile. "Jesus, the Saviour. I saw Him as plainly as I see you now. It was no trick. I stood there looking at Him, and then He vanished. And Eva, my wife, was lying there at the foot of the piano.

" 'I know now who my God is!' I cried out. 'My God is Jesus!'

"Divine gave me a peculiar look and sat down. He said nothing, but I know he had seen Jesus as clearly as I had. When I took Eva away a few days later, he made no effort to stop me.

"We went back to California; but we were in such a state we were still slaves to Divine. So we opened one of his missions at Redondo Beach. We ran it until last March, when Eva received word to return to New York or be lost. She left me a note:

" 'I am gone to see my father, M. J. Divine.'

"Gradually I began to come to my senses. I heard she was in a hospital in New York, in a critical condition, and continually calling for me. I started to hitchhike to New York. Arrived a little more than a month ago.

"People have been kind to me. I've never asked for a nickel, but I've never needed money. I live at the Y. M. C. A. Even my bus fare back to California has been provided me. I leave tomorrow—alone. I found my wife, but she won't come with me. She is still suffering from the delusion that M. J. Divine is God.

"It took me a long time to find her. The District Attorney's office gave me a detective to help me—a man named Johnny Cordes. He took me everywhere through Harlem—and he gave me money, too. But we never found her. No one would tell us anything about her.

"I knew she was working somewhere. Everybody works for Divine and gives him their money—every cent of it. No, no; they don't have to. Not at all. But they do. They insist on giving it to him. He teaches that God owns all the money in the world, and that if you voluntarily give him your money you will be rewarded a hundredfold. He also teaches that you must love nobody but the divine Father—Father Divine, of course. Oh, I know of so many families he has split—so many children he has forced parents to abandon!

"I found Eva through this letter written me by her daughter. You see, there, she wrote that she was working as a governess for a family in West End Avenue."

The letter gave the address and the apartment number.

"I went there and saw her. She looked thin and ill. She wouldn't talk to me.

" 'Eva,' I said, 'I want you to come back. If you don't, I'm going to a newspaper or a magazine and tell the whole story.'

"She looked at me as though I had blasphemed. I never saw such horror on anybody's face.

" 'If you do that,' she said, 'I'll deny it.'

"Then she backed away from me, slowly. She backed into the elevator. The door shut on her, and the cage went up. I haven't seen her since."

"You've tried to?" I asked him.

"Oh, yes. But I can't find her again. She won't answer the phone. When some one does answer, it is only to say my wife isn't there."

"So you've given up? You're beaten?"

He nodded his head mildly.

"Yes," he said. "I'm beaten. I can't fight any more. There's no more fight left in me."

To Be Accounted For

a story by Achmed Abdullah

*A Flaming Tale of Sudden Love, a Woman's
Guile, and a Dark and Sinister Revenge*

HE MET HER first at the ultramodern chromium-glittering Mayfair apartment of Carleton Trevor. He had not seen the latter since Oxford days; called on him one evening, a few days after his appointment to the London consulate; and was shocked when he saw the other's purple-veined, alcohol-sodden, prematurely aged face that stood out above the immaculate white of his evening-dress shirt like a flabby blotch—rather a diary of the deeds its owner should not have done.

It embarrassed Prince Hossayn Abdelkader deep down in his meticulous Arab soul. It saddened him, in a way. He felt tongue-tied; and Trevor was amused.

"I know," said the Englishman, "what's biting you. Expected to find me the same clean-limbed, clear-eyed, pipe-smoking undergrad, all for cricket and football and Merry England—that it?"

"Not exactly. But—oh . . ."

"Something like it. Well—since those innocuous old days a whole lot of water has passed under the bridge and a whole lot of excellent vintage champagne down my gullet." Trevor spoke without either bitterness or regret. Pleased he seemed with himself and his philosophy; grossly surfeited with the good things of life. "I do look a bit florid—don't I? An aura about me of silks of China and French perfumes and jewels and unsalted caviar." He laughed. "Can't help it, my dear fellow. That's me."

"The whole of you?" the Arab asked gravely.

"The *blooming* whole. You see—I'm all in favor of lovely baubles. Baubles made of gold and pearl. And baubles made of soft white flesh."

"Different from what you were at Oxford."

"Quite." Trevor lit a corona-corona. "And you, I fancy, are just as you used to be? Full of high idealism?"

A silence fell between the two men. The years of the past, the years when he and Carleton Trevor had been friends, stared at Hossayn and grimaced.

Years of Oxford youth. Fair years. Good years of decent young enthusiasms, decent young ambitions, decent young falterings and gropings and uncertainties. And now—oh yes!—staring at him, staring out of the past like sardonic, obscene gargoyles . . .

Hossayn gave a shudder. He did not know what to reply; and once more the other was amused.

"Each to his taste," he remarked. "You're satisfied with your own life—aren't you? Not yet thirty, and already consul general of that brand-new Iraq kingdom of yours. Going some! And picked for a big job back home—if one is to believe the papers."

"Yes." Hossayn spoke not without pride. "Minister of Foreign Affairs, if I make good."

"You'll make good—never fear. You're so blinkin' shortsighted that you don't even recognize temptation when the painted hussy comes your way. Very well. Go ahead. Live your life as you like it—and like it as you live it. But kindly grant me the same privilege!"

"And yet . . ."

"Oh"—a little impatiently—"don't preach virtue to me, or I'll put you in a class with my revered and reverend uncle, the Bishop of Ilchester. He's another one of those masterful, swaggering, bullying moralists, topheavy with self-righteousness and greasy with the oil of purity. Virtue may have its rewards, but so has . . ." He interrupted himself, laughed, as the door opened. "Rise and turn, old fellow," he went on, "and bow your prettiest to Miss Carolyn Wilton."

She had come from the inner room, dressed in a loose negligee of soft clinging wistaria charmeuse, her bare feet in gold-threaded French slippers. If the situation was embarrassing to Hossayn, it was not to her. She looked at him and found him not bad-looking—narrow-hipped, wide-shouldered, his skin dead-white, his features hawkish. He looked at her and found her amazingly lovely—with her high-bridged nose, her red, adventurous lips, her broad forehead, the tumult of her short dusty-gold hair.

She acknowledged the introduction with a smile. She sat down. And she proved both her position in the house and her utter lack of self-consciousness when, on the butler appearing with the cocktails, she gave him a message for her maid:

"Tell Katie to put out my black velvet dress for tonight and the ermine wrap."

Then she turned to the two men, speaking lightly of this and that and the other thing. And not long afterward Hossayn got up to go.

She said, "Some day you must tell me all about the Orient. I find it *so* thrilling."

The words were ordinary enough. Hossayn had heard them many a time in Europe, with just that faintly rising intonation, from the lips of romantic debutantes, smug matrons, and intellectual spinsters; had heard them—and casually dismissed them. But somehow tonight, as he bent over Carolyn Wilton's slim hand, then straightened and looked at her, the words seemed to be endowed with a different meaning, a personal meaning; seemed to hold at their core the significance of an intimate and vital message. And when he returned to his consular office near the Asia Docks—he had purposely chosen his quarters there to be close to the people of his own country, his own Arab race and Moslem faith, stevedores and waiters and small tradespeople who lived thereabouts and whose interests he was serving—he told himself, with a queerly chilly finality, that he was in love.

Throughout his life, as he had lived it heretofore, his brain and not his passions had ruled him; he had always treated the softer emotions with scornful disregard. Now, when love had come to him suddenly, violently, unreasonably, he suffered all its extremes. His thoughts wantoned with his fancies. His past existence seemed but a record of trite drab memories.

That night was the first since his arrival in London which he did not spend in work for his government or in researches among the leather-bound tomes, books mostly on economics and international law, that crowded

his shelves. He sat down at his desk and, being a versifier of sorts, began writing an Arabic poem:

Death will come to me because I cannot forget a certain
   girl.
Night tossed a handful of golden stars
Into a blue pool—and called it her eyes.
God wrote a new moon into the heavens—
And called it her forehead.
The velvet of Damascus is woven from her hair.
Her feet are small and sweet as little sins.
Her hands . . .

He interrupted himself. He tore up the page. He walked up and down.

He thought of his great-grandfather, Prince Murat Abdelkader; of the Persian slave girl whom the latter, when he had been well advanced in years, had bought, after much haggling, from her previous owner, the Sultan of Muscat.

He smiled ironically; and early the next forenoon, having telephoned to make the engagement, he met Carleton Trevor at the Savoy Club, sat down, and said:

"I'm in love with Miss Wilton . . ."

For once, the other found himself startled out of his usual saturnine placidity.

"You—wh-what?" came his stammered query.

Calmly the Arab repeated his statement, adding:

"I think you ought to know."

The Englishman had regained a little of his equanimity. He hid a carefully prepared yawn behind a shaking hand.

"Don't tell me," he suggested. "Tell her."

"I can't," was the even reply, "as long as she lives under your roof."

"Jolly nice of you to be so concerned about my honor."

"I was not thinking of your honor. I was considering my own."

"These delicate points are beyond me. The fact of the matter is that you want me to give her up—eh?"

"Unless you are in love with her."

"One isn't in love with that sort of woman."

"I am."

There was a pause. Then Carleton Trevor broke into disagreeable laughter.

Of course you realize," he asked, "that I'm putting up for her—financially?"

"Oh, yes," said Hossayn. "But I'm a very rich man. I shall give her double whatever you give her."

Again the Englishman was startled—startled, now, in his conventional Western morality which he had thought scotched these many years. Momentarily he felt conscious of a sullen anger as he looked at the Arab; crystallized in his heart, for the least fraction of a second, all the hatred and contempt which Occident and Orient have felt for each other since the world was created from a mote of star dust. Involuntarily he clenched his fists. A curse was on his lips, an insult.

Then he controlled himself.

"That's all very well," he remarked. "Very sporting—and all that sort of thing. But, really, you can't buy a woman. I mean, not exactly. After all"—with slurring, malicious intent—"you aren't in Bagdad."

"Nor do I intend buying her."

"But you told me . . ."

"I shall simply pay for her apartment, her food, her clothes, her luxuries . . ."

"As I've been doing heretofore. So I don't see . . ."

"Wait! There'll be no obligations. Once she is free from you, she can choose what man she chooses, what man she loves—you or me."

"Or perhaps a third man?"

"Perhaps. I hope she'll choose me. If she does, I shall beg her to marry me."

"Are you serious?"

"Very. But—I repeat—there'll be no obligation on her part. Not the slightest. I trust you will make that last point quite clear to her."

The other frowned.

"D'you expect *me* to tell her?"

"It would be more fair all round—don't you think?"

As before, instinctively Trevor clenched his fists. Then he laughed.

"I'll do it!" he exclaimed. "I'll talk to Carolyn." He rose. "By the way—know anything about women?"

"Not much."

"I, on the other hand, know a lot."

They were silent. They looked at each other; looked away. There was between them a delicate equilibrium of brittle artificial courtesy which one fleeting negligible or wrongly interpreted word might have destroyed; which might have crystallized, in both, the ancient bitter enmity of West against East and East against West.

They were careful not to speak this word. They smiled, politely and falsely.

"Yes," the Englishman resumed. "I know a lot about the female of the species. I've learned—from Carolyn and from other women. Want me to teach you?"

"Don't bother."

"No bother. It'll be a pleasure. Listen! Here begins the first lesson." Trevor paused. "Woman is rather a tangled sort of trinity. One third of her is angel, one third devil, and the last third . . ."

"Yes . . .?"

"The last—and vital—third is whatever man chooses to make of her."

"I don't understand."

"I didn't think you would," was Trevor's dry comment.

He left the Savoy Club. Twenty minutes later he told Carolyn Wilton, who was stretched out on her couch playing with an Angora kitten.

She laughed.

"D'you know, dear boy," she said, "I've an idea it'll be rather interesting. . . ."

On Monday of the following week she moved into a smart little Curzon Street house. It reflected her own taste in pink-and-white boudoir, in toilet articles of tortoise shell and gold, in a profusion of pillows of orchid satin covered with rose-point lace. And it held a flavor of Hossayn's soul in the deep-toned Kermanshah rugs on the floor and in the tulipwood cabinet filled with mellow things of Asian lands; twelfth-century Moorish pottery, a miniature copy in enamel and silver of the Tamamushi shrine, three Sassanide plates of robin's-egg blue, and a collection of exquisite and fragile porcelain of the days of Harun-al-Rashid that glowed with rust red and apple green and imperial yellow.

She broke one of these, a few days later, by accident.

She noticed the fleeting expression of almost physical pain that came over Hossayn's eyes as the small vase crashed on the floor.

Thereafter she broke several more—by way of experiment.

She stopped breaking them when Carleton Trevor told her that any Bond Street jeweler would give her the pick of his emeralds for the collection; and she was very angry—not at herself but at Hossayn.

"Silly ass—the Arab boy friend!" she said. "You know, he never let on that those things are valuable."

"You didn't expect he would, did you?" replied Trevor, smiling darkly. He paused. "There's a new supper club on Whitehorse Street. The Supreme—wrongly called. Shall we dine there tonight? It's such gorgeously bad taste. You'll simply adore it, my dear."

He took her out frequently—quite as frequently as Hossayn, who raised no objections. For he lived up to the literal meaning of the agreement. An agreement, to him, was a stout and rectangular entity which permitted of no evasions of interpretations. Carolyn was under no obligation. It was her right to choose—him or Trevor or a third man.

Of course there was his hope, his longing, that he would be the chosen. And he spoke of it one day to Mustaffa Yar, the priest of London's single little mosque that catered to the religious needs of the humble Moslem workers and shopkeepers who lived near the Asia Docks. Hossayn kept up a certain friendship with him—for reasons of Islamic politics and, too, because the other was a scholar well versed in the Arabic classics.

Mustaffa Yar took no personal interest in Hossayn's affairs. He neither pitied him nor sympathized with him. "Let each man brush away the sand from his own threshold," was his tolerant maxim. But, being a wise priest, he was a clever politician. He believed that church and state must stand and fall together. And he knew that these last few weeks, around the Asia Docks, gliding Oriental tongues had been busy swapping salty scandal anent Carolyn Wilton and Hossayn—and that, given the latter's official position, was bad. It was dangerous. So he decided to be outspoken.

"Is it true," he inquired, "that you intend marrying the woman if, belike, she should choose you?"

"Yes."

The priest sighed.

"May I be frank?"

"Why not?"

"Then," brutally, "the woman is evil. I have heard —tales."

Hossayn smiled.

"Evil," was his calm answer, "is merely a point of view. Besides, I love her."

"Love—bah!" Mustaffa Yar exclaimed angrily. He pointed through the open window whence, beneath a sunset of dirty crushed rose-pink, hiccuped the thick sensuous symphony of the Asia Docks, with the voices of men and women mumbling haltingly, passionately, and a street organ gurgling some cloying ballad. "That sort of love—down there! Love of the senses, the flesh! It is a lie, a snare, an infidel act! To find happiness there is like dragging for the moon reflected in the water!"

"Even that is possible—to love. Indeed, there is nothing which is impossible . . ."

"To the human body?" sneered the other.

"No; to the human soul. You see—my love is not altogether of the flesh."

Hossayn spoke the truth as he saw it.

There was indeed in him, in that illogical counterplay of moods and forces which is meant by love, a great longing for Carolyn Wilton. But this longing was tinged, was even overwhelmed, by a delicate spiritual quality.

It is true that, when he saw her, he read in her violet-blue eyes—and reflected within himself—the suggestion and promise and hope of infinite dreams, infinite thrills. He was both too honest and too natural to deny it. Yet even more strongly was there in him the desire to read the mystery of her woman's soul. He tried to fathom this mystery; and—perhaps because there was little to fathom except a glittering shoddiness—he did not succeed. So he swayed emotional incoherence into intellectual coherence, thereby proving that he knew nothing about women—either good women or bad.

He gave her costly gifts. He composed subtle and charming Arabic poems to her which he translated, word for word, into careful English—and she would listen, reclining on a couch, yawning a little, her eyes half closed, her white pleasurable hands toying with the Angora kitten. All his thoughts he devoted to her, all his time, while the gossip and scandal of it drifted through the reeking streets that coiled about the Asia Docks.

They talked of it, one night, in the back room of a restaurant which was for Arabs only—though, ludicrously, the sign above the door proclaimed:

"He neglects important business," severely remarked Kasim Hydar, the paunchy shopkeeper, who for weeks had endeavored to reach the consul general to ask his assistance with the customs clearing of a shipment of Levantine medicine that, according to the narcotics squad, contained more opium than was reasonable.

"Over two months now my nephew has been in jail for the mere matter of stabbing a Greek sailor," sighed Arslan Djelali, the ship chandler. "And his mightiness does not reply—though I've written him innumerable times."

"In the days of the Turkish sultans," said Shukri Nazir, the stanch old Tory, "he would have been recalled and properly punished."

"Aw," came the crude comment of William Gladstone Mohammed, London-born and bred, "wot d'ye expect? He's nuts about that yellow-haired dame."

So, rightly, they complained. For, these days, Hossayn was seldom to be found in his office. His mail was unopened, his files dusty and untouched.

The love of Carolyn Wilton was in his blood. The mystery of her woman's soul was, enigmatic and unriddled, in his own soul. Nothing else mattered. Behind him lay life as he had woven it himself, close to the loom of his racial and religious traditons and prejudices. Beyond it lay a new life, throbbing with a puissant and seductive rhythm—the future with her, if she chose him.

It was utterly inconsistent with his principles as he had fashioned and obeyed them in the past. Nor did he stoop to pretense or argument or excuse. He hardly knew what was happening to him; knew only that daily, nightly, a tempest of desire took him bodily, literally by the shoulders, and pushed him toward the small house on Curzon Street.

There he would sit, looking at her, a tumult deep in his heart, while his words would be polite and coherent and slightly chilling. For he was conscious of a certain fear—the fear that she might say no if he brought it to a point.

Carolyn Wilton, on her side, surrounded him with an adroit wire-drawn net. She did not care for him. Not in the least. He was not her sort, as she put it to herself. But she had no intention of letting him go. Not only was he extravagantly generous without ever trying to interfere with her freedom—too, he amused her with his stilted courtesy that was—oh—in such contrast to the passion in his eyes. And she was curious to find out what he would say, how he would behave, when, finally, his passion got the best of him.

Carleton Trevor looked on and watched and smiled and said never a word—except one evening of late winter as he and Hossayn walked down Bond Street together.

"How're you getting on, old fellow?" he asked.

"Getting on?"

"I mean—with untangling that tangled trinity called woman."

"I never think about woman in the abstract. I am too busy thinking about one woman—Miss Wilton."

"Oh—you still call her *Miss* Wilton?"

"Indeed," said Hossayn coldly.

Trevor laughed.

"Didn't I promise to give you a few pointers about the female of the species?" he demanded. "All right. Here begins the second lesson. God hates a coward. And woman, for once, is not contrary. She does too."

And again he laughed, then slapped the other heartily on the shoulder and walked off, swinging his cane.

Then spring came, singing its topical song, flowing like a clear stream over the heart of Hossayn, charging it with a great tenderness, leaping into his blood with an impetuous yearning like the yearning of all creation, enwrapping him with the haunting and dream-colored mystery of love.

He feared no longer. He would ask her. Let her choose. Today. Now.

And deep within him he felt, knew, that she would choose him—inevitable it seemed to him, like the mating of fire and wind—and a song was in his heart as he turned up Curzon Street, entered the house where she lived, and found the hall door ajar—the maid had stepped out to mail a letter.

He passed soft-footedly through the outer hall. Near the threshold of the small salon he stopped.

He saw Carolyn Wilton stretched out on the couch, Carleton Trevor in a chair quite close to her. He heard her voice:

"Lost *all* your money?"

"Most of it. I thought you ought to know."

"Don't you worry about me, darling. Hossayn will keep on footing my bills."

She sighed. In her heart, too, spring—a fair imitation of it—trembled and danced, clouding her usual practical intuitions.

She asked, "How proud are you?"

"Don't know the meaning of the word. Why?"

"Because—you see—since you *aren't* proud, I'll support you . . ." She interrupted herself; went on quickly: "At least for a while— until . . ."

"Until my rich aunt dies. I know."

He took her in his arms. She sighed again.

"You do know how to kiss," she whispered.

"Better than the Arab boy friend?"

"Why—he's *never* kissed me. Never as much as tried. Isn't he a scream darling?"

She laughed. Her laughter was harsh, strident.

And then Hossayn left the house, unnoticed, and returned to his office. He beheld the files of government reports, dusty and untouched, the heap of unanswered correspondence; and he thought of her laughter—and he was conscious of a thick, murderous surge of hate. It receded almost immediately.

He shrugged his shoulders.

"Allah, Allah!" he whispered. "The time I have lost!"

Chilly-eyed, he turned a page in the book of his life. This chapter—he reflected—was done with.

He mentioned it only once, some days later, to his cousin, Ali Mehmet, an attaché of the Iraq legation in Paris, who had come to London to help him straighten out the accumulated consular affairs.

"Life," he announced in his slightly didactic manner, "is the moonlight which is near. It is also the rain which is near. I do not bother about the moonlight that floods a far garden."

"Suppose," suggested the other a little maliciously, "that the far garden has once been yours—a most precious belonging?"

"What of it?" Only a fool tries to strip two hides off one camel."

Ali Mehmet smiled. He pointed at Carolyn Wilton's miniature that, framed in exquisitely carved gold, stood on the desk.

"Why, then," he demanded, "do you . . .?"

"Do I keep it where I can look at it? I adore beauty. Consider our great-grandfather. When he was well past eighty, he bought, paying her weight in silver twice over, a Persian dancing girl—for no better reason than that her feet were narrow and her eyes steel-gray."

"And then, because she laughed at his white beard, he had her sewn in a leather bag with a scratching cat and thrown in the river. You are, I take it, less savage than our revered great-grandfather—or, possibly, more decadent?"

"Possibly," agreed Hossayn.

He lit a cigarette. He moved the miniature so that the sunlight struck it, accentuating the loveliness of the face. . . .

And when, during the following week, Carolyn Wilton died of a mysterious poison, Scotland Yard, unable to discover its nature, dismissed the case as accident or suicide—it was doubtless a coincidence that, twenty-four hours before her death, Prince Hossayn Abdelkader replaced the exquisitely carved gold frame around her miniature by one of plain black ebony, saying to his cousin, Ali Mehmet:

"It is better taste than gold—don't you think?"

"Yes," agreed the other. "After all, we come by our good taste honestly. Consider our great-grandfather—and the little Persian dancing girl."

And Arab smiled slowly at Arab.

Vox Pop

CLEAR AND CONSTRUCTIVE

WACO, TEX.—If there were nothing else in *Liberty* but Bernarr Macfadden's editorial page, I would buy it. So clear and constructive. Each editorial page goes into my scrapbook for preservation and future reference.—*Ray Rowell, Sr.*

ASHEVILLE, N. C.—Bernarr Macfadden's editorial, "Enforce the Laws or Get Out," in July 21 *Liberty*, deserves the highest commendation. It will take this spirit to accomplish what he has in mind. There is a question as to whether we have the nerve, courage, and determination to face facts like men and do our duties. Keep us reminded. Perhaps he will some day wake us up. We have sense enough, if we would only use it.—*John E. Calfee.*

COLD WAVE SWEEPS GEORGIA

COLUMBUS, GA.—I almost passed up "Mutiny in the Arctic," by General William Mitchell (beginning in June 30 *Liberty*), in favor of some thrilling fiction, but found truth far stranger than fiction. I almost froze while I read it on a night in June in Georgia.—*W. C. Mitchell*

PS.—If you decide to kill *"Movie Reviews"* by Beverly Hills, save me the Vital Statistics.

A PROPHET WHO FORESAW OUR DAY

NEW YORK, N. Y.—Nearly one hundred years ago Lord Macaulay, great English historian, made a prediction for the United States which seems remarkable now, in view of the economic crisis through which this country is now passing. Writing from London May 23, 1857, to the Hon. H. E. Randall of New York, he cited his fears for the future of America as his reason for being unable to reckon Jefferson as a benefactor of mankind. In part, Lord Macaulay's letter read:

"I have long been convinced that institutions purely democratic must sooner or later destroy liberty or civilization, or both. You may think your country enjoys an exemption from industrial evils. But the time will come when hundreds and thousands of artisans will be out of work. Then your institutions will be fairly brought to the test. Distress everywhere makes the laborer mutinous and inclines him to listen with eagerness to agitators who tell him that it is a monstrous iniquity that one man should have a million while another cannot get a full meal. There is plenty of grumbling and sometimes a little rioting.

"I have seen England pass through such critical seasons. Through such seasons the United States will have to pass and I cannot help foreboding the worst. The day will come when in the State of New York a multitude of people none of whom has had more than half a breakfast or expects more than half a dinner, will choose the legislature. It is possible to doubt what sort of legislature will be chosen? On one side is a statesman preaching patience, respect for vested rights, a strict observance of public faith. On the other is a demagogue ranting about the tyranny of capitalists and usurers and asking why anybody should be permitted to drink champagne and to ride in a carriage while thousands of honest people are in want of necessities. Which of the two candidates is likely to be preferred by a workingman who hears his children cry for bread?

"I seriously apprehend that you will, in some such season of adversity, do things which will prevent prosperity from returning; that you will act like people in a year of scarcity, devour all the seed corn and thus make the next year not of scarcity but of absolute distress. The distress will produce fresh spoliation.

"Either some Cæsar or Napoleon will seize the reins of government with a strong hand, or your Republic will be as fearfully plundered and laid waste by barbarians in the Twentieth Century as the Roman Empire was in the Fifth; with this difference: that the Huns and Vandals who ravaged the Roman Empire came from without; and your Huns and Vandals will have been engendered within your country by your own institutions."

Such was the prediction for America made by Lord Macaulay more than three quarters of a century ago. Judge for yourself how nearly it has come true—*E. T. F.*

234

WHISKERS IN THE NORTH

CHAMBERSBURG, PA.—Harry T. Fisk, in illustrating a scene from General William Mitchell's series, "Mutiny in the Arctic," in July 14 *Liberty*, pictured the men on the Greely Expedition as freshly shaven as if they had just stepped out of a barber shop. Or maybe they don't grow whiskers in the north!—*Curtis Lawyer.*

LONGER DRESSES—MORE MARRIAGES

NEW ORLEANS, LA.—The increase in marriages is due to the fact that the dresses are longer this season. So luck to the femmes with broomstick limbs, knock-kneed joints, weak ankles, and the like. But beware, young men, beware!—*Jerry Trosclair.*

EARTH A LUNATIC ASYLUM?

CHICAGO, ILL.—W. A. Crolfman's letter in July 7 "Vox Pop," claiming that Mussolini has almost killed Italian freedom, reminds me of what George Bernard Shaw once said. He said that the earth was only a lunatic asylum for the rest of the universe.

Just as long as Mussolini, Hitler, and Dollfuss rule, we can be certain that Shaw was not far off the right track. —*J. G. Mishkin.*

JOKERS IN LAWS

NEW YORK, N. Y.—There is only one remedy for our disregard for law and our system of enforcement. Take our laws now on the statute books and revise them to meet our present needs. Put teeth in all laws that can be and will be enforced. Stop putting jokers in laws.

Ninety percent of the reading public cannot read the laws as they are put on the books. Let us have them plainly written, that he who reads may understand.—*Ben Butzel, Author of Digest of Insurance.*

HE WAS WITH GREELY

DETROIT, MICH.—I listened with great interest to the broadcast by *Liberty's* editor about the Greely Arctic Expedition and read General William Mitchell's articles "Mutiny in the Arctic" beginning in June 30 *Liberty*). My father, the late Richard Cullen, was thirty-five years in the Appointments, Commissions, and Personnel Division of the War Department, and knew General Brainard and other survivors of the Greely Expedition. In his effects I found a photograph of Lieutenant Kislingbury, who was said to have been guilty with Dr. Pavy of insubordination at times on the expedition. I thought it might be of interest to those who read General Mitchell's great series.—*George R. Cullen.*

SOME DUMB, OTHERS ASLEEP?

REDONDO BEACH, CALIF.—M. Falkenberg of Amelia, Ohio, who wrote in the June 30 "Vox Pop" arguing that governors be put on automobiles to hold speed demons down to thirty-five miles an hour, should get wise to himself. If we don't go fast we are out of style.

Some people are dumb and others have been asleep. Mr. Falkenberg must have been asleep during the last few mechanical inventing years.—*A. L. Cameron.*

SOUR ORANGES

LA VERNE, CALIF.—It was purely disgusting to read the two letters from our Native Son and Daughter from California. If they don't like California, let them move.

A person may buy cheap vegetables and sour oranges if they care to, but there is no need of it if they would only pay a little more.—*Charles Hall.*

EVEN AFTER BEING MARRIED SIXTEEN YEARS

IRVINGTON, N. J.—Is sex education necessary? I say— absolutely! We are all products of sex, therefore it is the study of life itself.

The majority of the youngsters learn about sex on the streets and the impression they receive is wrong. To safeguard all this, it should be taught in the schools, where the truth will be told in an intelligent, scientific manner that will leave no stain of filth or indecency.

Even after being married sixteen years, I do not know all the fundamental facts about sex. Had I received that knowledge in my school days I would now be capable of explaining it all to my growing son.—*R. A.*

REAL PUZZLES

APOPKA, FLA.—I am simply delighted to have real puzzles to work on. Please keep those Cockeyed Cross Word Puzzles going and I'll never miss a *Liberty*.—*H. R. Whitcomb.*

PICTURE WITH A TYPEWRITER

KINGMAN, ARIZ.—"The Roué's Daughter," by Adela Rogers St. Johns, in July 14 *Liberty,* was like a refreshing breeze over a scum-covered moral swamp. Rare indeed are fiction writers who can paint a picture such as that with a typewriter.—*Chet Hymer.*

OUR ROAD LEADS TO ROME

ROME, ITALY—Liberty has become a part of me. Its illustrations are extremely characteristic, and I was furthermore very much surprised to note the reading time placed at the head of each story and article. Another great surprise was furnished for me by the enormous circulation of *Liberty*—more than 2,000,000 copies! This is something that really astounds me as a European and as a writer.—*Franco Catalano.*

NO SUCH WILD STATEMENT

CAMDEN, N. J.—Matthew Woll's article "Is Red Russia Striking at American Industry?" in the July 21 issue of *Liberty,* contained false and slanderous statements about workers in the New York Shipbuilding Company's Camden yards.

The strike at the Camden shipyard on March 27 was called and conducted by this, the Industrial Union of

Marine and Shipbuilding Workers of America, and not by the Marine Workers Industrial Union. The latter never had a single man in the Camden yards at the time.

Our union is completely independent of the T. U. U. L. and the Communist Party as well as of the American Federation of Labor. No office or committee of ours ever walked out of a Washington code hearing with any such wild statement as Mr. Woll attributed to us.—*John Green, Vice President and Business Agent, Industrial Union of Marine and Shipbuilding Workers of America, Local No. 1.*

WHO GOT GYPPED?

BALTIMORE, MD.—So you gypped us of page two and thought you'd get away with it! But The Case of the Curious Bride installment in July 21 Liberty gave you away. About two-thirds down the first column of page 24 the story was getting interesting. Then a line followed announcing that it was continued on page 2, column 1—and there was no page 2, column 1.—*J. Beckner.*

[You gypped yourself, fella. That was a supposed extract from a newspaper that Earle Stanley Gardner was using, and he put in the "Continued on page 2, column 1" only to make it look realistic—just like the newspapers do with their stories.—VOX POP EDITOR.]

TURN TO PAGE FORTY-SIX

GUIDE ROCK, NEB.—And so the Princess Kropotkin has kropt up in Hollywood. My word, fancy now!

Will this very interesting lady be the one to at last really relate the résumeé of the comings and goings of the place as it should be, or will she, like Adela Rogers St. Johns, put a white frosting on the whole affair and serve it up much as rather a sickening dessert after a very fed-up repast of erstwhile palaver?—*Billy C.*

SAD HOUR FOR PAPA BEE

BELLEVILLE, ONT.—Some say that woman has at last come into her own; that since the dawn of history she has been held down by man, but that now, exasperated by his wars, his political greed and exploitation, she is determined to oust him from his leadership. In short, it is a war of the sexes. And woman, being man's chief incentive, will triumph.

In such eventuality, it is difficult to picture the predicament in which we men would find ourselves. A warning may be found by viewing the bee situation. While bees do not fight or have nationalistic tendencies, they have no tariff barriers, immigration restrictions, political graft, or unemployment.

But it was a sad hour for papa bee when he first let mama bee bring home the honey and listened to her newfangled ideas on birth control!—*B. P. M.*

HE BUYS A STAMP AND AN IDEA IS BORN

MOUNT VERNON, N. Y.—The other day I purchased a postage stamp, and I realized that in this small transaction every one was receiving the same amount of value for his money. An idea came to me which, I believe, will provide a solution for the present financial troubles of our country.

Why not apply the same kind of control to the sale of all articles which we now apply to stamps? Equalize the purchasing power of the dollar. Fix prices at retail and wholesale so that the price of every article would be the same to all.—*P. J. Rose.*

CHINS OVER THE EDGE

GREAT FALLS, MONT.—Why is it that in relatively minor auto mishaps we so often read of a young child being severely injured? The answer is that parents permit children to stand in the car with their chins over the edge of the lowered door glass, or in other equally exposed and dangerous positions.

Why not teach the children to sit securely in the seat while the car is in motion? Haven't we enough crippled and maimed children without adding yours?—*Mary Frances Costello.*

PREPARE TO BE SLAUGHTERED

ST. PAUL, MINN.—General Robert Lee Bullard's article "Can Our Army Defend Us?" in July Liberty is another link in the chain of war propaganda calculated to secure profitable military positions for him and his like.

Magazines and newspapers are acting only to further this propaganda. *Liberty,* as a champion of fairness, should present the antiwar side as well as the militaristic viewpoint.—*M. L.*

BROWNWOOD, TEX.—Lieutenant General Bullard's article, "Can Our Army Defend Us?" should be of special interest to the youth of America, because the youth will have to fight in the next war and, unless we are prepared, will be slaughtered.—*H. E. Patterson.*

TWO-STAR "B" LETTER

NEWTOWN, IA.—Your star system of rating motion pictures is not satisfactory because it does not allow for the different types of pictures. Suppose you classify all productions into four or five general types according to the predominating characteristics. Call them "A," "B," "C," and "D," and I promise you will get results. As an example, rate them as three-star "C," pictures or four-star "A" pictures.—*E. G. Alger.*

NO ANGEL

KEW GARDENS, N. Y.—Mae West, she's no angel, but she gets away with it, and I think she would make an ideal Cleopatra in a movie, as every one knows Cleo was no angel either.—*Paul A. Gerard.*

"Disney's Folly" Makes History

by Beverly Hills

★ ★ ★ ★ SNOW WHITE AND THE SEVEN DWARFS

Based on the fairy tale by the Brothers Grimm. Produced by Walt Disney for release by RKO-Radio pictures. Running time, 82 minutes.*

THIS IS WALT Disney's dream come true. For years he has hoped to make a feature-length film, a wholly animated production without human actors.

Snow White has a rare and elusive charm. It is a lovely translation of the old fairy tale created by Jakob Ludwig Grimm and Wilhelm Karl Grimm—the fantasy of the beautiful little princess who flees her wicked stepmother and comes to dwell in the depths of the forest with the seven dwarfs who labor by day in a jewel mine.

But the stepmother consults her magic mirror, summons all her black wiles, and sets out to kill the little princess.

Like all Germanic folk tales, Snow White has its vein of cruelty. It has fearsome things reaching out of the forest darkness to terrorize the fleeing Snow White; it has its horrible witch with her lust for blood. But the fable also has its beauty, its humor, its tenderness.

The birds, the squirrels, the forest hares, the fawns, all the shy folk of the woodland, do their best to help Snow White. Here the film achieves a lyric loveliness impossible to anything of flesh and blood. Too, the fantasy, unbelievable as it may seem, possesses its tense and moving moments.

The dwarfs are individual and delightfully characterized, quaint little beings of fantasy.

Snow White is something brand-new under the Hollywood sun.

*Recommended for children.

VITAL STATISTICS: Story's been left much as the Grimm Bros.—Jakob Ludwig & Wilhelm Karl—conceived it late in the 19th century. Chief differences: Animals and birds have been given human characteristics, dwarfs have been named Sleepy, Sneezy, Grumpy, Happy, Bashful, Dopey, and Doc and characterized sharply. Squatty, by the way, is a ringer for Dopey but wears a beard. Grimm Bros. won undying fame but few riches. . . . Snow White's been 4 years in the making, tying with Chaplin's *Modern Times* for the longevity production record. Hollywood called it Disney's Folly. At world premier, however, all Hollywood paid $5.50 a ticket, cheered Disney, speculators got $50 a seat. . . . Disney artists are known as Disney's hands, work for from $19 a week to about $350 tops. . . . None of the offstage voices in Snow White get credit, are sworn by contract to secrecy as to their identity, ride around in comfortable cars nevertheless. . . . Walter Elias Disney is a 1-goal-handicap polo player, loves his 2 children to distraction, is happily and once married, he's of Chicago birth and Missouri farm upbreeding. Studied drawing at Chicago night schools, was turned down for ill health when he applied as a postman in Chicago, went home, put on make-up and got the job. Spent two years driving a Red Cross war ambulance in France. His first art job was drawing farmyard animals for a Kansas City ad agency. While working nights over a drawing board a fat mouse ran out, made friends with him, got named Mortimer Mouse, later became Mickey Mouse after quite a struggle to crash world of animation.

★ ★ ★ ½ DISNEY ACADEMY AWARD REVUE

Presenting five award films: *Flowers and Trees*, 1932; *Three Little Pigs*, 1933; *The Tortoise and the Hare*, 1934; *Three Orphan Kittens*, 1935; *The Country Cousin*, 1936. Created by Walt Disney. Produced by United Artists. Running time 44 minutes.

Walt Disney, the Aesop of Hollywood, is now a screen tradition. He is one of the few immortals accepted by the town that has become (in its own opinion) the art center of the world. Charlie Chaplin is the only other immortal —and Hollywood is beginning to doubt about him, now that the sound film seems to have terminated his pantomimic career.

Disney's cartoons have more than expert drawing and sound synchronization. Not that they do not possess these virtues to a greater degree than any other film-cartoon effort. But they have something bordering on actual genius. Disney's efforts have imagination, a pleasant shrewd humor, an imaginative fantasy rare these days.

This revue combines the Academy award films of the past five years. At least one, *Three Little Pigs*, is a high point in Hollywood history. Your Beverly Hills regrets that his favorite actor, Donald Duck, is not present in any of these award films. But you will find that study in frustrated genius, the Big Bad Wolf.

VITAL STATISTICS: *Three Little Pigs,* what with its original run; reruns, rereruns and rererereruns, is the most popular film Walt Disney ever made. Considering its length and cost, it's also the most successful. Though Disney's starred the three li'l' porkers since, they've never been able to equal their first wowishness. They may retire and grow into satisfied old hams. . . . In past five years Disney and his stooges have tried to make cartoons more and more lifelike. His artists have worked hard studying the human form and its vagaries in action, and, no matter how beastly the cartoon character, have tried to make it act superhumanly natural. Disney thinks the agelessness of the comic cartoon, granting no startling change in our optical speed habits, will depend on its life-like qualities. He's been working for almost two years now on his first six-reeler, *Snow White*. It will take another six months and when finished will be ready to be hung in the Louvre of Motion Pictures. . . . Though Mickey Mouse is Disney's favorite character, Mickey's never won the Academy award, and hangs his head every time Walt goes by. . . . Curiously, Mickey, though he's come close to it, has never married Minnie. Disney feels when a man's married his jokes are over. . . . Mickey Mouse and Donald Duck get most fan mail, but Three Little Pigs still sell gadgets. . . . Donald Duck has just become a star, is putting Mickey into the shade a bit, and as a reward has got himself Donna Duck, a bit fiery in the temper and squawky in the disposition, but a real girl friend. . . . Disney artists, inker-inners, inbetweeners, and story men are all serious; can't stand whimsicality; rarely laugh.

What Makes Sammy Run?

a story by Budd Schulberg

*Once In a Blue Moon Such a Story As This! A Tingling
Tale of One Man's Way with the Thing We Call Success*

AL SAT WITH a friend in a booth at the Vine Street Brown Derby watching the people watch each other.

It's a funny thing, Al said, if you watch an animal while it eats, it stops. But here in the Derby several hundred people pay, and pay well, for the privilege of being watched while they eat.

Al is a writer. He writes scenarios, but he could say that because he worked on a newspaper for ten years, and he didn't forget it. He remembered going down to New York and begging for a job, making a pest of himself because he needed twenty dollars a week to be a man in this world. Al was getting five hundred now. That was because he had no push. He seemed content with being small fry. He was lazy. He would never get anywhere. When other writers gave him good ideas for stories he would give them credit. He was a washout.

A big man with a fat body carefully hidden in smartly tailored clothes stopped at the table. He squeezed Al's hand affectionately.

Saw your picture, Al, he said. Tuhriffic!

And he pressed his pudgy hand against Al's as if to indicate that further expression failed him.

That's the original phony, Al said, as the fat man left his table to squeeze somebody else's hand. I happen to know he told Sol Morris my picture stinks.

Al looked around at the new star who had just come in with her husband and her lover, at the too-flattering caricatures of Hollywood celebrities on the wall, at the too-revealing starched uniforms of the waitresses.

Sometimes I feel if I passed my hand over all this it would topple down like a house of cards, Al said. Just like that. Pfffffffffft.

Whenever I think of it I think of a little kid we used to have on the paper. He was fifteen years old, a little ferret of a kid, sharp and quick. Sammy Glick. Used to run copy for me. Always ran. Always looked thirsty.

Good morning, Mr. Manners, he said to me the first time we met. I'm the new office boy, but I ain't going to be an office boy long.

Don't say ain't, I said, or you'll be an office boy forever.

Thanks, Mr. Manners, he said; that's why I took this job so I can be around writers and learn all about grammar and how to act right.

Get the hell out of here, I said.

He raced out too quickly; a little ferret. Smart kid, I thought. Smart little kid. He made me uneasy. I guess I've always been afraid of people who can be agile without grace.

In three weeks Sammy did more running around that office than Paavo Nurmi in his whole career. It made me feel great. Every time I gave him a page of copy, he'd run off with it as if his life depended on it. I can still see Sammy racing through the office.

I guess he knew what he was doing. The world was a race to Sammy. He was running against time.

Sometimes I used to sit at the bar and say, Al, I don't give a good damn if you never move from this seat again. If you never write another line. I default. If it's a

race, you can scratch my name right now. Al Manners does not choose to run. And it would run through my head like that. What makes Sammy run? What makes Sammy run? Does he know where he's going? I asked one of the reporters:

Say, Tony, what makes Sammy run?

You're drunk, Al, he said. How the hell do I know?

But I've got to know, I told him. It's important. Don't you see? It's the answer to everything.

You're nuts, he said.

Three weeks later I had my first run-in with Sammy Glick.

Those were the days when I was writing my drama column and I used to bat it out around four o'clock and then go over to Mac and Charlie's and forget.

One morning a storm from the general direction of the city editor blew at me.

Why in hell don't you look what you're doing? he said.

What's eating you? I said cagily.

That column you turned in last night, he said. It didn't make sense. You left all the verbs out of the last paragraph. If it hadn't been for that kid Sammy Glick it would have run the way you wrote it.

What's Sammy Glick got to do with it? I said, getting sore.

Everything, he said. He read it on his way to the linotypers. So he sat right down and rewrote the paragraph. And damned well, too.

That's great, I said. He's a great kid.

A few minutes later I came face to face with Samuel Glick himself. Nice work, I said.

Oh, that's all right, he said.

Listen, wise guy, I said. If you found something wrong with my stuff, why didn't you come and tell me? You knew where I was.

Sure, he said, but I didn't think we had time.

But you had time to show it to the city editor first, I said. Smart boy.

Gee, Mr. Manners, he said, I'm sorry. I just wanted to help you.

You did, I said.

Sammy seemed very satisfied. Don't you think it's dangerous to drop so many verbs? he said. You might hit somebody down below.

Listen, I said. Tell me one thing. How the hell can you read when you're running so fast?

"That's how I learned to read, he said—while I was running errands.

It made me sore. He was probably right. Somebody called him and he spun around and started running. What makes Sammy Glick run? I pondered. It must have something to do with centrifugal force, only deeper.

A couple of weeks later I turned in my column and went down to the bar. The telephone rang for me. It was Sammy. He said, The boss says your column is four inches short.

What the hell, I said. Tell him I'll be right up.

You don't have to worry, he said. I took care of it myself.

You, I said stupidly. I knew he had me.

Sure, Al, he said. I dashed off a four-inch radio column to fill, and the boss liked it.

Oh, he's seen it already, I said. Then why the hell did you call me? Why don't you just take over my column?

I just wanted to help you, he said.

Sure, I said, Joe Altruist, and hung up.

But the pay-off came the next morning. I had just started on the column when the city editor came over.

From now on write it six inches shorter, he said.

O. K. by me, I said, if you can give be one good reason.

From now on we're using Sammy Glick's radio column, he said.

You mean Sammy Glick the copy boy? I asked.

No, I mean Sammy Glick the radio columnist, he said. His stuff looked good today.

Maybe you'd like to know he copied the first paragraph from Somerset Maugham, I said.

Maybe that's where you need to go for your stuff, he said.

So that's how Sammy got his start. He was smart enough never to crib from the same writer twice. When it came to wisecracks, he rolled his own. I hated him so much I began to admire him. Every other copy boy was a nice guy. At least if you bent over, they'd ask you to stand up and turn around before stabbing you.

But I began to see what made Sammy run. Though I couldn't see just then where he was running.

After Sammy Glick had been writing his column for a couple of months he came up to me one day and said, Say, Al, next Monday is my birthday, and since you sorta gave me my start I thought maybe you'd like to have dinner with my girl and me at the Algonquin.

I'll never forget that girl, or the day either, and there's a real story in that too. Everything Sammy did was a story. That's why I'm telling you all this. Because Sammy is a genius, one of our big Americans, Napoleon in a double-breasted suit. Some day he's going to lie in a museum, stuffed, labeled: This Is Sammy Glick. In an Age that Could Never Stop Running, He Ran the Fastest.

We met in front of the restaurant. He was standing with a spindly-legged, thin, pale, vague little girl. She would have been an angel, only her face was made up like an actress, heavy red lipstick and eye shadow and too much powder. I wanted to take my handkerchief and wipe it off. The poor little kid. The blue eyes and the frail body and the sad look were hers. They grew out of the shadow of the tenement right up through the crowded sidewalk. There was a little of the gutter and a little of the sky in her. I could see her staying after school, lost somewhere between the two covers of a book.

And then, later, almost grown up, evening elbows on the dusty sill, looking up at the stars, clean stars, high over a Hundred and Eighteenth Street.

Miss Rosalie Goldbaum, he said, meet Mr. Al Manners. He has the column next to mine.

Oh, Sammy has told me so much about you, she said.

Sammy smiled. We walked into the Algonquin lobby. He was nineteen years old.

Dinner was what I would have called uneventful. Sammy was almost too busy looking for celebrities to pay much attention to either of us. Miss Goldbaum was shy, very sweet, and frankly unaffected. Except when she talked about Sammy. And I encouraged her. Perhaps I had been misjudging Sammy, I thought. Perhaps there was another side to him. He was a thoughtful lover, and slowed down to a walk for Miss Goldbaum.

You know, Mr. Manners, she said, writing that column isn't what Sammy wants to do.

Of course not, I said; they forced it on him.

He just does that to make a living, she said.

It's a damned shame, I said.

But he writes *me* the loveliest things, she said, and some day he's going to be a great writer. Because he's a poet.

Sammy was looking across the room at George S. Kaufman. He was lost in thought. Miss Goldbaum edged her hand into his. Sammy played with it absentmindedly, like a piece of silverware.

Gee, Miss Goldbaum said, sometimes when I look at Sammy I just can't believe it, so artistic and everything, and him just a little kid right out of the Bronx.

Her tight little world was bursting with Sammy Glick. All her craving to live and her blood beating to possess and to be maternal found expression in this one smart little guy. She had little pointed breasts, miserable and sad, and they seemed to me to be reaching out for Sammy, the way black-eyed Susans tilt themselves toward the sun. She was boring me. So I caught George Kaufman's eye, and he came over, and was introduced, and had a drink with us.

Sammy was in his element, artificially gay, trying his best to out-wisecrack Kaufman. He was obsequious, sniveling, unsure of himself, and very bold. It would have been funny, only I had seen Sammy too long.

Kaufman stayed only a few minutes, and soon Miss Goldbaum yawned, and I said I had a lot of work to do before getting to bed, and Sammy looked at Miss Goldbaum and said, We both appreciate your celebrating this way with us. She nodded. Yes, Sammy said it exactly right. And they were gone, walking down the steps to the subway arm in arm.

When I turned to Winchell's column next morning there it was, the bold-face print laughing up at me:

When rising critic Sammy Glick celebrated his nineteenth birthday yesterday at the Algonquin, Al Manners and George Kaufman were on hand as principal cake eaters.

You didn't have to be a master mind to figure out how Walter got that item, and when Sammy came in I gave him one of my searching looks.

I see where Kaufman got himself a plug in Winchell's column, I said.

Yeah, Sammy cracked, you should have been there.

Listen, Samuel, I came back. You got enough gall to be divided into nine parts.

Aw, don't be sore, Al, he said. I can't keep hiding under your desk. I gotta spread my wings a little.

You didn't even give Miss Goldbaum a break, I said. You're a disgrace to the rodent family.

Listen, he cracked. She gets a break three times a week.

You . . . stink, I ended lamely. I was too sore to be smart.

O. K. by me, he said, walking off. Some day you'll cut off an arm for one little whiff.

Then another thing happened. It all began when a tall timid guy came in with a manuscript under his arm and asked for Mr. Glick. He had written a radio script, and since Mr. Glick was an expert on radio he thought maybe Mr. Glick would be so kind as to read his stuff.

I should be happy to help you, Sammy said, a little different than he had ever talked before. I could feel at that moment something loud and strong pumping inside that little guy, like a piston, twisting him up and forcing him on.

After the tall guy had gone, Sammy sat down and read the stuff. He smiled as he read it, and when he hit the third page he laughed out loud.

Hey, this is good stuff, he said; funny as hell.

What's it about? I asked doubtfully.

Brand new angle, he said. The guy won't have anything to do with the girl. So *she* kidnaps *him*. But he still says nix and gets her arrested. In the court it looks like curtains for her, but they clinch and decide to get married, and the babe is saved because he's the only witness and a guy can't testify against his own wife. Pretty hot!

The guy who wrote it came back the next week.

You have an idea here, Sammy told him. Of course it's rough, and it needs developing, but maybe with a little work we could fix it up, he said.

You mean you'll help me! said the dope.

I think I can pull something out of it, Sammy said, and then I'll give it to my agent.

Say, I didn't expect all *this,* said the dope.

When the guy had gone, Sammy asked me, Say, Al, who's a good agent for me? I want to sell this story to Hollywood. I got the title all doped out—Girl Steals Boy.

Why not Leland Heyward? He only manages Hepburn and a couple of dozen other stars, I said.

Is he good on stories? Sammy asked.

Pretty fair, I said. He makes a couple of thousand a week out of them.

Well, I'll think it over.

I thought that was the end of it. It should have been, if life didn't confound us ordinary sleep-and-eat people by producing geniuses like Sammy Glick. Life is choppy, full of rip tides and sudden breakers, and some guys scream once and go down, and others fight their way to the surface and still go down. Some have water wings; they have a genius for self-preservation. It's them we see when we raise our water-logged heads above the foam, floating, just floating over us as nice as you please— Sammy Glicks, every one of them.

Two weeks later Sammy rushed in, exultant and jumpy.

Shake hands with God's gift to Hollywood, he said, grabbing my hand before I had time to stick it in my pocket.

Don't use the name of the Lord in vain, I said. You mean you sold that story?

Five thousand dollars, he said. We should have had a better price, but this is my first story.

It's a disgrace, I said, five thousand.

Well, that's just the first, he said, and there's plenty more ideas where this one came from.

You mean from the guy who wrote this one, I said.

Aw, he said, he had nothing on the ball but a prayer. He's lucky I bothered with him.

Like Miss Goldbaum, I said quietly.

And all of a sudden I hated Sammy Glick. Before, I had been annoyed, or disturbed, or just revolted. This was one hundred percent American hatred.

The next morning I read something in the film section of the morning paper that revealed the fine Bronx hand of Sammy Glick:

Sammy Glick, prominent radio columnist, has sold his first screen story to Colossal for $10,000. Titled *Girl Steals Boy,* this is the first of a series Colossal has contracted for, according to Mr. Glick. Collaborating with him was Eugene Spitzer.

What I can't understand, I thought, is how Eugene Spitzer ever got mentioned at all. I was very bitter. All of a sudden I was jealous of Sammy Glick, and congratulating myself on not being like him.

One day, a week later, Sammy didn't show up at all. Maybe he's sick, I thought at first, but I quickly discounted this optimism. Guys like Sammy Glick don't get sick, unless it helps them get out of a contract, or lands them an insurance payment. The afternoon passed.

Sammy came in around suppertime. He wore a new suit. He also wore a new expression. I liked it even less than the old stock. He had a blue check shirt and a red carnation in his buttonhole. He held a cigarette loosely between his fingers. My Sammy Glick, my little copy boy.

Hello, Obnoxious, I said.

I came in to say good-by, Sammy said. I'm off for Hollywood.

How did this happen? I asked. Metro wired that they just couldn't get along another day without you?

Not exactly, said Sammy seriously. My agent sold me to Colossal on the strength of that story.

And that's strength, I said. How about Eugene What's-his-name? Does he go too?

Colossal just wanted me, Sammy said simply.

Well, I said, our gain is Colossal's loss.

No more of these pebbles for me, Sammy said. It's two hundred and fifty bucks a week for me, starting a week from Wednesday.

There was a short pause, during which time I reviewed the history of Sammy Glick, complete from fifteen a week to two hundred and fifty. It was America, all the glory and the opportunity, the push and the speed, the grinding of gears and the crap.

See you in the Brown Derby, Sammy was saying.

Then I got nostalgic. I was always a soft guy, and I said:

Sure, kid, and remember, don't say ain't.

That was too much for Sammy. He didn't like it. He didn't like to be reminded. There are two kinds of big shots: those who tell as many people as they can that they started out as newsboys at two dollars and peanuts a week, and those who take every step as if it were the only level they knew, those who drive ahead in high speed and never bother to look back to see where they've been. I began to have a strong hunch that Sammy fell roughly into the latter category, only more so.

I watched Sammy walk out of the office that day, and then I stood at the window and watched him as he appeared on the street below and jumped into a taxi. I sound like a sucker, but I felt just a little sorry for Sammy Glick. I felt the way I did on the Commencement platform, the last days of college, watching the guys; thinking, You poor uneducated guinea pigs, you're smug, you've got no springs, and you're going to take some awful bumps. And it's not your fault; they've poured you into a mold, like jello. *They* is the villain, but don't get me wrong.

I never said Sammy Glick wasn't arrogant, deceitful, four-flushing, crude, cruel—well, I could go on like this all day. But that's what Sammy learned. He learned it on the sidewalks in the Bronx and he learned it well. He knows where he's going, and he's running fast. And when you know that, when you know what makes Sammy run, you know something.

A couple of months passed, and then I got *my* break. I don't know yet how it happened; you can bet dollars to supervisors I didn't get it by stealing any stories from Eugene Spitzer. One of the Warner Brothers must have got the idea to round up all the drama columnists in New York, and when they pulled in the net, there I was, floundering with the rest.

The day after the news broke that I had "surrendered to Hollywood"—it certainly wasn't a battle—a girl's voice came trembling over the telephone to me.

You probably don't remember me, she said. This is Miss Goldbaum—Rosalie Goldbaum.

Her voice sounded funny to me. It was shrill but dead, like a high note on a cheap piccolo.

I told her I was glad to hear from her again, which was a lie.

I've got to see you, she said.

Oh, hell! I thought. Meet me at the Tavern at seven, I said.

I got there fifteen minutes late, and she was sitting in a booth. I noticed that her shoulder blades stuck out. Her eyes were red. When I took her hand and said,

243

Gladtoseeyou, it was rubbery and soft, like a half-blown balloon. She said, Oh, it was so good of you to come.

There was something too intimate and uncomfortable between us.

You're looking swell, I said.

I read you were going to Hollywood, she told me. You'll see Sammy Glick.

Somehow I sensed I shouldn't wisecrack about that. I can, I said guardedly.

Will you—Mr. Manners, would you see him for me?

Sure, I said. When I run into him I'll say hello for you.

I knew it was more than that. I wanted to find out.

It's not that, she said. You could find out why he never writes, she said. Never, not once, not a single letter and she kept mumbling it as if trying to make herself believe it was true.

Sure, I said, I can ask him; but after all, it's new to him out there, and, getting adjusted and all, it's hard to write.

Can you imagine me, defending the slob? It didn't sound convincing.

You don't understand, she said. He promised to send for me the second week he was out there. I got rid of everything I couldn't take along. I was all set. He told me not to worry; he'd send for me in a couple of weeks. He told me the only reason we couldn't go together was he didn't have the train fare. Said he'd send me his second week's salary. Now I don't know what to do.

Skunk, I said.

Tell him I don't understand, she said. Ask him why. Ask him why.

She was crying. The waiter was standing over us impatiently. It was embarrassing.

Do you want yours with onions? I asked.

She wiped her eyes with her napkin. Her mascara was running.

Before I left, I slipped her twenty-five bucks. Just to salve my conscience for knowing a slime like Sammy Glick. She put it into her purse as quickly as possible, as if her hand was trying to put something over on the rest of her.

Give me your address in Hollywood so I can pay it back, she said.

Write me care of Warners', and tell me if you hear from him, I said.

I looked after her as she turned down to Broadway and the crowd sucked her in like an undertow. And I stood, thinking what New York and Sammy Glick had done to Miss Goldbaum, this little female toothpick of humanity, thin and straight and strong for its size, but easy to break for a grown-up man, or a grown-up city.

All the way out to Hollywood, Miss Goldbaum kept running through my mind, and when I got out there, the first thing I did was go over to Colossal and look up Sammy.

His secretary had a bigger office than our city room. She said Mr. Glick was in a story conference.

I waited an hour and fifteen minutes. I was all steamed up about this thing. Finally Mr. Glick made his appearance. He didn't wear a tie. Instead he wore a big yellow scarf, with a big yellow handkerchief to match. If you put his suit on a table you could have played checkers on it. He was no longer the thin, pale, eager little kid that used to say Thank you, Mr. Manners. He had one of those California tans, and he was beginning to bulge at the waist. But he hadn't stopped running.

Well, Al, he said, so they finally pulled you into the racket. I didn't think you were smart enough.

We sat down in his office. His desk looked as long as the runway in a burlesque theater. He swung his feet on to it. I noticed he was wearing camel's-hair socks.

How's the gang? he asked. Still selling their souls for twenty kopecks?

They all send regards, Sammy, I said.

Great old bunch, he said meaninglessly; but once you get the Indian sign on the producers out here the dough comes rolling in so fast you use it for wall paper.

Miss Goldbaum was asking for you too, I said.

Sammy stopped running for a moment. He looked at me and I knew he was wondering how much I knew. Even through that sunburn he paled.

How is she, Al? he asked.

Swell, I said, just swell. High and dry.

I couldn't help it, he said.

He was frightened. And it's a funny thing the poor guy meant it. He had to come out here. He had to move along. There was something in him that wouldn't be checked, something that had to run loose. And sometimes it was so strong it ran away out ahead of him. That's what Miss Goldbaum got for loving a guy like that. I guess it can happen to any one up in the Bronx, and the Bronx is just like any place else these days, only faster and harder.

Al, he said, I'll write her. I'll tell her it just isn't the place for her. I'll send her a thousand bucks. Damn it, you know how those promises are; it could've happened to anybody.

Give her a break, Sammy, I said. And then, for no reason at all, I said, Give everybody a break.

Sure, he said, sure. What are you working on over at Warners'?

I don't know, I said. But I've got a hunch it's the ninth episode of the Mr. Wu series.

Don't be a sucker, Sammy said. Turn down the first three stories they give you. They'll think more of you.

I guess I'll be seeing you around, I said, getting up.

I sold five stories last month, said Sammy, under a different name, because I'm under contract over here.

He made no bones about it. He was glorifying the American rat. He put his arm around my neck affectionately as he walked me to the door.

Here's a hot one Lubitsch told me, he said.

I heard that three weeks ago in "21," I told him when he finished.

Just one more tip, he said. If you want to get into the real dough out here, write something on the outside. Write a play. Like me. When I get it produced it will be $2,500 a week and my terms.

I'll do it tonight when I get home, I said.

Eight weeks later, when I was still waiting for an assignment, I get a little printed notice in the mail: Mr. Samuel Glick requests the pleasure of my company at the opening of his play, *Live Wire*, at the Hollywood Playhouse.

Sammy's car picked me up that night and brought me to his apartment. He was having a cocktail with Public Beauty Number One. Sixty million people would hock their lives to shake this girl's paw, and here was Sammy gurgling champagne with her.

Well, the play was really pretty good. The scene was a radio station and there was plenty of excitement and fireworks. All the time I keep thinking this seems awfully familiar. And then I think maybe I just dreamed it, like people do sometimes.

One or two people yell Author, author! and Sammy takes a bow, and some one sets a basket of roses on the stage, and all of a sudden it is a big success and I am sitting next to a hit author, and every one is stepping over me to shake his hand, and he is modestly denying that he must have worked very hard on it, saying it just came easy, three or four nights' work, and then every one is amazed, and some one says a new genius has come to Hollywood, and Sammy says, Oh, I wouldn't say that exactly.

Going out the lobby, Sammy said he was thirsty, and I said come up to my place and have a drink; but Sammy said, How about the Brown Derby? because he wanted to see more people.

And the Beauty said, The Vine or the Beverly Hills? I guess she would have liked to go to both.

So we got to one or the other, and it took Sammy ten minutes to get to a table, so many people flocked around him and his favorite star, and all the time I'm trying to think where I saw this play before.

Finally, when the Beauty said, Excuse me, I have to comb my hair, and went out to the ladies' room—even movie idols do—Sammy said, Well Al, you haven't told me what you think about the play.

I think it's just like something else I've seen, I said.
You're pretty smart, he said.
All of a sudden it came to me: *Five-Star Final!*
As long as you know, he said. I might as well tell you. I used exactly the same construction as *Five-Star Final*, scene for scene, only I changed the characters, and I made it funny.
Those people don't know what a genius you are, I said.
The star came back, stopping at three tables en route.
Sammy, she said, when will you write a play for me?

When he can find one, I said.
I don't want to write for you until I feel something great, Sammy said, something that's—you.
She moved closer to him.
I gotta go, I said. Thanks for everything. It was an evening I'll never forget.
Good-by, Mr. Masters, she said, feeling very proud and democratic that she had remembered my name.

I didn't see Sammy for six months after that. But I used to read about him in the papers. *Live Wire* went to New York and he sold it back to Colossal for $150,000. Then Parsons carried a story that he and the Beauty were secretly married, but both their agents denied it, and finally they said, We're just good friends, very good friends. Then DeMille got him to write his recent epic.

The next time I saw him was at the preview of my first picture at Pasadena. I ran into him in the lobby on my way out.

Hello, Sammy, I said.
You've got some smart stuff here, Al, he said, but the story line isn't straight enough.
No, I said; it isn't exactly Five-Star Final.
He didn't bat an eye. After all, he said, there's only one Five-Star Final.

I was about to say something, but Sammy's limousine was at the curb and he was gone. I got involved in a story conference on the sidewalk, but I couldn't keep my mind on it. The more I thought about Sammy the more I realized he had more drama than all my characters put together. My little office boy was going up. He was a human rocket. Would he reach the moon, or would he break like a Fourth-of-July firework, splattering his sparks into the sea?

By the time Al had finished his story, the Derby was completely empty. He and the other guy looked at each other in silence. Al stared at the caricature of President Roosevelt above the door. As he stared, an aggressive little man, a little dark ferret of a man, pushed the door open energetically and stood expectantly awaiting the head waiter. He was followed by four others, all of whom seemed to be talking to him at once.

There he is now, Al said.
Speak of the devil, said his friend.
Of course everything I told you is confidential, said Al, strictly on the q. t.
Hollywood is a jungle and the smaller animals have to run for their lives.
Mr. Glick and his party came down the aisle. He saw Al, and stopped.
Hello, Al. How's tricks?
Can't complain. You're looking good, Al said.
That's the funny angle on this whole thing, said Al, studying his glass, after Sammy had passed. My agent tells me I may go to work for him next week. And I'd still rather have my name on a Sammy Glick production than any picture in town.

If Christ Came to New York

by the Rev. Dr. Charles M. Sheldon

*Breadlines and Bankers, Hovels and Towers—What Would
Jesus Think of Them? Here's a Heart-Warming Answer*

FOR THE GREATER part of His earthly life, Jesus lived in a little country town called Nazareth, which lies on a slope leading down into the fertile plain of Esdraelon. The last time I was there, I thought it was one of the most peaceful and really beautiful spots on this globe.

I went up into the little room where they say He used to work at His trade. It was a small dusty room with a rude bench with some tools on it, now used by a local carpenter. I thought, while standing there, of the astonishing history of that Carpenter whose words have come down through mankind's history to revolutionize character and mold thinking, literature, art, and music.

The old streets that Jesus trod on His way to the carpenter shop are much the same now as then. Mary's Well, to which He went no doubt every day to draw water, is still in the same place. The only thing that makes the ancient town look different from Jesus's time is a traffic sign in the little square around the well, which reads: "Speed Limit, Ten Miles."

A far cry, you say, from this humdrum village of the Old World to the metropolis of the New. But is it so far? The men and women who crowd the streets of New York do not wear the flowing robes of the men and women of Nazareth. They ride in blatant taxicabs and clangorous hacks, not on the backs of soft-footed camels. But, for all that, they are the same kind of folk that Jesus saw every day in Nazareth.

People have not changed. The same sick that need a physician, the same sinful that need a redeemer, the same hungry that need food, the same shivering that need shelter, the same hearts that need comfort, the same death that needs resurrection.

Somehow I cannot make myself believe that Jesus would dislike New York. He loved Jerusalem, which was the New York of the land in which He lived. And if He came to New York, I have no question He would love its sweep of height and its impress of material power, its promise of human exaltation and glory in achievement.

He could hardly help liking the look of the city if He came, as I assume He would come, from the air or water and glimpsed that most beautiful of urban spectacles, the castle-fringed sky line of New York.

A workman Himself, He would marvel, I should think, at the ingenuity of a people that could conceive and execute these towering monuments. A poet, He would

246

appreciate the artistry of a people that could take so ugly a thing as a skyscraper and translate it into an urban epic. A philosopher, He would respect the wisdom of a people that had built its house on a rock.

"Here is the modern equivalent," He might say, "of a city that is set on a hill and cannot be hid."

I imagine Him walking up the canyon that is lower Broadway and pausing on the steps of old Trinity to observe the money-changers of narrow Wall Street. Now, you say, He has come upon a phase of New York life that He cannot possibly approve. But wouldn't He remember what we mortals so often forget: that not all Wall Street men, especially since 1929, are rich? And wouldn't He know in His divine wisdom that not all these hurrying figures with their worried faces were worshiping mammon simply because they toiled for their subsistence in mammon's mart?

But He threw the money-changers out of the temple? True—but I wonder if Jesus wasn't teaching us a political lesson, not a financial one. I wonder if He was not teaching a lesson which might well be applied right now to this war-threatened world.

Jesus drove the money-changers out of the temple not because they were money-changers but because they were in the temple. After all, the temple was His house, His Father's house. It was His duty to defend it—and He did. He did not provoke a fight but He did resist invasion.

Whether Jesus would think that the same principle of resisting invasion also applied to industrial war, and especially to sit-down strikes, it would be interesting right at this time to know. I suppose it would depend on His views as to whom those great industrial temples belong. What do you think?

It is but a short way from the steps of Trinity to the steps of City Hall. Many a less distinguished visitor has taken it in a gleaming automobile, driven through crowds of cheering men and women. But Jesus, I feel, would prefer to make the journey on foot, unnoticed by the passing throng.

I do not imagine Him suddenly or sensationally making Himself known to the press and the newsreel men and the radio studios, or even to the churches. I seem to think He might go about in His own way doing good. Doubtless, in His own good time and in the right place, He would have an audience with the people, would do just what He did when He spoke from the temple in Jerusalem: teach the same eternal truths for the redemption of the world from sin. But I do not find myself imagining Jesus all the time holding revival meetings.

By that, I do not mean that He would not seek to proclaim to New York His message of rebuke for selfish lives and His eternal appeal to turn around and go the other way. But it would be characteristic of His personality often to walk the streets of New York unknown and unrecognized, going His own way, doing good, unadvertised, and without press notices.

Do you not remember reading how He walked along the road by two of His disciples and did not make Himself known to them? Would He not be like that part of time, even in New York?

I do like to think, however, that He might influence the city's leading men and women to start a work of redemption that would be permanent and continuous. I picture Him visiting individuals and doing through them what He might not be able to do in sensational addresses.

That was a part of His method when He was here before. Why not now?

For example, I have found myself wondering if, when He reached the City Hall, He might not have an audience with the mayor—not a public reception but a personal talk. So He would remind him—wouldn't he?—that "A prophet is not without honor, save in his own country." I can even picture him encouraging Mr. LaGuardia with the cheery warning:

"Woe unto you, when all shall speak well of you!"

The more I think of Jesus in New York, the more I am inclined to think He would do His most effective service through this impress of His matchless personality on individuals, high and low, which would give them the inspiration to make it a city of God.

Sometimes during my ministry, when I was pastor of a church, I found myself writing letters to my men members to tell them how much I thought of them. One week I wrote one hundred such letters. The following Sunday, all those men were in church. It strengthened my belief that men are hungry for affection, and many of them go starved for it all their lives.

How otherwise can you account for the astounding hold that Jesus had on a group of illiterate and common men, so that they were willing to die for Him after a brief two years' knowledge of Him.

Was it not just plain simple affection that He felt *and showed* for them?

I was reminded of all this the other day when I read an item on the front page of the Morning Shudder—or was it the Evening Depression?—about a man who had committed suicide, leaving a note in his employer's office to the effect that for a quarter of a century he had done his faithful duty as an employee, and had never had a kind word said to him or a friendly notice.

The City Hall in New York stands midway, as perhaps it should, between the skyscrapers of lower Broadway and the hovels of "the Bowery, the Bowery, I'll never go there any more." Of course the Bowery of the song is as dead as the Bouerie of old Petrus Stuyvesant; but the people are still there, the poor and sometimes starving people, who need a helping hand.

For many years an organization with which I am connected has maintained in this region a breadline for homeless and hungry men and a mission called the Bowery Mission into which come every night the men who are without home, or friends, or hope.

We have known men who have been teachers, and men who have had homes and money, men of education and culture to be in this breadline. They know they will get a cup of coffee and a sandwich when they get up to the window; but as they drift off into the cold dark we cannot help wondering where they will sleep, and God knows what will happen with another tomorrow.

I do not have to draw on my imagination very much to see Jesus getting into this breadline some bitter night. He was himself a man of sorrows and acquainted with grief. Into this breadline, therefore, He steps and takes His turn. What questions do you suppose He asks as He becomes a part of that line as it shuffles along? What is the cause of it all? Who is to blame? Society? Drink? Unemployment, which covers so many economic sins? Heredity? Environment?

As Jesus moves along with this line of broken men, perhaps He feels with them the burden and the problem of earthly existence, and wonders how long it will be before humanity will obey the teaching: "Whatsoever ye would that men should do to you, do ye even so to them," and "It is more blessed to give than to receive," and "Man shall not live by bread alone."

It is not beyond the possibilities that He might enter the mission itself. If He should choose to enter and sit down side by side with men who have drifted in to get out of the raw wind, what a thrill it would be to hear hymns that spell His own love for a dying world, to hear rough-clad men rise and give testimony to the saving grace of Jesus, until the walls of the mission seem to glow with heavenly light and eternal hope!

Is it not within the realms of possibility that Jesus Himself, who said, "Come unto me, all ye that labor and are heavy laden, and I will give you rest," might actually feel the human need of comfort and the thrill of satisfaction with His own wondrous influence over lost souls in all the ages?

Does not even the Divine need comfort?

Is not God Himself hungry for the love of men?

I don't see Jesus getting the same uplift out of the Red agitators in Union Square a little farther uptown. I don't know, of course, but I find nothing in His teachings or in those of His disciples or of the apostle Paul to make me feel that He would favor in New York, any more than He did in Jerusalem, the bringing about even of desirable ends by violent means.

He would have admiration, no doubt, for the zealous spirit which leads some of these young orators to exhort the people in what they believe, no matter how mistakenly, to be a righteous cause. But His wisdom would convince Him—would it not?—that they were for the most part "blind guides, which strain at a gnat, and swallow a camel." And he might gently remind them that "if the blind lead the blind, both shall fall into the ditch."

As for "the lewd fellows of the baser sort" who can think of nothing better than to exploit the unwary with their self-seeking demagogy. He might be inclined to give them as short shrift as He gave the money-changers in the temple; or He might simply dismiss them as He did the vain repetitions of the heathen who thought they should be heard for their much speaking.

Perhaps He would see more hope in the loft section of lower Fifth Avenue, where so many of the humbler members of His own race toil in the garment industry. He would rejoice, I should think, this "Lord of Lords who learned a trade," that these earnest men and women had done likewise, and were able to support themselves by the work of their hands in their adopted country. He would rejoice, too, I feel sure, that they had been able to achieve in an industry once racked by strife such measure of peace and good will toward men that they have long served as a model for those seeking better relations between employer and employee.

Now up Fifth Avenue, past the shining windows of the great department stores, through the hurrying crowds of women spenders, Jesus might make His way. Would His heart be heavy because the faces of so many of these lilies of the field were brighter than nature ever intended a lily's face to be?

I wonder. Even the men of His native Nazareth smear kohl above and below their eyes to heighten their warm Oriental beauty. They did it in Jesus's time. I can't imagine His being one to cast the first stone.

Weary with much walking, I can imagine Jesus finally entering one of those great towers—perhaps the Empire State, perhaps the lofty Radio Building in Rockefeller Center—which rise higher than Nazareth is wide.

It is here that He would at last realize New York.

At His feet would lie the city of the tabloids: of glittering hotels and stuffy night clubs, of white lights and red lights.

Beyond would lie the city of the guidebooks: of the Aquarium and the museum, the Stock Exchange, the Woolworth Building and the Metropolitan and the Chrysler, Grant's Tomb and the bridge.

Still beyond—eastward to Brooklyn, westward to Jersey, southward to Staten Island, northward beyond the towering Cathedral of St. John to Harlem, the Bronx, and Westchester—would lie the city nobody knows *except the people who live in it,* the city of homes.

I wonder now if Jesus, standing on his man-made peak —the nearest to the sky that man has yet built—might not be saying to Himself:

"What a heaven on earth this City of New York *could* be!"

My Sex Life

by Mahatma Gandhi

Has India's Leader Forsworn Celibacy?
Here Is His Own Frank Reply to the Charge

IN 1906 I took the vow of celibacy in the conviction that it would help me to be of better service to my country. From that day forward my life became far more open and free than it had ever been before. It was celibacy that gave me the independence I desired for my work. It revealed a richness and fullness in life beyond anything I had previously experienced or even imagined. I have never had the slightest occasion to regard my decision as a mistaken one. Indeed, the opposite has been true; more and more, celibacy has seemed to me one of the greatest blessings possible to bestow.

Not long ago, however, a sensational story was brought to my attention. Like all rumors, and particularly unfounded ones, it appears to have traveled very widely and very quickly. It began in a native newspaper in India. From there it spread to the pages of a Bombay newspaper, and since this paper has a large circulation of readers, it soon reached England, and perhaps even America.

The story was to the effect that I had given up my celibacy and had resumed sensual relations with women.

I believe that this story had its real beginnings in my campaign against the creed of untouchability, the belief that for centuries has separated the people of my country. When I began to fight against it, insisting that there be no discrimination against untouchables, a group of ortho-

dox Hindus who had previously been my friends broke with me and started to vilify me with all the resources at their command. They pointed to the number of women among my close followers and declared that my pretended "saintliness" in reality was "sinfulness." They dragged before the public eye the woman doctor, Sushila Nayar, who for years has been a constant companion and whose "crime" and "sinfulness" consist of giving me massages and medicated baths!—treatments, incidentally, that are conducted entirely without privacy, and during which indeed I often transact business with my co-workers.

Hitherto I have ignored these charges. I did not think that they deserved the dignity of being acknowledged, much less answered. But when close associates of mine are made to suffer, and when the rumor reaches the ears of friends in other countries, the air needs clearing.

I have no secrets of my own in this life. I think that I have confessed my weaknesses. It happens that I am not sensually inclined; but if I were, I hope that I would have the courage to make the confession.

As I have said, I began the practice of celibacy in 1906 when I was living in Phoenix, South Africa. A detestation of sensual connection even with my own wife had been developing in me for some time. I determined to test myself, to see if I would have the strength and resolution to maintain celibacy, and to see what effect it would have on me, mentally and physically. When I had determined that I could maintain it and that it would benefit me in my lifework, I took the vow.

It was on that day that true freedom began, and not only for myself but for my wife. My wife became a free woman in the most significant sense of the word—she became free from my authority as her lord and master. For my part, I became free from her—free from my previous slavery to her.

There were a great many women around me at this time. It might be said, then, that there was the opportunity for promiscuity. But no other woman had ever had any attraction for me in the sense that my wife had. I had never experienced a sensual urge toward other women. Nevertheless before I took the vow of celibacy I had been conscious of a certain restraint standing in the way of full, open friendship between the two sexes. I think it is a consciousness that no woman, perhaps, can ever entirely rid herself of when she is in the society of men.

But my celibacy changed this. I discovered that it drew me irresistibly to woman as the mother of man. She had become too sacred for sexual love, and so every woman became at once a sister or daughter to me.

Celibacy, in my case, has been governed by no orthodox rules. I have never believed that to practice celibacy one must become a hermit. The restraint that demands abstention from all contact with the opposite sex, no matter how innocent, is a forced growth having little or no vital value. Therefore I never tried to avoid natural, normal contacts with women.

And I found that there was a greater pleasure in such friendship than there had ever been before I took my vow. I found that I could work with all women to far greater advantage. Sex was no longer an invisible barrier between us. Women came closer to me; they gave me their confidence as I think even the closest of my friends among them would have hesitated to give it to me before.

When I returned to India from South Africa, therefore, and invited women of my own country to join the civil-resistance movement, they answered with a wholehearted and joyous response, with a perfect trust that I do not think would have been possible otherwise. My vow had given me a special fitness to serve womankind. The easy access which they gave me to their hearts was a wonderful revelation. The old beliefs and conflicting creeds of India dropped away, and we faced one another as equals.

For example, Moslem women would not veil themselves before me, a thing that would have been unthinkable in other circumstances, as any one who knows the power of the custom of purdah—the veil—will realize. How otherwise could I have overcome this obstacle, the barrier of the veil, when I appealed to these Moslem sisters to support our movement? How otherwise could I have appeared to them as the close and trusted friend, entirely without motivation except in the interest of our movement, that I wished to be?

And so, from that day forward, there has been no false privacy in my life. In my dwelling I sleep at night surrounded by women, for they feel safe with me in every respect. There is nothing to make us strangers and enemies.

All these great benefits celibacy has given me. I would be weak and foolish indeed were I to relinquish them!

Nevertheless, if I were sexually attracted to women, I think I have courage enough, even at this time of my life, to become a polygamist, to take not one but several wives. For I have never believed in free love—secret free love or open free love. Open free love I have always regarded as dog's love. Secret free love seems to me nothing more than a cowardly evasion.

I hope that this will serve to repudiate the lie that has been circulated about me. People may disagree with my beliefs; they may attack my celibacy; they may attack my idea of nonviolence—but I do not think it can be said that any one who has come under my influence has ever been turned into a coward.

Barbara Comes to Town

a story by Thyra Samter Winslow

The Story of a Wise Child and an Untied Apron String

THE LONG-DISTANCE operator called and presently I heard Cousin Rhoda's voice on the telephone.

"Did you get my letter?" she asked.

I told her yes, I had got her letter. Rhoda had written she was coming in town to meet her daughter Barbara, who was on her way home from boarding school.

"Will you help me out, darling?" Rhoda pleaded. "Billy is ill with tonsillitis. I simply can't get away. I telephoned Barbara, but she wouldn't stay in school another day. You know how it is—all the girls leaving. She gets in New York this afternoon. Please say you don't mind taking care of her! She'll be no trouble, I'm sure, and she'll be thrilled at anything you do for her. I'll pick her up tomorrow or the next day. You're sure you won't mind?"

I told Rhoda I didn't mind at all. It would be fun taking charge of a little girl for a couple of days.

Before she hung up Rhoda said a significant thing.

"Barbara is starting to romance a bit," she said. "Just a phase she's going through. If I were you I wouldn't believe a thing she says!"

I went to the station to meet Barbara. I hadn't seen her since she was eleven, a pretty but rather leggy child with a stare that must be called vacant. I knew that now, at fifteen, she'd be a big girl, and I suspected the usual boarding-school affectations.

The train was one of the usual school "specials." Groups of anxious relatives were waiting. When the train arrived there was much milling about as overdressed girls in traveling suits and little girls in sweater dresses were claimed.

I felt I'd know Barbara when I saw her. I didn't see her! After asking questions of several women who looked as if they might be in authority, and being buffeted around with no help, I reached the conclusion that Barbara had not taken the train. Well, she had my address. I felt the best thing to do was to go home and wait for word from her. We were eating dinner when the doorbell rang. There was Barbara! She looked more grown-up than I had imagined her. Her legginess had given way to the lovely slenderness of the very young. She wore the exaggerated clothes of a college girl, a bit too sporty, a trifle too nonchalant. Her hair was puffed out too much and her lips were very red.

We greeted each other with perhaps too great a show of affection.

"When did you get in?" I asked.

"Just this minute," she said. "The special was delayed, so when you didn't meet it I came right out."

"But I did meet it," I said.

Barbara laughed.

"Well, the truth is," she said, "I came on an earlier train. I knew you wouldn't care. I had a tea date."

I had understood that Barbara was too young for dates.

"Don't be put out," she said. "I'll tell you about it."

She told us at dinner. A boy she had met at school—the cousin of her roommate—had made the engagement three weeks ago.

"I thought Mother would be here and it would be all right," she finished.

"Would your mother let you go to tea with a boy?"

"My, yes!" said Barbara. *"Of course* she'd let me go to *tea!* My goodness, at school they *want* us to have tea dates. They think tea dates teach us things—what to do at teas. Of course we can't have *luncheons* or *dinners* with boys, and we can't have *night* dates—that's against the rules. But teas—my, yes!"

Barbara told us pleasant and decidedly innocent incidents of her school life. We were pleased to find she hadn't grown into one of the bold youngsters we had heard so much about.

In the evening we took Barbara to the movies. She seemed delighted. They were allowed to see so few pictures at school. A nice natural little girl! The next day Barbara

got two telephone calls. Each time a feminine voice asked for her and the conversations were similar:

"Yes, Jane darling. . . . I'd *love* to, Jane. Isn't it wonderful! . . . Any time you say. . . . I think so, Jane. Yes, darling. 'By." And—

"Yes, Mildred darling. . . . I'd *love* it! That would be simply *wonderful!* . . . Whenever you say. . . . That will be swell! 'By."

On the word " 'By" Barbara's voice rose as if for a salutation instead of a farewell.

"That was Jane," Barbara said after the first call. "That was Mildred," she said after the second. She didn't smile. "Two of my best friends at school. Live here in New York. We're going shopping. I haven't enough money for *real* shopping until Mother comes. I know I'll be simply crazy over New York shops. You don't mind if I go?"

"Where are you going to meet them?" I asked.

"I'm going to meet Mildred at Lord & Taylor's at one. For lunch. And we'll meet Jane later."

"I'll take you to meet Mildred," I said. "And if I think you two will be all right—"

"We'll be all right," Barbara assured me. "New York girls always go shopping alone."

Mildred was waiting at Lord & Taylor's, a lovely blonde girl dressed quite like Barbara. Her lips were too red.

I took them to luncheon. They giggled through an amazing amount of indigestible delicacies.

"Where are you going to meet Jane?" I asked.

Mildred looked blank. But I had noticed that Mildred's responses were often vacuous looks of not quite understanding. Now Barbara looked at her rather severely.

"We're meeting Jane at three at Lord & Taylor's," she said.

"Oh," said Mildred. And a minute later, "Oh, I see."

They went away together, giggling.

Just before dinner was announced the telephone rang. It was Barbara. She was at Mildred's. Did I mind if she stayed to dinner? Mildred's mother would ask, if I thought it was necessary.

"That's quite all right," I said. I wanted her to have a nice time. "You'll come home immediately after dinner, won't you? I don't want you to be out late."

"Oh, yes," she said.

I said, at dinner, that it was lovely to see a young girl so ready to do what an older person suggested.

She was home before nine.

"I've had a wonderful day!" she told me. She described a dress she had seen.

The next morning, feeling it my duty, I took Barbara on a short sight-seeing tour. I asked her if she wanted to take the girls with her, but she said Mildred had to go to the dentist and Jane was busy too.

We went to the top of the Empire State Building and Barbara exclaimed prettily about the view. I showed her other "points of interest."

We got home in the middle of the afternoon. I was pretty tired. I asked Barbara if she didn't want to lie down. She said she guessed she'd read a newspaper. In the current topics class they had told her to keep up with what was going on. She seemed restless.

The telephone rang, and Barbara ran to the library to answer it when she was told it was for her. The conversation was similar to the conversations of the day before. I went to my bedroom. Forgetting that Barbara was telephoning, I picked up the receiver to get a number. To my surprise a masculine voice was talking to Barbara. I didn't want to eavesdrop, so I hung up, went downstairs again.

"Whom were you talking to?" I asked.

Barbara looked at me oddly. Then she smiled.

"I was talking to Hal. He's the boy I had tea with. I promised to have tea with him today. I didn't think you'd mind, as long as we were allowed to have tea dates. Because I'm on my vacation I thought maybe I could have dinner with him too. I'll be home awfully early."

It seemed innocent enough.

"You might ask the young man to come in when he brings you home," I said. "I'd like to meet him."

"I'd love to," said Barbara. "You'll like him. An awfully nice boy!"

Barbara was home before ten. Her escort was with her. I was a little shocked at seeing him. He seemed at least twenty, a good-looking sprawling blond youngster quite past adolescence.

"You seem older than I thought," I told Hal. I never did get his last name.

"I'll be a junior next year," he said.

"Barbara's such a child to go with college men," I ventured. "She's only fifteen."

Barbara gave me a curious look.

"Do you really believe that?" she asked.

"Of course. Your mother was married—let me see—sixteen years ago. It was very romantic. She met your father when her parents took her to Italy. And she married him there." I explained to Barbara's young man: "Barbara was born in Italy. Her parents didn't return to America until she was four."

"You think that's all there was to it?" Barbara was amused.

"What else?" I asked.

"Oh, my!" Barbara said with the attitude of talking to a backward child. "You know *why* my mother went to Italy, don't you?"

"Yes," I told her.

"Well!" said Barbara.

"What do you mean?" I was curious now.

"I thought every one understood." Barbara was a bit condescending. She turned to Hal.

"I told you about it?"

He nodded.

"I can't believe," she smiled, "that in these days such a thing would be a family skeleton. You knew Mamma was taken abroad because her parents wanted to break up an a affair she was having with a musician?"

"Of course," I said.

"Well, they didn't break it up quickly enough. When she met—shall I say?—my father, she knew it was time to get married. They stayed abroad long enough so that people wouldn't worry about my age. Folks were so old-fashioned in those days!"

She looked at me with a little smile. Perhaps I was showing my amazement.

"Didn't you notice when you first saw me how large and bright I was for my age?"

"You were large," I admitted, "but not too bright."

"I had been kept back purposely. But even so, I could speak French and Italian." Her manner was sprightly now. "So you see Hal's just the right age for me. And that's why mother allows me so much freedom. I'm nearly seventeen!"

She did look seventeen!

The next day Barbara had an engagement with her schoolmates. She stayed at Mildred's for dinner. At nine the telephone rang.

"It's Barbara," she said. "I'm having such a good time with the girls I wondered if you'd mind if I stayed all night. Wait a minute—Mildred's mother wants to ask you," Barbara said.

I waited an extremely long time.

"Wait just a minute," Barbara's voice said again.

"This is Mrs. Morris, Mildred's mother," a voice said. "I'm sure you won't mind if Barbara stays all night with us."

I didn't like the voice. It had a metallic sound.

"I'm sorry but I'm afraid I must ask you to send her home," I said.

"You don't mind if I stay a little longer?" Barbara was back on the telephone. "Mildred is having a party and we're having such a nice time. Hal is here and will bring me home."

It seemed a shame to spoil the child's evening.

"Don't stay too late," I said.

It was one o'clock when Barbara returned.

"I had a grand evening," she said. "Mildred's mother was awfully sorry you wouldn't let me stay."

I was glad to see Rhoda the next morning.

"I hope I was right in not letting Barbara stay all night with one of her friends," I said.

"I should say you were!" Rhoda was emphatic. "Barbara knows she isn't allowed to do that. Goodness knows what they planned!"

I was a little annoyed at her suspicions.

"I knew you wouldn't object to tea dates," I said. "Barbara explained that at school they let her go to tea with boys."

Rhoda groaned. "I told you not to believe a word she said. Barbara," accusingly, "why did you make that up?"

"It was the only way I could get out to tea," said Barbara.

"How about those other days? Jane? Mildred?" I was suspicious now.

Barbara gave me an impish smile. "I don't know any girl named Jane. That was Hal. I told him I'd call him by a girl's name when he telephoned."

"But you have been with Mildred?" I asked.

"Not since the first day."

"The woman on the telephone!" My voice was shrill.

"That was a woman we spoke to in a speakie. We couldn't quite put that one over."

"Well," I gasped, "Barbara's at an age where she should be able to take care of herself."

"Fifteen isn't very old," Rhoda said.

"Seventeen is older." I tried to look wise.

"It is," Rhoda agreed. "But Barbara happens to be fifteen."

I smiled. "Barbara told me about her age."

"I still don't know what you're driving at."

I tried to explain. Rhoda shook her head, sighed. Barbara chortled.

"She sure fell for it! So did Hal! I tried it on him first. Awfully romantic. I caught an earlier train to New York instead of the special because I heard college boys would be on it. Hal was the best-looking boy on the train. He really is awfully nice. I didn't want him to know my real age, but I never dreamed any one else would believe that." She gave me her best smile.

"I'm glad you've had a taste of having a growing girl around," Rhoda said. "The thing I don't understand is that I warned you about not believing Barbara's stories."

"I really won't make up another thing!" Barbara promised solemnly. She brightened, changed the subject.

"Mother darling," she said, "when we go shopping I'll show you some of the darlingest dresses. Cheap, too. And a riding habit. Mine's too warm. The riding master said to tell you my system needs riding every day. I don't care much for riding but I'm willing to ride a lot this summer if it's for my *own good!*"

Why We Have Wars

by H. L. Mencken

"War Survives," Says a Sardonic Philosopher, "Simply Because So Many People Enjoy it—Let's Renovate Human Nature!"

THE UPLIFTERS WHO try so violently to downpull war are very earnest folk, and some of their arguments are so powerful that no answer to them has ever been discovered. But meanwhile war continues to be popular. Who, indeed, is really against it—that is, honestly to God against it, as everyone is against smallpox and work? Probably not five percent of the human race. Perhaps another five percent may be induced, under pressure, to sign petitions against it, and even to swear solemnly that they will not serve the next time war comes. But let the bugles blow a few sharp blasts, and the second squad will be howling for blood instanter, and in a little while all save a corporal's guard of the first squad will be howling too.

As for the rest of the people, they are for war all the time, whether for good reasons or for bad. They delight in it as a cat delights in catnip, or a dry congressman in radiator alcohol. There is no easier way to get their confidence and their votes than to start honing the sword and talking darkly of Huns at the gate. In the whole history of the United States I can't find a single example of a politician who ever lost anything by advocating going to war. But on the other side I can show you almost countless examples of politicians who were ruined by talking incautiously of peace.

Go back, for instance, to the War of 1812. If there ever was a senseless bloodletting on this earth, it was that one. England had a magnificent war machine in full operation. The United States had next to nothing.

Moreover, the reasons advanced for going to war were of the flimsiest. Some of them were downright imaginary, and most of the rest were obliterated by a neat English backdown before the war actually began. But by this time the plain people were aflame with military libido, and there was no containing them. Poor little Jimmy Madison, trying to hold back, was greeted with angry roars, and in a little while, like any other enlightened politician, he allowed himself to be converted, and plunged the country into the carnage with pious hosannas.

The war went the way that might have been expected. The Americans, with the aid of a noble band of profiteers, improvised a small and expensive but very smart navy, and it quickly gave a good account of itself on the sea. But on land there was little save a long series of disasters.

Certainly there was plenty of meat in this war for pacifists; and after it had gone on for a while, the few who were then to be found in the country got together and demanded that the slaughter and arson cease. Some New England Federalists, dumb even for politicians, were seized with the idea that there might be something in this movement for their party, so they joined it hopefully. With what result? With the result that their rivals, the Democratic-Republicans who had made the war, accused them of plotting to separate New England from the Union and hand it over to England. This of course, was not true, but nine out of ten Americans believed it the moment they heard it, and in consequence the whole Federalist Party was wrecked and some of its leaders narrowly escaped

being lynched. Open any school history book, and you will find elegant woodcuts of the two loudest advocates of this idiotic war, Henry Clay and John C. Calhoun, and long accounts of their tremendous services to their country. But you will have to search even the thickest schoolbook very hard to discover any mention whatever of their two chief opponents, George Cabot and Theodore Dwight, and what it says about them will probably turn out to be very sniffish.

The same tale might be told of every other war in which the United States has ever been engaged, and, indeed, of every war in which any other nation has ever been engaged. The chief heroes of all wars, next to the generals who lead the troops to slaughter in the field, are the high-powered rabble-rousers who promote the business behind the lines, and keep it going when it threatens to lag.

There are cases, of course, of opponents of war who have lived down their ill fame by swallowing the principles that had been so costly to them. But the really earnest opponents of war always fare badly. The head of the clan in France, Jean Jaurès, was assassinated on July 31, 1914, two days before the first of 1,357,800 Frenchmen were butchered.

Someone once said that if all the diplomats of the world were hanged there would never be any more wars. There is enough truth in this to make it sound plausible. But that getting rid of the whole diplomatic pack would abolish war altogether is by no means likely, for war survives on earth simply because so many people enjoy it.

Enjoy it? Did I really intend to write that word? And if so, have I gone *mashuggah?* Not at all. There is, indeed, nothing in all this world that can match war for popularity. It is, to at least nine people out of ten, the supreme circus of circuses, the show beyond compare. It is Hollywood multiplied by ten thousand. It combines all the excitements of a bullfight, a revival, a train wreck, and a lynching. It is a hunt for public enemies with a million Dillingers scattered through the woods. It is the dizziest,

gaudiest, grandest, damnedest sort of bust that the human mind can imagine.

The pacifists always make the mistake of assuming that the people do not like war, and would not miss it if it were taken away from them. Precisely the same sort of mistake was made by the prohibitionists in 1919, with results so sad that I hate to recall them. The truth is that what the human race really finds it hard to endure is peace. It can stand the dull monotony for ten years, twenty years even thirty years, but then it begins to fume and lather, and presently we are in the midst of another major war and enjoying its incomparable exhilarations.

The whole body of the people, high and low alike, are all the same when the bands begin to play and the tramp, tramp, tramp of marching men converts every heart into a cocktail shaker. The recruits that the pacifists drum up so easily in times of peace are not to be taken seriously. Nine-tenths of them are simply either fools who will sign anything, or snobs who like to fancy that they are superior to the general run. These snobs entertain themselves by pretending that they can't be fetched by the blather which so easily upsets the rest of us, and by taking mighty oaths to refuse to serve in the next war. That many of them will try to keep out of the trenches I have no doubt, but all of them, save a few cripples, will be lined up along the curbstone as they were in the last war, howling incitements and encouragements to the boys in the ranks.

Here I do not except even the rev. clergy. They will not holler as loud as the rest; they will holler twice as loud, as they have always done in all wars since the days of Cain and Abel, and on all sides. In 1912 or thereabout I came into contact with a band of pacifists mainly made up of clergymen, and got to know some of them well.

Along came 1917 and the grandest hullabaloo ever enjoyed by the freemen of this republic. When I thought to inquire about my pacifist friends I naturally expected to find them locked up in some hoosegow or other, charged with treason. But the first one I encountered was now a four-minute man touring the movie parlors and bellowing for blood like a starving tiger. The others had all gone the same way. There was one exception—a clergyman. This holy man stuck to his guns throughout the war. He was denounced in the newspapers, got a great many threatening letters, and came near being thrown out of his pulpit. But he refused to budge, and the last time I heard of him he was still a pacifist. His case, however, was so extraordinary as to be almost unique. It would not be unreasonable to liken him to an honest politician or an odorless polecat.

Even the sassy young intellectuals who rage against war in the colleges, hurling defiances at their teachers, are no better than the rest.

To listen to pacifists, one would think that when the United States went into the World War there was wailing and lamentation from one end of the country to the other. But every one who was alive and reasonably sober in those days knows that the country really stepped into it with shivers of delight, and that nine Americans out of ten had a roaring time until the show was over.

Here I by no means except the actual soldiers. To be sure, it was unpleasant to be killed, but every buck private of healthy mind believed confidently that he would escape, and those who didn't plainly couldn't do any mourning over it. It was also, of course, unpleasant to be wounded, but not every one was wounded, not even a majority, not even ten percent, and the overwhelming bulk of those who collided with shot or shell recovered afterward and had something to be proud of for the rest of their days. There were some young men, unfortunate beyond the common, who didn't escape but were wrecked for life; but statistics prove that their chances of coming to that unhappy fate would have been almost as great if they had stayed at home.

The choice before the average youngster, when war breaks out, is not between enlisting in the army and staying home to become President of the United States, or going into the movies at $10,000 a week, or marrying a girl with four or five doting stepfathers, each worth $100,000,000. It is between enlisting in the army and taking a job in a filling station, or following the plow, or adding up long rows of dull figures, or sitting day after day in an unventilated classroom while half-dead pedagogues try to teach him things that don't interest him.

War, to this typical, this normal young fellow, is a colossal release. The problem of making a living in a stupid and unappreciative world departs from his shoulders. He ceases to be a nonentity and becomes a public figure, cheered by his relatives, his friends, and the populace in general. There is someone to feed him when mealtime rolls around, someone to clothe him, and someone to tell him what to do. He has a gun in his hands and feels like a man. His country needs him, and tells him so with many a slap on the back, though in a little while it may forget him. No more lordly life is imaginable. It combines all of the advantages of a sure income, good and racy company, and a job full of thrills. The soldier stands proudly above all the ordinary laws. Even the laws of economics are repealed for him.

And the rest of the population? My belief, born of close observation in two wars, is that those who stay home enjoy war even more than those who take a hand in it. Every day is full of tremendous excitements, and they are of kinds that peace simply cannot offer. The minute war breaks out the whole country heaves a vast sigh of satisfaction. All the rules are suddenly suspended. There are new and better jobs for everyone. Bands play in the streets. Soldiers go clumping by. Every girl has two beaux, and every boy has three girls. The old fellows make speeches, hunt spies, try to get their share of the easy money. The old girls knit socks, cheer the parades, and dream of handsome generals coming home to steal them from their husbands. I'll begin to believe war can be abolished when the pacifists show me a way to change all this. What I call for, of course, is a complete renovation of human nature. Science is mighty and may accomplish anything in time; it may even accomplish this. If, when, and as it does so I'll begin to believe we have seen the last of war. But not before.

Must We Be Prepared For HELL?

an editorial by Bernarr Macfadden

HELL IS AN appropriate name for war. The hordes of the satanic realm are then loosened. The moral standards of the civilized world were materially lowered by the last war. Another conflict may take us back to the cave-man period.

In the last war we thought we were fighting to save democracy.

In the coming war we may have to fight to save humanity.

If the human race is to become a lot of untamed brutal killers . . . if civilization and all it stands for is to be cast to the winds . . . then our destiny will be early oblivion.

Our President has been acclaimed by many of our people for his recent outspoken criticism of war-mad nations. Although Japan was not mentioned, it was quite evident and freely admitted that the outrages committed by this nation against China were the direct cause of his dramatic utterances.

It is entirely in order for laymen to express themselves in reference to the ghastly horrors of the Japanese-Chinese war. Theirs are merely individual opinions.

But when a high official talks, his words resound throughout the world, and he is supposed to be the voice of the nation, and we . . . the entire citizenry . . . must be responsible for the views expressed.

It took some courage to assume the attitude presented by the President in his Chicago speech. The "peace at any price" advocates must have been unpleasantly surprised. And the first reports indicated that the Japanese fiercely resented this outspoken criticism, although second thought apparently changed their attitude, as their reply indicated an inclination to give reasonable consideration to the viewpoint of the various critical foreign governments.

The Japanese standard of conduct differs greatly from our own. Human life in that country appears to be valued lightly. And there is but little friendliness in their attitude toward our people.

Our citizens are naturally wondering if the President is prepared to support the position assumed in his recent speech with force of arms . . . and that may be necessary.

Practically everything that is worthwhile in life requires a certain amount of effort . . . a struggle . . . sometimes a fight. And even war is often required to preserve peace.

The people of this country, however, will go to almost any extreme to avoid entering another war. We spent our treasure with prodigious liberality in the last world contest. Europe still owes us a huge sum of money that will doubtless never be paid.

And the diplomats of Europe have a habit of "using" our officials when dealing with a hectic situation. Ex-Secretary of State Stimson greatly displeased Japan by his attitude on the Manchuria problems. We were the "goat" on that occasion. And notwithstanding our supposed isolation, we are apparently being used in a similar manner on this occasion.

However, our idea of isolation is but little more than a dream. In fact, we have never isolated ourselves from any of the really important affairs of the world, notwithstanding our refusal to join the League of Nations or to become a member of the World Court. We have always dabbled in important world affairs through an observer, and we are one of responsible members of the Nine-Power Treaty which so vigorously opposes Japan. And the unanimous decision of these Powers will bind us morally, if not actually.

An eruption is likely to occur at any time in Europe that will set the world afire with another murderous conflict.

Can we stay out? That is our great problem.

If we are forced into another war we will be as thoroughly unprepared as we were in the World War. One would think we would have sufficient intelligence at least to prepare our citizens physically for such a conflict. Such an effort would be an investment that would become invaluable for developing the health and vitality of the nation. The deplorable need of such preparation was dramatically demonstrated in the examination of our young men during the World War.

Intelligent and thorough preparation—that is the one safe procedure that might enable us to avoid such another conflict.

Let us hope that we will take this needful precaution.

Found—The Fountain of Youth

by Edward Doherty

I DIDN'T BELIEVE it. It was too unlike the pictures my mind had painted. It upset too many of my theories. I had expected to see a straggly line of gaunt figures limping painfully down the road, men and women leaving bloody footprints in the dust behind them, women falling and getting up and trudging heroically on again. I pictured grim, tortured, fanatic faces, swollen legs, blistered and bunioned feet.

And instead of that I found forty or fifty people walking toward me with powerful swinging strides. I found faces glowing with happiness and health, faces tanned or sunburned, young faces even on elderly men and women. They came toward me swiftly, singing.

No, I didn't believe it!

"This isn't the bunch I'm looking for," I said to the driver. "The people I want are those who have hiked all the way from Cleveland."

"These are Bernarr Macfadden's Cracked Wheat Derby hikers," the driver insisted, "whether you like it or not."

I didn't believe it until I saw Mr. Macfadden among the marchers.

I had never seen a "Cracked Wheat Derby," had never met any one who had taken part in one, had never given the hikers much thought, save to pity them. Like a hundred million and more other Americans, I avoid walking whenever I can. If I have to travel only a block or two, and the car's handy, I take the car.

The car had taken me six miles down the road to meet these people. They had hiked nineteen miles or so every day for fourteen days, and had six more to go before they reached their goal. But they looked less tired than I felt.

Cracked wheat Monday [they sang];
Cracked wheat Tuesday,
Cracked wheat Wednesday,
Cracked wheat Thursday,
Cracked wheat Friday,
Cracked wheat Saturday too!

I got out of the car and walked with the crowd—not very far—and talked to Mr. Macfadden.

"What do you think of them?" he asked me.

"It's fantastic," I said, "but they all look young; even the old men and women look young."

"They've found the Fountain of Youth," he said. "It flows out of their feet. I wish every man and woman could learn that. Nobody needs any gland transplantation, any operation, to become young again. He needs only to walk. These people are proof of that statement. Talk to some of them and you'll be convinced."

"How do you do it?" I asked one of them, when they halted about noon. "Are you all professional athletes? You're all used to walking?"

"Athletes?" he said. He roared with laughter. "That's a good one. Say, where were you when we started out? You should have seen us. You should have seen me!

"Say, a few months ago the doctors told me I might drop dead any minute. You should have seen the way my wife looked at me when she thought I wasn't looking!"

"Let me get this straight," I said. "A few months ago you were dying. Then you go on this 260-mile hike —and—"

"And get myself another fifty years of life," he interrupted. "First let me introduce myself. I'm W. G. Barnard of Warsaw, Illinois. I'm a salesman. I used to go everywhere in a car. I never took any exercise except with a knife and fork and spoon. I ate anything and everything, especially meat and potatoes and lots of white bread. I put on a lot of weight. At my heaviest I weighed 212 pounds.

"I used to get heartburn after every meal. I took soda mints to relieve the pain. I had to have bicarbonate of soda by the handfuls, and glasses and glasses of seltzer water. I was better stocked than your corner drugstore. But I didn't get alarmed until I was refused a life-insurance policy.

"A smart young doctor put me on a diet of grated carrots, fresh-vegetable salads, and fruits—no fatty meats, butter, starch, sugar, coffee, tea, or beer, no white bread, no candy. That helped, but I found I needed exercise. So I decided to take the hike from Cleveland to Dansville.

"Man, I thought I'd die that first day. And the next. But you should have seen me a few days later, taking those mountain paths without even puffing.

"Oh, there were plenty of blisters, Charley horses, sprains, and stiffnesses along the way. But fresh air, sunshine, exercise, diet, pure water, and sound sleep cured everything. I feel like a kid again. No fooling!"

A slim young woman came running up as Mr. Barnard talked. He introduced her as Miss Flora Hanes of Akron, Ohio.

"How about you?" I asked her.

For answer she gave me two pictures. One was of a rather fat woman, the other of a slim figure in an evening gown.

"Those are both me," she said. "You can call them 'before and after' if you want to. I've taken off ninety pounds just by walking and by eating the right kind of foods. I've had to throw away all my old clothes—or have them altered. But it's worth it. It's worth everything in the world to be healthy again! And the hike was glorious!"

"Glorious?" I couldn't help asking. "Hiking nineteen miles a day is glorious?"

"More than glorious," Miss Hanes answered. "Ask anybody. Ask that lady over there—the one putting on new stockings. She was so all in after the first day she thought her whole insides had dropped. She phoned her daughter to come and take her home. The daughter arrived the next morning, thinking her mother was near death.

"But Mama had had a good sleep during the night, the first real sleep in years. And she thought she'd try it another day.

"At the end of the second day the old lady told her daughter to go home. Yesterday and today she led the march."

I asked this woman later how she felt.

"I feel that I've just begun to live," she said. "I feel that I've cheated myself for more years than I care to admit—because I didn't get out and get God's sunshine and wind and rain on me, because I didn't use the legs He gave me. I can never forgive myself for those misspent years. Why, it's like a miracle—to be so well again, to have such a hunger, such an enormous appetite, to sleep so soundly, to enjoy life so fully."

Just before the "chuck truck" pulled up, I met Edna Milligan, who claims she was much fatter than Flora Hanes ever was—before she started the march from Cleveland. Mrs. Milligan was known to the hikers as "Kate Smith," not only because of her avoirdupois but also because of her sweet singing voice.

"I weighed 222 pounds when I started this little walk," she told me. "I've lost a lot of that. Maybe thirty pounds. I can't tell exactly, for I haven't weighed myself recently. You know how I got this way? Doing lip service to my own cooking. I'm a swell cook. Rather, I used to be. I was too good a cook! But I've got new ideas now. I've found out about live foods. There are dead foods and live foods. No more dead stuff for me—no matter how wonderful it tastes.

"I've found out you can do wonders on cracked wheat. We've had cracked wheat every day on this hike. And I love it. We marched so far every day. Then we get hungry and start singing 'Cracked wheat Monday, cracked wheat Tuesday.' Pretty soon up comes the truck with the cracked wheat. After a little while we're full of pep again. Pep. Energy. Strength. Enthusiasm."

The cracked-wheat truck came down the road in a cloud of dust, and everybody began to sing again.

I talked to one of the men in the truck just before he began to serve the steaming bowls.

"Did you ever see a happier bunch of people?" he asked me. "Look at them! Everybody laughing, everybody smiling, everybody crazy about everybody else. You wouldn't believe it—how they get along with each other. I mean like they all grew up together. But I never saw a meaner, grumpier, more complaining lot in my life than these same people during the first few days. They hated each other. If they hadn't been so dog tired at the end of the day that they just fell down and went to sleep, they'd have murdered each other. Have some cracked wheat?"

"No," I said.

"It won't hurt you," he assured me. "In fact it might do you some good. It's just cracked wheat, with raisins on it, and butter. And you can have brown sugar or honey, or both. Go on, try a bowl—with raisin coffee."

"What's that?"

"Raisins and hot water. One of the most delicious drinks you ever had!"

I ate the cracked wheat and drank the raisin coffee; and asked for more.

I watched the hikers as they ate and drank, and realized they were having a real picnic—realized they had had a picnic three times a day. I felt quite humble as I got back into the car and rode the six miles back to Dansville. I began to wonder whether I shouldn't walk more; take more thought as to the things I ate and drank.

But I consoled myself with the idea that perhaps this was all just a temporary thing, and that these people had been benefited as much by faith as by walking and diet. They were just kidding themselves that they had found the Fountain of Youth.

But I couldn't get away with it.

At the Physical Culture Hotel in Dansville I met two of the group who had completed the hike the day before, two of the 102 who "finished strong."

One of these was Jess Hyde of Binghamton, a man of forty-five. He was so eager to join the Cleveland hikers he walked from Binghamton to Cleveland.

"It was nothing," he said. "I did it in a week. It's 400 miles from Binghamton to Cleveland, by road map. The way I went it was a little more than 350 miles."

Only a little more than 350 miles! He made it in a week! And then took it easy with the Cleveland hikers. Six hundred and ten miles in three weeks!

"I didn't want to be on the road Memorial Day," he said. "Too much traffic. So I got up at four o'clock one morning and walked thirty-two hours straight. I covered 105 miles in that time."

"You didn't stop to eat?"

"Nope. I just took a little orange juice now and then, or a little water when my lips were dry."

"You've hiked before?"

"Oh, yes. This is my third hike with Mr. Macfadden."

"Tell me," I said. "What do you get out of it? Have you really benefited?"

"Well," Mr. Hyde answered, after some thought, "let me give you an example of how I've benefited from walking—and proper diet. I've never been sick since I started walking—I mean walking long distances. I've never even had a cold. And last winter, when I got caught in the elevator machinery on the roof of the Security Mutual Building in Binghamton, I suffered a very slight injury when I should have been killed.

"I got pulled into the cable drum before I knew what was happening. My hand was crushed to a pulp; but I had strength enough to pull it out. One of my fingers didn't come with the rest of the hand—but you can't save everything in circumstances like that.

"I made a tourniquet, walked downstairs, and several blocks to a doctor's office. On the way to the hospital I stopped at the building, so I could notify the office that I was hurt and would be off the job for a day or two.

"My hand was crushed, and I was bruised all over. I had lost a lot of blood, and naturally I was suffering from shock. But I was in the hospital only six days. If I hadn't been a walker I couldn't have stood all that."

Then I met Dave Power of Los Angeles. David Will Power. He's forty-six. He gained a reputation among the hikers because on the last day of the hike he ran about nineteen miles in one hour and fifty minutes, and came in breathing naturally. It was his custom to run a mile or two after the daily hike—"just for fun."

Mr. Power styles himself "a hundred percent raw vegetarian, and an ardent believer in nuts, fruits, grains, and vegetables, sunshine, and outdoor exercise."

"I make it a practice to run nine hours every week," he said, "and to take at least two twenty-five to thirty-mile hikes a week. I have walked over Mount Hollywood several times without a change of pace. It's about 1,600 feet high. My blood pressure was 136 when I started, 138 when I finished. I finished with a sprint.

"I once climbed Mount Shasta, which is nearly 15,000 feet high and has an 80-percent grade near the top. I met eighteen or twenty CCC boys at the bottom of the mountain. They were preparing to climb the peak, too—kids of eighteen or nineteen. They told me to go on ahead, so I couldn't be a drag on them. They'd catch up to me.

"They were eating when I joined them. They were eating meat and white bread and heavy truck like that. And how they howled when I put some balls of garlic in my juicer! That's all I put into my stomach—a little garlic juice and a spoonful of honey mixed in it.

"I started ahead, and stayed ahead. I got to the top an hour and thirty minutes before any of them arrived. And only three of them arrived."

I said, "Marvelous! But why? Do you take these hikes and these long runs just for the fun of it? Or because you think it'll bring back your lost youth?"

"I'm a World War veteran," he answered. "I was gassed and wounded in the war. I developed pulmonary tuberculosis. The tops of both lungs were affected. That's why I started outdoor exercising. That's why I started eating nothing but live foods.

"And if you think it didn't bring back my youth, you're crazy! I have perfect control of my breath now. I can walk. I can run. I can do a standing marathon—taking 180 steps to the minute and keeping it up for two hours and a half—without breathing heavily. I have no more t.b. than a granite cliff."

His words made me wonder if I wasn't foolish not to take up walking. I'm not getting any younger. I could do with a little of the zest and endurance and health I observed in the Macfadden hikers. I could use a lot of that youth they found as they hiked through the glory of the American countryside.

I mentioned something of this to Mr. Macfadden.

"Good!" he exclaimed. "The more miles you walk, the more days you will enjoy. By all means, get out and walk. Tell all your friends to walk. Tell all Americans to walk. How I'd love to see this country on its feet!

"Walking is a superb physician. It'll take all the surplus fat out of your body—and out of your mind too. It'll build muscle and sinew. It'll build stamina, character, strength, beauty of body and soul.

"But it's such a simple, natural remedy that most people will scorn it. They think it's tiring to walk. Well, it is—until you get used to it. After that it's a joy.

"I've been preaching the gospel of walking for half a century; and finally I'm getting somewhere. This year we had the largest class of hikers. One hundred and twelve started. One hundred and two finished. Next year I hope to have twice or three times as many. You're cordially invited to come with us."

"Thanks," I said. But I said it with a mental reservation. I don't think I've got the guts to do it.

Those Delirious Dodgers
by John Drebinger

What Will They Do Next? . . . A Look
At Baseball's Strangest Phenomenon

WHEN BURLEIGH GRIMES accepted the managerial portfolio of the Brooklyn Dodgers Baseball Club, he fell heir to one of the strangest phenomena in the history of the national pastime—Brooklyn baseball.

It being perfectly safe to assume that nowhere in this wide, wide world is there anything quite so extraordinary as that, it should be of interest to one and all to take a deep look into the thing just to see what it is. Even the first glance reveals that here indeed is something without parallel, precedent, or reason.

Witness the recent escapade of Van Lingle Mungo, Brooklyn's ace hurler, as a fair example of the unpredictable. Mr. Mungo, let it be said, is a fervent lover of action. The early-season peacefulness of rival players on the diamond had failed to satisfy his desires. So, in desperation, the estimable Van paid an early-morning visit to the room of one of his teammates. Jimmy Bucher, invaded Dodger, was both an accommodating soul and the possessor of a good right. Third-baseman Bucher served Mr. Mungo. So did Manager Grimes when he heard details. Mr. Mungo, for his adventurous spirit, won a Grade-A shiner, a thousand-dollar fine, and suspension for three days without pay. That gives you an idea. Let us look further.

Where else, for instance, did one ever see three players pile up on third base for a triple play as the inglorious finish to a rousing three-base hit?

Where else has one ever seen a runner, twice within a week, pass a comrade on the base lines for no other startling effect than to wipe out the joys and benefits normally to be accrued from a home run smack over the fence.

Where else did they ever fire two successive managers, each with another year to go on an unexpired contract?

Where else would they ever think of paying one manager ten thousand dollars a year for running the ball club in Flatbush, while laying out fifteen thousand dollars to another to keep out of there and tend to his vegetable garden in Glendale, California?

And where, oh where, does one ever see so guileless an outfit strive with an almost studied perversity to keep its team steeped in the throes of second division in a locale whose fans are the hottest, most ardent baseball enthusiasts on this or any other globe?

Just what started all this is so enmeshed in general bewilderment and antiquity that even the ablest baseball historians have never been able to get in accord on the matter. Some have even been so unkind as to blame it all on that grand old Oriole, the late-lamented and lovable Wilbert Robinson.

Certain it is the two fitted each other close to perfection, and if Robbie deserves a place in baseball's Hall of Fame for no other reason, it certainly is for the fact that he survived it all for eighteen years!

He was bluff, gruff, but with a heart as big as the gap one usually found between his second baseman and shortstop. He may have lacked imagination, but he loved the unexpected, a commodity with which his Dodgers supplied him in endless profusion.

In the presence of the writer, Robbie once gave his outfit a dressing down that surpassed even the most vitriolic blasts from John McGraw.

"Partridge," he stormed, "it don't look like you ever can stop a ground ball with anything but that chicken breast of yours, does it?"

"It does not," amiably agreed that luckless culprit.

"Well, just for that, you're fined fifty. And you, Herman, what in hell were you doing down on second base when the play was at first?"

"Oh, I just thought Petty was covering the bag."

"Well, that thought will cost you just fifty."

"Make it a hundred."

"I'll make it two hundred," roared the aroused Robbie. "And you, Hendrick, who ever told you you could play third base?"

"Well, you asked me to play there, Robbie," was the meek response from the soft-spoken Harvey.

"And I suppose if I told you to jump off the grandstand roof, you'd do that too! A fifty for you."

And so it went down the line. Not a player escaped. The total fines must have aggregated more than fifteen hundred dollars. Yet not a dime of it was ever collected from the pay checks of the players.

Babe Herman! In such a setting he was a natural. He came up as a first baseman, and forthwith continued from there to do everything backward. Yet he could sock that apple, never failed to do the unexpected, and Robbie loved him.

Subsequently he was converted into an outfielder, and Max Carey was assigned to act as tutor. One day in Pittsburgh, Max, in center, finally managed, after much arm waving, to get the Babe, playing right, to come in close for Sparky Adams. Sparky was retired in the infield, and Paul Waner came up.

Frantically Max waved Herman back. But the Babe, totally oblivious to it all, remained fixed. Waner swung and pulled as perfect a line single as ever whistled off Big Poison's bat. Right in its path stood Herman; and to save his face he caught the ball for an out!

And on returning to the bench he almost floored Carey with the remark: "Well, Max, we certainly are catching on to this inside stuff pretty fast."

For a player who could miraculously escape getting killed in the performance of his duty and who almost flawlessly could run down harmless flies into damaging triples, he made the most amazing catches imaginable.

Rabbit Maranville was another. He was with the Dodgers only a short time, but long enough to convince every one he fitted admirably into the general scheme of things.

That, of course, was before Rabbit's great reformation.

Once Robbie tried to install an 11 P.M. curfew such as John McGraw enforced with an iron hand with the Giants. He assigned his clubhouse man, Dan Comme-

ford, to do the checking in when they took to the road. On the second day Dan threatened to quit both jobs.

"A man's got to get some sleep," complained Dan; "and how do I get that working in the clubhouse all day and then sitting up all night? A couple came in at one. A few more at two. Some more straggled in at three, and two haven't come in yet—but I guess they'll show up at the park."

"See that," said Robbie, with the air of a man who had just proved his point with a noble experiment. "McGraw can do that with the kind of club he's got, but you can't do that sort of thing with this club."

Dazzy Vance! A prima donna, yet a likable fellow and a genius and one who formed another rare combination with Robbie. Dazz did not like relief work; there were a number of other things he wouldn't do; and he always insisted on his four days of rest.

But Robbie gave in on all points so long as the old Dazz-marine came up to the mark on the fifth and did a first-class job, which Vance invariably did. He turned in more complete games than any other pitcher, ruled the roost as the league strike-out king, and rated for a time as just about the greatest pitcher of his day. He was a star of the first magnitude in as weird a setting as ever was provided for a gem. And Robbie was ever careful never to give offense to his ace.

One day in Philadelphia the Dodgers were desperately trying to hold a one-run lead in the last of the ninth. The Phils had a man on second and Chuck Klein at bat. Down in the bull pen Vance was tuning up; not for today, however, but for tomorrow. Robbie sent a courier down to Dazz with the request that he try to save this one.

Vance came up, pitched one ball straight as a string down the groove, and Klein larruped it over the fence.

Robbie was furious, but dared not say a word to Vance. So he took it out on Hank De Berry, the catcher.

"Hank, why in hell did you let him throw that one right down the middle?"

"Now, listen, Robbie," replied Hank quietly. "You know I haven't told the big fellow what to throw in the last ten years, so how can you expect me to start in the ninth inning of today's game?"

That left Robbie with no answer, and he made no effort to find one, as very soon some other problem would come to perplex him. And there were no end of problems; for, in addition to what was going on out there on the ball field, a bitter feud behind the scenes was being fought during all this time. The McKeever and Ebbets factions were battling each other hammer and tongs, with Robbie riding in the middle as president and manager. Only the ballplayers, although they never realized it at the time, actually reaped a harvest from this odd situation. Some of them were receiving the most outlandish salaries imaginable as each of the two warring factions sought to force the other to quit and sell out.

The classics, however, were the Giant-Dodger conflicts. Came one series that set an all-time record for something or other. Somebody on the Dodgers came up with the bright idea that the club needed new signals and that the Connie Mack system was by far the best.

Unfortunately, this inspiration hit the club only a few minutes before game time, and, instead of matters clarifying, the confusion became all the greater as everybody tried to explain to everybody else what his notion of the new signals happened to be. The result was no end of commotion, until finally Herman stepped up with a thought that only the Babe could ever concoct.

"Aw, hell," he said, "let's play without signals. I'm mixed up enough."

So they played without signals, and won. They won the next day. Then they knocked over the Phillies. In all, they won five straight without a signal being flashed from the bench.

But on the sixth day this dream of heaven came to a crash. Del Bissonette let a "home-run ball" go right down the middle for a third strike with the winning runs on the bags, and Robbie fell back with a groan.

"See that. You can't win ball games without signals. Tomorrow we go back to signals."

The feud between Robbie and McGraw always caused a chuckle among the boys, for it was foolish to see these two old gentlemen glaring at each other like a couple of school kids. Although almost as hasty in temper, Robbie was far quicker to forgive and forget and always stood ready to bury the hatchet. But McGraw remained adamant. He carried hates and grievances much longer. Only when trouble finally overtook an old friend would McGraw's generous spirit blot out everything else.

That time came in 1929, when McKeever ousted Robbie as president. McGraw at once went to bat for his old pal, and succeeded in getting McKeever to let Robbie remain on as manager with a two-year contract.

The Dodgers almost won a pennant in one of those two years. They embarked on their last Western trip that year in first place. But then came the inevitable tail spin and they finished fourth. It also finished Robbie.

Max Carey succeeded him. Max, a scholar and former theological student, was another odd link in the weird assortment in Flatbush. He used to play chess with the writers, to the utter consternation of Robbie.

In fact, there were no end of talented accomplishments on that club's roster. They could boast of some of the most skilled bridge, golf, and poker players to be found in the major leagues; and yet, as Robbie once remarked:

"How can so much brain turn out the dumbest baseball I have ever seen in all my fifty years?"

Max really had some fine theories on managing ballplayers. But things were by now in too much of a jumble for any of it to make sense.

Two weeks before the 1934 training season opened, the directors fired Carey, paid him off for a full year, and installed his coach, Casey Stengel.

Casey, part sage, philosopher, and clown, but a capable baseball man for all that, promised for a time to make a success of it. He had a terrible outfit last spring, but from July to the end managed to win more games than any other club in the league except the pennant-winning Giants. But the idea of bouncing a manager with still a year to go on his contract seemed to have captivated the fancy of the Dodgers' directors. So they bounced Casey, and now it's Burleigh Grimes.

Burleigh is as learned and as serious about baseball as ever was Carey and, to boot, far more hard-boiled. He comes with a wealth of experience, and has played under some of the greatest pilots in the game, including McGraw, Robbie, McKechnie, Hornsby, and McCarthy.

He says he will put an end to all this foolishness. It should prove highly interesting to see what Burleigh does to the Dodgers. Or perhaps the question should be put: What will the Dodgers do to Burleigh?

Is DiMaggio Baseball's Wonder Man?

by Daniel M. Daniel

A Sports Expert Surveys the Facts Behind a Swift, Dramatic Rise to Fame

WHEN BABE RUTH slid from the peak of baseball achievement into retirement, experts announced that time would not bring even his approach as a producer of diamond drama, splasher of color, and manufacturer of home runs. But almost immediately time answered the challenge. We got Joseph Paul DiMaggio, Jr., center fielder of the New York Yankees.

Coming up from the San Francisco Seals in 1936, Joe won unanimous acclaim as one of the most amazing recruits the game had seen. Having fought through that critical second year—the most trying in a baseball player's career—with results hitherto not achieved by a major-league sophomore, Giuseppe presents a most intriguing subject for the fans and a more than alluring clinical exhibit for the writers.

Just how good is this lad DiMaggio? Is he truly the baseball wonder of today, the paragon to be of tomorrow, the man who will threaten the accomplishments of Ruth and the run-making records of Lou Gehrig?

Here is a young man who, at twenty-three, is confronted with the opportunity to make a million. It has required no deep study in colleges, no business acumen, to bring him face to face with that golden chance.

He is big, strong, well put together, fleet of foot, keen of eye, every inch of him an athlete in splendid condition. He can hit a baseball with consistency farther than anybody else. He can throw even as Thor hurled his hammer. He has come hurtling into a fame which not even Ruth or Ty Cobb approached, with two seasons of American League competition. As a consequence, many experts do not hesitate to pronounce DiMaggio the number one player.

However, there are recognized authorities who see DiMaggio's aspirations and his place in the game in serious jeopardy from counter-challenges by Joe Medwick, left fielder of the St. Louis Cardinals and winner of the National League's most valuable player award for 1937, Hank Greenberg, the chief slugger of the Detroit Tigers, and Hank's teammate, Rudy York, who established himself as a vehement factor in the home-run struggle last season.

DiMaggio is menaced, too, by a pitcher—the nineteen-year-old Bobby Feller, strike-out remarkable of the Cleveland Indians, who seems to have it in him to revive the ancient glories of Mathewson and Johnson.

Certainly it is no rose-strewn path which lies before DiMaggio.

Giuseppe failed to land the American League most valuable player award for 1937, but it is my personal belief that he was the number one player for that year and that he is destined to scale the real heights in 1938.

At the risk of boring you with figures, let me quote a few to make my arguments clear.

Last year DiMaggio hit .346. He won the home-run championship of the major leagues with 46. In his own circuit he finished six ahead of Hank Greenberg. His closest home-run rivals in the National League were Medwick and Melvin Ott, of the New York Giants, who tied at 31.

With 418 bases on 215 hits, which included 35 doubles and 15 triples, DiMaggio built up the most impressive offensive record in the major leagues in 1937.

Charley Gehringer, who won the American League batting championship and the most valuable player award last season, outhit DiMaggio by twenty-five points. But when you consider that Gehringer's total bases came to a mere 293, that he belted only 14 homers and drove in just 96 tallies, you begin to wonder what that committee was about when it passed up Giuseppe of the Bronx.

In winning the National League batting title with .374, Medwick compiled a total of 406 bases, drove in 154 runs, and got 41 passes.

On the defensive side of baseball, there are many qualified experts who believe Gehringer to be the greatest second sacker of all time.

But our Signor DiMaggio is no slouch himself in the art of defense and the science of stopping enemy runs. Joe's style of fielding, on fly balls, liners, and grounders, bears the mark of baseball genius. He also displays a better arm, by far, than the much-talked-about Bob Meusel showed for the Yankees, a stronger wing than Jack Murray displayed for McGraw's Giants.

This may be disputed by some of the old guard, who figure that baseball died when Matty quit the Giants and Ty Cobb lost his magic art with the Tigers. But there are just as many strong arms in the major leagues now as there were in the "good old days." It is important to remember that in the old days the ball was dead. Outfielders played in. The throw to the plate was far shorter than it is now, with that lively leather being belted far and wide.

Please remember also that DiMaggio has attained his high position in only two seasons of major-league baseball. In a few more years he is likely to crash the all-time outfield composed of Babe, Ty, and Speaker.

DiMaggio is the fans' ballplayer, the ballplayers' ballplayer, and the managers' ballplayer. And in *my* book he is the greatest player in baseball.

Very Much Alive

a story by Margery Sharp

*A Crazy Story? That's What You May Think to
Start With. But Wait Until You Get Into It . . .*

SHERRARD HAD FORTY-FIVE minutes to wait for
his train, so he checked his suitcase and turned out
into the Euston Road. He had three days' leave, and was
about to spend two of them in unpleasant travel just to
keep a luncheon engagement with a lady in Scotland.

As he strolled along the sight of a tobacco shop reminded him that he was short of cigarettes. He was struck
by the oddity of the window. The boxes and packets were
simply piled in one corner, leaving the rest of the space
bare. The one word "Hamble" showed on the glass.
The whole establishment, in fact, had a take-it-or-leave-it
air which Sherrard found unusual. He liked the unusual.
He went in.

Behind the counter sat a large unshaven old man wearing a knotted handkerchief instead of a collar. His jacket
needed cleaning, or perhaps burning. His features were
heavy and sad. But he had the aura of one who is his
own master, and Sherrard rightly guessed him to be Hamble in person.

"What kind of cigarettes have you got?" asked Sherrard.

"Nothing much," said Mr. Hamble.

Sherrard looked round and saw that this was true. But
there was a case of cigarette holders, and as the lady he
was going to visit lost about one a day, Sherrard began
making a selection. To do so, he put down on the counter
a couple of books, a Euripides, in the original Greek,
and a work on philosophy.

Mr. Hamble examined him thoughtfully for some
minutes and appeared to come to a decision.

"Do you mind," he asked, "if I tell you a rather remarkable story?"

Sherrard said not at all, he would be delighted.

"It's an animal story," said Mr. Hamble apologetically, and cleared his throat.

"As a small child," began Mr. Hamble, "I frequently spent my holidays with a maiden aunt who lived in a small villa on the Italian Riviera. One day, as I was running back through the garden in response to the luncheon bell, I was surprised to see a bear in my path. Bears, in the imagination at least, are by no means unfamiliar objects to a small boy, and I dare say I should have taken it quite calmly but for the fact that this bear walked upon its hind legs and also wore a small Homburg hat. I fled, howling.

"In but a few moments, of course, all was explained. The animal belonged to a band of gypsies who were exhibiting it through the neighborhood, and hoped to offer us a private show. Later that afternoon, in a secluded grove, I came upon them again. This time the bear was eating a cold leg of pigeon, and to do so had thrust back his furry muzzle, revealing a human face.

"This incident made a deep impression on me, and for many years after I was a good deal confused in my relations with all the larger quadrupeds. At home in London, when taken to the zoo, I was quite convinced that all lions and tigers, apes (and of course bears) were really human beings exercising a profession as regular as that of butcher or baker."

Sherrard said he understood perfectly.

"Years passed," continued Mr. Hamble. "My parents died. I had never been clever, but I found myself a niche in the secondhand furniture trade. My first independent purchase was a stuffed bear."

He paused, evidently awaiting comment. Sherrard said he thought it very natural.

"It was *not* natural," corrected Mr. Hamble. "The market for stuffed bears—upright—is extremely restricted. I did not intend bidding for it. My lips moved, as it were, of their own accord. 'Five pounds!' I cried, and the animal was mine.

"It cost another ten shillings to transport. I set it up on the pavement outside my shop, hoping to gain some advantage in the way of publicity. I placed a small Homburg hat on its head. It attracted, as I had hoped, considerable attention. Business looked up.

"For the first week my new acquisition remained, so to speak, passive. Then, one particular sunny day, I noticed that the Homburg hat looked very shabby, and I replaced it by a hard straw. Several passers-by noted the change with approval. The weather broke, it rained every day, and I grew very tired of either hauling the bear inside or wrapping him in dust sheets. I remembered a mackintosh cape, Inverness style, which had belonged to my father, and put that on him instead. You would have been surprised to see what a change it made. He still looked like a bear, but he also looked rather like a Ger-

man professor. My charwoman reported that he had given her quite a turn, and I noticed one or two customers murmur a word of apology as they brushed by. Perhaps the most curious point was that when the rainy spell ended, and I took the cape off, the bear looked not more but less natural. He looked unclad—like a German professor in his combinations. Fortunately, among a variety of secondhand clothes, I possessed an academic gown which fitted him very well.

"I ought to say that he was already, in a small way, a public figure. Every one in Paddington knew him, and the variety of his hats (for he had several others besides those I have mentioned) was a constant source of friendly interest. But this gown, by attracting the notice of students of London University, opened wider spheres. I had observed for some time the presence of a new type of customer—young men in flannel trousers, tweed jackets, and large mufflers—who bought, if they bought anything, secondhand books.

"At last two of them approached me with an offer of five shillings for the loan of the bear for Saturday afternoon. They wished, they said, to take him to a football match. I thought it over; the bear had certainly done his best, he had brought me innumerable fresh customers, and it seemed hard that he should never have any pleasure. I decided to let him go—refusing, however, the five shillings. His new friends were delighted, and off he went in their car, wearing a large purple muffler and a knot of purple ribbon. I put in an umbrella after him, in case of rain."

"I hope he got back all right?" said Sherrard.

"He got *back*. He got back well after midnight, smelling strongly of drink with his gown torn, and having lost his umbrella. I was extremely annoyed, and I spoke pretty sharply to his companions; but they were in no state to appreciate the justice of my remarks. In fact I doubt whether they heard them, for a day or two later they returned, quite unabashed, with an invitation to a club dinner. This time I was harder to persuade, but they assured me it was to be a most decorous function, sanctioned by the university authorities, and that the club was one for the advancement of theological philosophy.

"I have mentioned already that the bear strongly resembled a German professor, and this seemed just the sort of thing he would enjoy. I let him accept. But I stipulated that I should call for him myself at ten-thirty, and I actually did so, though I had some difficulty—the debate was still in full swing, and he was taking the chair—in getting him away.

"This incident, too, had consequences. The taxi fare was six and six—to me a not unimportant sum. In fact, I considered it far too much, and I was very nearly decided he should not go out again. Then it occurred to me that it was really he who had sold many things for me at a profit; he was therefore entitled to cash credit. Next day

I began a separate account for him—on one side his personal sales, on the other taxi fares, new clothes, and so on.

"I counted as his all sales made to customers who looked at the bear before they looked in the window; and he did so well that he was soon able to buy himself an opera hat, a silk muffler, and a new umbrella—all very necessary, for from this time his engagements rapidly increased. Were you in London in '38?"

Sherrard said he had been abroad.

"Then you can have no idea," said Mr. Hamble impressively, "how very popular he became. Perhaps it will help if I tell you that on certain occasions—Boat Race night and the Cup Final—he had to have a special policeman detailed to look after him. Like a Cabinet minister. He was the acknowledged patron of London University, without whom no academic function (of the lighter sort) was complete. He attended every sporting event, and usually finished the evening with the victorious team.

"My own life, of course, became more and more bound up with his, for I kept to my rule of always calling for him, and this rather cut me off from the social enjoyments of my neighbors, who were nearly all whist players, and who disliked my having to leave in the middle of a hand. Soon I ceased to frequent them, and without regret. Tradesmen's card parties had small charm for me; I breathed, vicariously, a wider air.

"But let me," said Mr. Hamble, "abridge. For a time all went well. Business continued to prosper. I did not perhaps keep our accounts as carefully as at first, and the bear was a bit extravagant, but I took pride in his appearance, and my own wants were few. The change in our relations came about very gradually. I began to feel a slight reluctance to turn out so frequently and so late at night. It annoyed me to hear people refer to the establishment, as 'the Bear's,' instead of 'Hamble's'; and one evening in November—the fifth—as I sat waiting to go and fetch him from a Guy Fawkes dinner, these dissatisfactions came to a head.

"I had had a hard day's work, the fire burned brightly, there was a program on the wireless I should have liked to hear. But at ten-fifteen I would have to go out. For the third time that week. It suddenly came over me that the people who called my shop 'the Bear's' were right: it wasn't my shop at all; it was his. I was working twelve hours a day to support him in a life of idle pleasure.

"And there were other points—trifling perhaps—that rankled. He was always losing umbrellas. It seemed absolutely impossible for him to go out with an umbrella and bring it back. And he lost not only his own but mine as well, whenever I lent them him. I suddenly came to an astounding decision.

" 'All right,' I said, 'you can get back by yourself.' And I locked up and went to bed."

Mr. Hamble turned to Sherrard beseechingly.

"I assure you," he said—"I never thought of anything more than his spending the night on the pavement, and having lost his umbrella, and it coming on to rain. That was the very worst I anticipated. And in the morning—for it *did* rain—I hurried down at half past six with a large towel. But he wasn't there. He hadn't come home. I waited till nine, and then I hurried to the college where he had dined. It was built round a quadrangle, in the center of which, as I entered, I observed the remains of a large bonfire. I observed them quite idly.

"At the lodge I made inquiry of the porter, giving the names of the bear's particular hosts, only to be told that they were one and all in the hands of the police. They had gone, explained the porter, too far: a bonfire in the quad might pass, but not the carrying of flaming torches through the London streets. They had all been arrested. 'Was there a bear arrested with them?' I asked. The porter shook his head. I felt a foolish relief. At least they had had the decency, I thought, not to implicate him. 'Then, where is he?' I asked. 'I have come to take him home.' The porter shook his head again—but this time pityingly, and he pointed through the lodge window to the heap of ash . . ."

"What?" cried Sherrard, genuinely shocked. "He'd been burnt?"

"Cremated. I knew without another word. I asked, 'What time did they light it?' And the porter answered, 'About half past ten.' "

There is always something a little absurd in the emotions of the stout. Mr. Hamble was very stout indeed, and the object of his affection a stuffed bear; yet Sherrard did not find his distress wholly ridiculous. It was too sincere. To give the old man time to recover, he picked out six cigarette holders and laid a note on the counter in payment. Mr. Hamble violently blew his nose.

"That's all," he said abruptly. "I never so much as riddled through the ash. I hadn't the heart. In a day or two they came around, those students, full of regrets and explanations. I wouldn't listen to them. I sold the business, moved here, set up as a tobacconist, and I've never prospered since. I expect," said Mr. Hamble, "I haven't had the heart." He looked at Sherrard earnestly. "Now, as a man of education," he said, "and a man of the world, what d'you make of it?"

Sherrard hesitated.

"It's certainly a remarkable story," he said. "It's one of the most remarkable stories I've ever heard."

Mr. Hamble moved his big shoulders impatiently.

"I know *that*," he said; "but would you call it unique?"

Sherrard began to reflect.

"No," he said at last, "not unique. In fact, I believe a good many men have a bear of sorts."

"I never heard of another," said Mr. Hamble jealously.

"Not an actual bear, as yours was. But an idea, or an objective, possibly unworthy, to which everything else is

271

sacrificed. It may be a golf handicap, or land, or stamps, or basic English. With women it's very likely to be a house."

Mr. Hamble pondered.

"You were beginning to find him out," said Sherrard seriously; for the bear by now was almost as real to him as it was to Mr. Hamble. "You say yourself that your relations were changing. So long as you believe in your bear, nothing else matters; but if once you find him out and still can't get rid of him—that's the devil. Perhaps it was just as well it ended as it did."

Mr. Hamble shook his head again.

"I'll think it over," he said. "Mind, I don't say you're right, and I won't hear a word against him, but I'll think it over."

Then he looked at Sherrard with a sudden, unexpected shrewdness.

"And what," he asked, is *your* bear?"

Sherrard counted the cigarette holders lying in his palm: six of them, at half a crown each. They would all be lost within a week; not only lost, but forgotten. . . .

"My bear," he said, "has golden hair and brown eyes and is unshakably faithful to the memory of her late husband."

"Ah!" said Mr. Hamble. "And have you found her out yet?"

Sherrard let the holders slip one by one from his fingers to the counter.

"Not yet," he said. "But now *you* shall advise *me*. Shall I catch my train to go up to Scotland to have lunch with her, thus wrecking a much needed leave, or shall we both go out and get a drink?"

It took Mr. Hamble some moments to answer, and even then he did not do so in words; but he reached up to a peg behind him and from it took down a small Homburg hat.

How To Dance the Big Apple

by Eleanor Powell

*From an Expert of Experts, with Some New Steps of Her
Own! A Blithe Lesson for All Who Have Rhythm in Their Feet*

AMERICA'S HAVING A fad for revivals this year, not only of clothes but of dancing—which is why, if you go to almost any night club tomorrow night, on at least one number you'll be asked to get up and do a square dance just like grandpappy used to do when there was a shindig in the barn. Of course there'll be a phony touch to the whole thing, a flavor of the satirical. This will be 1938 grinning a little at 1898.

We've taken a perfectly respectable dance like the old-fashioned hoedown, adjusted it to slacks and swing skirts, and dusted it off for swing use. We do it with shoulders hunched and stomachs out; we set it to flash Negro music played on trumpets instead of to The Irish Washerwoman jigged on a fiddle; we call it the Big Apple. And it's not far removed from a ceremonial hop they throw in East Africa when they want to put the voodoo on some wayward tribal brother—which would have been a shock to grandpappy, who didn't know that his early American version came to the red barn via slave ship from a jungle glade, and the boys who originated it trucked on down to a set of tom-toms that would have made even Krupa of the Goodman band forget his traps for a while.

As a matter of fact this particular craze started in a down-South cabaret, and some visiting college fellows took it up. But of course. Then famous professional Arthur Murray caught on, and that was that.

I'm going to tell you how to do the steps of this Big Apple thing because, whether you're twelve or eighty, if you've got anything but rust in your joints you'll be doing it sooner or later. If you dare put your head inside the Troc or any dance club in the country without being ready to get out and solo for the bunch while the ring pecks on in place, you might as well stay in the porch swing and save your money.

At home, when you're using a phonograph or a radio, be sure, first, that you've got the right music. It's got to be a fox trot in four-four time, with a persistent tempo, or you'll lag. Then you start off the same way they do in the niteries, with one person calling out what steps to do, and every one else in a circle around him, holding hands. You get in rhythm, all of you, by pawing at the floor with your right foot, and then the leader says, "Hokay now— and a one, and a two, and a three and a *four*. And *to* the left. . . .

The first step I'll give you is called the "Chuck-a-boom," and I think it's the best of the lot. I've got a right to; I made it up myself. You see, Chris Schonberg and some of the boys heard a one-cylinder engine Chuck-a-booming away next to my set one day, so they ran up a tune and I figured out a dance to go with it. Chet Forrest and Bob Wright did the lyrics. Now Paul Whiteman's introducing the tune at the Cocoanut Grove and Bill Robinson is making it his finale in the Cotton Club show, and Dave Gould, Metro's dance director, is planning an entire ensemble built around the Chuck-a-boom for my next big musical.

The advantage of the step is that you can do it not only to its own song but to any four-four fox trot; you can do all of it or just a little, alone or with a partner. You can do it with all arms and legs at the Palomar—or just with your heels at the Waldorf. This is it in essence; after you've caught on you can vary it all you like:

Hop four steps forward on your right foot, left foot dragging a little; then four steps ahead on your left foot.

Back four steps on the right foot, and another four on the left. Now, with feet together, make four little jumps on the corners of an imaginary square—and then Chuck-a-boom four times. Chuck-a-booming is done with the heels alone, while you're standing still, feet together; and it's a very fast drumming: right heel, left heel, right heel, pause. That spells Chuck-a-boom once. Do it three times more, and then you can repeat the whole thing or start something else—whatever the leader feels like. Your partner simply faces you and does everything backward. Then you can do the hops in a circle too, or in a semicircle each way.

All the other steps that you will do in the Big Apple are simple ones, each with an identifying gesture. With the Susie Q it's clasping your hands and waving them back and forth. With truckin' it's holding one hand up in the air, wagging the index finger.

Truckin' was originated by Harlem waiters who carry their trays balanced on one hand and do a sort of shuffle-toddle around the café in rhythm to whatever the band's playing. Your body is held a little back and turns slowly while your feet do exaggerated things. Start with your left instep hugging the right calf, right foot pointing right; step down and forward on your left foot, toeing in; and turn both toes out on the second beat. Then start over with your right foot up.

For the Susie Q you clasp your hands and swing them against the rhythm of your feet as you travel to the side. Your right foot comes down flat across the left foot—and your hands go right; then your right toe comes up and turns to the right as the left foot steps left—and the hands swing to the left again. Repeat.

They had to go back to the most famous and popular of all dances to get the Charleston Swing. You do it in a simplified version by stepping forward on your left foot, kicking in a semicircle forward with your left leg. Reverse this going back, do it in tempo, and that's all there is. Your arms and the rest of your body can do anything you like.

Then there's the Duster, in which you hold the front of your pants or dress up a little, and shuffle in to your partner. As you go in you throw your hips forward, shoulders and head back, and when you retreat you throw your hips back, and your chin finishes last.

At parties—I wouldn't suggest it for a dance floor—you can do the bumps as a climax to all the steps you want to do with your partner. The leader, if he's good, will give you intervals when you can turn to the gal you're with and go to town any way you like. Here in California almost everybody starts off with the Balboa Double Shuffle. The boy begins with feet together; steps slightly forward on his left heel and then all the way ahead on his right toe; while he's bringing his right foot back, his left heel catches his weight again so he won't lose the rhythm; then he hesitates just a second, with all his weight on his right foot. After that he hops and kicks—left foot down, right foot kicking back; right down and left back; and he repeats this once, and then he starts over again.

This takes exactly five seconds to do but probably a good five minutes to learn.

The Shag is a simplification of this. Hop on your left foot, hop on your right, kick with left and right quickly. The girl does it all backward.

The variety of things you can do while you're still in the circle is limitless. Of course there will be at least one time when the boy will drop to his knee, ruining a fine crease with corn meal, and the girl will put one finger on his head and truck around him. (This is called the Organ Grinder.) Then the girl will kneel in turn—but I warn you this is expensive on hose.

Praise Allah speaks for itself. It's an old gag gesture: Everybody double-times in, raises his arms above his head, and tries to touch his toes without bending his knees. Then the circle spreads out again.

You can all play leapfrog around the circle, if you like. It's hazardous, especially if the boy is six feet three and the girl has a tight skirt on. But then—

Eventually, though, you're going to be asked to Shine for the folks, and if it's on a public floor you'd better be ready. The spot will center on you and every one will point and yell. That means you and your partner have to truck on in alone and do a few steps while the circle shuffles in place and claps in tempo.

When this happens to you, improvise only if you know you're good. Otherwise take it easy and do just the steps you've learned completely. It's here that you can revive a few crusty but good numbers yourselves: the Carioca doesn't have to be done to a rumba. You just stand with your hips sticking out behind you, your knees straight, and put your foreheads together. Then you can shuffle or peck or truck around each other.

There's one beauty of a thing you can try if the boy's husky. The partners stand side by side, hands in loose ballroom formation: that is, boy's left and girl's right clasped in front, boy's right hand on girl's waist, girl's left hand on his right shoulder. He stands still while she jumps in front of him so that they face each other. Then he jumps and comes down almost squatting, feet spread apart and knees pointing out; and she jumps simultaneously, twisting in the air so that she comes down sitting on his right knee. The third and final jump brings him up standing, bending forward with feet together; and she lands just in front of his left foot, facing toward his right. The whole motion of her final jump carries her along into the familiar back dip, in which she rests on the boy's left arm and is held by his right.

It's a question of timing and balance, but if you do it correctly you'll get the cup for the evening and maybe even a whole basket of big red apples to give you more energy for tomorrow night's dance.

What Swing Really Does to People
by Benny Goodman

*Jitterbugs, Whackies, Alligators, Gather Round!—Your High
Priest of Hot Music Rends the Veil from a Modern Mystery*

I HAVE BEEN WATCHING a new brand of fun blossom in America. Whether you are old or young, rich or poor, its magic brings you out of yourself and puts you in a stomping, romping mood. This latest fad in revelry is swing music.

Swing music is to moderns what old-time barn tunes were to jigging farmers, and strumming guitars and crooning were to black feet shuffling in the delta mud.

But first let me say that swing music is not expressed in sexy dancing with cheek to jowl, though to swing musicians, swing dancers and singers, and even to the swing listeners, this rhythm provides an outlet for the exhibitionism in every one.

Just what, then, is swing music? It is amazing how many people ask that question.

Jorge Oller, classic guitarist, heard my swing band and said: "Swing music is a new kind of symphony."

Szigetti, concert violinist, listened and said that he recognized swing as modern and original music.

Dancers express swing by becoming absorbed in its rhythm. Musicians, dancers, and singers express it in exaggerated tunes, motions, and tones, but in their exaggeration is new and undiluted joy.

Swing started down in the cabins and shanties on the Mississippi, where the Negroes strummed guitars; then it reached New Orleans honky-tonks, where some musicians started tooting horns to accompany the guitars. The rhythm was out of the ordinary accepted rhythm. Ragtime, jazz would have been monotony in those swingy musicians' lives who played in barrel houses and on the

steamboats plowing the river and mingled with the Memphis Beale Street blues makers. As swing music crept along the river, other musicians in bands here and there craving individual expression began to throw in a flourish. The flourish instantly communicated the barrel-house mood, the fun mood, from the musician to the dancers and the listeners. The musician was swinging out a tune, a contagious tempo, and the crowd caught it. The musician was "in the groove."

Swing music naturally brought along with it a new language. Its dancers are known as jitterbugs who do the flittercut. The musicians are "cats" who *send, ride,* and *go out of the world.* Its listeners are "alligators" and "ickies"; its most ardent followers are whackies, etc.

Every one who likes swing music has a pet definition for it. Something like "an itching sensation you can't scratch," or "just a lot of noise," or maybe "something to drive you outa your mind." To those who understand it, swing is a "neat streak," a "hot lick."

But really to know what swing music is you have to feel it *inside.* If you feel swing, then you can't help expressing it, any more than you can help eating, sleeping, crying, or dancing. To test this out on yourself, next time you hear a swing band playing hot, swinging it out, agonizing, ask yourself, "Do I feel that?"

"If you feel it, your eyebrows curl, your lips twitch, your anklebones pump, and your toes throb. You know it's the real thing.

But if your answer is muffed and lost in a blast of brass and reed and savage beats which leave you with all your breath and not a goose bump on your skin, then you, of course, do not *feel* swing. You do not yet understand what it really means.

But do not give up, because swing music has been on its way since the first twig rapped against another and the first bird pecked rhythmically on a hollow log. The new thing, swing, is old as the very base of music.

Swing has to get inside you—and it will eventually, although it has to crawl in, through your ears, through vibration, through your pores. You eventually become saturated with it, hypnotized. And then, when a cat *sends* a tune "out of the world," it fills every crook and cranny of your soul and mind. You start to shag! You peel the apple! You beat it down! You ride to town—ride right out of the world with the sender.

Don't you believe me? Then ask an alligator. There are millions of alligators in the United States, from coast to coast, from Canada to the Florida Keys.

If you watch an alligator dance, you know then that swing is more than movement, more than command. It pushes, tears and rips and groans and snorts, once it gets inside you. It is more than sound. It's rhythm, the base of all music, and it is real enough to have girls and boys everywhere, with all their senses, "pecking" and "posing" and "grinding the apple" with a rapturous frenzy in their eyes. That frenzy is like the word "sterling" on silver. It means that, through and through, they feel swing music. Theirs is the new ecstasy.

Swing, cat. Swing, alligator. Swing, little peach and apple peeler!

Does this leave you just as you were before? Have you listened and watched and shaken your head and called for your check and sallied forth home saying, "So that's the thing they call swing! Well, take it away. It doesn't mean a thing to me?"

Listen. A clarinet goes toodle-oodle-oodle. (That's the agony pipe *sending*.) The brasses jam in. Millions of jitterbugs answer, "Let her ride!" "Beat it down!" They start the shag, the Big Apple, flittercutting all over the country. They are swing-happy.

If you listen and nothing within you answers, don't sign off, because if you can consider what the idea of swing means to others, that might help you.

Those who really think swing is all right will tell you there is nothing like swinging out a tune to put it in shape. Certainly, they contend, swinging it out will start your foot patting. Nobody can mind patting his foot.

If you feel you are becoming swing-conscious, then there is a chance of your becoming at any jam session (when all the cats send) an expert listener. You'll begin quivering at any measure and bobbing in your chair.

That is how the thing gets you. You start co-operating. Then you collaborate. The next thing you know, you're whacky!

Swing music is not like a horse race or a World Series, although the idea is definitely a sporting thing. You may have a fair idea of what Joe DiMaggio is likely to do to Carl Hubbell's ball, and what the horse from the Whitney stables may or may not do; but with a *swinging cat sending*, you can never tell where he's going—only that he is going "out of the world." He points his brass or his reed toward the ceiling and "rides." That much is certain when he stands up and *takes* the tune. But only the god of Swing knows where he's going and when he'll stop with it. The rider doesn't know himself. And the listeners don't care where he goes, but that they are going with him "out of the world."

You'll see the whackies and alligators crowd around the band. You'll see their frenzied happy eyes, jerking shoulders, and pumping ankles. All right! They're *beating it down* with the rider. They have gone "out of the world" with the sender. In their frenzy, the swing listeners express what is perhaps the real meaning of swing—the outlet for fear, inhibitions, dreams, hopes. "Out of the world" in their abandon, they are free from job-fear, worries, from nagging friends and duty-calling love.

Swing music has gradually taken its place in the present. The reason for its appeal, some serious-minded folk contend, is that it offers, in its jamming of sound, release from the pressure of depression and war clouds, from the wail of hard times.

Is that the meaning of swing music and swing dancing to you? Is that what taking part in the Big Apple means to you? When you dance the Big Apple, do you beat out the pectin of emotion and thereby soothe your nerves and your frenzy and feel better adjusted to modern life?

You've got a right to your own opinion.

I know that when as a kid I had to discontinue my expensive lessons on the clarinet when my father was hit by a truck, I found solace in just playing on what I then called the "agony pipe." I improvised, sometimes thinking of the installments I owed the mail-order house where I had obtained the instrument. I was sad, thinking that now I could never reach my goal—to become a symphony man.

I took a job in an orchestra on an excursion boat. I began expressing everything I felt, the current of my heart and mind, on my clarinet. I had not learned to interpret meanings and emotions in my classical study. But in feeling I was portraying the essence of real music, true symphony, in my own way.

Now, a musician swings when he improvises . . . when he expresses, in his own way, his own interpretation of a tune, which is a feeling, an emotion.

Always swing music holds a natural, primitive beat, rhythm. Always it has stimulation, like music accompanying worship. In its own beat and bleating it has real pathos, as real as anything written by Mozart, Beethoven, Debussy. But I don't hold an academic angle toward swing music.

This is my angle:

For instance, "My Gal Sal" is an all-right number. But what are you going to do after you play it seven hundred times? Musicians, weary and bored, take it to town for fun, try to do something different with it, play around and lick it around, and first thing you know, one has taken it "out of the world."

Some say swing music is dying. I don't know. But I do know that all over the country more young musicians are playing swing. The process of taking trifling music of popular tunes and giving it musical substances of their own emotional understanding and individual invention and warmth is too much fun to all concerned.

Swing and jam sessions are really contagious. They are impromptu battles of wit and origination, always a game with each musician trying to outswing the other.

Swing is not just a stunt. It is serious music and has a place anywhere, because it offers a field of self-expression no other music offers. It has traveled a long way, up the Mississippi, from coast to coast, and into Carnegie Hall where a piano, guitar, bass drums, four saxophones, two trombones, three trumpets, and a clarinet beat it down, made it jam.

Where is swing music going? I don't know. Only, as long as the millions of people go "out of the world" with it I think it will continue to be a part of music and therefore is here to stay.

Stalin Talks About Hitler

an interview by
Princess Catherine Radziwill

*A Momentous Revelation of Russia's Aims
and Strategy, from the Dictator Himself!*

STALIN CHUCKLED.
He had just handed me a Reuters news dispatch—
one of a flood of such dispatches—in which the Nazi
government sought to convince the world that its hesitation about repeating its Austrian feat in Czechoslovakia
was due not to fear of any one but to Hitler's wisdom.

"Do you believe that?" he asked.

"Certainly not."

"Well, you are right not to believe it," he agreed. Then
he chuckled again.

I glanced once more at the dispatch. The final sentence
read: "Europe owed it solely to the *Fuehrer,* with his
splendid nerve and his boundless love of peace, that this
dangerous game did not result in a catastrophe."

This time I chuckled, too. I had just come from Prague
—where I had gone to study the Czech situation for
Liberty—and I knew first hand just how ridiculous this
explanation of Hitler's background really was.

"What Hitler was really afraid of," continued the Man
of the Kremlin, "was that Russia would move. He was
thinking only of himself, not of the peace of Europe."

That this was true no informed person could doubt.

The Czechoslovakian crisis is a thing of the past, but
the lesson to be learned from it is definitely of the present
and the future: the peace of Europe, and perhaps of the
world, was maintained solely because a direct hint was
given from Moscow to the Czechoslovakian government
to fear no one and to call its troops to the colors, because,
no matter how much Hitler might boast, Germany could
not afford to lose its prestige by rushing into a war which
it would be by no mean sure to win. For Stalin, the best
informed man in Europe, knew that the German army was
not yet in a condition which would allow it to resist a
well equipped enemy.

"Hitler," said Stalin, as if in answer to my question,
"is not such an ass as some people think. He would like
nothing better than a close alliance with Russia."

An alliance between Communism and Fascism! A
Moscow-Berlin axis! Here was news indeed. Yet who
could doubt that a friendly understanding with the man
in front of me was today the main objective of every
European government?

"Will he get it," I ventured—"that alliance?"

"Russia doesn't need alliances," Stalin replied. "Russia
can take care of itself."

He stopped for a few moments; then went on:

"I love Russia, and no one knows what I suffer when
I hear it slandered and maligned. Peter the Great also
loved it, and made out of it an immense empire. Everybody admits this today, but everybody seems to have
forgotten how much blood he shed before he succeeded in
his endeavor. Nothing great can be done without blood
flowing, because blood is the only thing which can cement
the fragments of a tottering edifice. And it is not so long

ago that the entire structure of Russia was tottering and about to fall. It had to be saved. I hope I saved it, but I don't know. . . . I wish I knew." . . .

As he spoke, he rose from his seat, a magnificent, colossal figure, a man profoundly convinced of the justice of his cause, determined to restore to his country the place from which she had been banished.

"Napoleon the Third once said, 'The Empire is peace,' " he went on. "I say the same thing, but more truthfully. Soviet Russia means peace, wants peace, will and can enforce peace. Soviet Russia is not aggressive, it hates aggression, but it can meet it and defeat it. It will remain faithful to its treaties, without immediately resorting to war in order to enforce them."

Watching this man—so strong, so poised—I realized more clearly than I ever had before that Soviet Russia holds the key to the entire European situation. She holds it because she is the great unknown; because, so far, no one has been able to discover the real strength of her army or the intentions of its leaders.

Stalin remains the man of mystery, a sort of Old Man of the Mountain.

What will Stalin do? What can Stalin do?

These are the questions which one finds on the lips of almost every European politician one talks with.

Not so long ago the annual maneuvers of the Red Army were countermanded without any reason being given for this unexpected decision. An English publication went so far as to say that it was a proof that Russia as a military force had ceased to exist. Stalin was asked to contradict this statement, but he merely smiled.

"Why contradict it?" he asked. "It serves our purpose. We do not want our enemies to know whether we are strong or weak; they will discover it themselves if they ever dare attack us."

This is the mystery which weighs on the minds of politicians all over Europe and overshadows every decision they find themselves called upon to make.

How can Hitler attempt to sweep Czechoslovakia off the map as he swept Austria off, if he is not sure that Russia won't attack him from the rear? How can France think of fighting Hitler, if it has reasons to dread Stalin with his Red troops rushing to the *Fuehrer's* rescue? How can England afford to become entangled in a quarrel which is not her own, if her hopes of being friendly with the new Russia might be dashed to the ground by any untoward move she might make?

Of course Hitler would like nothing better than a close alliance with Stalin. And, in spite of Stalin's cryptic remark about not needing alliances, he may get one. Lately the *Fuehrer* has turned all his diplomatic attention upon Russia, and is now trying to negotiate an accord with the Soviet government, which Stalin has really wanted to complete a long time and has simply awaited a favorable moment to do so.

This does not mean that Hitler loves Stalin, or that Stalin sympathizes with Hitler, but both men seem to understand that together they might achieve a start on the road toward the peace which they both need.

Russia knows, and I know, that what she needs most at the present day is reconstruction—internal reconstruction," said Stalin. "Within an incredibly short time, as you will see for yourself, Russia will again be prosperous and rank among the most industrially successful nations in the world.

"People call me a monster, but this does not trouble me. Napoleon was called a monster. So was our own Peter. So were all the men who made something out of nothing. I have always thought of my country, even during the dark days when I was an exile in Siberia, or a prisoner in a dungeon. I still always think of her, and because I do, I shall see to it that, while ready to fight—which I can safely say no other country in Europe is at present—she does not get into any fight but uses her power to maintain peace everywhere."

Stalin paused as if to let this momentous statement sink in; then he added: "That is a fact of which I am proud, especially when I remember the negligible quantity Russia was but a short time ago, and how the tables have been turned to Russia's advantage."

My thoughts flew back at once to the recent situation in Czechoslovakia, and the Dictator's must have, too, for he went on to speak of Hitler in much plainer terms than the head of one government usually employs in speaking of the head of another.

"Surely this means something," he said. "Hitler was all ready to march into Czechoslovakia, his advanced posts had reached its frontiers, when he was made to feel that one step farther might mean Russian soldiers facing German ones, and you saw what happened. Yet no threat was uttered, no menace was used. The existence of Russia simply became to him a serious fact to be taken into serious consideration. He knows that a conflict with us might mean his own ruin."

"If this is so," I asked, "why did not Soviet Russia use the same tactics when poor Austria was invaded?"

"Because, for one thing, there was no treaty or understanding between Austria and Soviet Russia; and, for another, Russia did so much in the past for Austria and was rewarded with such dire ingratitude, it would have been folly to rush to her rescue."

"So Soviet Russia means peace?" I mused.

"Undoubtedly," was his unhesitating reply. "And Soviet Russia is strong enough to prevent war from breaking out again to disturb humanity."

Stalin made his last statement with a justifiable pride. Thanks to him, Russia has once more become a determining factor in European politics, such as it was during the reign of Alexander III. Thanks to him, the old Realm of the Ruriks is again coming into its own, because Russia now, such as it has become, can be declared outside the pale of civilization, together with those who rule it, but it can no longer be ignored, and its voice must be taken into account when questions of international politics arise.

Fortunately Stalin realizes extremely well that Russia and he himself have everything to lose if they become entangled in European complications. They will never allow themselves to get embroiled in other people's quarrels or dissensions.

Russia thinks only of herself, and Stalin thinks only of Russia. So today he stands the best defender the world has against the criminality of another war which would sweep away the last remnants of our seemingly doomed civilization. One question still troubled me.

"But what do you make of Spain and China? Doesn't their fate disturb humanity?"

"This does not concern Soviet Russia," was the astounding reply. "Only Russia concerns Russia. What goes on elsewhere doesn't interest her beyond a certain point. Soviet Russia won't fight for the advantage of its neighbors and competitors. But it will fight tooth and nail whenever its interests are threatened.

"Russia is working at its own reconstruction. Russia is on the road to become the greatest nation in the world, and so long as I am responsible for its welfare, I will not allow it to deviate from that road. It is not a road that leads to war, in spite of the fact that war holds no terror for Russia."

Once more Stalin paused as if to emphasize his own awareness of the significance of his words.

"Nor for her rulers," he added grimly.

Then, quite unexpectedly, he chuckled again.

Church,
State,
and Sex
by Benito Mussolini

HUMAN RELATIONS TODAY are beset with all sorts of intricate theories. Many great scientists and philosophers have investigated human behavior and conduct and have proposed the most drastic changes in our social relations. Institutions which have been part of the very structure of civilization for centuries have been attacked as wholly erroneous, and we are daily being presented with new fads and strange palliatives as remedies for real or imagined ills of our present-day civilization. So prevalent has been the showering of ideas for our social relations that they have carried with them numerous offshoots from what has given to life its potential backbone. And in the speculative realm scientists and philosophers have dabbled in numerous schemes and perhaps more than all in that which concerns the social relations of mankind.

Right now, in bad times, the scientists and philosophers have been seriously occupied with economic relations; but whether times are good or bad, there is never lack of discussion of the social conduct of mankind and more especially of the sex conduct. The trend has been to attack the whole institution of Christian marriage and to substitute for it various forms of union with broader liberties and a decrease of those responsibilities which have for centuries and in practically all civilization been lifelong.

As a statesman, it is fitting that I should inquire into the probable effects of some of the new departures from long-established custom. I first would view them from the standpoint of their influence on the state. There are those who say that the individual comes before the state and that governments are established to serve the individual. But whether it is the government that serves the individual or the individual that serves the government is an idle question, as the two are so profoundly interwoven in common interests that service to one ends up by being service to the other. In other words, we would be chasing the question in an endless circle about a bush if we should ever undertake to fix absolutely whether the one or the other is the aim of the nation.

And so, in dealing with the question of the relation between the sexes, whatever policy would result in national good would also result in good to the individual. Conversely, what would be a sound benefit to the individual would also eventually achieve a benefit for the nation. Therefore, in the examination of the problem of the proper relation between the sexes, it is almost quite safe to say that if we were to take care of the interests of the state, we would, in the long run, take care also of the interests of the individual.

Life is continuous and must go on. It must also be so with a nation if that nation is to endure and have a heritage. As life is transmitted from the father and mother to the child, so the nation must transmit its being if it is to live. Nations beget nations as well as human beings. To appreciate this fact we have but to examine the vast new empires come from the loins of mother nations and nurtured and cradled by them, later to assume the form of sovereign states and to take their places in the concourse of nations as complete entities attaining their full national stature.

The nation has the responsibility of handing on to posterity that which it has achieved and especially those civilizing attributes which have made eternal some of the nations of antiquity and even many others up until modern times. In the same way the individual has a like responsibility of transmitting the sum total of life reached during his lifetime. What progress the individual may see in a lifetime may be infinitesimal compared with the ages which mankind has lived, but progress there is, and it is for the individual to hand on what he has compassed to his posterity.

The responsibility of both the individual and the state is therefore very forcibly brought home to us and the interdependence of the one upon the other is notably self-evident. Our people, then, must be indeed alive to the necessity of national continuation and national expansion. If the state is to be great and to remain great, it must have a strong and virile people ready to face the responsibilities incumbent upon them for the preservation of the race.

This is a day when men and women preach the shirking of the duty of begetting sons and daughters. Strength is not built on the apathy of the sluggard, and national strength is not achieved in a life of listless ease. No nation is destined to leave its mark on civilization if it fails to step forth and take up the duty of a great nation not alone by living, but by living to strengthen and expand through the utilization of all its attributes, until its whole spirit is handed on in an unending stream from generation to generation with progressive force and virility. Those nations which have failed to strengthen and expand have passed away and are forgotten, while those which took up the burden with virile zeal and expanded are today the great models of all time.

There is therefore need, above all, for a well ordered family life. This is still the basis of the state and will continue to be the basis of the state for all time. In it we find not alone the nucleus for the units of the nation, but also the crystallizing point of all the cherished human emotions and passions. Any influence which tends to impair its integrity tends also to impair the power of the state.

The nation must have a sense of family integrity. We all know too well the arguments in support of family disintegration, but beyond the immediate selfish interests of wife and husband there are the superior interests of the offspring and their raising to the full height of their capabilities beyond the state of infancy. He who evades the duty upon him to create a family evades a responsibility akin to that which calls him to the colors in time of national danger. It is a twofold duty, imposed not alone by God and the nation but also by the call of life itself.

We who have been endowed with life are endowed with a power to carry on life and "to seek it more abundantly." We are here to receive it, live it, and pass it on. This is nature's own mandate upon us, and for that mandate she has filled us with an ever-present urge to beget children. What manner of woman is she who within herself desires to evade the duty of having children? We all know well how it is the culmination of a good woman's greatest and dearest desire to bear the child she can love and cherish and bring to capable manhood. It is as true today as in the centuries of antiquity that, blessed with a large family, she can proudly gather them about her and say with that dutiful Roman mother, "These are my jewels."

The good woman does not desire to shirk her responsibility, but instead is saturated with eagerness to respond valiantly to nature's call to produce her kind.

The responsibility of the man is even more marked than that of the woman, even though it is less immediate and founded more on social ties than on animal instinct. Despite the waves of feminism and the successful ripples of cries for sex equality, the man must remain by nature and by circumstance the answerable authority for the creation of the family. Neither in his own interest nor in the interest of the state can he live his life riotously. There are compulsive controls and there is necessary discipline for physical and sociological reasons. And, when all the factors are counted up and the results and aims reckoned, we must arrive at the point of recognizing that the virile and expanding state is best blessed by the institution of an unbroken marriage where the one family is kept inviolate and integral, strong in the fact of its own solidity.

The will of the man can more than often impose that integrity, for the woman fortunate in bringing to life a cluster of offspring is not prone to seek change. Her joy more than recompenses her for the trials and difficulties which keeping the family intact entails.

On the man again devolves the duty of accepting the large family. For him deliberately to set about preventing the creation of that family is, as I have said, little short of evasion of a national duty in times of stress.

Upon the woman who desires children and fails for one reason or another to bear them, the sympathy of the world must be bestowed; but upon the man or woman who refuses to shoulder the responsibility of them and deliberately contrives to prevent their conception and birth, nothing can be bestowed but the most vehement condemnation.

The great though long untenable opposition to the large family has been based on economic considerations. It is contended that it is much better to have few children and educate them right than to have many and be forced to deprive them of the advantages they would have had if the economic condition of the family had been less meager.

The cry of national poverty is not new; and it has already been proclaimed as certain to outgrow and outdistance the increase in the population. Malthus over a century ago calculated that the population was bound to increase faster than the food supply, but if any theory has been exploded, that theory has been completely disintegrated and annulled, for even the workman enjoys today, in all the world, far greater economic advantages than he ever dreamed of a century ago.

The cry of "bringing up a few children in the right way" sounds pleasant and beautiful, but it is neither sound nor praiseworthy.

It denies a fundamental requirement of character in that within a large family the give-and-take of life is more profoundly embedded into the child's character than in a household where he is coddled by the excessive love bestowed on an only boy or girl by the foolish filial extravagance of a fond parent.

The friction and conflict among brothers and sisters steel the child for the greater battle which awaits him in the greater world of his future career.

Returning to the economic plea for a small family, this cry is constantly recurrent. Let us remember that it is the selfsame cry that was heard a century ago, and yet practically every country has doubled its population within the last half century and some have tripled the number of their inhabitants. Even more compelling is the fact that the standard of life, instead of becoming lower as population increased, has become higher—and even to the point at which it may be said that the workingman of today enjoys luxuries that were enjoyed only by the nobles of a century ago.

To all those suggestions which include a slackening of the family ties, we must turn an unsympathetic ear. Those who would relax the rigidity of a family régime, would likewise relax the duty toward the state. Widespread and easy divorce throws the great basic institution on which the state rests seriously out of balance and results in confusing the great forces on which the nation must depend for its continued virility and prowess. Companionate marriage again is just an attempt at a royal road to evasion of the responsibilities of parenthood. It is not willing to face boldly the ups and downs entailed by the choice of mates and the greater burden of passing on the life that has been given to us to others of our own creation. There ought not to be "ifs" and "ands" in accepting this charge.

The state, nature, and the soul require that life be transmitted or death will be the final mark of the emptiness of our existence.

Again we must not be completely overcome by the trend of some modern thinking—that in the marriage relation there is merely a thankless duty.

There are joys and contentment which family alone can give, and, beyond it all, there is the inherent pride in offspring which remains alive in all those who have achieved true maturity.

If we permit this life to pass from us without having tried to continue the eternal flame, our lives will have been lived in vain, for with both individual and nation, and even above all, there is that great and fundamental purpose running through all life—namely, that it shall hold on forever, clinging and grasping for eternity through myriad generations, and unbroken until the unending infinite.

When we think of careers and the glories of the world, we must realize that we should achieve them in vain did we fail to pass on to another generation the thread of life which was intrusted to us on our entry into this life.

How Hitler
Has Changed the Bible

by Maxwell J. Flagg

Here, Word by Word, Is Evidence of His Astonishing Move to Make Holy Writ Fit Nazi Ideas . . . Read These Parallel Passages for Yourself

HAVING FAILED TO unite the Protestant Church in Germany, Hitler's Bishop, Ludwig Mueller, now attempts to revise the words of Jesus. Unable to purge the opposition, he purges the Bible. His aim, he frankly admits, is not to translate but to "Germanize' the Scriptures. The first objective of his purge is the Sermon on the Mount. The revised Sermon on the Mount is

offered to "his compatriots in the Third Reich by their Bishop" under the title, German Words of God.

The *Reichsbischof*, or *"Reibi,"* justifies the venture by claiming that the Germans have become "alienated" from the teachings of Christ partly by the "dogmatism" of the Church, partly because Martin Luther's language is "obsolete." Every people must "reinterpret religious values and truths in terms of its idiosyncrasies."

He proceeds to defend Jesus against His enemies in the National Socialist camp. Nazi extremists wish to eliminate the Bible entirely and to re-establish the ancient Germanic gods. The Reibi patiently attempts to show these radical compatriots the error of their ways.

"One often hears," he asseverates, "the expression 'Christ was a Jew.' " The Reibi evades the genealogy of the Lord; His teachings, he contends, are not Jewish. "Christianity did not grow out of Judaism; on the contrary, Christianity evolved from the battle against Judaism, so that Christian and Jew are to each other as fire is to water."

"It must be admitted," the Reibi concedes, "that church tradition, the order of the service, many church hymns preserve so-called Judaisms—that is to say, Jewish words and expressions. But the National Socialist awakening which we have experienced has opened our eyes to the impossibility of retaining words and expressions so alien to our nature. With the reformation of our national life, all that is un-German will disappear of its own accord, even from the ecclesiastic vocabulary."

The idea of translating Jesus' words into colloquial language is by no means new. If Realmbishop Mueller had contented himself with a translation into modern German, there would be little reason for quarreling with him. But he has not. He deliberately alters the obvious intention of the Sermon on the Mount; he adds and omits passages to suit the philosophy of his party. The figure that emerges is no longer Jesus of Nazareth but Jesus of Naziland. He is no longer the Prince of Peace, but Realmleader Jesus, bearing a suspicious resemblance to Realmleader Hitler and Realmbishop Mueller.

Let us discover how Hitler's bishop rewrites the Sermon on the Mount:

St. Matthew, Chapter V

King James Version	Nazi Version
3. Blessed are the poor in spirit: for theirs is the kingdom of heaven.	Blessed is he who trusts in God with childlike simplicity he has communion with God.
4. Blessed are they that mourn: for they shall be comforted.	*Blessed is he who bears his sorrow manfully*; he will find the strength never to lose courage nor to abandon himself to despair.
5. Blessed are the meek: for they shall inherit the earth.	Blessed is he who practices good comradeship; he will make his way in the world.

The Realmbishop's Jesus preaches not meekness but race pride! After the next few verses, which do not differ materially from the original, we come to:

9. Blessed are the peacemakers: for they shall be called the children of God.	Blessed are *they who keep peace with their compatriots*; they fulfill the will of God.

The Jesus who goose-steps through the pages of Realmbishop Mueller addresses himself not to all men but primarily, if not solely, to Mueller's racial compatriots. It is obvious that the Reibi does not approve of peacemakers who desire to maintain peace among all children of God irrespective of race and nationality.

Verse 21 is the crucial test. How will he meet it?

Jesus reiterates in His sermon the commandment: "Thou shalt not kill." The Jesus of Realmbishop Mueller objects neither to the death penalty nor to killing in battle. He does not object to killing at all, except under certain conditions.

21. Ye have heard that it was said by them of old time, Thou shalt not kill; and whosoever shall kill shall be in danger of the judgment.	*You shall not commit assassination*; such a murderer is guilty and must be condemned to death.

Jesus exhorts us to refrain even from being angry with a "brother" without cause. The Reibi applies the injunction only to the "folk comrade," the racial compatriot, the party member.

Softening the Biblical "Thou shalt not commit adultery" (verse 27), the Realmbishop asserts: "*A pious tradition among your people condemns adultery.*"

Jesus continues (verse 28): "But I say unto you, That whosoever looketh on a woman to lust after her hath committed adultery with her already in his heart."

The bishop limits his condemnation to those "who lust after a woman *who belongs to another man.*" Obviously he considers it perfectly proper to lust after a woman whose affections are still unmortgaged.

Between verses 31 and 32 the Realmbishop injects a National Socialist sermon on marriage and divorce:

31 and 32. It hath been said "Whosoever shall put away his wife, let him give her a writing of divorcement; But I say unto you, That whosoever shall put away his wife, saving for the cause of fornication, causeth her to commit adultery: and whosoever shall marry her that is divorced committeth adultery.

Have a care and labor that your family life is genuine and truthful, in that way you serve your people; if your family life is false and untruthful, you injure your people.

A marriage which has become untrue is not a genuine marriage.

Adultery gives you the right to divorce; but do not resort lightheartedly to divorce. It affects not only you but the community. And even if a marriage has been annulled according to the external letter of the law, if inwardly something is wrong in the sight of God, you are still an adulterer.

The bishop disagrees with the injunction (verse 34) "Swear not at all." He modifies it: "You must keep God's honor, your people's, and your own so high and sacred that *you will not swear an oath over a trivial matter.*"

Shall a Nazi turn the other cheek?

"Yes," says Jesus. "No," says the Realmbishop.

38. Ye have heard that it hath been said, An eye for an eye, and a tooth for a tooth:

In popular parlance it is still said: "What you do unto me that I will do unto you," or an "eye for an eye, a tooth for a tooth." That is in accordance with natural human instincts.

39. But I say unto you, That ye resist not evil: but whosoever shall smite thee on thy right cheek, turn to him the other also.

But I say unto you: It is better to live with your compatriots in such a manner that you get along together amicably.

The communion of your people is a high and sacred weal for which you must make sacrifices.

Therefore go as far as you can in reconciling your adversary before you and he are completely at odds.

If your comrade strikes you in the face in his excitement it is not always proper to return the blow at once. It is more manly to maintain superior composure. Probably your comrade will then be ashamed.

In Chapter VI, verse 2, the bishop eliminates the reference to the synagogue. He then proceeds to present an abbreviated version of the Lord's Prayer:

9 to 13. Our Father which art in Heaven, Hallowed be thy name. Thy kingdom come. Thy will be done in earth, as it is in heaven. Give us this day our daily bread. And forgive us our debts, as we forgive our debtors. And lead us not into temptation, but deliver us from evil: For thine is the kingdom, and the power, and the glory, for ever. Amen.

Our Father in eternity Thy truth be sacred to us. Rule thou in our hearts. Thy will be done. Give us our daily bread. Forgive us our debt As we, too, wish to forgive our debtors. Strengthen us in temptation, and make us free from the bane of evil! For thine is the Realm, And the Power, and the Glory in Eternity.   Amen.

It is difficult to escape the conclusion that the Realm (Reich) in the mind of the Reibi is not the kingdom of heaven but the Third Reich of Hitler!

The Reibi agrees with the Author of the Sermon on the Mount that "no man can serve two masters." It is obvious that *he* serves only one—*der Fuehrer.*

He tells his compatriots (like the Bible) that "whatsoever ye would that men should do to you, do ye even so to them." "Embattled comrades," the Reibi assures them, "will accompany the German Christian through the strait and narrow gate." There is a warning against "false prophets, which come in sheep's clothing," but nothing is said of translators in bishops' clothing who deliberately distort the spirit of Jesus.

The copy from which our extracts are taken is the fourth edition of *Deutsche Gottesworte*. It is not copy-righted in the United States and is probably intended only for the Reibi's compatriots.

To give the Reibi his due, some of his interpretations, while prosaic, are rational enough. He loses nothing of the Sermon on the Mount—except its divinity, its universality, and its beauty.

The Price of Peace

by Neville Chamberlain

*An Authorized Publication of His Views, from
Papers and Addresses of England's Prime Minister*

MY FATHER AND brother had qualifications far greater than I for the highest office of Premiership, but I look upon my position today as a continuation, perhaps I might say a consummation, of their lifework.

I entered on my duties at an age when most people would think of retiring from active work.

I do not think it is the long hours or the hard work that form the most alarming aspect of the duties of a Prime Minister.

It is rather the knowledge that in all the perplexities and the problems which rise up day after day in front of any Government in these troublous times the ultimate responsibility of the final decision must rest upon the shoulders of the Prime Minister.

No major point of policy can be decided, no real fateful step can be taken without the assent, either active or passive, of the Prime Minister, and if things go wrong he can never escape the reflection: I might have prevented this if I had thought or acted differently.

I believe it is that ultimate and inescapable responsibility which is the real root of the anxieties which have worn down the energies of our recent Prime Ministers.

I have the good fortune to be able to count upon the assistance of a lady whose affection and understanding have for many years made all my troubles seem light.

She has shared all my plans; she has been privy to all my secrets; she has never divulged one.

She has rejoiced in my successes, she has encouraged me in my disappointments, she has guided me with her counsel, she has warned me off dangerous courses, and she has never allowed me to forget the humanity that underlies all politics.

I did not seek to enter the House of Commons when I was nearly fifty years of age because I had idle time on my hands that I did not know how to fill up. I went because I was brought up in a house where public service seemed to be a natural part of a man's life.—And I should be unhappy if I were deprived of the opportunity of doing public service so long as I have power to perform it.

I was reading a very interesting book the other day.

The writer, after discussing the credibility of various theories on future life, expressed his opinion that the really incredible thing was life itself, and that the greatest miracle was man's existence in the world.

I suppose I have got so used to man being here that I can hardly imagine the world without him.

But I know what is a really incredible thing, and that is that *I* should be occupying the office which at present I hold.

I remember that Mr. Gladstone used to say that the politician who entered the House of Commons after he was forty could no more make a success of his career than a lady of the same age who started to be a ballet dancer.

I suppose the popular view would be that Cabinet Ministers, like generals, should be young; but there is something to be said on the other side.

I am tempted to recall a Chinese proverb—at least it was said to be Chinese—that used to be quoted by a famous admiral in defense of old men in office. This is the proverb: "One decrepit camel still bears the burden of many asses."

I always think that a man's character and principles are influenced very largely by his upbringing.

Children generally model themselves on the standards that they see adopted by their elders, especially if they know that those elders are generally respected.

I was brought up in a household where we were taught the importance of telling the truth even though we got into trouble in doing so. Perhaps that is a reason why I have developed this habit of plainly saying what I believe to be true.

Another rule of conduct which was also impressed on me when I was young what that you should never promise anything that you did not think you were able to perform.

But there was something else in the example of my father's life which impressed me very deeply when I was a young man, and which has greatly influenced me since I took up a public career. It was my observance of his deep sympathy with the working classes and his intense desire to better their lot which inspired me with an ambition to do something in my turn to afford better help to the working people and better opportunities for the enjoyment of life.

At first I thought anything I could do in that direction would be done locally in serving on the Council of my native city; but when afterwards I decided to enter upon national politics, the background was still the same, and I have not yet lost sight of it.

To me, the very idea that the hard-won savings of our people, which ought to be devoted to the alleviation of suffering, to the opening out of fresh institutions and recreations, to the care of the old, to the development of the minds and bodies of the young—the thought that these savings should have to be dissipated upon the construction of weapons of war is hateful and damnable.

Yet I cannot shut my eyes to the fact that under the present conditions of the world we have no alternative but to go on with it, because it is the very breath of our British being, our freedom itself, that is at stake.

Do not let us forget that this freedom has come down to us from the past, bought for us at a price. If we wish to keep it we must pay the interest on that price in each succeeding generation.

We pass no judgment upon the political systems of other countries, but neither Fascism nor Communism is in harmony with our temperament and creed.

And yet, whatever differences there may be between us and other nations on that subject, do not forget that we are all members of the human race and subject to the like passions and affections and fears and desires.

There must be something in common between us if we can find it, and perhaps by our very aloofness from the rest of Europe we may have some special part to play as conciliator and mediator.

An ancient historian once wrote of the Greeks that they had made gentle the life of the world. I do not know whether in these modern days it is possible for any nation to emulate the example of the Greeks, but I can imagine no nobler ambition for an English statesman than to win the same tribute for his own country. I believe in liberty. Without it there can be no true democracy.

For the preservation of democracy I would fight myself, and I believe the people of this country would fight.

Were Britain attacked, she would know how to defend herself—as she always has done in the past.

But our present program of defense is the surest way of avoiding the dread necessity of fighting at all.

Happiness In Our Time

by Maurice Maeterlinck

A Distinguished Refugee Speaks to a World Torn by War

MARCUS TERENTIUS VARRO, antiquity's greatest encyclopedist, tells us that the problem of happiness is susceptible to two hundred and eighty different solutions, almost every one of which has been defended by some sage.

We must believe that none of these solutions is correct, since we are not yet happy.

There is no solution, no universal prescription, because happiness is not the same for all men and is found only within ourselves.

If God asked you one day: "What do you wish to make you happy?"—what would you reply? Reflect before answering. Possibly your wish may be realized in this world or the next. What you ask is what you are, what you will become, what you will be.

Say to any man, giving him a serious look: "You are not happy, isn't that so?" He will be disconcerted and won't immediately answer you.

Imagine today your happiness or your paradise. Dream it as delicious and magnificant as possible. Suppose that a God should make it a reality and install you in it definitively. Before the year ends you will be longing to leave it to see if you may not be happier elsewhere.

Count the good and bad moments of your life. Forget the misfortunes and you will be happy, forget the happiness and you will be one to be pitied.

One accustoms oneself to unhappiness more quickly than one had expected. One doesn't accustom oneself to happiness, because it is brief and because during the little time one possesses it one doesn't know what it is.

Happiness is but a single day that it does not even completely fill. Then night falls and only memory remains —to become immortal. Our imagination is very *limited* when it deals with happiness. It doesn't go far, it doesn't see far, save when it dwells upon unhappiness.

Man has not yet learned to be happy.

One should learn to be happy as one should learn how to die. Most men live only not to die.

Let us learn to hope without hope. That is the last secret of our happiness.

What I Saw in Europe's Last Hours of Peace

by Cornelius Vanderbilt, Jr.

*Stirring!—A Close-up of Mighty Men and
Humble Hordes at Grips with Destiny*

I WISH THERE were some way of wiring these words for sound. For how otherwise, without the accompaniment of roaring planes, thundering tanks, and troop trains, the thud of marching feet and the sharp bark of orders, can I explain the nature of those last hours?

Ever since May, when *Liberty* anticipating trouble across the Atlantic, had sent me on a "scouting trip," I had been sticking my nose into spots where sometimes others didn't think it ought to be. From the Scandinavian countries I had gone to Danzig and Poland, Soviet Russia, Hungary, Yugoslavia, Slovakia, Bulgaria, Albania, Rumania, as far as Turkey, then doubled back through Greece, Syria, Egypt, Italy, Spain, and France, ending up with a several-weeks motor tour of Germany, Belgium, and the north coast of Africa. General Gamelin had sent me through the Maginot Line; General Brauchitz through the Siegfried.

Thrice I'd entered Danzig Free State. In Warsaw I'd lunched with Josef Beck and General Smigly-Rydz and received their assurances that Poland could hold out indefinitely against any enemy. The kindly general had sent me by air to visit Lodz, Cracow, and Lwow, where Poland had her major planes concentrated. The officers had done everything to let me see as much as was militarily possible—and I hadn't been greatly impressed.

I had come into Athens, Greece, just in time to meet democratic King George and Prime Minister Metaxas. We had played charades after dinner, and together, with a tablecloth over their heads, they'd come into the room, these two rulers of ancient Greece, representing a donkey—which was their name for Hitler!

In Cairo I'd cocktailed with the young King of Egypt and been given his word of honor that Hitler or Mussolini would never control the Suez Canal. Egypt was prepared to sink boats in it first.

And in Russia Molotov had assured me that as long as he remained in power Hitler would never gain a toehold—but that if war came to Europe Stalin would win in the end because every nation would have revolution.

In Italy I'd attended a concert at Pompeii with King Victor Emmanuel and the Prince, and listened to the applause they received from 30,000 people there in the neon-lit arena—applause far greater than that which greeted Mussolini and Ciano. And for a week I'd wandered up and down Italy and talked with dozens of people who all said—quietly, of course—that they would rather burn Rome than see her go to war for Hitler.

Down in Spain I'd rambled ten days; chatted with Franco in a barbershop in Madrid, and with his new Cabinet of generals, and looked with apprehension upon the large number of German officers and troops still there.

And on the French Riviera I'd had a pleasant evening with Wallie and Edward, and heard him prophesy war.

In Copenhagen, Denmark, I had enjoyed a horseback ride with the King of Denmark, who feared German annexation of Denmark. In Brussels the King had asked me to dine with him, and afterward had traced what he thought Hitler might do if war ever broke out again. But Belgium was well prepared for any onslaught, and the King prophesied nothing would happen.

I dined my first evening in France out at Chantilly with American Ambassador William C. Bullitt, his daughter Anne, Mrs. James Roosevelt, the President's mother, and Anne and Johnny Roosevelt, his youngest son. Upon reaching Paris I called up an American girl I knew and asked her to go "slumming" with me.

"Look at the women—they're all crying," she said, as we sat in the dining room of the Gare de l'Est, one of Paris' largest railway stations, the evening of August 17. All around us I then noticed the reddened eyes of the women and the brave little faces of the children as husbands, brothers, fathers, and sweethearts silently swept out of Paris during the quietest, most secret mobilization I have ever witnessed.

Excusing myself for a moment, I sent *Liberty* the following telegram:

FRANCE SECRETLY MOBILIZING STOP GERMANY RUSSIA NEGOTIATING STOP SOMETHING MUST BE UP

Next morning at eight I was awakened by a pleasant voice over the telephone: "Mr. Vanderbilt, the interview you have been requesting with M. Daladier will be granted at eleven o'clock this morning."

Now, I happened to remember that Daladier was out of town, at the seashore, so I asked if I could postpone the "interview" until later in the afternoon. The man I was told to ask for was M. Bressi. There were two Bressis, I learned; both apparently held unimportant positions.

At 4:30 P. M. I presented myself, however, at Premier Daladier's office. After giving my name I had scarcely sat down when two gentlemen stood before me. One of them displayed a gold badge. Instantly I was escorted out into the street, down to the Quai d'Orsay (Foreign Office), and up to the office of Pierre Bressi, Chief of Intelligence!

Out came M. Bressi, bowing. He led me into a small room and he came to the point very quickly.

"You sent a press cable saying the French army was being mobilized? According to Section —— of the Criminal Code of France, I can have you imprisoned for the duration of a war for spreading false information. This cable was read by the Minister of the Interior at a Cabinet meeting. Said other Cabinet officers, 'How dare this fellow Vanderbilt send such secret information—' "

"Just a minute, sir," I broke in. "You have just admitted the information to be true. You said the Ministers asked how dared I spread such secret information."

"But, Mr. Vanderbilt, I never said it wasn't true. We have a free press in France. Any one can print anything he likes if it is true. But newspapermen usually play ball with us."

"I understand, M. Bressi. You don't want the world to know you are mobilizing now. But I happen to know you are, and why."

"If you are insinuating that our missions to Russia have failed—"

I rose as if to leave the room.

"Just a minute, Mr. Vanderbilt. You cannot leave this office. Your conversation has been transcribed. Threats and insinuations won't help you."

I said, "I didn't know I was making threats. I bear France no ill-will. I ran away from home, M. Bressi, when I was only seventeen, to enlist in the army, spent twenty-two months with the A. E. F., and thought I was helping to keep 'the Hun' away from our joint doors."

Bressi yawned. The telephone jingled. He lifted the receiver nonchalantly, then shouted: *"Who told them?"* He turned on me: "Other American newspapers are printing the news you sent out. Who is spreading this secret information?"

An hour later I called upon Mr. Offee, secretary to the American Ambassador, and told what had happened to me. He instantly called Bressi's office and made an appointment for Mr. Bullitt to see Bressi next morning.

"Gosh," said I, "I didn't come here to cry on your shoulder over troubles of my own. Why did you do that?"

"For the reason that this morning, when Mr. Bullitt called upon the Premier, M. Daladier assured him that France was not yet mobilizing, and that the Russian negotiations were still going along splendidly. Now, since your talk with Bressi the picture has entirely changed. What France has got to realize is, if she plays ball with us she plays it all the way or not at all."

An hour and a half after Bullitt called upon Bressi at the Quai d'Orsay I lunched with him at the American Embassy residence. The luncheon was attended by Daladier, General Gamelin, Foreign Minister Bonnet, the admiral in command of the navy, the president of the Bank of France, the new Air Minister, the Chief of Press, and others. Afterward we chatted with President Lebrun. Shortly, said he, France would have 6,000,000 men mobilized!

Flying over Belgium, Holland, and Denmark, I nearly choked at the news: Germany and Russia had concluded a non-aggression pact—as Princess Radziwill had been prophesying in *Liberty* for the past two years they would do.

As dawn rose on August 22 my plane landed in Gdynia. A taxi quickly took me to the Free State. Everywhere in the Corridor and in the Free State there were trenches, fortresses built underground, soldiers. The Germans seemed more cocky than the Poles. And I noticed, as I had earlier in the summer down in Bavaria, that large oil paintings of Hitler replaced the bleeding head of Christ on most church towers!

Reaching Danzig city, I dropped in to see Edward Piszcz, editor of the leading local paper. He was panicky. He advised me to see Förster.

"Danzig will return to the Reich within the week," boasted Förster. It went back just eight days after!

"And what if Poland and France and England fight?" I asked him.

"Germany will crush them all. Besides, England is too scared to fight, and France too degenerate."

Boarded an afternoon plane for Berlin. Arriving, went immediately to the Ministry of Propaganda and sent my card in to Herr Doktor Josef Goebbels—who in March 1933, officially expelled me from Germany for writing that the Nazis had set the Reichstag afire!

How long will it take you to mop up Europe?" I asked Goebbels. Pounding his desk, he answered: "We cannot fight much after November 1. I think we will master Poland, France, and England in sixty days."

"And after that, Herr Doktor?"

"Can't you guess?"

"You mean America?" I asked, and added, "But that is fantastic, sir. How can you capture the United States, with the 3,700 miles of ocean and land in between?"

"We do not expect to do it that way," he smiled. "We will take it from within."

The rest of our conversation was so extraordinary that I am telling it to President Roosevelt and to no one else right now.

Berlin streets were alive. Practically every one, including women, wore uniforms. All seemed in a hurry. I was glad to clamber into my warm seat in the plane, and happier still to land at dawn in Paris.

After breakfasting at the Crillon Hotel, I watched with amazement French *poilus* erecting antiaircraft guns in the fountains—of all places—on the Place de la Concorde. Driving up to Le Havre, I saw hundreds and hundreds of French peasants digging in their back yards, many with their bare hands, working feverishly to build underground shelters. Le Havre was a beehive of activity. Several large liners had just canceled their sailing dates. The *Washington,* of the United States Lines, swerved into the roadstead. Boarded her, together with Mother Roosevelt and several hundred others.

Reaching Southampton at midnight, we were all astonished to see the large number of vessels there, guarded by British troops. Next morning in London I tried in several places to purchase a gas mask. The polite British clerks told me if I would leave my name and address they would see what they could do for me in a fortnight —or, "Sorry, sir. Why not try your Embassy?"

My taxi driver finally said: "Oi'll git me ol' loidy's sir." He was back in half an hour with a mask, marked "Eliza Powell, Chelsea, London."

"But what will she do?" I asked.

"She don't need it, sir, where's she's gone. She passed away last night."

I found it fitted reasonably well, and paid him what he wanted for it.

Ran into Sir Nevile Henderson and Winston Churchill crossing Downing Street from No. 10 to the Foreign Office. Churchill had nothing to say, but when I asked him if war was coming he nodded his head several times.

Prime Minister Neville Chamberlain and Mrs. Chamberlain left No. 10 a few moments later for their usual walk in the Park. Plainclothesmen kept a crowd far back, but I was lucky in being able to have a few words with him and with General Viscount Gort, chief of the British General Staff, who joined him.

Early that evening sirens began sounding all over London. In less than three minutes by my watch the streets were clear. Like moles, every single person had dropped below the pavements—the subways gobbling up most of them. The "test," as it later proved to be, was over in fifteen minutes and every one came back as quietly as they had disappeared.

I dined that evening with Lord and Lady Kemsley at Chandos House. Kemsley is the publisher of the *London Sunday Times,* the *Daily Sketch,* the *Manchester Guardian,* and nineteen other big newspapers in England. His brother Lord Camrose publishes the London *Daily Telegraph* and twelve other British newspapers. Ten days before, he had lunched and spent nearly two hours with Hitler at Berchtesgaden, at which time the Fuehrer had assured Kemsley he was striving his hardest to preserve peace, and would, unless "England forced him to give her the beating she had long deserved."

This Is No Time To Talk of Peace, Mr. Macfadden

by Fulton Oursler

IN THIS ISSUE of *Liberty* magazine there is an editorial by our publisher, Mr. Bernarr Macfadden, called "War? Maybe? But Let's Stop, Look, and Listen." In it Mr. Macfadden states his belief that if England is faced with the certainty of invasion, peace at this time would be a logical step and would preserve the Democracy of England intact.

I never like to disagree with Mr. Macfadden publicly or privately, because I respect his views and because he is not only my publisher but my friend. Today, however, more than ever before, men must remain inflexibly true to their own convictions in the face of the crisis that confronts the United States and must boldly speak their opinions. Otherwise Democracy itself is already a failure. It is in that spirit that I rise to disagree with Mr. Macfadden's conclusions in this matter.

No one today, not even Churchill or Hitler, can say whether England will be invaded. Only Hitler knows whether there will be an attempt at invasion; but whether England is successfully invaded, or whether she negotiates a peace now, one fact, in my opinion, is certain: She will not in either of those contingencies retain her

Democracy intact. She may retain the shadow of Democracy, as Germany has done under a one-party system in which everybody votes yes to the Dictator, but that is the most she can hope for.

There is only one way in which Democracy can be retained intact in England or in the United States and that is by the defeat of Hitler and what he represents—the totalitarian idea. There is not room in the world for these two ideas—Hitler says so! The issues between the two are very simple. Under Democracy the government is the servant of the people. Under Nazism the people are the slaves of the government. The question is purely one of freedom as against slavery—and slavery will be the ultimate answer to negotiated peace. Such a peace would give Germany 90 percent and England 10 percent —for a little while. England would lose even that in the end, and our turn would be next.

The message of the President at the opening session of Congress made this abundantly clear. The situation today is that Hitler desires nothing in the world so much as a negotiated peace. The reasons for this should be obvious right now. He has conquered western Europe

THIS ship must not come in.

and by an immense superiority of airplanes, arms, and ammunition he is able to batter away at the lives and property and the spirit of the English people. That is the way things are now, but it will not be so for long.

America, the Arsenal of Democracy, is speeding up its production with frantic zeal. More and more planes are going over to England. Ships will soon be carrying munitions there. Before long, in spite of all difficulties, America's production will be at its matchless peak and England will have more planes than Germany and more ammunition.

All this is coming soon to be, and when it does come Hitler faces almost certain disaster. He has two courses open to him. One is to smash England by a knockout blow before America's production reaches its peak. He knows how hard it is going to be to deliver that knockout blow. If he could call it quits now he would have gained everything and would lose very little. That is why there is such a strong undercurrent for a "realistic peace" now.

It is like a cup of cold water offered to a world thirsting for peace. But the drink is not what it seems. It is loaded with arsenic and if civilization swallows what is offered, the result will be the death of freedom.

I am indeed thankful that Mr. Macfadden does not approve "yes men." He believes in the educational value of free discussion and likes to see both sides of any important question. That accounts for my reply to his views as expressed on the editorial page.

a short story by Eleanor Roosevelt

Of Dark Days That Pass Away,
and Shining Faith That Endures...

ST. NICHOLAS' EVE, 1940, was cold and the snow was falling.

On the hearth in Marta's home there was a fire burning, and she had been hugging that fire all day, asking her mother to tell her stories, telling them afterward to her doll.

This was not like St. Nicholas' Eve of last year. Then her father had come home. Seven-year-old Marta asked her mother to tell her the story over and over again; so her mother, whose fingers were never idle now that she was alone and had to feed and clothe herself and Marta, sat and knit long woolen stockings and talked of the past which would never come again, and of St. Nicholas' Eve, 1939.

The war was going on in Europe in 1939, but Jon was only mobilized. He was just guarding the border, and was allowed to come home for the holiday. Marta's mother said:

"On Monday I got the letter, and on Tuesday, St. Nicholas' Eve, he came. I got up early in the morning and started cleaning the house. I wanted everything to shine while your father was home. Soon I called you,

and when you were dressed and had had your breakfast, you took your place in the window, watching for him to come. Every time you saw a speck way down the road, you would call out to me, but I had time to get much of the holiday cooking prepared and the house in good order before you finally cried, 'Here he is!' and a cart stopped by our gate. You threw open the door and you ran down the path. I saw him pick you up in his arms, but he was in such a hurry that he carried you right on in with him and met me as I was running halfway down the path."

Her mother always sighed and Marta wondered why her eyes looked so bright; then she would go on and tell of Jon's coming into the house and insisting on saying: *"Vroolyk Kerstfeest,"* meaning "Merry Christmas," all over again to her and to Marta, just as though he had not greeted them both outside.

They both felt sorry that the two grandmothers and the two grandfathers could not come that year. Little Marta loved to think about her grandfathers. One grandfather could tell her so much about the animals and the birds and make them seem just like people, and her

297

mother's father could tell her stories, long, long stories, about things that happened in cities, about processions and having seen the Queen, and so many wonderful things that she could dream about after the visit was over. It was a disappointment when the grandparents could not be with them for this St. Nicholas Eve.

Little Marta did not know it, but to her father's parents it was more than a disappointment. They had wanted so much to see their son again. Like all mothers, his mother feared the worst where her own boy was concerned. Perhaps she had had a premonition of what the future held, but, as with all peasants, the hard facts of life are there to be counted, and the money saved for the trip would keep food in the larder if the winter was going to be as hard as everything indicated, so they did not travel.

Marta's mother had told her that perhaps St. Nicholas, on his white horse with his black servant, Peter, would not bring any presents that year to fill her wooden shoes, but Marta would not believe it. Her first question to her father was, "Will St. Nicholas forget us?"

"No, little Marta," said her father. "The good saint will come tonight if you go to bed like a good girl and go quickly to sleep."

Marta put her little shoes down by the big fireplace, and her mother took her into the bedroom and tucked her away behind the curtains which shielded her bunk along the wall on the cold winter night.

On Christmas morning Marta woke and ran to look for her wooden shoes. "St. Nicholas has been here!" she cried, "and he's given me many sweets, a doll, and bright red mittens just like the stockings mother made me as a Christmas gift."

Then the whole family went skating on the river and there were many other little girls with their fathers and mothers. Every one glided about, and the babies were pushed or dragged in their little sleds. The boys and girls chased one another. Sometimes long lines took hands and, after skating away, gathered in a circle, going faster and faster until they broke up because they could not hold on any longer.

Then at last they went home to dinner. On the table a fat chicken and a good soup.

At first they ate silently, and then, as the edge of their hunger wore off, they began to talk.

"Marta," said her father, "have you learned to read in school yet? Can you count how many days there are in a month?"

"Oh, yes," replied Marta, "and mother makes me mark off every day that you are gone, and when we are together we always say, 'I wonder if father remembers what we are doing now,' and we try to do just the things we do when you are home so you can almost see us all the time."

Her father smiled rather sadly, and then her mother said:

"Jon, perhaps it is good for us all that we have to be apart for a while, because we appreciate so much more this chance of being together. There is no time for cross words when you know how few minutes there are left. It should make us all realize what it would be like if we lived with the thought of how quickly life runs away before us."

A curious look came into his eyes and Jon thought for a moment with anguish of what he might have to do some day to other homes and other children, or what might happen to his, and then he pulled himself together and you could almost hear him say, "This at least is going to be a happy memory," and turning to Marta, he began to tease her about her fair hair, which stuck out in two little pigtails from the cap which she wore on her head. Seizing one of them, he said:

"I can drive you just like an old horse. I will pull this pigtail and you will turn this way. I will pull the other one and you go that way."

Such a jolly, happy time, and then, as the dusk fell, Marta's father put on his uniform again, kissed her mother, and hugged Marta tightly, saying, "Take good care of *moeder* until I come back."

Then he was gone and they were alone again. The year seemed to travel heavily. First, letters came from Jon, and then one day a telegram, and her mother cried and told Marta that her father would never come back; but her mother never stopped working, for now there was no one to look after them except God, and He was far away in His heaven. Marta talked to Him sometimes because mother said He was every one's Father, but it never seemed quite true. Marta could believe, however, that the Christ child in the Virgin's arms in the painting in the church was a real child and she often talked to Him.

Strange things Marta told the Christ child. She confided in Him that she never had liked that uniform which her father went away in. It must have had something to do with his staying away. He had never gone away in the clothes he wore every day and not come back. She liked him best in his everyday clothes. She was never afraid of him then, and he had a nice homey smell; something of the cows and horses came into the house with him, and, like a good little country girl, Marta liked that smell. She told the Christ child that her mother had no time to play with her any more. She had to work all the time, and sometimes tears fell on her work and she could not answer Marta's questions.

There was no school any more for her to go to, and on the road she met children who talked a strange language and they made fun of her and said now this country was theirs. It was all very hard to understand and she wondered if the Christ child really did know what was happening to little children down here on earth. Sometimes there was nothing to eat in the house, and then both she and her mother went hungry to bed, and she woke in the morning to find her mother gone and it would be considerably later before her mother returned with something for breakfast.

Thinking of all these things as her mother told the story again on this St. Nicholas' Eve, 1940, Marta took off her wooden shoes and put them down beside the open fire. Sadly her mother said, "St. Nicholas will not come tonight," and he did not. Marta had an idea of her own, however, which she thought about until Christmas Eve came. Then she said to her mother, "There is one candle left from last year's feast. May I light it in the house so the light will shine out for the Christ child to see His way? Perhaps He will come to us since St. Nicholas forgot us."

Marta's mother shook her head but smiled, and Marta took out the candle and carefully placed it in a copper candlestick.

Marta wanted to see how far the light would shine out into the night, so she slipped into her wooden shoes again, put her shawl over her head, opened the door, and slipped out into the night. The wind was blowing around her and she could hardly stand up. She took two or three steps and looked back at the window. She could see the twinkling flame of the candle, and while she stood watching it, she was conscious of a tall figure in a dark cloak standing beside her.

Just at first she hoped the tall figure might be her father, but he would not have stood there watching her without coming out into the candlelight and picking her up and running into the house to greet her mother. She was not exactly afraid of this stranger, for she was a brave little girl, but she felt a sense of chill creeping through her, for there was something awe-inspiring and rather repellent about this personage who simply stood in the gloom watching her.

Finally he spoke:

"What are you doing here, little girl?"

Very much in awe, Marta responded: "I came out to make sure that the Christ child's candle would shine out to guide His footsteps to our house."

"You must not believe in any such legend," remonstrated the tall dark man. "There is no Christ child. That is a story which is told for the weak. It is ridiculous to believe that a little child could lead the people of the world, a foolish idea claiming strength through love and sacrifice. You must grow up and acknowledge only one superior, he who dominates the rest of the world through fear and strength."

This was not very convincing to Marta. Why, she talked to the Christ child herself! But she had been taught to be respectful and to listen to her elders and so silence reigned while she wondered who this man was who said such strange and curious things. Was he

a bad man? Did he have something to do with her father's going away and not coming back? Or with her mother's worrying so much and working so hard?

He had done her no harm—at least, no bodily harm—and yet down inside her something was hurt. Things could be taken away from people. They had had to give up many of their chickens and cows because the government wanted them. That had been hard because they loved their animals and they had cared for them, and it meant also that they would have little to eat and much less money when they lost them. But that was different from the way this man made her feel. He was taking away a hope, a hope that some one could do more even than her mother could do, could perhaps make true the dream, that story she told herself every night, both awake and asleep, of the day when her father would come home; when he would put her on his shoulder and they would go skating on the canal. Somehow this man hurt that dream and it was worse than not having St. Nicholas come. It seemed to pull down a curtain over the world.

Marta was beginning to feel very cold and very much afraid, but all her life she had been told to be polite to her elders and ask for permission to do anything she wished to do. She said, "I am hoping the Christ child will come. May I go in now and will you not come into my house?"

The man seemed to hesitate a minute, but perhaps he decided it would be interesting to see the inside of such a humble home where there was so much simple faith. In any case, he wanted to impress upon this child and upon her mother that foolish legends were not the right preparation for living in a world where he, the power, dominated, so he followed Marta into the house.

Marta's mother, who had been sitting by the fire knitting when Marta went out, was still there, yes, but in her arms was a baby and around the baby a curious light shone, and Marta knew that the Christ child had come. The man in the door did not know; he thought it was an ordinary room with an ordinary baby in a woman's arms.

Striding in, he said, "Madam, you have taught this child a foolish legend. Why is she burning a candle in the hope that the Christ child will come?"

The woman answered in a very low voice, "To those of us who suffer, that is a hope we may cherish. Under your power there is fear, and you have created a strength before which people tremble. But on Christmas Eve strange things happen and new powers are sometimes born."

Marta was not interested any more in the tall figure in the cloak. The Christ child was there in her mother's lap. She could tell Him all her troubles and He would understand why she prayed above everything else for the return of her father. St. Nicholas would never again leave them without Christmas dinner and she could have a new doll and the sweets which she longed to taste again. Perhaps, if only she went to sleep like a good little girl, there would be a miracle and her father would be there. Off she trotted to the second room, and climbed behind the curtain.

Marta could not go to sleep at once because, though there was no sound from the other room, she still could not free herself from the thought of that menacing figure. She wondered if he was responsible for the tears of the little girl up the road whose father had not come home last year and who had not been visited either by St. Nicholas.

Then before her eyes she suddenly saw a vision of the Christ child. He was smiling and seemed to say that the little girl up the road had her father this year and that all was well with her. Marta was happy—fathers are so very nice. Perhaps if she prayed again to the Christ child, when she woke up He would have her father there too, and so she said first the prayer she had always been taught to say and then, just for herself, she added:

"Dear Christ child, I know You will understand that though God is the Father of all of us, He is very, very far away and the fathers we have down here are so much closer. Please bring mine back so that we can have the cows, the pigs, and the chickens again and all we want to eat and the tears will not be in my mother's eyes." The murmur of her prayer died away as she fell asleep.

A long time the power stood and watched Marta's mother, and finally there came over him a wave of strange feeling. Would any one ever turn eyes on him as lovingly as this woman's eyes turned on that baby? Bowing low before her, he said, "Madam, I offer you ease and comfort, fine raiment, delicious food. Will you come with me where these things are supplied but where you cannot keep to your beliefs?"

Marta's mother shook her head and looked down at the baby lying in her lap. She said, "Where you are, there are power and hate and fear of people, one of another. Here there are none of the things which you offer, but there is the Christ child. The Christ child taught love. He drove the money-changers out of the temple, to be sure, but that was because He hated the system which they represented. He loved His family, the poor, the sinners, and He tried to bring out in each one the love for Him and for each other which would mean a Christlike spirit in the world. I will stay here with my child, who could trust the legend and therefore brought with her into this house the Christ-child spirit which makes us live forever. You will go out into the night again, the cold night, to die as all must die who are not born again through Him at Christmastime."

The man turned and went out, and as he opened the door, he seemed to be engulfed in the dark and troubled world without. The snow was falling and the wind was howling, the sky was gloomy overhead. All that he looked upon was fierce and evil. These evil forces of nature were ruling also in men's hearts and they brought sorrow and misery to many human beings. Greed, personal ambition, and fear all were strong in the world fed by constant hate. In the howling of the wind he heard these evil spirits about him, and they seemed to run wild, unleashed.

This has happened, of course, many times in the world before, but must it go on happening forever? Suddenly he turned to look back at the house from which he had come. Still from the window shone the little child's candle and within he could see framed the figure of the mother and the baby. Perhaps that was a symbol of the one salvation there was in the world, the heart of faith, the one hope of peace. The hope he had taken away from Marta for the moment shone out increasingly into the terrible world, even though it was only the little Christ child's candle.

With a shrug of his shoulders he turned away to return to the luxury of power. He was able to make people suffer. He was able to make people do his will, but his strength was shaken and it always will be. The light in the window must be the dream which holds us all until we ultimately win back to the things for which Jon died and for which Marta and her mother were living.

IV

Pin-ups and
War Bonds

(1941-1945)

THE EARLY DAYS of World War II found America an ambivalent nation. Abroad, the major countries of Europe were engaged in a conflict that made no claim to end all wars; rather it was a grim struggle for survival with the bombing of cities added to the timeworn horrors of the battlefield.

At home, the population stood divided. Large numbers of Americans wished to declare immediate war on Germany and jump in with full force on the side of Britain and its allies. Others pointed out that World War I had failed to make the world safe for democracy, and insisted that this time the United States should stay home.

Astride this plunging controversy sat President Roosevelt, who had run for a history-shattering third term in 1940. Needless to say, the third term had added fuel to the fury of *Liberty* publisher Bernarr Macfadden, who became a vigorous Willkie supporter during the election.

The nation compromised by trying to do everything possible short of fighting. "Bundles for Britain" became the slogan of the people; lend-lease the language of diplomacy. *Liberty* did its bit by running articles by John Gunther and others who reported vividly on embattled London during the blitz. Edward Doherty, an editorial stalwart from the days of Al Capone, went overseas to file dispatches like "I Saw the French Army Collapse" and "How It Feels to be Bombed." *Liberty* also heightened anxiety on the home front by printing "Can Hitler Conquer America?" by Pierre van Paassen, and "Hitler's Hellish New Weapons," by Wythe Williams.

To blunt the impact of horrifying reality, Americans tried turning their minds to lighter matters. Once more, silly songs swept the land, among them "Three Little Fishies," "Cement Mixer," and "The Fuehrer's Face." For the first time in history a teen-age bloc emerged to be known as bobby soxers, and zoot suiters writhed to the voice of reedy young Frank Sinatra.

All at once, pop music turned an unexpected beam on *Liberty*. In 1941, Jule Styne (music) and Frank Loesser (words) wrote a song called "I Said No." It was sung by Betty Jane Rhodes in the Paramount musical

Sweater Girl. In the song, a pretty girl answers the ring of the doorbell. The young man at the door begins to fast-talk her—"He whispered of pleasures I'd missed," the girl confides musically.

Was he trying to seduce the girl with glib words and golden promises? It seemed so, but the girl is firm. "I said No," she carols. He replies by pleading, "Please, pretty baby." Finally, the girl's resistance collapses: "I said Yes-yes-yes-yes—that's how I subscribed to *Liberty* magazine!" Instead of being a base seducer, the young fellow was a door-to-door magazine salesman, a flourishing breed at the time.

With a catchy tune and surprise ending, "I Said No" became a hit-parade song which brought *Liberty* fresh attention, especially from the younger generation. But it injected no joy into the magazine's editorial offices. As the new decade began it became increasingly apparent that Bernarr Macfadden, the man who enjoyed diffusing himself, had finally spread himself too thin. His life had become a whirling pinwheel of political campaigns, health resorts, cracked-wheat derbies, and parachute jumps. Of all his activities, magazine management seemed to interest him the least.

This produced a dilemma which—even as war continued abroad—won the front page attention of *The New York Times*. Bernarr Macfadden was forced out of his own magazines, with the so-called suppliers (printing, paper, ink, etc.) seizing control of Macfadden Publications. It was a tribute to the continuing charisma of *Liberty* that the new owners expressed highest hopes for its future, even though other Macfadden periodicals were far more robust.

For a time Fulton Oursler stayed on as editor-in-chief, but after Pearl Harbor he left for a post in the war effort. By this time the magazine had of course dropped all vestiges of George Sylvester Viereck and his slanted thinking. With America in the war, it printed a defiantly patriotic editorial aimed at Captain Joe Patterson, whose *Daily News* continued to be surly and isolationist.

Several other innovations were visible after the departure of Macfadden. With the success of *Life* as a picture magazine, *Liberty* attempted an illustrated section. It also began a policy of condensing best-selling books such as Joseph Davies' *Mission to Moscow*. Each of these weekly condensations was headed "Reading Time: One Evening." The feature was a great success and remained a part of the magazine until the bitter end.

To a large extent though, *Liberty* retained its old editorial policy. Articles hopped nimbly from battlefield experiences to "Houses I Have Haunted," by Boris Karloff. Full tribute was paid to Betty Grable, who had become *the* Pin-Up Girl of the fighting forces. In Hollywood, "Oomph Girl" Ann Sheridan reigned supreme as sexpot, while the fabulous proportions of Jane Russell's bosom were of endless fascination to all G.I.'s. On the home front, kids ran loose as parents worked nights in defense factories. With V-Girls haunting the streets of cities, *Liberty* had a chance to print a reassuring "Youth Has Flamed Before."

Liberty's fiction dealt gently with the war. Soldiers in *Liberty* stories were less likely to be shooting at Japs than meeting pretty, bewildering girls at the Stage Door Canteen. Stories by Sinclair Lewis, Somerset Maugham, and other literary titans avoided the subject of war altogether. One atypical piece of fiction, in the old Floyd Gibbons-"Red Napoleon" genre, was Fred Allhof's "Lightning in the Night: A Story of the Invasion of America."

Here, at last, is a serial from which one installment can be neatly excerpted, and so we have done.

The new *Liberty* might be groping editorially, but it was suddenly healthy otherwise. Indeed, during the war, came two of the precious three years when the magazine showed a financial profit. While other publications suffered from the wartime paper shortage, *Liberty* with its supplier-owners always seemed to have enough to print on. Consequently, of all American magazines, it alone was able to guarantee its claimed circulation. Advertisers were impressed and used the magazine as never before.

In this healthy fashion, *Liberty* made its way through the years of World War II . . . .

We Have Only Just Started to Fight

by Gen. Charles de Gaulle

Free France Speaks! . . . A Stirring, Historic Challenge

THE SO-CALLED RULERS of Vichy went to a great deal of trouble to find men who could be charged with the blame for France's military disaster.

Acting under Hitler's long whip and Mussolini's hammer, it was essential for them to show that France had been at fault in declaring war and that all those who had made the decision were culprits and must be punished.

To the men of Vichy, all those who saw that France was threatened are criminals; all those who said that France must fight are criminals; all those who refused to rush into bondage are criminals.

But these men are quite logical in their infamy, for nothing else will satisfy the enemy they have taken as their master, and naturally the capitulationists of Vichy have their own interests at heart. If they can succeed in making people believe that France was at fault in declaring war, then they themselves will appear to have been justified in putting an end to the conflict.

They might even make this insane argument seem reasonable: that they "saved" France by surrendering her!

So they hope. But I refuse to believe that the enemy and the "rulers" of Vichy can deceive the remaining free peoples of the world. I refuse to believe that they can deceive the peoples of occupied as well as of unoccupied France.

The sense of logic of the French is too proud and too firm. The Frenchman knows that those responsible for the collapse are not the men who wanted to defend France but the men who, while holding high positions in the government and the defense forces, betrayed their trust by not preparing France for the approaching conflict; the men whose responsibility it was to build a modern military machine for the country, but who, instead, refused to consider anything but the outdated conceptions of the past; the men who surrendered without calling on France's full, mighty strength of resistance.

France found herself driven back momentarily by a method of warfare for which her chiefs had not prepared her. In those first black moments of defeat, France might have doubted herself; she might have doubted her allies.

Blinded by despair, certain Frenchmen forgot the two thousand years of France's heroic past, the innumerable times when France plunged to the depths, had risen again overnight and turned defeat into glorious victory.

But France is France. Her spirit has not changed.

Deep in the heart of her there is a secret spring of courage, fortitude and reckless daring that always in the past has responded to the crisis and that now once again will astound the world with its irresistible strength.

Crushed, humiliated, surrendered to the enemy, already France is beginning to rise from the abyss to hurl back the foe.

I have good reasons to say that this fighting France of our ancestors is re-forming her forces for the struggle.

There may be some confusion in her first blows for freedom, for the powers opposing her are ruthless and determined and their tentacles are sometimes cleverly hidden. But the new France will return to the battle with ever greater strength, and she will take her part with honor and glory in the inevitable victory.

For no Frenchman alive today has the right to have any other thought, any other hope, any other love, than the thought, the hope, the love of France.

And every Frenchman alive today knows his duty. It is a simple and hard duty, and it will be accepted gladly.

It is his duty to fight.

The enemy believed that with the armistice and the work of the capitulationists of Vichy, the war was ended.

The enemy was gravely mistaken.

For France retains some very valuable weapons. She has the spirit of her people. She has certain outposts of empire in strategic places. She has great forces over the sea that have refused to bow their necks in surrender.

A certain Italian paper said:

"France has signed an armistice and thereby admitted her defeat. We shall now teach France how to behave herself. There are several questions that cannot be 'negotiated' or 'bargained' about. One of these is Tunisia, which, without reservations, shall be included in the Roman Empire."

So says the Italian enemy. So he says! But the France that signed this armistice was not free France. Free France wants no part of it. Free France is determined to continue the war, with all her millions of people, throughout the thousands of miles of her empire. She will fight on, she will not perish, she *will* win the war."

To the Ladies

by Princess Alexandra Kropotkin

THE FOUR PRETTY King sisters, nieces by marriage of ex-Senator William H. King (Dem., Utah), are such unusual girls in this day and age that I think you'll like to know about them. While they sing swing of warmest harmony for stage, screen, and radio, they also sing hymns in church on Sunday, and they neither swear, smoke, nor drink, not even coffee or tea! What's the answer? They're *Mormons*—born and raised in the strict creed of Brigham Young, which they still practice through all their contacts with show business. . . . Driggs was their name originally—Louise, Alys, Donna, and Yvonne. William King Driggs, their father, is a Mormon teacher of music in Utah schools. One of their granddads was Parley Pratt, a founder of Mormonism, and another was Lars Mortensen, pioneer from Denmark who wrote some of the old Mormon hymns composed between Indian fights during the long prairie trek. The sisters' favorites are: "Come, Come, Ye Saints"; "Jesus, Once of Humble Birth," and "Love at Home." "We ought to marry Mor-

mons," said Donna, "but if we don't, we'll hope to convert our husbands. All Mormon girls are missionaries at heart." Louise, married to band leader Alvino Rey, hasn't converted *him* yet. . . . Outside of Utah, Mormons are thickest now in California, around Hollywood and Los Angeles. They befriend each other cordially wherever they roam, and when two strangers from Utah meet, they always ask, "*Are* you or aren't you?" At a Detroit party the King sisters once asked Jack Dempsey, who nodded yes. Is Jack *really* a Mormon, I wonder? . . . It's been years—at least two generations—since Mormons gave up polygamy, yet the after-effects are still numerous. The King girls have so many cousins they've never learned half their names!

Fresh from a trip through agricultural California, I greatly appreciated the opportunity of meeting Vice-President and Mrs. Henry A. Wallace at a Washington social affair. You can imagine how pleased I was when the Vice-President spoke to me of my father's book, *Fields, Factories and Workshops,* as one of the first of its kind to promote thought here. I have a childhood memory of Father reading the manuscript aloud in our kitchen while Mother did the supper dishes. Somehow that scene always seemed to link me to American democracy.

In a Washington suburb I picked up a homemaking trick from a young governmental employee's wife who needs to economize. Her twin beds have headboards upholstered in the same material as the bedspreads.

First, the wife bought two boxspring beds on legs, two mattresses, and *three* spreads. A carpenter cut beaverboard to simulate headboards. She padded them; covered them with the third bedspread cut to shape; attached the boards to the wall; pushed the beds up against them. They look very smart and expensive—but cost far less than regular beds of that type.

A new beauty book, specially helpful to parents of young girls, is Constance J. Foster's *The Attractive Child.* (Published by Julian Messner, Inc. $2.75.)

"What is salsify—a professional career, a disease, or a vegetable?" A lady fired this kindergarten question at my host, Senator Peter Goelet Gerry (Demo., Rhode Island), and me while our picture was being taken in his South Street house, once owned by ex-President Hoover. The senator and I both answered, "Vegetable, of course. Same thing as oyster plant."

The lady confessed that she had flunked the question in a recent exam for a government job. "I thought salsify must be a verb," she said, "like falsify." She pronounced it that way, too.

Vegetables cooked and uncooked are combined as follows by one Washington hostess to make a balanced, sustaining meal for informal occasions. . . . Cook separately 2 cups green peas, 4 medium-sized potatoes. Drain peas thoroughly. Slice the potatoes. Sauté both together in 2 tablespoons hot oil or frying fat. Season to taste; sprinkle generously with uncooked chopped green peppers and arrange as a vegetable plate, adding to each portion a few cooked asparagus tips and 2 thick slices raw tomato dressed with sweet cream, lemon juice, and minced parsley.

Thirsty for a drink of water, I couldn't line-buck the reception crowd at the hospitable home of Mr. and Mrs. Eugene Meyer. A kind stranger in evening clothes volunteered to convoy me to the refreshment tables. On our way we encountered my friend, Congresswoman Edith Nourse Rogers (Rep., Massachusetts), who said, "I didn't know you two were acquainted." We told her we weren't, whereupon Edith introduced Admiral "Jerry" Land, chairman of the U. S. Maritime Commission. . . . It seems I had picked up an *admiral* to get me a glass of water!

Inside London
by John Gunther

I'VE JUST RETURNED from six weeks in wartime, war-bound London—six of the most stimulating and exhilarating weeks I ever spent anywhere. I visited bomber stations and coastal defense establishments; I met eleven Cabinet ministers, including Mr. Churchill; I talked long hours with old friends; I interviewed the heads of six refugee governments; I looked at plenty of destruction; I learned something about courage, common sense, hope, and sacrifice.

There are lessons in contemporary London for every American, now that we too are engaged in the greatest war in history, fighting the same heinous enemy.

No Londoner who lived through a really big blitz—like the one on May 10 last—is ever likely to forget it. No one who felt the hot breath of a land mine on his cheek is ever quite the same again. Everybody I met in London had at least one blitz story to tell—stories of heroism, comic relief, fear, narrow escapes, acute discomfort, harrowing agony of mind. I heard what London looked like when thousands could not get home from work, when the glass was inches deep on every street, when fires lit up half of London, when the gas and water failed, when—one small, odd touch—burglar alarms kept ringing all night long because show windows had been broken. Nor can any visitor to London fail to be shocked at the amount of material damage done. Some streets look like the ruins of Herculaneum. Some streets have simply disappeared.

Nevertheless, the first point I would make in this article, the first lesson I would attempt to draw from the experience of England is that bombing, no matter how savage, no matter how merciless, is nothing to be afraid of. Do not worry about bombing.

I was about to write, "bombing never wins." Perhaps that would be an exaggeration. Bombing *might* win, if it went on long enough on an immense enough scale. But it hasn't won so far. The British people have beaten the blitz to date.

Amazingly few people are killed by bombs. Comparatively few are made homeless. Greater London contains more than 8,000,000 people; scarcely 60,000 live in public shelters now, and many of these could return to their homes if they wished. Bombing causes lack of sleep, yes; it may disorganize transportation temporarily; it may set some bad fires; but it does not destroy a city, it does not vanquish a people, if the people have stalwart spirit. What Londoners hated most about big raids was the noise. That and the lack of sleep.

The most common reaction to raids among ordinary folk is, first, anger; second, courage. Once, when bombs were falling like lumps of rock out of an apocalyptic sky, a woman stood outside her burning house, shook her fist upward, and shouted, "Bloody child's play, I call it!"

Once, surveying the broken ruins of a residential street where house after house had been blotted out, a visitor asked the air-raid warden what he thought about it.

Imperturbably—and with complete good humor—the warden replied, "Seems 'e [Hitler] was a little extra-spiteful last night, sir."

The British government has in effect reversed its bomb-shelter policy. At first the authorities sought to concentrate on deep shelters—shelters far underground, where every one would be comparatively safe. They soon gave up this idea. If the population of London had stayed underground on the night of December 29, 1940, London might have burned down over their heads. The idea now is that all able-bodied men and women should stay *above* ground, watching on rooftops and putting out fires. Anybody, even a child, can put out a small incendiary bomb if he gets to it quickly enough. And very, very few people get killed.

So, first of all, I would say to people in America: Bombs may come. Take sensible precautions. Bombs may cause destruction. Bombs may be a nuisance. But don't be afraid of raids. Do not fear bombs. You can conquer them.

A greater enemy than bombs—I speak quite seriously —is boredom. There have been no serious raids on London since early summer (though other British cities have been pasted hard and often), and the resultant lull has produced a certain amount of lethargy and complacence. Discomforts and sacrifices are harder to bear when everything is quiet, when excitement and the sense of danger are missing. People are more inclined to slacken down, even people with morale as superb and solid as the British, when no attacks are imminent. I heard more than one Englishman say, "You know, believe it or not, we all loved the blitz!" A good sound raid shook the average Londoner out of his normally colorless and routine life. It was the kind of supreme experience when every individual saw his own fate and history face to face. I even heard Englishmen of standing and intelligence say they wished more raids would come. "What this country needs," I heard more than once, "is a good stiff raid once a month."

But no visitor, no foreigner, has any right to mimic that remark. Only those who have lived through a blitz have any right to wish for more. Consider the case of the tactless American who, leaving London after a short raidless visit, turned to his hotel porter and sighed, "Well, I certainly hate to go without seeing at least one raid." The porter looked him over and replied soberly, "My wife and child were killed in the last one, sir."

Another "enemy," if so it may be called, is the blackout. No American can appreciate the intensity and comprehensiveness of the London blackout until he's seen it —or tried to see through it. Along about 4:30 in the winter afternoon the streets begin to empty. Shops close at four, so that people can get home more easily. I have walked from New Bond Street to Park Lane, through the choicest streets of Mayfair, at about 5:15 P.M. and encountered not more than two or three pedestrians in six or seven blocks. People dive into their homes or hotels as if they were retreating into caves. At dusk the heavy black curtains are pulled over every window; by 6 P.M. London is black as pitch. (Traffic lights are reduced to small crosses and are hooded from above; automobiles use shuttered parking lights.)

The blackout, practically every Londoner will agree, is an unmitigated nuisance. It is the one thing that almost every one complains about. People yearn for light at night more than for any other single thing. The blackout condemns the great majority of people to life indoors after sundown (taxis at night are almost as scarce as eggs or oranges); it drastically impedes their instinct to gregariousness; it is a kind of emotional suffocation. Moreover, it is downright dangerous. Traffic accidents are caused mostly by the fact that the pedestrian, as a rule, can see an oncoming automobile and therefore thinks that the automobile can equally see him; but it can't. More deaths are caused in England by blackout accidents than in raids, I'm told.

So I would suggest that another lesson from London is that we in the United States avoid blackouts as long as possible, and then go in for them with great care and discrimination.

The pinch in England is severe. There is no getting around that. People eat less, simply because there is less food to go around. On the other hand, there is no real privation. No one is undernourished, and certainly no one is starving.

But the American visiting England encounters certain shocks. In six weeks, living in a luxurious hotel, I had exactly one egg. I saw beefsteak twice. I had ham once. I never saw pork or lamb. There is plenty of bread and plenty of potatoes, and so no one needs to be hungry. But milk is short, and so are most fresh vegetables except cabbage and sprouts. You get a pat of butter per meal about the size of a quarter, and a cube of sugar about a quarter inch square. Fruit is scarce, and so is cheese.

At my first dinner party in London I sat next to a titled lady very famous in America. The waiter passed small lumps of sugar with the coffee. I never take sugar in coffee, and I shook my head. Whereupon the titled lady hissed at me, *"Never* refuse sugar!" I called the waiter back, got my single lump, and gave it to her. Calmly she put it in her handbag.

Nobody dines out in London on anything like the prewar scale, largely because it's so hard to get around in the blackout. Nor do country-house weekends flourish any longer. Coal is short, to say nothing of petrol for private cars. Houses are apt to be drear and chilly, and a guest feels that he is taking preciously rationed food from his host and his host's servants. There are, of course, exceptions to this general rule. A few great houses still do maintain the old tradition. But not many. As one distinguished writer muttered to me ironically, "The greatest achievement of the war so far is the abolition of the country-house weekend."

In a London hotel your choice of food is limited, but you won't be hungry. Bread and potatoes are, as I say, plentiful, and you can always—or almost always—order game, fish, or chicken. These luxuries are, however, fabulously expensive. My breakfast consisted of a tablespoon of tomato juice, toast, and coffee. (Orange or other citrus juices are, of course, all but unknown.) At lunch, which costs anywhere from two dollars up, you may have either a soup or hors d'oeuvres (served very skimpily), and then a choice of whatever fish or meat is on the menu—not both. The fish and meat courses take the form of stew, patty, hash, or ragout, as a rule. Desserts, with a minimum of sugar, are limited as a rule to cake or custards, though I had stewed fruit and ice cream once or twice. Dinner is about like lunch. Most people eat in restaurants if they can afford it; it's best to reserve a table and get there early. You can get beef—sometimes— in some "black house" restaurants.

The chief shortages, when I was in London (I skip items like silk stockings, typewriters, cosmetics, fountain pens, lipsticks, small metal gadgets, paper clips, and so on), were paper, alcohol, cigarettes, and above all, matches. Newspapers are down to a single sheet folded to make four pages, except the *Times*, which is bigger. Whisky was hard to get in shops and extremely expensive in hotels; I paid as much as eight dollars a bottle. Cigarettes are very short, though usually you could get Turkish or Egyptian varieties at about one dollar for a box of twenty. The cheap cigarettes smoked by the enormous majority of Englishmen have practically disappeared.

In all fairness, however, let me state that never once did I lack for a cigarette when I wanted one. For one thing, I had brought a good many with me. For another, the headwaiter or floor waiter could almost always get a package of something or other, if you didn't care what kind. Shops seldom had them in stock, but hotel servants could manage to procure them somehow. Of course the millions of Londoners who did not have the luck to live in a good hotel found it harder to get cigarettes than I did.

Matches are the scarcest article of all. As a rule, I got two matches per day at my hotel, with breakfast. If you have no lighter, you are out of luck. Nor can you buy a lighter in London for love or money, except some surviving jeweled specimens at £ 100 or more. The government is now planning the manufacture and distribution of a "national lighter," to cost about seventy-five cents, but it had not appeared by the time I left.

Clothes, are of course, rationed just as strictly as food is. A man gets 66 clothing coupons a year. A new suit costs 26 coupons, an overcoat 18, a pair of shoes 7, a shirt, 5, and so on. Add it up and you will see that you do not come out with much of a wardrobe. The coupons do not represent value; what they represent is permission to buy. You may have £ 100 in your pocket, but you can't buy a sixpenny handkerchief without a coupon. In London I needed a pair of rubbers badly. I couldn't buy them, no matter what I was willing to pay, until the proper authority gave me permission, *i. e.,* three coupons.

From all this there are several points to make. Few Americans, I should say, realize how severe the pinch in England is. (The pinch in Germany is, of course, infinitely more severe.) Probably in our own country we shall never have to suffer from shortages so acute or serious. We are blessed with an abundance of food and raw materials. We do not need to import food, as England does. The lesson from England is nevertheless clear, striking, and obvious—that sacrifice is necessary to wage war, that the need of sacrifice becomes more urgent as a war goes on.

One striking phenomenon in England is what might be called equality of sacrifice. The war has pitted and scarred every man, woman, and child in Great Britain. Nobody is exempt. Of course the poor have suffered most—even though unemployment has been virtually wiped out and wages have gone steadily upward. But the rich have suffered too, and make no mistake about it. The very rich are, in fact, on the verge of disappearing as a class. They are finished. Taxation begins at a flat 50 percent (with certain exemptions) and in the upper brackets it reaches 95 percent. Nobody in England can make more than about $16,000-$20,000 per year *out of income,* no matter how large his gross income is. Taxes take all the rest. A very rich man may have more than $20,000 a year to spend, if he chooses to use his capital; but $20,000 is the approximate limit so far as actual income is concerned.

One more lesson for Americans is of primary and paramount importance. Many British have been bombed out of their homes. Their families have been scattered, their children sent abroad. They endure the discomforts of the blackout. They are deprived of many amenities of life, and they pay fantastic taxes. Yet they remain good-humored, staunch, tolerant, and united. This is the chief lesson we have to learn from London. The British endure hardships almost inconceivable to us, and endure them smiling. They have not lost their sense of balance, their instinctive fairness of mind, their humor, above all their kindness. They have sat naked on the edge of complete disaster—after Dunkirk, for instance—and come up stronger than before. They are tough—don't minimize that. But they haven't succumbed to any hysteria. They've kept their feet, kept their heads, kept their free minds. Through the greatest crisis in their history they have remained completely adult. Let us hope that we in our country can do likewise.

It would be foolish to assert that the war has broken down the old social castes of England. Dukes are still dukes, and navvies navvies. Nevertheless the amount of what might be called "democratization" is considerable. To take just one instance: About 60 percent of pilots in both bomber and fighter commands of the R. A. F. are sergeants, *not* commissioned officers. These are the men who saved England in the Battle of Britain in September 1940; these are the men whose long-range bombers traverse the Continent almost nightly, attacking Berlin, Brest, the Ruhr, the Rhineland, and other enemy objectives. Very often commissioned officers serve in bomber crews *under* a sergeant, a noncommissioned officer, who is in command.

Another point—which we will do well to watch closely—is the enormous activity of women in war work, which also serves to shake a country up, to demoralize it. As every one knows, British women take part in actual military service. There are three main organizations: the Auxiliary Territorial Service, which functions with the army; the Women's Royal Naval Reserve, associated with the navy; and the Women's Auxiliary Air Force, which operates with the R. A. F. Thousands upon thousands of British women have enlisted in these organizations, and are known as "Ats," "Wrens," and "Waafs." Additionally, of course, thousands more women perform war work—everything from sweeping railway platforms to labor in munitions plants—in nominally civilian fields. Uniformed women toil side by side with men in the aircraft batteries which guard the periphery of London. I mentioned this to a Cabinet minister of great eminence. He grunted with ironic humor, "Thus, day by day, we march back to the Stone Age!"

London is not the capital of one country. It is the capital of six or eight. The Yugoslavs, the Norwegians, the Dutch, the Belgians, the Czechoslovaks, the Free French, the Greeks, the Poles all maintain their headquarters on British soil. Polish soldiers guard British shores; Polish and Czech and other foreign flyers fight with the R. A. F. One small but pertinent point is that instructions on R. A. F. dinghies (lifeboats) are printed not merely in English and French but in Czech and Polish too. In one R. A. F. bomber station I met pilots of seven different nationalities. It may well be that the rudiments of a future international air force, to protect peace in the world to come, are in process of creation on English soil. This is a movement which we in the United States should watch with closest sympathy and attention.

I asked almost every one I met in England: "What will England be like after the war?" I got a fascinating variety of answers. Two points stood out. Almost every one agreed that the future England would be a different kind of England; they couldn't predict just what the difference would be, but in any event it must be an England *worth having saved*—in other words, a better, stronger, healthier England for sons and daughters to grow up in, admire, and love. The million little men in England are doing their jobs. The A. R. P. wardens, the fire watchers, the shopkeepers, the country constables, the men and women in the factories have served the country—and helped save it—just as staunchly as have the army, the navy, and the R. A. F. The little man has made prodigious sacrifices. And he doesn't want to be let down.

Second—and here too there is a lesson for America—almost every one I met thanked Providence for the leadership of Winston Churchill. They have found that democracies need leadership even more than dictatorships do. What England has achieved after terrible ordeals, is unity of morale, of spirit, and of command. Every one knows that this war is going to be long, difficult, and dangerous. People, in fact, don't talk much in terms of when victory is going to come, although their confidence is absolute; they think of victory rather in terms of a job to be done, and that will be done. Finally, they know what this war is for, what it is about. Not all of us in America know this yet, fully and instinctively. The British know it is a war for the right of peoples to be free, and for survival as a nation.

The Pirates of Mascarenhas

a story by C. S. Forester

It Might Mean a Rope's End, but the Prize
Was Worth the Gamble to One British Sailor

THE LIFEBOAT HAD reached safety. Her sail was filled with the breeze off the sea, sucked in by the burning heat of the African continent, and the first mate could sit relaxed in the stern sheets, the wind comfortably over the quarter, the sheet caught in a single turn over the cleat, the tiller in his hand, and the boat heeling pleasantly and riding the swell with the masterly ease that never fails to stir the heart of a lover of the sea. It might be a yachting trip in the Clyde, thought the first mate dreamily—many nights without sleep had reduced him to a state close to hypnosis.

"I'm going to have a pint of water," he announced pleasantly, "and I'm going to have it now."

Shaggy heads lifted themselves at the words. The second engineer had been guarding the water breakers. That had been the duty allotted him when the ship was torpedoed, and he had been carrying it out for more days than he could remember. All he knew now was that he had to guard that water, and three times a day dole out a miserable cupful to each man.

He glared at the first mate, and then at the men crawling toward him, like a lioness defending her cubs.

"It's all right, Mac," said the first mate. "We're safe now. Any one can have a pint of water."

He nodded toward the green island that pushed its shoulders over the horizon.

"This wind'll hold till nightfall," he explained further, "and we'll be there in two hours. That's Mascarenhas. We haven't got to make the African coast."

Eight days of thirst, of lying cramped in a tiny boat, of exposure to the equatorial sun, had reduced them all to a state of torpid misery from which only the prospect of water could rouse them. When the land had been sighted an hour back, the fact had hardly penetrated

their dazed consciousness. After eight days of thirst and exposure it seemed to them as if they were doomed to nothing else than thirst and exposure for the rest of their lives.

"Smith's dead, sir," said a croaking voice from the bows. Smith had been injured when the torpedo hit the ship.

"Well, he'll have a shore burial," said the first mate. In these eight days he had grown accustomed to looking on the bright side of things for the sake of his men. The second engineer was pouring water. The sound of it was to the first mate music more splendid than Bach's Mass in B minor, which he had heard in Liverpool Cathedral the last time he had been home.

The men drank in turn. When they reached shore they would drink, and drink, and drink, and the first mate had heard somewhere that such drinking after prolonged thirst might be fatal. This would be the best way of slowly bringing them back to normal. The first mate knew his duty to his men.

He put the tiller over and hauled in on the sheet as the boat rounded the tip of the island. Far beyond, there was a thin gray-green line on the horizon which indicated the mainland of Africa. This island of Mascarenhas was one of the few residual scraps of the Portuguese Empire which had once stretched world-wide. The steep slopes were vividly, tremendously green with the vegetation nurtured by the equatorial rainfall. Where the horns of the island drew together to offer shelter from the winds and the Atlantic surf, the slope was scattered with little white houses and there were a few small boats round the dilapidated pier. But what caught every one's eye was a big ship that rode to her anchor there. She was huge, 20,000 tons of her towering out of the water, well kept and glittering. The British sailors, sunbaked, bearded,

half naked, stared at her morosely. They read her name, *Regina di Sicilia*, and her port of origin, Genova.

"Italian," commented the first mate. "Took refuge in the neutral port when Musso stabbed us in the back."

As the boat neared the ship they came under the lee of the land, and the sail flapped and the boat lost way and drifted under the blazing sky.

"We'll show 'em," said the first mate. "Where's that flag, Brown?"

It was a dingy little red ensign which had found its way into the boat heaven knew how. It hardly moved in the heavy air, but the dull red with the faded union in the corner was recognizable to any one. The crew of the *Regina di Sicilia* saw it as they came lounging up to the ship's side, and the defiant gesture roused them to action. They shouted jeeringly at the British sailors. The words were unintelligible, but there was no mistaking the import of the gesticulations that accompanied them. The Italians lined the rail and spat in unison, and their hands moved in the age-old signals of contempt. The first mate shouted what he thought of them, but they either did not understand him or made out that they did not.

The chugging of a boat motor shifted the point of balance of the scene. A Portuguese boat had put out from shore to them. The colored sailors on board seized the lifeboat's painter and took her in tow, and the Italian jeers died away in the distance as the lifeboat brought up to the pier.

The port police and the port doctor were awaiting them, and the British consul came hurrying down just as they were helping the British sailors out of the boat. Eight days of it, eighteen men in one boat, left them so cramped and weak that they could not stand without assistance.

The first mate stood swaying in the sun, trying to keep his head clear. He did not want to reveal any military secrets as the port authorities questioned him. He gave the name of his ship but not her destination nor her position at the time she was torpedoed. He reserved that information for the British consul after the port authori-

ties had helped away the sailors and carried off the dead man for burial. Then he asked eagerly if any news had been received about the other two boats, but the consul shook his head.

The first mate remembered the sudden storm which had swept down on them the second night—the desperate bailing, the long hours spent tossing insanely and jerking madly to the pull of a sea anchor. Not many boats would live through that—he did not know how his own had managed it. After that, his duty done, he fainted dead away.

Two days later he and his men were walking through the odorous lanes of the town, recovered; dressed in clothes procured for them by the consul, and awaiting the chance of a passage back to a British port. They had shaved off the beards acquired during the voyage— all of them except one or two who had come to like the effect—and they prowled restlessly in the tropical heat and the drenching rain. The colored police eyed them askance, for officers and men from the *Regina di Sicilia* were in the habit of coming ashore as well, and every one in Mascarenhas feared lest the whole town should be torn apart in a battle between the two nationalities.

The first mate and the consul were standing by the pier gazing out at the Italian ship.

"We've only got one gun between us," said the first mate pensively. The revolver which he had brought with him from his sunken ship pulled his coat out of shape on one side. "Can you tell me where I can get some more? Half a dozen or so?"

"Is it piracy that you have in mind?" the consul asked, and the first mate nodded.

"I suppose you could call it that," he admitted.

"Every one would call it that," said the consul. "They'd hang you for it—the Portuguese authorities here, I mean—as sure as a gun if they caught you at it. And I don't mean maybe, either. They'd be hopping mad with you. They've got their neutrality to think about. Suggest anything like this to them, and they'll be seeing pictures of Lisbon bombed by the *Luftwaffe* tomorrow."

The first mate's expression did not change.

"But if they didn't catch us?"

The consul spread his hands.

"There'd be the devil of a row," he said. "Notes, protests, diplomatic representations—everything all the way up the scale."

"Everything except action," the first mate grinned.

"Yes," reluctantly from the consul. "But that's not what I'm worrying about. It's you. I tell you, man, they'd hang you for piracy. I don't think they would hang all of you, but they'd put all the rest in jail for ten years. And if you had seen the jail they have here in Mascarenhas you'd know that you were the lucky one."

"Yes," said the first mate. "And now tell me where I can get hold of some guns."

The consul sighed.

What passed further between those two after the consul sighed is not publicly known at all. But in the forecastles of a dozen ships at sea today, where the scattered crew still do their dangerous duty, the story is told of how the first mate assembled his men that day at Mascarenhas and made them a speech.

"I want some of you," he said, "to take a chance of being hanged. There's quite a chance of it, and if you're not hanged there's still the chance of rotting in jail. Who'll take the chance with me?"

The seamen did not take their eyes from his face—they did not even glance at each other to estimate the opinion of the meeting. They had all known the first mate for a long time and they trusted his judgment.

"Nobody wants to drop out?" said the first mate. "I'm warning you men that what I have in mind is piracy. No other word for it—just piracy. And if we are caught we're hanged. You're still all agreeable? Right! As a matter of fact, I didn't expect anything else. Well, which of you can handle a revolver?"

It was while the first mate was making his plans and giving his orders to his crew that Senhor Joao de Sousa came into the story. It might have been pure coincidence, but if it was, it was a peculiarly fortunate coincidence. It is beside the point to argue that Senhor de Sousa was notoriously pro-Axis in his sentiments. When sentiments cost nothing they can very easily be assumed.

Whichever way it was, Senhor de Sousa remembered that tomorrow was the anniversary of the March on Rome. It was an occasion that called for a celebration on a grand scale, and Senhor de Sousa sent a most cordial invitation to the officers of the *Regina di Sicilia* to dine with him in honor of the day. The first mate, lounging by the pier in the fast gathering evening, saw the *Regina di Sicilia*'s boat land a mass of officers in tropical white. They walked up to Senhor de Sousa's house, and their host came effusively out to meet them, his portly form more portly than ever in white and his hospitable good will demonstrated by the amplitude of his gestures. There was not much colored blood in Senhor de Sousa's veins. His swarthy pendulous cheeks fairly bulged as he smiled, and he led the way indoors, exuding hospitality and perspiration.

The first mate pitched the end of his cigar into the water and walked back to find his crew. It was quite dark when they filed down to the pier and scrambled into the lifeboat. They untied without a sound and silently lifted out the oars. For a few moments they drifted while they bound the oars with rags, and then they crept out quietly toward the *Regina di Sicilia*'s riding light.

The first mate had an orderly and tidy mind. Every man knew what he had to do, from the initial muffling of the oars onward. The lifeboat reached the accommo-dation ladder unobserved, and the first mate was the first man up it, his pistol in his hand. He wanted no shooting unless it were absolutely necessary. The pistol was useful, for one glimpse of it was enough to terrify into silence the two men who composed the anchor watch.

The first mate kept them quiet while the men who followed him bound them and gagged them and laid them helpless on the deck, and then the first mate ran up to the bridge, while the second engineer took a party forward to secure the crew and another party hurried aft to make sure of the stewards.

Up on the bridge something nearly went wrong, for the first mate came unexpectedly upon the Italian wireless operator, who, by the decision of his captain, had been adjudged not to be an officer within the meaning of Senhor de Sousa's invitation. His captain's decision was a disastrous one for the young man in question. There was a moment of surprised recognition as the two bumped into each other, and then the first mate put into a single punch all the exasperated hatred he felt toward the nation that had stabbed his country in the back. Training in a hard school had taught the first mate to hit as hard with his left hand as with his right, and that single punch, brought up from his hip with his body weight behind it, was enough to silence the wireless operator instantly.

The first mate made sure that the prostrate figure was harmless, and then looked forward. A score of the ship's crew had been caught lounging on a hatch cover. They were already lined up against the rail with their hands over their heads. The first mate was glad to see that young Jones had the sense to sit back on the hatch cover, with his revolver supported by his knee, for that was the best way to keep a long line of men covered.

Mysterious little noises were coming from forward, and now there appeared a fresh long line of men, walking in procession with their hands on the tops of their heads. The first mate had thought a good deal about how to keep a large number of men prisoners and harmless, and he had decided that, despite the apparent advantage of locking them up, it would be safer still to keep them where they would be under observation. From aft came another little procession, of stewards and petty officers, all with their hands on the tops of their heads, so that the whole crew was now herded together. Four revolvers menaced them from different points. Young Jones stood up on the hatch cover and addressed them like the superintendent at a Sunday-school treat.

"Squattez-vous," he said, and then, as they did not understand, he explained what he wanted in vivid pantomime. The Italians lowered themselves on the deck, their hands still high. The first mate was reminded of a gymnastic class. Jones had a lot of sense. If the Italians wanted to make a rush, they would waste time by having to get to their feet first.

The second engineer showed up on the deck, pistol in hand.

"There's another one up here, mister," called the first mate softly. "Send up and get him."

The first mate was now the captain of a ship and the second engineer was now one of his officers, hence the use of the honorific "mister." Not that the first mate nor the second engineer thought it out that way—it was purely spontaneous.

"I think that's the lot, sir," said the second engineer.

"Very good, mister. Take your party below and get steam up."

The first mate had time to brood now as he leaned his elbows on the rail. Below him the deck was thronged with a mass of sullen humanity, seated, their hands on their heads, menaced by the revolvers of Jones' party. Overhead the stars hung low. To his left the lights of Mascarenhas gleamed across the water. The first mate wondered how long they would be left undisturbed like this. He wondered how long it would take the second engineer, finding his way round a strange engine room, to get up steam—damned good job that the ship was oil-fired. Somewhere up among those lights were a couple of ramshackle eighteen-pounders intended to protect Mascarenhas from stray aggressors. The first mate wondered what sort of practice they would make at night if the alarm were given. From that it was a natural transition to wondering what it would be like to be hanged. The first mate contemplated all sort of unpleasant ends, but this was the first time he had ever thought about hanging.

The whistle of the voice tube went off at that moment, taking the first mate by surprise to such an extent that he almost jumped from the deck. He had not realized until then how keyed up he was to face any unexpected emergency. He took out the stopper and listener.

"Pressure's rising, sir," came the voice of the second engineer.

"Five minutes more and there'll be enough for the winches."

"Thank you, mister," said the first mate.

Over the silent water from the lighted town came the sudden sound of a boat motor, and directly afterward the first mate could see the faint white of a boat's bow wave against the black water.

"Stand by there forward to up-anchor," called the first mate.

The boat was undoubtedly headed toward the ship.

"Cast off the boat and get that accommodation ladder up," ordered the first mate. As long as the ladder was down it gave no clue to the fact that the ship had been seized, but on the other hand it would provide easy entry for the Italian officers or the Portuguese police—it was not an easy decision to make. But he wanted no shooting. He did not want to add murder to piracy—unless, of course, it was utterly necessary.

The ladder rose out of reach just as the boat was approaching, and the latter swerved away. Somebody hailed the ship unintelligibly. For that matter, the first mate did not know whether the language used was Italian or Portuguese.

"No comprehend," he hailed back.

Another voice hailed from the boat, and there was a sudden flutter among the prisoners below.

"Shoot any man who moves or speaks, Jones," said the first mate, and then to the boat, "Try again-o."

The voice-tube whistle made him jump again, and he hurried to answer it.

"There's enough steam for the winches, sir," said the second engineer. "Enough for slow ahead."

"Thank you, mister."

The boat turned again and was heading back to the ship's side.

"Hoist away there forrard," said the first mate.

The towering steel side of the *Regina di Sicilia* offered only the coldest welcome to a small boat. But the noise of the capstan at work had the effect of driving the occupants of the boat frantic. The bellowings that came up from it were, even to the first mate's ear, in two languages, and the first mate could even distinguish individual words which were of the type that every seaman recognizes. The first mate went to the rail and replied in kind. Thanks to the ubiquity of the British Mercantile Marine, the words he used were understood by the occupants of the boat. The darkness was punctured by the flashes of a pistol, and the stanchion close beside the first mate rang as a bullet hit it. The first mate withdrew from the side. If anything happened to him, the enterprise might still miscarry.

"Last shackle coming in, sir," hailed a voice from forward.

The first mate rang down for full speed and went to the wheel. The propellers churned the water mightily, and as the first mate spun the spokes he felt the rudder bite as it took hold. The ship was gathering way and the first mate headed her out to sea. Another futile volley of revolver shots followed her, and from the battery above the town came an echoing crash and a long orange flame as they fired one of the eighteen-pounders. The first mate never knew where the shell went.

The beat of the engines slowly quickened. As the *Regina di Sicilia* gathered speed the motorboat dropped more astern and finally gave up the chase. A quartermaster came forward and relieved the first mate at the wheel, so that he could pace the bridge and give his thoughts free play again. There was a three-mile limit to equatorial waters, but he had no idea whether pirates were safe outside that limit. Probably not. Probably the Portuguese would hang him if ever they laid hands on him. But it did not matter. He had added a nearly new 20,000-ton ship to the available tonnage. It was only then that another thought occurred to him. Prize money! By golly, there ought to be prize money in this. The Admiralty or Lloyds or some one would fork out handsomely. He was probably going to be a rich man.

"Bring those men aft, Jones," he ordered. "We'll give them a bit of lifeboat practice."

The first mate rang down to stop the engines, and as the ship lost way the covers of the boats were cut free and the boats swung out.

The first mate was reminded of a scene in *Mutiny on the Bounty* as he leaned against the rail and watched the Italians getting out their oars for a long pull back to Mascarenhas. One of the British seamen shouted jeeringly at the castaways.

"Stop that!" said the first mate.

FALA

"A uniform always gets 'em!"

An Open Letter to Capt. Joe Patterson

DEAR CAP'N JOE:

Maybe you remember *Liberty* Magazine. After all, you should. You started it twenty years ago. We remember you around here with considerable kindliness, even though after a few years you did sell us down the river into a fate that at times seemed worse than death. So maybe we're entitled to talk back to you a bit frankly.

As we remember it, Cap'n Joe, you used to be a pretty good guy, with a genuine feeling for the welfare of the little people. We never pass your imposing building without glancing at the quote from Lincoln chiseled over its doorway: "He made so many of them"—meaning, of course, the little people God loves so much. We think you really mean that—at least you did when you put it up.

We're sure you're a pretty smart cookie, too, or else you couldn't have built the biggest—and, who knows, maybe the best—newspaper in the country.

But lately, Cap'n, we can't figure out just what you're driving at. The editorials in your *Daily News* seem predicated on the assumption that people are just no damn good. They don't make you sound like a man who loves people. They are often contradictory and seem meant to create suspicion and further discord rather than the tranquility which the little people everywhere want.

Let's start with a simple fact and see where it takes us. War falls heavily on the little people. Its recurrence must be prevented if the human race can find within itself the power to do so. Any plan aimed at preventing war should get the support of a man who professes to love the little people.

We know, of course, that you think affairs on other continents are none of our business and that we were foxed into this war by the clever British and the "messianic" Roosevelt.

But, Cap'n Joe, isn't it obvious that if we hadn't helped the British and Russians keep fighting we would now be at war anyway? If England, Russia, and China had succumbed to the aggressors, would not their resources now be ranged against us instead of fighting on our side? Our only alternative would have been to make a cynical deal with Hitler and Tojo and let them steal what they wanted from their neighbors while we stole what we wanted from ours.

You know we could never have done that and kept our soul. Besides, it would probably have led to war anyhow and on an even bigger scale.

The "turtle" psychology you advocate for the future seems to us to assure that bigger war some day. We have learned from this present conflict that fortifications don't mean a thing any more. Smart guys on the other side can always figure ways around them. Thus your idea of maintaining our armed strength at a high point and to hell with the rest of the world looks dangerous to us. Some future aggressors may grab the rest of the world while we "mind our own business" and then come and take us apart.

No, Cap'n Joe, the time has come when, for the sake of the little people, we must make a sincere effort to settle the world's squabbles through cooperative international effort. We all ought to concentrate on getting an organization that will work, and on avoiding the sort of toe-in-the-water commitment which is sure to keep it from working.

You and your paper can do a great deal to help bring this about or to prevent it. Before you go any further you owe it to the little people to think this whole thing through again. Why don't you take a nice long walk some day and do that? Make it soon, willya, Cap'n Joe?

PAUL HUNTER
Publisher

Do These Kids Know All the Answers,?

by Helen Gilmore-Herman

A Lively Look at a Quiz That Seemed Too Good To Be True

ONE HOT DAY the end of June 1940, Louis G. Cowan sat in his Chicago office overlooking Lake Michigan and cursed his good luck. Mail was piled mountain-high on his desk, letters were still coming in by the basketfuls, his telephone was an incessant jangle. In brief, he had a brand-new success on his hands—with just one fly in the ointment: Nobody would believe him. Well, not exactly *him*. It was his Quiz Kids they wouldn't believe. People refused to accept the fact that those five youngsters whom he had put on the air a few nights before were on the level. Either the kids were reading off the answers from pieces of paper in front of them, or they'd rehearsed them before they went on the air. Or—

Mr. Cowan picked up the nearest letter and read: "In a country that has a national food and drugs act for inspecting what goes into our stomachs, why isn't there some provision for inspecting what goes into our ears? What do you mean by trying to foist adult child impersonators onto an intelligent radio audience?"

The discouraging part of it was that Mr. Cowan had foreseen this doubting-Thomas angle from the reactions of prospective sponsors, and had hit upon a most effective scheme, as he thought, to scotch it. He had asked Dr. Harold A. Swenson, professor of psychology at the University of Chicago, to sit in on the first session and assure the radio audience of its legitimacy.

"I'd like to say I know for a certainty that these children had no advance knowledge of the questions," Dr. Swenson had said. "Their performance has been amazing and is truly a splendid tribute to our American educational system. . . ."

There it was—plain as the nose on your face, from an unimpeachable source. There, also, was the charge of adult child impersonators! Laughable if it weren't so lamentable! What more could be said to convince the unseen radio audience? Nothing—except to keep on saying it!

So a campaign of educators, editors, and other prominent people was launched. The psychology has worked. Now that the Wednesday-night dial audiences are used to the chirping wisdom of these youngsters, the charges of fake have disappeared.

Of course the kids themselves made the going a bit tough. For instance, a question like this is asked: What is the difference between a majority and a plurality? Ho-ho, think you listeners, I know that one! Whereupon one of the children says a majority is more than half and a plurality is enough to elect—well, roughly what you had in mind yourself. But Joe Kelly, their genial questioner, interposes, "No, I don't think that's quite the idea on plurality." Promptly one of the other kids raps out an answer, clean as an incision: "A plurality is the excess of the highest number of votes cast for any one candidate over the next highest number."

Well, by this time, if you're anything like the rest of us, you're mad enough at being outdone by some eight- or ten-year-old to explode, "What is this? A fixed game?"

Jane Withers, Hollywood's young pride and joy, tried to stump the kids with this one: There are four requirements for a man becoming President of the United States. He must be a native American, he must be at least thirty-five years old, he must have lived in this country for the fourteen years preceding his nomination. What essential requirement remains for him?

Lois Jean Ashbeck's bright little face snapped as she retorted, "He must be nominated—oh, and he has to be elected."

Jack Lucal, thirteen, answered this one: There is found on the earth an element that was at first discovered on a distant heavenly body by the use of a scientific

318

instrument. Name the element, the heavenly body, and the instrument. Jack promptly replied, "Helium was discovered on the sun by means of the spectroscope."

There's an interesting story in connection with how the program originated.

Something less than a year ago Mr. Cowan was trying to dope out a new type of quiz. His mind wandered. News at home had been too exciting; he was to be a proud father in September. He visioned his son (but of course it would be a son!) growing from a baby to a bright little fellow in school. That suggested exams and quizzes—and suddenly, presto, there it was! A quiz for kids, bright youngsters who would knock their elders' hats off.

Pence James, a Chicago feature writer, dropped by and Cowan asked him if he had happened to run into any particularly clever children in the course of his newspaper travels. He supplied some names, three of which eventually went on the air. Sidney L. James (no relation to Pence), of *Time* and *Life* magazines, was the next step in the program. He became so enthusiastic that he undertook to dig up questions while the hunt went forward for the children.

One of the most urgent needs was the right master of ceremonies. Requirements proved tricky: he must have radio experience, a broad background of general information, and a way with the kids.

Joe Kelly, who emcees the National Barn Dance program, was finally selected. Not because of his educational background, but because the youngsters liked him and he seemed to be able to get more out of them than any one else by way of extracurricular comment in front of the microphnoes.

Joe, who abandoned school at an early age for the career of entertainer, is still a little bewildered at finding himself in charge of some of the brightest school children in the country. Just goes to show, he sighs, that you can't play hooky from destiny. Now he's right back in school, boning up like mad in his spare moments.

Many people are asking how the children are chosen. It's all very simple. Any one may recommend a child. These recommendations generally come from friends, teachers, members of the child's family, and sometimes children themselves ask to be considered. Extensive questionnaires are sent to the candidates, and those showing the most promise are personally interviewed. The interviews are long and exhaustive, to determine the extent of the child's general knowledge and presence of mind in giving oral answers, which is, of course, what the youngsters will have to do on the program. The only restrictions are that the child be not over fifteen and, for purely practical purposes, that he live within the Chicago area. Eventually, however, it is hoped that children from all parts of the country will be included.

The questions are gathered largely from the radio audience. Some 30,000 are received weekly, from which Sidney L. James makes a careful selection. A portable radio set is awarded to each listener whose question is used. Sometimes small country schools have worked together to compose a question, which means a radio for the classroom if it makes the program.

The five contestants receive a $100 United States Savings Bond. But the real reward is the friendly fun of the contest.

Five youngsters compose each quiz board and the three having top scores for the broadcast are invited to return the following week. This was believed at the time to be a far-visioned scheme for maintaining a constant turnover in the personnel of the children and still hold enough experienced hands to carry the newcomers who might at first be a little nervous. But they reckoned without Cynthia Cline, Gerard Darrow, George Van Dyke Tiers, and now Jack Lucal.

Cynthia has developed into the dean of the whiz kids, with fifteen bread-and-jam sessions to her credit, as of the present writing. Her ambition is to become an opera singer, and her studies in that direction make her the musical expert of the program and able to answer such catch questions as this: What singer, radio commentator, and Presidential candidate all have the same last name? Could you have answered that one? It's Thomas, of course.

Besides enjoying the healthy sports of a fourteen-year-old girl, Cynthia writes songs, creates dances for which she has won competitive prizes, and, as the height of nonchalance, composes verses during her spare moments in the midst of a broadcast. Asked by one of the guest educators to dash off a poem on the stars in the sky, she wrote:

In the blackness of the night
The stars stand out like candles bright
And all across the Milky Way
They make the summer night like day.
And sometimes you see them slide and fall
Against the heavens' curtained wall.

Gerard Darrow is the Quiz Kids' eight-year-old prodigy. At the present time Gerard is not on the program, but his phenomenal record of fourteen sessions makes him an integral part of any story written about the youngsters. Just as Cynthia is the board's musical expert, Gerard was its naturalist. At the age of four he could name, identify, and give the characteristic calls of 365 birds. People used to get a distinct shock when they asked the tiny tot what he wanted to be when he grew up and he solemnly answered, "An ornithologist." As a direct result of his appearances on the program, several Chicago schools have invited the little fellow to make nature-study lectures before their assemblies.

Another bright and shining light is George Van Dyke Tiers, thirteen, who at the age of three was the subject of a Movietone newsreel. The picture showed Van naming states and their capitals, together with principal countries and capitals of Europe and Asia, and spelling such words as psychology and Czechoslovakia. Van has been a veteran of eleven programs.

The current challenger is thirteen-year-old Jack Lucal, who is chalking up an excellent record. Out of nine appearances he scored first place in six. He comes from Oak Park and River Forest Township High School and is planning to study for the priesthood.

So the Quiz Kids roar along to the tune of millions of radio listeners. In their simple unaffected performance is a profound inspiration to the mother and father of every child living in the United States of America. As Dr. Joseph J. Schwab, instructor in the biological sciences at the University of Chicago, said: "These children are admittedly endowed with high intelligence, but there are thousands in America like them and they prove how our modern schools are making the most of whatever aptitudes children have."

Whole schools are swelling with pride when one of their students makes the broadcast. Themes dealing with them are assigned in English classes, and school newspapers send reporters to interview the underage Information Please broadcasters.

In fact, the Information Please boys had better look to their laurels, for if this keeps up, the kids will be challenging Messrs. Fadiman, Kieran, and Adams any minute now. Not a bad idea, Mr. Cowan.

They Had Magic Then!
a story by Sinclair Lewis

*A Short Story of Acting and Love . . . by
a Novelist Who Is Also an Actor Himself!*

WHEN LILY LAYTON retired from the stage, back in 1915, the reviewers wound lilac ribbons into their typewriters and wailed that she was "a mocking flame, thistledown in the breeze, the last exquisite bloom of the age of Sarah Bernhardt."

It was universally believed that any one so delightful must be somewhat wicked, and that she drank champagne out of slippers almost continuously. The lamentable truth was that Lily had never but once drunk champagne —at the golden wedding of her father, who was foreman of a hat factory in Danbury. In private life this "mocking flame" was a subdued glowworm, and only in the anonymity of costumes and lights and music on the stage did she dare let her fancy go. It was shyness which beguiled her to marry Mr. Albert Puddington Gooch, and retire from acting, at only thirty-five.

Albert was a heavy man, born in Kansas City. He was fond of chess, golf, and thick watch chains, and he had made two million dollars out of the Five Cities Laundry Company. He firmly told Lily that she loved him and depended on him; he told her that she was tired of twenty years of rehearsals and touring; and so, with a never-ended meek surprise, she found herself married to him, with a bulky brownstone house in Manhattan for winter and, for summer, a cobblestone villa at Graham's Beach in Connecticut.

Now she was sixty, and for two years she had been a widow. But she still felt married to Albert and to the laundry business, and the theater seemed lost to her as the roses of Nell Gwyn.

Mrs. Gooch—no one called her Lily now—arose at ten in the morning. She would willingly have been up at six, because she liked the newness of the June mornings here on the shore, but for twenty-three years Albert had asserted that she was a frail skylark, and he was a man, by golly, that could afford to have a wife who elegantly slept late.

Soft in a chiffon negligee, she had breakfast by a window overlooking an inlet, but for a frail skylark she did pretty well: tomato juice and oatmeal and bacon and eggs and English muffins with blackberry jam. She looked no more than thirty-five. Perhaps time had halted during her years of loafing and Albertry, when she had no life in the theater and not much outside it. Her neck was uncorded, her mouth was babyish, her hair remained golden —with aid from a recipe invented by Albert himself—and when she put on horn spectacles to read the morning paper, she looked like a girl playing gramma.

She dressed slowly, in a suit of amber-colored English flannel with shortish skirt, amber silk stockings, and sports shoes with fringed tongues, of which she was childishly proud. She put on fringed gardening gloves and sunglasses, and went out to try to think of doing something with the primulas in the rock garden.

She picked off three dead leaves, moved a pebble two inches, and put a watering can away in the tool chest. From the lawn she looked up at the front of Cobble Cottage: the lower porch of bumpy cobblestone arches, the roof of violent green tiles. It was the stanch abode of Albert Gooch, and there would rarely be any repairs for Lily to enjoy fussing over.

It was now eleven-thirty, and so far this morning she had said no word to anybody, except "Good morning" to Bessie, the substantial maid who had brought her breakfast. Lunch would not come till one-thirty, and it would already have been ordered by the militant cook-housekeeper hired fifteen years ago by Albert.

She thought of telephoning some one—but whom? Her days had no emergencies; they followed the Albertian routine. Today was Monday. On Wednesday she would be dining with Judge and Mrs. O'Rafferty from Brooklyn; on Friday she would have Alderman and Mrs. McGhoul, from Utica, for dinner; on Saturday she would go to the dance at the country club, but go home at nine-thirty, because Lily didn't dance. That is to say, Albert hadn't danced.

Yet she was not bored, because there had never been any one to ask her if she was bored.

Joyfully she did think of something exhilarating to do. She would go shopping. Nothing was needed for the house; the morosely punctilious cook and the wordless Bessie, the maid, would have seen to that, and as to Lily's wardrobe, it had been chosen, down to the last lipstick and beach hat, by Miss Agatha Blitzen of Highup & Swan's. But still, Lily might find something, some new kind of woolly animal, for Albert's niece in Spokane.

She felt as though she ought to ask Cook's permission for going away only two hours before lunch, but, so impulsively that it took her only ten minutes to put away her gardening gloves, she darted off.

She plodded up the weedy lane from Placid Point to Trumbull Avenue. She stopped to watch Joe Silva paint a catboat. She stared into the windows of Ye Poke About Shoppe, with china cats, and Ye Ann Teak Sanktuaree, with porcelain dogs, and The Misses Lambkill: Teas and Luncheons. She stopped to watch a motorist with a West Virginia license buy gas.

The day was hot and humid and dispirited. She wished she had stayed home. On Trumbull Avenue she was more awed than usual by the superior mansions with white pillars, which much resembled the old native Connecticut families who owned them and to whom the words Albert P. Gooch had never, in twenty-five years, been anything but a foreign expression signifying zero.

She came to the town hall: white clapboards and wide green shutters, and on top a prim lantern with a gilded nutmeg for weathercock. The hall contained a sizable auditorium where, in winter, the villagers conducted dances and basket suppers and heard glee clubs from the minor colleges. Lily Layton Gooch, the hermit of matrimony, had never been inside the town hall. She stopped now, for across the front of it, as indecorous as a Hawaiian lei across the shirt front of a senator, was a sign of painted canvas:

THE BEACH PLAYERS
Lincoln Earlhill, Mgr.
10 Wks. of Summer Stock
Broadway Successes with
Professional Actors

This would be the first time during Lily's exile that the village had had any theatrical production more ambitious than *Charley's Aunt*, as presented by the Clambake Boating Club, with the plumber's assistant as Lord Fancourt Babberley.

Diffidently she entered the hall.

A madhouse of young men and women in shorts and jerseys were sweeping, tacking canvas on frames, lugging furniture into the auditorium, or standing in corners and loudly repeating parts. On a tall screen of black paper, in golden letters, appeared the legend: "Through these doors you enter an enchanted world," and below it, a roster of actors from the Age of Illusion.

The names ran alphabetically, in three columns, and at the top of the second column the shy lady saw the name "Lily Layton."

She skimmed through the others: Maude Adams, Margaret Anglin, the Barrymores, Blanche Bates, Marie Doro, and returned to her own. She had not felt so incredulous since the moment when, as a particularly unworldly baby of fifteen, she had received the telegram from David Belasco's secretary offering her a job on Broadway.

She looked about, with a desire to thank these dear kind people for remembering her. None of them noticed her, except when she was in the way of the furniture movers and a man yelled "Gangway!" She peeped wistfully at their excited unheeding faces, and turned. She sighed that there was no Miss Layton any longer, but only Mrs. Gooch.

Out of the box office a thin, very bald man popped, yelping, "Lily! I don't believe it! What are you doing here? Don't you remember me? I'm Ben Malon. I was company manager when we were touring Sussex Sands. Not so young as I used to be—well, I guess none of us are, no sir—so I came up here to run the business end for the kiddie-kar outfit. Like to meet 'em?"

Before Lily had time to be shy about it, Malon had yelled, "Hey! Linc! Come and meet your betters!"

Lincoln Earlhill, the manager, was twenty-five and looked like an Apache Indian; in winter he did a strange ineffectual thing called "teaching drama" in a Western college; summers, he devoted what money he could wile out of his relations to small impromptu theaters. He greeted Lily with a reverence she had not known these latter years.

"I never thought I'd have the privilege of meeting you. Of course I'm not old enough to have ever seen you on the stage." Lily winced, then forgave him. "But I've read everything about you. Would you like to see our layout here? Oh, come on!"

She was pleased when, gaily, not waiting for her consent, Linc seized her arm and marched her down the auditorium aisle and up rickety pine steps to the meager stage. It was only twenty feet wide, the curtain looked like a decayed sheet of oilcloth rolled around a fence rail, and there wasn't enough room in the wings to hide a dwarf. But Lily was content. These ten years past she hadn't been going back on opening nights in New York; she didn't seem to know these preposterous new stars, and they didn't seem to remember her. To walk across a stage, any stage, aroused her.

"Look. We only got two dressing rooms for the whole gang. But they've got good light," said Linc. He led her into a coop smelling of chalk, dust, mice, and old paper, with eight stools distributed at four kitchen tables bearing milky old mirrors in pine frames.

"Well—But I've had it worse than this on the road," said Lily.

"That's what I tell the kids! I'd like to have 'em meet you. It'll be an inspiration. Look. Would you come out and meet our leading lady—Sophie Anscoff? She's only twenty-two but I think she's a real genius. She played with the Group Theater—right on Broadway—once! She'll be awfully proud to meet you."

Lily would have gone with this adoring young man even to meet a critic.

They teetered down sinister dark stairs to the yard back of the town hall. It was quite a dirty yard, strewn with abandoned jalopies, shaky benches, secondhand tombstones, and the wreckage of political reputations; but amid the debris a young man clad chiefly in optimism was stippling a piece of scenery which was lying on the ground, a young lady was turning an old-fashioned hat-rack into a gilded throne, and on a discarded church pew, devoutly reading Stanislavsky's *My Life in Art,* was Sophie Anscoff.

She was beautiful as a thunderstorm is beautiful; her black hair was in elf locks and seemed the darker above her atrocious costume of orange sweater and crimson slacks. Her nails were red lacquered and they appeared to be the only very clean portions of her fine brown hands.

Lily and Sophie looked at each other scrupulously and hated each other as fire hates dry wood. But the innocent Linc babbled, "Soph, this is Lil-y Lay-ton! Sure 'nuff! She's been living here since she retired."

"Layton?" queried Sophie huskily. Oh, she was an actress, all right; she was good, quite good, but not good enough to keep an old trouper from perceiving that Sophie knew perfectly well who she was. With her first really pleasant viciousness in a long while, Lily cooed, "Yes, I was on the stage myself once, Miss Uh."

"Oh, yes, I remember now," crooned Sophie. "Didn't you use to do Barrie and Molnar and all those caramel-sundae parts? Isn't it curious how that sentimental eye-wash has disappeared from the theater now?"

Linc Earlhill scolded, "Oh, Soph, for Pete's sake, don't get started on the Social Significance! Just let me tell you, people like Miss Layton and Ethel Barrymore, back in the days when they could still get romantic scripts, really made the stage in this country. They had magic then."

"Ah, yes. Magic . . . magic!" sniffed Sophie.

Through a tight throat Lily croaked, "So you don't believe in magic—in romance—in illusion?"

"No, I don't. I'm down on all this charm stuff. All phony."

"I see. And just what do the young discoverers propose to put in its place?"

"Realization of character. Identification. Concentration of attention. Reality. Power!"

"What nice words those are. Well, I'm glad to have seen you all. Good day!"

Lily knew that the embarrassed Linc was trying to iron it out, but she marched through the alley beside the town hall and homeward. As she passed the drug-store she disapprovingly saw that the theater youngsters were sitting at the counter ruining their stomachs with ham sandwiches and malted milk. She wanted to round them up and take them home for a decent meal. But she told herself that she was hurt and hungry, that she was finished forever with the untrained and bumptious brats who were ruining the theater today.

She lay awake till two that night.

She was asking herself if there wasn't something to what that wretched young Sophie female had said. If she had depended more on power and knowledge and less on charm and Albert Gooch, mightn't she still be in the theater, instead of being the servant of Bessie and Cook and a house of cobblestones?

Of course she vowed that she would never go near the Beach Players again, and of course she went to their opening night, when they presented, or thought they were presenting, *Brief Moment.*

She assumed that a woman of her Goochian respectability couldn't possibly go to the theater alone, though just why she couldn't in this gray marsh-scented community where the most perilous night rovers were wild pussycats, she couldn't have told you. She went with old Mrs. Dr. Jones from Schenectady—two shy, quiet, pretty women in embroidered Chinese shawls, ignored equally by the Old Families and by the arty summerites to whom summer theaters were almost as amusing as sailing or psychoanalysis. . . . She had once been Lily Layton; she had once been a magnet to waiters as the consort of the vigorous cigar-smelling Albert Gooch. She was nothing now but Row G, Seat 16, while up there on the stage a congenital orphan like Sophie Anscoff was for two hours the dictator of the world.

Except for Sophie, the performance of the Beach Players was bad; it was atrocious; and the setting was a brown blur with some chairs and a couch. As for Lincoln Earl-hill's direction, you couldn't exactly say that it was bad; you could only say that there wasn't any direction. If three or more actors were speaking, the idea was for them to make a neat stage pattern by standing side by side in line, like a college glee club.

Lily was alternately hot and cold; gloomily pleased that these young interlopers were so bad, and embarrassed that fellow craftsmen could ever be so sloppy. She had never in her life walked out on a play, and she didn't now, but that night—after getting rid of Mrs. Dr. Jones, who had also disliked the performance but, like a true layman, for the wrong reasons—she sat alone on her terrace, looking into the moist darkness with only the riding light of a yacht to keep it alive, and tried to assure herself that she was glad these brats had shown themselves up.

It didn't much relieve her that Sophie had been good. Sophie overplayed, she made with the eyes, she gasped and beat the breast, but she had life in her and protest. Lily brooded, That beastly young woman! I hate her. A born ham. But—if she had the training and the direction, she'd be another Kit Cornell!

Not till Friday night of that week did Linc Earlhill come to her.

He was hungry-looking, he was tired and scared, and he talked in an anxious cataract, with none of the small pomposities of a college instructor.

"I saw you at the show Monday evening, Miss Layton. I could see you didn't like it. And how right you were! It was fierce—and it's been getting worse all week. I guess I can't direct. I get so sore I lose my temper, and then the actors do what they want to, especially Sophie. I could choke her to death! Oh, she might become a good actress—"

"I thought you were in love with her."

"Yes, I guess I am—anyway, I certainly hate her just now and—oh, yes, I hate her, and—Miss Layton, I want a thousand dollars. Right away."

"What?" She didn't sound like Lily Layton or Peter Pan; she sounded like the relict of Albert Puddington Gooch, who invented bookkeeping.

"I know. I got an awful nerve. But I've put in all I could get my hands on, and if I can't raise another thousand bucks we can't get through the season. The theater will go bust, and that would be a tragedy."

"Do you think so, Mr. Earlhill? It's a very bad theater, you know."

Linc stood over her chair so that she resembled a white rabbit in the shadow of the Leaning Tower of Pisa.

"Yes, and why is it bad? Because none of us has a chance, except in the summer theaters. For every job on Broadway there's a hundred competent kids scrambling for it and praying for it and willing to cut throats for it. How the deuce are we going to learn to act and direct by acting and directing? And then, when semi-amateurs like Sophie and me try to learn, a big-time star like you just laughs at us and says we're bad! You used to love the stage, and the stage loved you, and it made you. Give us a chance!"

Lily made one of those swallowlike rises of hers that had once been famous, crossed to her demure white desk, and wrote a check for a thousand. Then she adventured:

"Do you think it might help you if I came and acted in one of your productions? I'd just expect Equity minimum salary, and—" She was appalled; she answered herself: "Oh, that's a silly suggestion. I'm all out of training."

She was in her lilac-silk chair again, smaller than ever. As awkward as a brown bear in the zoo, Linc knelt by her, kissed her hand, and cried, "That would be the biggest thing anybody ever did for the theater!"

"I don't think Sophie would agree with you."

"She'd better, or else!"

The Beach Players were to do, for their fourth week, the recent Broadway success, *Daughters Don't Understand,* starring Miss Lily Layton as the Mother and featuring Miss Sophie Anscoff as the Daughter.

It was an Intellectual Play, with a great deal of conversation in it, mostly to the effect that the world was a good deal upset and that the Younger Generation didn't like it much, and didn't like their parents at all. Having been created by an Intellectual Playwright, the central character was, naturally, an Intellectual Playwright, who was the Mother. No intellectual ever stoops to writing about anybody except playwrights, novelists, critics, and poets—though you may work in a doctor, provided he does more talking than operating. The law is that if a customer doesn't find these superior people and their love lives important, he'd better stay home or go to *Hellz a Poppin.*

When Lily read the script, she flinched. Where were the fairy lights, the green-gold robes, the guttural villain, the cloudy moon above enchanted woods? She didn't understand a single line of all this talk about the World Today—she never did understand it. Yet during rehearsals she was more excited than the youthfulest apprentice, and much more scared. She knew so many more things to be scared of, from having a stone wall (made of canvas) fall on her, to the major tragedy of coming out onstage with a petticoat showing. With glorious idiocy, she went clear into New York to get her make-up at the seedy old drugstore on Sixth Avenue with which she had dealt twenty-five years ago. From the comments of Bessie and Cook upon this escapade, one would have assumed that Lily had, at least, eloped to Peru with a Russian gigolo.

She tried to be one with the youngsters by coming to the first rehearsal at the town hall in sneakers, sweater, and slacks, but she who had nonchalantly worn tights as a fairy princess now felt depraved and extremely un-magic in masculine trousers, and at the other rehearsals she wore her smuggest gray-blue suit and white buckskin shoes with the highest heels on record.

The play concerned Daughter's revolt against the dramatist Mother and their rivalry for the same young man. In the final act Daughter suddenly grows up, turns on her elders, and wins the hero—a person whom one would distinctly not want to have in the household.

Lily made the Mother easy and smiling; her most vicious lines she gave so lightly that she seemed amiable. She heard Sophie Anscoff wail to Linc, "Oh, good Lord, that woman is going to go and get dainty on us!"

Lily reflected, with considerable less timidity than a week ago, And how! You watch me, you young unemployable!

She was disappointed that the company were all on time for rehearsals. It would have been pleasant to have been there ahead of them always, and to have looked with quiet superiority as they straggled in. But they were punctual, they worked hard, they were ambitious—and all of them, save Sophie, were artistic ditchdiggers and vegetable cooks.

Where were the charms and grandeurs of the old days, when the theater had been a shrine, a sanctuary from the world and its vulgarities? Where now was that great gentleman of the stage, Chesterton Gaul, who had never read a book in his life yet who became, at will, king, bandit, or beggar, and whose smile had always lifted the frightened little Miss Layton? Oh, well, he was an old man now, living in an actors' home and forgotten, and every year she sent him red roses, and he answered, on paper with a crest, in a note that was equally courtly and misspelled. And where were the tenderness and wrath with which David Belasco could turn a kitchen wench into a serene goddess? Linc's well meant direction consisted in spotting the players about the stage in nice geometrical patterns which seemed to have no purpose except to bunch them in front of the star during her best scenes.

Lily's only real fun at the rehearsals was in warfare with that young anarchist Sophie. The other beginners, as she sat with them on a plank bench waiting her turn at rehearsals, were indifferent to her; they had never heard of her, and most of them did not know that there had ever been any theater before Orson Welles. They weren't interested enough to ask her advice—poor woman, she would have been so pleased to give it!

But Sophie could be depended on to keep up a very high level of offensiveness. She knew who Lily was, and didn't like it. As Lily sat by the fireplace (which, in rehearsals, was a grocery box), suavely gesturing with her cocktail glass (a small paint can), Sophie threw the lines back at her only too quickly, too harshly, looking her hatred of the suavity. Well, hate is at least never dull.

It was clear to Lily that she'd better know her lines. There wasn't going to be any pampering of the glamorous old-time star. And she learned them. She drafted Bessie, the housemaid, to cue her every evening, and that was a feat. Only Cook herself was solider and soberer and less approving of play-actin' and goin's-on than Bessie, who had also originally been hired by Albert Gooch. But half by impertinence and half by whimpering, Lily coaxed her to listen, over and over, to such bejeweled lines as

"I sometimes think that virtue is founded more on deafness than on good sense."

Her part went on like that for eighty sides and till two in the morning, when Bessie fell asleep in her chair. Lily kept at it, tramping all over the bedroom, glaring, moaning, stammering, yanking at her own soft hair. At dress rehearsal she did not miss one line, and so she came, in this war of attrition, to the set battle of Opening Night.

Lily was sick-scared. *They* were out there in front. They, the Audience, the eternal censorious godlike They, who were not human at all but a dark diabolic mass of beings without faces, who laughed in the wrong places and coughed all the time and could destroy you if their super-human intelligence was not satisfied by the sweat and terrified desire that you, a working woman, put into your part.

Would They jeer at her for daring to try and come back? Would there be guffaws along Trumbull Avenue after the show?

She clutched the edge of a backing flat till the pattern of the canvas was imprinted on her fingertips. She was muttering her entrance line over and over, but even while she said it, she was convinced that she had forgotten it. She was shaking; she was blind and deaf. She could not hear one line on the stage—and yet she must have heard them all, for on her cue, exact, she came mincing onstage, and They applauded and believed that she was as cool as a traffic policeman.

In the play the time was supposed to be December, but in real life it was very much July, and across the back of her shoulders, under her furs, Lily was sweating like a threshing crew. In the play she was supposed to come into a hostile group of her Daughter's friends; and in real life that was just what she unfortunately did. There was altogether too much realism in the hostility with which Sophie and company looked at her as Lily piped the flatly coy line, "Will you aged philosophers please give an aspiring author a cup of tea—and not too much Italian vermouth in it?"

It is possible for two actors to do a quarrel so alarming that the audience will believe they really hate each other, yet all through it to be saying, with kind and lively eyes, "Come on—you're doing fine—sock me again— isn't this a grand scene!" But when Mother and Daughter closed in a violent duologue later, there was in Sophie's eyes nothing but hostility and contempt for old-time stage technique.

Lily was dismayed, and thrown, and she stumbled on a line. Before the stage manager, whom she could see through the fireless fireplace, squatted on his stool, could prompt her, it was Sophie who gave her the line. That was very nice of Sophie, and Lily was grateful, until she saw that Sophie's eyes were still impenetrable with hatred. Then Lily, who had naïvely meant to help this child, accepted the challenge.

Poor Sophie Anscoff!

She was up against a woman who was generous but who had trouped with seasoned hams that could illegally keep the eyes of the audience on them by shivering, grinning, looking at the feet, balancing a highball glass on the back of a chair, or holding a match until it almost burned their fingers. Lily did nothing so crude as that; she merely used a look of tender surprise, plus a series of bright chiffon handkerchiefs. She fluttered them, she put them to her lips and to her eyes, she dropped them on the floor and looked for them, she squeezed them into damp agonized little wads in a desperate hand.

The wicked audience loved her for all this naughtiness, and watched only her and never looked at the fine desperations of Sophie. By the end of the second act the obdurate Sophie knew that she was licked, and as for getting credit for her high-class emoting, she might just as well have gone home and read a good book.

In the third act Lily did not need even the hokum of a handkerchief. She was sure of herself now. Twenty-five years of indolence were gone, and she was swimming, swift and confident. She just held the handkerchief in her hand, as a threat to Sophie, and began acting.

The Mother was supposed, in this final act, to be shamed and defeated by Daughter's unflirtatious integrity, and to do something like slinking out into the night. But Lily smiled as wistfully as Lillian Gish; she made the audience love her for her frailty and hate the hard Daughter for her self-righteousness. She took Sophie's blows not on the jaw but on trembling lips, and where she should have slinked, she simply stole, and on her exit the audience sounded like the surf, while Sophie, center stage, stood and wondered who had blacked the lights out on all her talent and glory.

Only one person was adequately angry at Lily Layton for her skilled misbehavior that evening, and that was Lily.

She was having to share a dressing room with the five other women in the cast. Four of them tried to congratulate her, but she stopped them with smile and uplifted hand, and thus stopped the ardent Ben Malon and Linc Earlhill when they blundered into this jungle of dressing gowns and cold cream and silk stockings rolled up like doughnuts. But as for Sophie, she stooped over her mirror and neither congratulated Lily nor said anything else.

When Lily was ready to go, her Bessie, who had been indignant at being shanghaied as a theatrical dresser but who was excited now and admiring, brought from the door the news that General and Mrs. Whippany would be pleased to offer Miss Layton their compliments.

For twenty years Albert Gooch had hoped that the Connecticut Whippanys—judges, shipowners, bishops, college presidents, brass artificers since 1657—would sometimes invite his lovely bride to one of their mansions, or at least say something more passionate than

"Haryou." He had died hoping so, but now Lily snapped, "Tell them I can't see them. I have a headache—or I would have, if I looked at their fishy faces."

"Yes'm," said Bessie with respect. She had never heard Mrs. Gooch talk that way.

Lily escaped with no more word to any one.

She whirled around her terrace at home like an infuriated mouse, wishing that she were an actress.

Then Linc Earlhill was there, crying, "I couldn't tell you, with all those people around, Lily!" Yes, he called her that, but the ex-Mrs. Gooch didn't even notice it. "You did the most wonderful acting tonight that I ever saw." Well, she reflected, the young gentleman hadn't seen much acting for comparison. "I realize what a hopeless director I am and what amateurs my company are—especially Sophie. I think I'll fire her."

"Oh, no! You said you were in love with her!"

"I guess I am, at that. I'd marry her if she were willing, which she isn't. She thinks I'm a dried-up Colorado Yankee. Oh, yes, I suppose I'm crazy about her, but not as an actress. You certainly showed up that imitation Nazimova tonight!"

Never had Lily sounded so maternal: "Linc, you *are* stupid! Sophie played circles around me tonight. She played that brat so well that I wanted to kiss her, and the only way I could keep the audience from seeing how she was stealing the show and prevent their laughing me right out of Graham's Beach was to keep on mugging, so that nobody ever looked at the poor baby. You better marry her—do you hear me?—and not let her get away."

"Yes?"

"Before the movies tie her up with a seven-year contract."

"I'll try."

The doorbell was ringing. They heard Sophie's voice: "I've got to talk to Miss Layton. Is she still up?"

"You mean Mrs. Gooch, don't you?" grumbled Bessie. "I'll see."

Lily commanded Linc, "Go in the living room there and leave the door open and listen. Perfect! This is the old farce technique."

Sophie floated toward Lily as if she were enchanted. "Miss Layton, I never knew what acting really was till I saw you tonight."

"It was all hokum."

"Oh, I knew that, of course."

"Oh, you did, did you!" said Lily.

"Sure. I'm not *that* dumb! But for the first time I saw that illusion and loveliness are almost as important as reality."

"Almost?"

"Yes. And I can't express them yet, so I'm going to quit Linc and the company."

"But I thought you loved him."

"Sure I do. But what the dickens! He's so dry. I'd like to touch a match to him. Maybe I'd be willing to marry him, but I don't want to waste my time acting with a director like that. He thinks he knows it all. He won't listen to me! So I'm going back to New York end of next week, and see if I can't find me a Belasco—"

"Oh, shut up! You've found one!" said Linc, as he made a spirited entrance. "I get the point." He kissed her with the ardor and grace of a two-months-old pup.

The two of them sat at Lily's feet, holding hands, while she recalled her touring days. Even Sophie did not consider Lily "dainty" as she told them of six months playing under canvas.

All the while, she watched these harsh, insistent young people, so unsympathetic to her and so incomprehensible, turn human in the spell of her fluid voice, and on Linc's shoulder rested the handsome angry head of Sophie.

They didn't say much but "Thank you" when they went, and Lily could hear them quarreling healthily as they swung up Reedy Lane.

Bessie, helping Lily undress, speculated, "Them actor folks sweet on each other?"

"They will be, if they'll quit being so conscientious."

"Think they'll make a go of it?"

"I don't know. But tonight, anyway—they had magic then. Bessie! Why do you and I let Cook bully us for being young, and then these kids bully us for being too old, and all of them decide between them what we're allowed to do? I'm going back to the stage. And tour. Even if it's character woman in a whodunit. And you're coming as my dresser. We'll get away from Cobble Cottage and Cook. We'll see the whole country again."

"Well, I never been west of Jersey, but—would we get near Baraboo, Wisconsin? I got a nephew there."

"Baraboo? Yes! That's the Ringling Theater. Bessie! Have I still got that old wicker trunk?"

"Up in the attic."

"Let's go have a look at it."

"Now? It's after one."

"Come on, Bessie! On to Baraboo!"

"O. K., Mrs.—Miss Layton," said Bessie. "I guess if you go and make up your mind to do something foolish, it's just about as sensible as common sense. Have they got banana royals out there? I always wanted one, but Cook would never let me have it."

How I Beat the Social Game
by Groucho Marx

*Being Some Pearls of Wisdom from a Hollywood
Funster Which You Must Read at Your Own Risk*

I'M NOT GOING to kid anybody. There was a time when, if I found myself staring at four or five assorted forks at a formal dinner table, I was in a quandary. But that was long before the Four Hundred became the Four Hundred and One and I became known as the Ward McAllister of Hollywood.

Friends who used to laugh when I sat down at the dinner table now flock to me for advice on etiquette. Hostesses rush to the telephone to ask what kind of wine should be served with the wienies, or where to place the guest of honor who has just put three spoons in his pocket. But the nicest compliment of all came from Emily Post herself.

Watching me in action at a fashionable dinner, she admitted that, in comparison with me, she knew nothing about etiquette. Her exact words, as I recall them, were, "If that Mr. Marx knows anything about etiquette, I don't."

And yet even applause and adulation can become tiresome. It becomes inconvenient having people barge up to you at all hours, asking how you managed to lick

with the carelessness of modern journalism. There was nothing in the house but a herring. Even *I* was out—which was fortunate, because that made one mouth less to feed.

That evening I was an unexpected dinner guest in Brooklyn. I mention that because it brings up a point that has been neglected by every other authority on etiquette. I refer to the uninvited guest, or, as the vulgarians phrase it, the crasher.

My advice is this: If your host has, for some reason or other, neglected to invite you to the party you're attending, do not embarrass him by calling his attention to the fact. Only a very low person would enter a home uninvited and say, "You're a fine one! Throwing a party and not asking me. I had a good notion not to come."

Under the circumstances, a gentleman enters the house blithely, through the front door rather than an upstairs window (which I consider the worst kind of social climbing).

He will not make an immediate dash for the bar. Not only because this sort of thing is crude, but because "party liquor," generally of an inferior grade, is served there. I have found that by slipping the butler a two-spot he will get you the stuff he (and of course the host) drinks himself.

In going out socially there are the following factors to be considered, and you'd better study them carefully, because I'm going to ask questions later.

CLOTHES

Since clothes make the man, a woman ought to give a lot of thought to her dress. Her host, if his manners are above those of a skunk, will inform her whether or not she's expected to appear in formal attire. And he should take pains to be specific; because I know a member of one of New York's first families (first as you drive up Tenth Avenue) who wrote on his invitation, "We're not dressing." Unfortunately, one of his guests, a charming and gracious lady who had recently joined a nudist colony, misunderstood.

As a general rule, a woman makes no mistakes in wearing a simple afternoon gown in the afternoon and a nightgown at night.

With men, dress is even less of a problem. A black tie is always appropriate, provided you're wearing a collar. Tails, I believe, look good only on dogs. And even *they* sometimes have theirs cut.

DINING

The experienced diner-out generally manages to be the first one at the table, so that, in the event he has been seated next to a cluck, he can switch the place cards.

If discovered doing this, the gentleman will not, of course, make snide remarks about the cluck. Instead he will adopt a more constructive attitude, gaily tossing off some such observation as, "I simply *must* sit next to the Countess Rittenhouse. The boys at the club tell me she's loads of fun, once you pour a few beers in her."

It is extremely bad form to accompany this remark with a leering "Eh, Countess?"

the social game—especially if you happen to be teaching Miss Garbo the Memphis Stomp or kissing the hand of a White Russian duchess. I'm sure she was a White Russian duchess because I've never met a colored one.

I could, of course, refer people to the standard books on etiquette, but I'm afraid they're of little practical value to a man who lives (as I do) without a footman, three wines at dinner, or Elsa Maxwell. What I have accomplished is simply the result of observing a few simple rules and keeping my nose clean.

It is a matter of record that in 1939 I attended 336 parties, with invitations to more than twelve of them. Of course you have to invite people to your house too. But I won't give much space to that because, with a little careful planning, you can see to it their invitations reach them when they're out of town.

As I say, this requires careful planning. Once, when I was in New York, I gave a dinner party for twelve friends who, the newspapers said, were attending a convention in Minneapolis. Well, it so happened that the papers were wrong. Only *four* of them went to the convention. The other eight came to my house and, please believe me, they were even more disgusted than I was

Now to the food—and about time, too. The first thing to bear in mind is that the salad is at your left and, unless it's asparagus, should not be touched with your fingers. The dish at your right (Countess Rittenhouse) should not be touched at all.

In dining out and finding the food unsatisfactory, a gentleman does not grumble and say that he could have had a better meal at home without having to wait until eight forty-five for it. And he certainly will not make threatening remarks such as, "Madame, if this schnitzel gives me ptomaine, you'll hear from my lawyers tomorrow." (If he *does* get ptomaine, he strives to make a friendly settlement.)

But all of that can be avoided by smiling at the hostess and saying, "Ella darling, I managed the soup and the salad, but this swill has me licked. How about rustling me up a couple of eggs?"

SOCIAL DIVERSIONS

Of all the good things of life, nothing is more popular than necking.

The real gentleman does not indulge in this pastime indiscriminately. He will never neck in a ballroom unless the dance floor is crowded; and he will make no attempt to kiss a young lady who has just yelled for a policeman. Obviously, a man in a uniform has more romantic appeal than the rest of us in business suits.

Most young women do not welcome promiscuous advances. (Either that, or my luck's been terrible.) In society they must learn how to keep a gentleman from pawing without offending him. For that I recommend flattery—some such personal remark as, "Did any one ever tell you that you resemble a weasel?"

QUESTIONS

All right, wise guy, we're going to see if you've been paying attention. The answers to the following questions will be found in a bottle two miles off Vincent Astor's yacht at Newport:

1. If, while carving a turkey, you drop it into the lap of the dowager at your right, do you (*a*) apologize profusely; (*b*) break into tears; or (*c*) say, "Madame, I have not given you the bird; I'll thank you to fork it over immediately"?

2. Should chives or parsley be served with a steak on a black eye?

3. Is it proper to use a nickname—say, "Stinky—on your calling cards, assuming that nobody ever calls you Roderick?

4. If you ask a young woman for a dance and she tells you her feet hurt—and then, thirty seconds later, you see her waltzing away with a young man who has more vaseline on his hair, (also more hair), do you ask her for an introduction to the chiropodist, or do you pretend you're dead?

5. When the lady grabs the check in a restaurant, should she slip the dough under the table to the gentleman or openly hand it to the waiter?

6. On leaving a night club that's been raided, who enters the wagon first—the lady or the gentleman?

7. When a young couple dining out has a spat, should the husband put his best foot forward or wait until he has a pair of spats?

8. Describe the design and colors of three of Lucius Beebe's vests.

9. How can you get a song writer away from the piano at a party without blasting?

10. Would you like to have me drop over some evening for dinner?

If you can answer seven of these questions, and have eaten the tops of four cereal boxes, write in for your Society Man badge.

330

Lamson to the Slaughter

a story by Edward Hope

When a Man Marries, They Say, His Troubles Begin.
But Here's a Soldier Who Collected His Beforehand!

OBEDIENTLY, CORPORAL LAMSON stood, but did not feel, at ease. Captain Carrick poked at the papers on his desk. His eyebrows wiggled. He raised his head and skewered the man before him with the pale, unwinking blue eyes that had been known, unassisted, to extract confessions from hardened offenders. The company called him Old Granitepuss.

"So you're going to get married, Lamson."

"Yes, sir."

"Congratulations." A muscle at the left-hand corner of the captain's mouth twitched but there was no other change of expression.

"Thank you, sir."

"Your love life, corporal, is none of my business. Matrimony is a holy institution and the War Department smiles upon it. That's why you've got a seven-day pass. And that's where I come in."

Captain Carrick's look was long and unwinking. Corporal Lamson murmured, "Yes, sir."

"When Sergeant Morris spoke to me about your impending nuptial rites, Lamson, I was reminded of the illness of your sainted grandmother last November. Just at Thanksgiving time, oddly enough. I recalled her miraculous recovery, widely attributed to your presence at her bedside. On a five-day pass."

"The doctors—"

"I know. They despaired of her life. You'll admit that I swallowed the yarn like a gentleman. But a gentleman retains his own opinions." Old Granitepuss sat back in his chair and continued not to wink. "I suppose you really *are* going to get married, Lamson?"

"Oh, yes, sir. It's Miss Christine Swithin, sir. She was down here with that Junior League show in April. The pretty one who played the piano and sang. I was assigned to the detail that acted as stage hands, the captain will remember, and—"

"M-m-m—yes. She has agreed to marry you?"

"Oh, yes, sir. If the captain would like to see part of a letter—"

"No, thanks, Lamson. I only wanted to be sure. I also wanted you to know that I haven't forgotten your grandmother's astonishing recovery. And its only fair to point out that if anything should go wrong with your marriage plans—if, for example, Miss Swithin should change her mind at the last moment and you should return to duty still a bachelor—I'm afraid I'd consider that a—remarkable coincidence. You see what I mean, corporal?"

"Oh, yes, sir. But there's no—"

"I haven't had time to look up Army Regulations on the point, but I am sure there is something definite about obtaining passes under false pretenses. And although the evidence might be purely circumstantial—That's all, corporal."

"Thank you, sir," Corporal Lamson said thickly, and saluted.

Corporal Larry Lamson pulled his blouse straight, sucked his guts up, and stepped from the burnished copper elevator onto the thick carpet of the Diana Soap Corporation's reception room, which was done in pale greens and indirectly lighted. It gave you the feeling that you were in a tank at the aquarium. A man with a briefcase and a look of determination occupied an armchair to the left. Two blondes with knees lounged in a settee to the right.

The girl at the desk had red hair that went perfectly with the color scheme. She looked up from her book and smiled. Her teeth were very white. She looked O. K.

"Hello, corporal," she said.

She was definitely O. K. Larry let his breath out and went over to her. Her greenish eyes seemed amused about something.

"I want to see Mr. Swithin," he told her.

"Really?"

"Well, no, not really; but I've got to."

"You wouldn't settle for his secretary? Mr. Swithin's in a terrific conference, and Miss Moss—"

The telephone buzzed and the girl answered it and listened. She spoke to the blondes: "Mr. Copley will see you now, Miss Torrell."

The blondes rose and undulated across the room and through the pale green arch beside the reception desk.

The redheaded girl looked up at Larry from under eloquently raised eyebrows.

"Wonderful thing, the human body," he said. "Full of fascinating curves."

"And all of them so movable! Do you insist on seeing Mr. Swithin? Because he's awfully hard to get a look at, and Miss Moss—"

"I'd love to meet Miss Moss, only I've got to see Mr. Swithin. I think he expects me, sort of."

"All right. I'll see, sort of. Corporal who?"

"Lamson."

The girl spoke to a couple of people on the telephone. "Miss Moss says he is expecting you, sort of, but he really is in conference. Will you wait?"

He liked her eyelashes, which were not pink, as most redheaded people's are, but dark and curved. "I'd be an awful fool not to," he said, and took the small chair beside her desk. A man on the dizzy brink of matrimony is under no obligation not to feast his eyes, if he maintains the detached attitude.

The reception girl looked at Larry's insignia. "Infantry, eh?" she asked. "Stationed around here?"

"Fort Rogers, No'th C'lina. Where'd you learn to read uniforms?"

"U. S. O. I'm a hostess three nights a week. Van Ryck House on Lexington Avenue. Why don't you drop in tomorrow night?"

"Guess I'll be a little busy tomorrow night. Anyhow, I wouldn't want to be trampled in the rush for you."

"Timid, eh?"

"Timid?" he said. "If you felt my pulse right now you'd think you had a machine gun by the wrist. I'm not looking forward to your Mr. Swithin. What's he like?"

Her brief, tilted nose developed a small wrinkle above each nostril. "Oh—he's all right, I suppose. A little stuffy, but maybe you're entitled to be stuffy if your family's been making soap for four generations and getting richer each time."

"He's going to be crazy about me," Larry said.

"How do you mean?"

"If there's one thing a soap millionaire likes to find climbing his family tree, it's a prominent corporal."

The redheaded girl's eyebrows were puzzled. "Maybe I'm not very bright. I still don't dig it."

"Ever meet Miss Christine Swithin?"

"But yes! She's terrific. She's about the beautifulest thing I ever saw. What about her?"

"She and I are sort of thinking of getting married."

The redheaded girl gaped. You could see her temperature falling as if somebody had turned on the cooling system.

"Oh," she said. "I—I'm sorry. If I'd had any idea, I'd have been—"

Larry laughed. "You'd have been what? Careful what you said about the old man? I asked you what he was like and you told me. What could be fairer than that?"

"I don't think it was fair of *you*—"

The telephone buzzed once more. The girl said: "Reception desk. . . . Yes, he is. . . . Just a minute. "Mr. Swithin would like to speak to you, sir."

" 'Sir'!" Larry repeated. "Snob!" He spoke into the phone: "Corporal Lamson."

The voice was the voice of Groton and Harvard and Oxford (postgraduate) and Economic Royalty. "Ah—hello, my boy. Look here. I did want to talk to you alone. Heard a lot about you from Christie, of course, and—But I'm tied up here and I don't know when I'll have a minute. You're coming to dinner tonight, aren't you?"

"Christie said—"

"Yes. That's right. Seven-thirty for cocktails. And you'll get a chance to meet the family. You and I can have our chat another time, eh? Sorry to bring you here for nothing, but—See you at seven-thirty, then."

"Yes, sir. Thank—" The telephone clicked off.

The redheaded girl's eyebrows were at work again. " 'Sir'!"she echoed. "Snob!"

"Get out," he said. "That's the army. Get so used to calling people sir, you do it automatically." He got up. "I'm not going to see him now, after all. Thanks for entertaining me."

"Not at all. I did nothing but my duty. Any girl in my place would have done as much."

He had to answer her impudent eyebrows. "I didn't even know who she was, the first time I dated her. She came down to Fort Rogers with a Junior League show, and I—"

"I hope you'll be very happy," the girl said, and he jabbed the elevator button with a vicious forefinger.

The family party did break up at last. Larry should have known that it would, but there had been moments when he despaired of any such happy ending.

He took his modest place beside Christie in the hall and said good night.

Good night to Mr. and Mrs. Smith W. Wrison (Mrs. Swithin's elder and icier sister, who was Christie's Auntie Grace).

Good night to Patterson Swithin (Mr. Swithin's younger brother, Christie's Uncle Pat, a savage caricature of the men of the upper classes).

Good night to Alan and Sue Lockerby (Christie's sister, who had—as Mr. Swithin had confided to Larry—married well).

Good night to Kenneth Swithin (an unidentified young man who had taken little part in the proceedings, being preoccupied with the decanter of whisky, and who was now, in a gentlemanly way, sozzled).

Good night, finally, to Mr. and Mrs. Swithin, who announced their intention of going to bed. They were bearing up bravely (nobility has its obligations) but you knew they were going to toss all night in troubled slumber. Your heart bled for them.

Larry looked around cautiously to make sure he was alone with his fiancée before he held out his arms for her.

She walked into them.

Christine Swithin was the most beautiful thing he had ever laid eyes on. Her eyes, her lips, her complexion, her ankles, and all the other items that are grouped for convenience under Figure, were unquestionable masterpieces of design and execution. She was poised. She was graceful. From the topmost light brown curl on her aristocratic head to the bottom lift of her exorbitantly fragile slippers, she was perfect. Neither more or less.

He gathered her into his arms. Once again her perfume dizzied him. He kissed her cheek and permitted himself the luxury of guessing that everything was going to be all right.

Her relatives, after all, had only their own standards to go by. If you make allowances for slum-born young men who turn into gangsters, you've got to make equal allowances for the very rich. He recognized extenuating circumstances and held no grudge.

He supposed Christie had been as miserable as he during the horrible family party. He supposed she too had been squirming inwardly at the things her father and the others said. But she had been properly brought up and she could conceal her feelings. Poor child, she probably expected him to blame her—

He kissed the tip of her perfect nose and laughed softly, reassuringly. Christie pulled away a little.

He said, "Golly! Are they always like that?"

"Like what, darling?"

"Oh—sort of before-the-war-before-last. Back in the good old days, when you read a few verses from the financial page at family prayers. Embarrassed at having a peasant in their midst, but keeping a stiff upper lip."

His laughter got the better of him. When it subsided, he kissed the lobe of her left ear, and was thus unable to see her face. He went on:

"Your father's a riot. He thinks he's right up to date. And he is, compared to the rest of them. He's caught up with the Coolidge administration. He's ready to admit that the lower classes are here to stay. He doesn't exactly like it, but he's willing to make concessions. He's even trying to be reasonable about letting you marry below your station. He's a yell."

Larry bent down to kiss her more thoroughly. But the expression on her lovely face turned his laughter into something not unlike a hiccup. His fingers went limp on her shoulders. He said, "Look here. I only mean—"

She spoke slowly, and there were little hunks of ice clinging to her words: "You think it's funny, do you?"

"Well, yes. Don't you? I mean, the whole attitude. 'We'll have to keep him dark till we get him ready to meet the best people. We'll get him a commission and have his uniforms made by a good tailor. We'll teach him to wear shoes and use a fork, and we'll beat that Middle Western accent out of him.' If that's not funny, I—"

She broke free and stared at him. Her nostrils quivered with rage. She said, "You don't seem to realize—"

"Now look here," he interrupted. "Either it's all terribly funny or I'm going to have to sock somebody. If I take it seriously I'll be pretty blasted mad. Let's get this straight."

"I'm getting it perfectly straight," she said, and generations of perfect upbringing went down the drain. "You think all the Swithins are ridiculous snobs—"

"That's right," he agreed. "All except you."

"Why except me?"

"I don't know. I thought a girl who'd let herself go for a common soldier—"

"I *didn't* go for you!"

"Sorry. I thought you did. That night I went over the hill to meet you, and we parked the car and—"

"You in-*suf*-ferable cad!"

"That's what I mean," he said reasonably. " 'Insufferable cad.' And your father says 'By gad, sir!' And your Auntie Grace speaks of 'the best people.' First thing you know, you'll be telling me never to darken your door again."

"Oh? Well, I will. I do tell you!"

"Oh, blast! Just when I was getting the hang of door-darkening!"

"Please go!"

"Out—into the night?"

"Before I ring—"

"I know: for Billings, the old family retainer," he said, wondering.

She threw a copy of the Social Register at him, but her aim was poor.

And so he went out of her life, laughing. His laughter carried him all the way back to the Hotel Thomas Jefferson. He was still grinning when he crossed the gilded lobby, and a smile lingered on his face when he switched on the lights in his room and saw himself in the mirror.

The smile came off. All at once he saw that some aspects of the situation were less hilarious. His mind's eye

tactlessly conjured up the face of Old Granitepuss and his mind's ear heard the captain's voice: "If anything should go wrong with your marriage plans. . . . I'm afraid I'd consider that a—remarkable coincidence."

Finally—after he had paced up and down in front of the room's two windows until the rug started to show the wear—he decided to wire Sinkers Purdy. Sinkers had a way of finding out anything he wanted to know. The night was cool for June, but Larry's hand stuck to the telegraph blank.

MARRIAGE PFFFT STOP SOUND OUT GRANITE ON CONSEQUENCES STAYING SINGLE

The redheaded girl was at the Van Ryck House U. S. O. club next evening, as she had said she would be. She was behind the ice-cream counter, and men of the country's armed forces were crowded four or five deep in front of it.

Corporal Lamson, Inf., tried to push into the front rank of ice-cream addicts. He collected (*a*) an unidentifiable elbow under the ribs, (*b*) a snarl from a sailor with a broken nose, and (*c*) a heavy foot on his toes. He decided to wait his turn, and in due course reached the counter.

The redheaded girl was too busy to look up. "What'll it be, soldier?" she asked.

"Just window-shopping," Larry said. "Can't decide."

"That's not fair. No loitering at the—" She raised her eyes and recognized him. "Why, Corporal Lamson! I thought you—"

"I thought so, too, but I was wrong. Listen: how about letting somebody else take the ice-cream fatigue?"

"I can't. It's my turn tonight and I—"

"Yes, but I've got to talk to you. It's important."

A bossy woman's voice stabbed him in the back: "Miss McKittrick!"

"Yes, Mrs. Forsom?" the redheaded girl said.

"Don't let yourself be swamped with the crowd. Do you need some one to help you?"

"No thank you; I can manage. What's yours, sailor?"

"Two vanilla, please, miss, and one orange ice."

Her speed with the scoop was worthy of a magician.

Larry leaned closer. "Let's you and I get out of this," he suggested.

"Can't, thanks. Want some ice cream?"

"Do I have to take some?"

"No. Take some and go away, or just go away."

He went away. He studied the situation, and thought of Mrs. Forsom, who seemed to be in command. She was standing beside a desk at one end of the room, watching things grimly.

Larry said, "Excuse me. I wonder if you can do me a favor, ma'am. The fellow who's going to marry Miss McKittrick is in our outfit. He couldn't get here tonight and he sent me with a very special message for her. Pretty important. I was wondering if somebody else could take over the ice cream and—"

Mrs. Forsom's faith couldn't have moved an anthill. Her expression would have looked fine on a codfish. "I haven't heard anything about Miss McKittrick's being engaged."

"No, ma'am. Maybe I shouldn't have told you. Only—"

"What's the young man's name?"

It nearly floored him, but he recovered in time. He said, "Larry Lamson."

Mrs. Forsom looked at him long and coldly. "Go and wait in the cardroom," she snapped.

The cardroom was on the floor below, between rooms dedicated to billiards and ping-pong. It was empty. Which was good.

Miss McKittrick pulled up in the doorway. She folded her lips in on themselves and moved her head slowly up and down, "Uh-huh," she said. "I thought so."

"But you came anyway."

"Curiosity. Anyhow, Mrs. Forsom seemed to think it was a matter of life and death. What have you been telling her?"

"Just that I had a message for you from Larry Lamson."

"Yes?"

"Well, maybe I put in something or other to make her think it was important. Because it is."

"Why?"

"Oh, come on! Don't stand there being Mrs. District Attorney. Come in and sit down and hear the message."

Her eyes seemed darker in this light. She asked, "Do you always get your own way about things?"

"Initiative is a quality noncommissioned officers are trained to develop," he told her, and demonstrated more of it by guiding her smoothly to the settee, which was screened from the door by a large lamp. She sat under the lamp, and he liked the lights in her hair. She was O. K.

"What would Miss Christine Swithin say to this?" she asked.

"Christie? She'd say she could have told you so, or blood will tell, or thank heaven she found out in time."

"Do you mean she's not going to marry you?"

"That's it. And I'm not going to marry her. Neither of us is going to marry the other. While we're on the subject, I might add that I *am* going to marry you."

"Really? You could knock me down with a left hook."

"I mean it. What's your front name?"

"What's that got to do with it?"

"I'm old-fashioned. I like to know a girl's front name before I propose marriage to her."

"How formal!"

"So what is your given or Christian name?"

"Katherine."

"Very well." He pulled his blouse straight and held his head high. "Wilt thou, Katherine, have this man Lawrence to be your lawful, wedded husband, for better or for worse, for richer or for not much poorer—because nobody could be much—"

"That's not very funny, corporal," she said.

"Funny? I'm asking you to marry me. I'm offering you a good man's love."

"I don't think it's very nice to fool about it."

"Fool? I'm not fooling. I'm as serious as the Articles of War. Do you know your lips are like—like nothing else in the world—and your hair with that lamplight on it is like the northern lights and . . . Wilt thou, Katherine—"

"Oh, stop it!" she said. "Got a cigarette?"

He produced cigarettes and lighted one for her.

"I wish you'd get over the idea I'm making fun of you," he said. "I'm talking about marriage. Love. Cottage in the country. Patter of tiny feet. Grow old gracefully together, unless—Look: you *could* learn to love me if you really put your mind to it and did your homework."

She asked wearily, "Is there something else you could talk about for a while?"

"I'm sorry," he apologized. He unbuttoned the pocket over his heart and fished out Sinkers Purdy's wired answer. He handed it to her. "If you don't think I mean it, read this."

He should have known better. The telegram said:

CPL. LAWRENCE LAMSON THOMAS JEFFERSON HOTEL NEW YORK BETTER MARRY SOMEBODY COMMA BABY EXCLAMATION POINT   SINKERS

Katherine McKittrick was on her feet all of a sudden, and she was very cold and indignant and desirable. She tossed the telegram on his knees and turned away. He only just caught her at the door.

He said: "Look! You've got it all wrong. I didn't think how you might take it. I— It isn't just that I've got to marry somebody. I don't have to. I can explain about that. The fact is, yesterday, when I was still engaged to Christie, I looked at you, and a voice inside me murmured—I thought it was indigestion at first, because I'm not used to voices inside me—it murmured: 'My boy, aren't you making a grave mistake? Isn't *this* the girl of your dreams, after all?' And I—"

"Please don't squeeze my wrist!"

"I'm not squeezing your wrist."

"You are! If you weren't I'd be upstairs by this time."

"Let me tell you about it. I got a seven-day pass—"

"I'm not interested. And the club is closing now and I'm going home."

"Let me take you home and explain on the way."

"I don't want to hear."

"All right. Let me take you home and you can put cotton in your ears."

His earnestness made her laugh and her anger slipped away from her, and she was lost.

He took her home. He told her about his affair with Christie Swithin, and about his grandmother's recovery, and about Captain Carrick's position in regard to remarkable coincidences. He told her how he had spent most of the day thinking about her and how he had decided to ask her to marry him not only because of what Old Granitepuss might dream up in the way of punishments—

"But what can he do to you?" she asked. "I mean, to compare with the punishment you may have to take if you marry somebody you hardly know?"

He shrugged. "Maybe it's technical desertion in wartime, or something. But that's not it. I want you to marry me because I love you. I know you don't know anything about me—"

"Don't I? Let's see. You come from Searsville, Indiana. Your father owned the village drugstore. Both your parents were killed in a train wreck when you were little, and your sister brought you up. Your big brother runs the drugstore and you own a quarter of it. You graduated from Indiana State—"

"Golly! Where did you learn all that?"

"You told me, in passing."

"*I!*"

"But you don't know anything about me."

"I know about your eyes and your hair and your complexion and— Maybe I shouldn't have been looking, but I saw one of your knees when you got into the taxi, and it was all right, too. You've got a nice voice and a sense of humor and— Are you going to marry me or not?"

"Of course not."

"Why?"

"I never marry total strangers."

"You could make an exception just this once."

"And I've got obligations that make it impossible for me to marry anybody just now."

He stared at her profile in the dim taxi. "Say! You're not married already?"

"No."

"Then what—"

"Don't you think you're pretty nosy?"

"You mustn't keep secrets from the man you're going to marry."

She made the nicest chuckly noise in her throat. She said: "All right. You win. My mother died when I was eight. My father remarried, and my sister and I never could get on with our stepmother. She didn't like Pinkie and me. Pinkie's my kid sister. So, two years ago, when I was making enough to support us both, we walked out. So I'm responsible for Pinkie. She's only eighteen and I have to keep an eye on her. She's got a good job now, so it's not the money; but she's too young to have good sense and she's cute enough to attract all the wolves and—" Katherine McKittrick shrugged.

"You're the Good Sense Department?"

"That's about it."

"Tell you a sensible idea. Marry some nice corporal in the army. Find one who's got an electrical engineering degree and owns a quarter of a drugstore. You can't hang around all the rest of your life—"

"It's not for the rest of my life. I promised I wouldn't get married till she was twenty-one, unless she did. That may be two or three years, but—"

"Suppose the right man comes along?"

"If he's the right man, he'll wait."

"Oh, he will, will he?"

"Naturally."

"I see. Say, what becomes of Pinkie these evenings when you're U. S. O.ing?"

"She's secretary to the head of a big defense plant. They work late three nights a week. He's a dear—like a father to her—so she's all right those nights, and I go to the U. S. O."

"You're sure the right man'll wait, are you? Because—"

The taxi stopped at Number 28 Powell Street, which was a slightly cockeyed alley in Greenwich Village. They got out.

"How much?" Larry asked the driver.

"Better keep him," Katherine McKittrick said. "It's easy to get lost down here."

"You mean I won't be coming in?"

"I'm afraid you won't."

"But we haven't settled this business about getting married."

"Haven't we?"

"Of course not. We've only just started. Listen. How about dinner tomorrow night?"

"Pinkie—"

"Bring her along. We'll keep an eye on her together."

"Well, but—"

"What time, where?"

"S-s-s-seven o'clock," she said doubtfully.

"I'll be here."

He bent forward suddenly and kissed her mouth, and retreated into the cab before she could gather her wits. "Good night!" he called through the window.

A week is a pretty short period of time, any way you look at it. Even if you don't squander nearly twenty-four hours of it on trains from and to camp, and another sixteen hours being engaged to the wrong girl, and twenty more before you get a chance to offer yourself to the right girl, it's a pretty small hunk of your life to accomplish anything important in. And if what you've got to accomplish is an entire courtship from the first careless rapture to holy wedlock, a week can slip through your fingers like seven watermelon seeds.

Larry's relief that he had escaped an entanglement with Christine Swithin (and all she implied) was second only in intensity to his conviction that Katherine McKittrick was the one woman in his life. He was perfectly willing to admit certain boyish fancies ever since Hilda Offenschultz, the baker's buxom daughter in Searsville, whom he had wooed at the age of eleven, but this was entirely different. This was the business.

He gave it his undivided attention.

And he started out with a stroke of luck the next evening, for Pinkie dined with Mr. Ricken, her employer, who was a dear and hence above suspicion.

Larry and Kitt had dinner together at a little place where you got steak for a dollar and a quarter. They went on to another little place where you could dance without being stuck with a cover charge. And from there—because it was Saturday night and Kitt could sleep late next morning, and because he still had most of the five hundred dollars from the sale of his car in Searsville for honeymoon expenses—they moved along to another place that had a cover charge but gave you a floor show for it.

It was a large, intimate, delightful evening. It ended in a date for Sunday lunch, and a kiss which was solemnized in the vestibule of 28 Powell Street because it was nobody's business but their own. Without the aid of a soothsayer, you could call it a happy sort of beginning.

And the luck held on Sunday. To begin with, Pinkie had a nasty cold-id-d-doze, just bad enough to confine her to the apartment without making it necessary for Kitt to stay home with her. So Larry took Kitt to an impressively expensive lunch, and afterward on an almost interminable subway ride to the Bronx Zoo, which worked out nicely. They walked in the mild June afternoon and talked about themselves and the war and love and snakes and movies and Kitt's eyes and lion cubs and related topics.

They dined magnificently, at the McKittricks' apartment, on canned soup and dill pickles and scrambled eggs prepared by Kitt, and Larry dried the dishes she washed; and Pinkie felt much better and sat on the sofa while Kitt and Larry danced to the radio. It was exactly the sort of thing the Swithins couldn't have dreamed of. And suddenly it was half-past eleven.

Kitt went with him out to the vestibule.

"Please, darling!" she said, after a while.

"Please, who?"

"Please, corporal!"

"Hah! You would, eh?" She resisted, but halfheartedly. "Honestly," she said, when he released her, "you've got to go."

"In a minute. Do you know we haven't said a word about marriage since the night before last?"

"I know. I thought you'd forgotten it."

"Forgotten!"

"You'd better. You see how things are. I can't think of it."

"You're right, you can't think of it. You haven't got the time. I'm due back at Fort Rogers for reveille Thursday morning, and here it is practically Monday. I've got to hop a train Wednesday night. So we'd better take steps. In the first place—"

"Larry, I can't. I've *told* you—"

"Ask for tomorrow afternoon off. We'll have lunch and go to the marriage license place—"

"No, Larry!"

"How do you mean, 'no'? Do you love me or don't you?"

Her voice was small: "I don't know. You're sweet, and I've never liked being with anybody so much, but—we've only known each other three days—"

"Three days or three years or three minutes! What's that got to do with it?"

"And—well, Pinkie—"

"I hate to hand you the radio stuff about Our Boys in the Fighting Services, but they are sending an awful lot of infantry in an awful lot of different directions. If you take too long to think it over, you may wake up some morning and—"

He had to hold her very tight to stop her trembling. When she was quiet, he said: "All right. Take it back. I'm probably on the list for O. C. S., and that'll mean—"

"It wasn't very nice to frighten me half to death."

"It was very nice of you to be frightened, though. And that settles it. Meet me for lunch tomorrow and—"

"No, darling! Honestly— Oh, damn! I don't *know!*

She twisted out of his arms unexpectedly and managed to get herself into the hall with the door all but shut between them. Through the crack she said: "Take me to dinner tomorrow night before I go to the U. S. O. Seven o'clock here." And she closed the door before he got over his surprise.

He walked over to Fifth Avenue and found an open-topped bus that suited his mood. The night was warm and you could smell wood violets and hear small soft birds rustling in trees. If you tilted your head back and let your eyes get used to the light, you could see real stars far above the palisades the buildings made on both sides.

He rode to 135th Street and had to pay another dime to get downtown again.

And the next day she disappeared. Desperately killing time until he could call for her, he spent the afternoon at the movies and didn't get back to the hotel until after six. When he asked for his key, the man handed him the little stack of messages:

5.21. Miss McKittrick called.
5.32. Miss McKittrick called.
5.34. Miss McKittrick called.
5.51. Miss McKittrick will not be able to meet you tonight.

And that was that. There was no answer at the apartment on Powell Street, though he telephoned every half hour till midnight. The telephone operator at Van Ryck House U. S. O. said they had word that Miss McKittrick would not be able to get there that night. . . .

In the morning, the Diana Soap Corporation's voice said icily that Miss McKittrick would not be in today; it was sorry; it did not know where she could be reached. The Ricken Precision Machine Company (arrived at by a process of elimination with the telephone book) also said icily that Miss McKittrick would not be in today; it whatever had happened to Kitt seemed to have happened to Pinkie too. And even Mr. Ricken, that dear, was reported out of town.

Monday dragged by, and Tuesday was worse. Larry conferred with the hotel porter and found that there was a train at 9.36 Wednesday night that would get him to Fort Rogers for reveille Thursday. As for the prospect of an interview with Captain Carrick, he didn't even care.

Penn Station, dimmed out, had a somber look that was appropriate. People went about their business grimly. Soldiers and sailors and officers of all ranks and services were everywhere, and M. P.s to keep an eye on them. It was nearly half-past nine when Larry paused before the gate of Track II and fumbled for his tickets.

"Larry!"

"Hah?" He didn't believe it. He turned, warily, not to make a fool of himself.

Kitt was there, right beside him, looking very formal and New Yorkish in black, with a perky little black hat tilted forward on her coppery curls. She took his arm in both of her small hands and squeezed until he could feel her fingernails.

"Darling!" she said. "I was so afraid I'd miss you!"

He swallowed hard and cleared his throat and stiffened his jaw. He said, "B-but—"

"I know, darling. It's a long story. I'll have to write it to you."

"What happened?" he managed to ask.

"No time to tell you now. Listen, Larry. Do you really love me—or did you find out, when I wasn't around, that it was all—"

He took her in his arms without shame, without even the slightest idea that other people might be watching, and kissed her mouth. "Do I really love you!"

"Then I can tell you. Remember I said I didn't know? I said I had to think? And—" She swallowed.

The public address system bellowed something about some train or other. Larry Lamson could hear it over the thumping of blood in his ears. He looked into Kitt's eyes, which were darker than he had ever seen them before. He said: "But—then—what about—when can we— It's going to be tough explaining to Captain Carrick, but I—"

Somebody touched his elbow. "All *aboard*, soldier!"

Kitt's arms were around his neck. She said, "Quick! They're closing it!"

He picked up his suitcase and let her push him toward the gates. "What about Pinkie?" he asked.

The man plucked him by the sleeve and he moved forward obediently. The folding grille closed between him and Kitt.

She stood close. "That's what I've got to write you. She eloped. That's why I— She ran off with Mr. Ricken and got married. Thought I wouldn't let her, so she sent a crazy note. I didn't find them till today."

"But then—"

Kitt's head bobbed up and down till the small hat jiggled.

"Run for it, soldier!" the gateman shouted in his ear, and Corporal Lamson ran for it.

The man in greenish fatigue uniform shouldered the broom and shovel and carried the G. I. can in his left hand. He moved along jauntily to the next drain on West Parade. The armed M. P., following at the prescribed two paces, didn't like the prisoner's method of locomotion. There was nothing you could exactly put your finger on, but the so-and-so's attitude was all wrong. A man on post punishment has no right, under military law, to look as if he might be going to break into a dance. On the other hand, a military policeman is not empowered to correct anything so vague and indefinable as a sort of generally sassy look.

The prisoner put the can down and applied the broom vigorously, if somehow flippantly, to the little accumulation of leaves and twigs at the drain. The M. P. hooked his thumbs in his belt and looked on critically. A small sound emanated from the prisoner.

"Cut out that whistling!" the M. P. snarled.

"Sorry. Wasn't thinking."

"Think, then."

The prisoner scooped up his sweepings and dumped them into the can.

"Wipe that smile off!" the guard barked.

The smile came off.

"What you got to smile about?" the M. P. inquired from natural curiosity.

"I was just picturing Captain Carrick's face," Larry Lamson said, "when I ask him for a pass to get married."

"To get— Say, you *had* a pass to get married."

"I know. My error. Wrong girl. Got the right one this time."

"Wipe it off!" the M. P. bellowed, and the conversation languished.

Pin Up!

by Ted Shane

Meet the Girl Who Is Number One in the Hearts of the Armed Forces and Number One at Movie Box Offices to Boot — Betty Grable, As American As a Banana Split and As Bright As Neon Lights

WHEN OUR FIRST Marines on Guadalcanal got things temporarily in hand, some home-minded gent did two things: (1) He tacked a sign to a coconut tree which read: "WPA Project No. 876¾." (2) Under it he pinned up a picture of Betty Grable.

It was a picture not entirely unfamiliar to the armed forces. Hundreds of thousands of copies of it have found their way to the farthest and damnedest places: serving to warm our chilled lads in Greenland or further heating a hut in remote Dang Dong. It shows the tasty Miss Grable rather poorly concealed in a bathing suit evidently several sizes too small for her, and kept warm by a pair of shoes and a bracelet. As her various selling points light up the landscape, she is casting a most vivacious come-hither smile over her right shoulder.

My statistician informs me it is the most pinned-up picture in the world. Betty's postman groans under two to three thousand letters a week—80 percent of them from the armed forces, including our allies, and most of them requesting this very same artistic study.

Let's adjust our specs and look more closely at this luscious phenomenon who is not only number one in the dreams of our armed forces but also number one box-office lure of the present moment.*

*Present box-office standing from motion-picture exhibitors' poll: 1. Grable. 2. Hope. 3. Abbott and Costello. 4. Crosby. 5. Cooper. 6. Garson. 7. Bogart. 8. Cagney. 9. Rooney. 10. Gable. Note that a fully clothed female fails to appear till the No. 6 position.

What is it the boys see in the Grable figure? Starting from the bottom up, Grable stacks up like this:

Shoe	5-C
Hips	34½ inches
Waist	24 "
Bust	33½ "
Glove	6¼
Head	22
Eyes	Definitely blue
Hair	Well—blonde

Five feet three and a half inches high and 110 pounds of dynamic flesh in weight, other Grable characteristics include a peaches-and-cream complexion and a pair of legs which even women like to look at. "It's not that Betty Grable has anything other women haven't," Bob Hope has said; "she just groups it better!"

But flesh is not all. Hayworth, Lamarr, Lamour, and Turner have their points and their fan mail. But it is Grable who is the G. I.'s sweetheart, the dogface's ideal. Grable is a World War II product. Like sulfa, plasma, and plastic bugles, she was born of Pearl Harbor. Before that she was little known.

She's not only streamlined and solid and functional-looking, but she's slangy and hep. She's Miss Waterloo, Iowa; she's the girl next door, as American as the funnies, the banana split, and as bright as neon lights.

A soldier writes to her as he might to his girl back home, associating himself with the role of her protector and escort. She's the workaday girl glorified and glamorized, easy to talk to, within his grasp, the girl he necked and took to the movies. Ninety-nine percent of the Grable service mail comes from the Army proletariat—the G. I.s.

She does hear from officers, too. Every day chaplains, who handle such matters, write from the field asking for her picture for the rest huts and tents. ("And be sure it's the one with the ahems showing," wrote one gentleman.) The captain of an aircraft carrier about to be commissioned to replace one that had been sunk wrote: "We want the new ship to be twice as good as the old one. So please send 200 of your 11x14 photographs in color to decorate our wardrooms. The old ship had 100."

Incidentally, only a snapshot of Betty is sent free. Something larger, at which a guy doesn't have to peer closely— say 5x7, costs a dime; while an 8x10 will set you back two bits. There's a paper shortage and the studio tries to discourage the latter requests, hence the charges. However, Betty pays for and sends out lots of 8x10s, especially where the recipient has a large bare spot on a damp foxhole wall to cover. Mama Grable and a couple of assistants handle this end of things.

Miss Grable has done her share of morale-manufacturing in the flesh. She practically danced her lovely legs off at the various canteens and broke a few Eleanor Roosevelt records for camp travel. Often she danced all night, showered, and showed up ready for work at the studio.

At one camp, ten empty rows faced her in front of the theater. Behind them sat the ordinary troops. "They're for the officers and their wives," a sergeant explained.

"I won't sing to empty rows," said Betty. She stepped off the stage, waved the soldiers standing in the rear to fill those seats, then went outside and sent more into the theater. Since there was still a long line of men waiting to get in, she decided to relieve their tedium by singing to them in a sort of preview of the show. Then she went back into the theater and did the show. Officers and their wives stood up that night—but there was no criticism of Betty.

Another time, on her way to a camp show, a sentry stopped her. "You're Betty Grable, aren't you?" he said. "I guess I don't get to hear you. I ain't relieved till you're finished."

"Oh, yes, you do," said Betty. And to his amazement and delight she went into the song-dance-and-patter act she had cooked up for the camp—without accompaniment.

She has also had direct military influence on the boys. Out at the Independence, California, infantry school, Sergeant G. Crane was having trouble teaching the lads the fundamentals of rifle drill. One day the sergeant pinned up on a bulletin board a series of photographs taken from a picture magazine. They showed Betty performing the Manual of Arms in her usual brief uniform.

"Look, you stupid so-and-sos," the sergeant would yell whenever some lad hit himself in the nose with his rifle. "If that dame can do it right, why can't you? Do we have to get her to fight the war?" I am told this had the desired effect; the men improved promptly.

The Army has expressed its gratitude in its own way. One day at a PX Betty squealed, "Look! Real chewing gum!" and spoke of the current civilian shortage of jaw waggle. The entire camp, to a man, came through with a package apiece; and since then tons of the stuff have kept rolling in.

On the home front Betty's emotions are geared to the lower-income tax group, too. Despite her agile mind and shallow if substantial wit, she is not a bookworm. Her tastes in literature run to Dick Tracy and Li'l Abner. A confirmed crossword fan, I regret that I cannot number her among my addicts. She obviously has too much good common sense. On the athletic side she is given to gin rummy and bridge (taught her by George Raft).

A hearty eater, she prefers maw's food cooked at home to eating out. She has been known to lead her men to a soda fountain rather than to a fancy gourmet layout. As for dieting, she laughs at it. "Hey, fellers," she has cried at a canteen, "toss me another doughnut—I'm on a diet!"

Her language, while not in the smoky style of some loose-lipped glamour gals, is decorated with a few damns and variations. One of her pecularities is a self-invented Ubangi double talk. If you should please Betty a lot, she'd say you were "Fonge-donge!"—with a soft g. Anything inanimate that pleases her is "krill-dill!" On the other hand, if she doesn't like something, a simple "It stinks!" suffices.

She is fond of discussing herself before friends. "I'm no singer and I can't dance. As for acting—bro-ther! But boy, oh, boy, my figure! That's talent!" While she may not be a favorite of the intellectuals, she dances, sings, and acts like the talented kid next door who wanted to get in the movies. In Technicolor, with cheerful music and the Grable externals, and hardworking uninspired charm and energy, her pictures have made more comparatively for her studio than those of any other star in history. *Coney Island* cost a million and a quarter, and will net over $2,000,000. She realizes that the practice of stripping to shorts and bras several times a picture helps at the box office. "It's not art," she sums up, "but who's kicking?"

She's never been hard up, but she knows the value of a dollar. Aside from clothes, she doesn't throw her money around. Naturally, she'd rather wear sweater and slacks than a *cheap* fur coat; a real diamond or ruby than a gaudy phony bauble. Yet she uses an inexpensive barber water favored by stenogs and Lockheed gals. She won't hire a secretary, does her own investing, bill paying, and bond buying. She struggles along at $2,500 a week on a seven-year optionless contract.

They like her at her studio because she doesn't put on an act like a lot of her Hollywood sisters. When she works, the help likes to drop in to watch and listen for the wisecracks. No one's ever seen her throw a tantrum when things go wrong and she has never had a personal maid in her life. First on the set mornings before they start, she's always on hand, never wearies no matter how often she has to retake a dull shot.

She has never gone Hollywood. She explains it this way: "I can't go Hollywood because I am Hollywood."

FALA

"The housing problem is getting more acute here in Washington."

Hollywood Canteen
by Elizabeth Wilson

Where Service Men Steal the Spotlight and Movie Stars Shine at the Kitchen Sink

OLIVIA DE HAVILLAND stood behind the snack bar at the Hollywood Canteen, handing out sandwiches and cakes to the men in service. Suddenly a tall gangling fellow stopped dead in his tracks and stared with mouth open.

"Are you one?" he asked in a slow Texas drawl.

"Yes," answered Olivia, with a grin. "I'm one. And she's one too," she added, pointing to a flaming redhead farther along the counter. "She's Geraldine Fitzgerald."

"Never heard of her."

"Didn't you see *Wuthering Heights*?" asked Olivia.

"No, ma'am," said the boy. "That was too deep for me."

"Well, surely you saw her with Bette Davis in *Dark Victory*?"

"No, ma'am. That was too deep for me, too. I only see your pictures, Miss de Havilland. They're simple."

Two nights later Bette Davis, shining light of the Canteen, was signing autographs. A six-foot-four marine shoved up to the counter. "Hello, sugarplum," he said, fresh as all get out. "You're kinda cute. But I sure think you stink on the screen."

An eighteen-year-old from the naval base at San Pedro swaggered up to hostess Eloise O'Brien and asked, "Is Joan Leslie here tonight?"

"No," said Mrs. O'Brien. "But that's Hedy Lamarr back of the snack bar, and there's Greer Garson."

"Aw, nuts," he said dejectedly. "They're too old for me. Say, is Linda Darnell here?"

Mary Astor was a hostess on the late shift one night when a sailor asked her to dance.

"Certainly," said Mary affably. "But I may as well warn you, I don't jitterbug."

"Don't jitterbug!" he sneered scornfully. "Jeez, you don't get around much, do you?" Then, on second thought, he decided to be gallant about it. "Lady," he said, swinging into action, "you'll learn."

And Mary did—the hard way.

At the end of a strenuous night Marlene Dietrich was sweeping the Canteen floor. A marine grabbed the broom from her. "I'll sweep this for you, babe," he said. "You must have enough of this to do at home."

A young soldier who was dancing with Olivia de Havilland asked her what kind of job she had. She told him she was an actress.

At the end of the dance he politely requested her autograph.

"Gee, Miss de Havilland," he said, blushing to the roots of his red hair, "I'm sorry I didn't recognize you. Isn't it awful, but I don't seem to recognize any actresses off the screen except the sweater girls."

This is the kind of stuff that goes on every night at the Hollywood Canteen—where Hollywood meets and entertains service men from all over the world. The critics who said that the movie people would never buckle down and make a success of the Canteen—and there were a lot of them—have had to eat their words. The Hollywood movie

Top-flight movie stars appear at this renovated night club, but there is no cover charge. Everything, in fact, is free.

Business is brisk, and why wouldn't it be, with Hedy Lamarr (not a motion picture) doing a waitress act at the counter?

great, with few exceptions, have proved that they are pretty swell.

The Hollywood Canteen is the dream come true for a lot of studio people. It was inspired by the success of the Stage Door Canteen in New York, and practically every guild, craft, and union affiliated with films helped to create it.

A lease for the duration of the war was taken on an abandoned night club which had appropriately been known as The Barn. It was in a bad state of repair. The carpenters, the painters, the plumbers, property men, grips, studio decorators, drapers, electricians, laborers—all the

multitude of crafts necessary to the existence of a studio —contributed man power, material, and money. One side of the Canteen was decorated by the artists from the Walt Disney studios. The Motion Picture Illustrators did the other side. Screen actor Richard Whorf, who used to design Broadway sets as a side line, designed the men's powder room. Now completely refurnished and rebuilt, the old night club has a value of $15,000. It cost the Canteen $200.

As the project gained momentum, Columbia studios dedicated the opening of *Talk of the Town* to the Canteen, thus giving it the first funds for its treasury. Since then

Lynn Bari attends to the serving, while Marlene Dietrich takes time out to dash off a few autographs for service men fans.

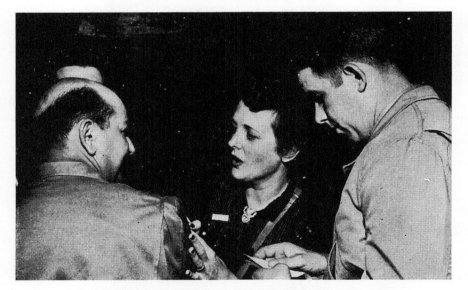

The stag line crowds in on popular Mary Astor, while one opportunist gets set to ask for an autograph as well as a dance.

several movie stars have made healthy donations. Stars and executives who sat in the "bleachers" on opening night paid fifty dollars for their tickets. There is an "Angel's Table" at which outsiders see the fun at twenty-five dollars each, and angels have not been lacking.

Everything, of course, is free. The uniform of any branch of service in any of the United Nations forces is an admission ticket.

The Canteen serves between four and five thousand boys on Saturday nights, and an average of 1,600 on week nights. Most of the food is donated. To encourage the boys

to write home, the studios supply two secretaries nightly to take dictation. One night over 200 letters went out. The soldiers seem to get a great kick out of playing what they call "Hollywood executive."

A few pretend to be bored, but at least 95 percent of the men get a terrific thrill out of the place. One had his picture taken with one arm around Rita Hayworth and the other around Ann Sheridan. "I used to dream of things like this. I never thought it would happen to me," he murmured, wonder-struck. Thanks to the Hollywood photographers, he had a print a few days later to send to his girl.

Another soldier was heard telling his pal, "There I was, dancing with this dame and handing her a swell line. 'What's your name, babe?' I asked. 'Dorothy Lamour,' she said. Right in my arms! Dorothy Lamour! Gee, I shut up like a clam. I couldn't say a thing."

But the boys just back from the Solomons are the ones who go right to the hearts of the movie stars. As Bette Davis explained, "They have something in their eyes. We can always tell when a boy has seen actual service. There was a marine here last night. 'You'll never know,' he said to me, 'what it means to see girls and hear music again. Just let me sit here, please!' "

Despite the million-dollar entertainment provided nightly, the boys' chief sport seems to be getting autographs. Curious to know what they do with them, I asked a number of boys who were crowding around Irene Dunne and Hedy Lamarr. Three quarters told me they were sending them to their girls. Another 15 percent were sending them "home," while 5 percent insisted they would keep them. The remaining 5 percent said, "I don't know, lady. This is the first one I ever got."

This is the first Hollywood Canteen the boys ever got, but it is doing its job like a million-dollar production.

"Which way is the stern? We want to see what a rear admiral looks like."

Without Mercy

a short short story
by I. A. R. Wylie

THE MAN IN the black uniform threw open the folding doors behind which he had been standing in close listening attention. The gesture was sudden and almost violent, as though he had expected to surprise some hostile trespasser. But the vast room into which he led the way was superbly empty. A magnificent mahogany table stretched along the wall facing the tall French windows and the balcony from which a flag drooped in heavy rain-soaked folds. Behind the table and under a man's portrait on which the light concentrated with theatrical intensity, twelve chairs were ranged. In the middle of the table was a small bronze casket. All these features were correct and familiar. Yet Ullrich Bohlen considered each of them in turn, seeming to suspect some change beneath their apparent rigid conformity to custom.

He gave an order. The two soldiers at his heels began a systematic inspection. They tapped the walls and examined the vast chimney behind the baroque mantelpiece. They worked rapidly and efficiently. When they had finished, Bohlen stood with his arms outstretched while they ran their hands over him. In turn they searched each other. All this was done dispassionately, as a matter of routine. The task accomplished, the soldiers ranged themselves stolidly on either side of the open door, and Bohlen took up his place at the head of the table. His lean dark face, which once had been handsome, stared back

at him from a mirror. It had a blurred look like that of a photograph taken slightly out of focus.

But he continued to listen. Beyond the tense immediate silence his ear, trained to the evaluation of every sound, made note of the dark murmur that rose from the invisible street beneath the balcony. It was like the murmur of the sea. Actually it was the murmur of a people. He had heard it often enough before; but in those other days it had had a different quality.

Men were coming down the marble corridor. Their footsteps sounded measured and ominous. They entered in silence, cautiously separate. There were ten of them. They wore various uniforms. They were of all ages. They had nothing in common but the insignia on their arm bands and their expression, which was hard, somber, and wary. They too appeared to be listening to the murmur and to be estimating it.

They took their places at the table, standing. The two soldiers passed behind them, slapping them over methodically. They then drew to attention.

"Everything in order, general."

Bohlen touched a bell concealed under the table edge.

The answering footsteps were light and staccato, like those of a dancer dancing to some secret rhythm on the dark floor of those disembodied voices. The man who entered was the man of the portrait. His gesture of greet-

346

ing was fluttering, almost womanish and indefinably menacing.

The whole room seemed to stiffen to attention. But the voices outside paid no heed. They flowed on inexorably, beating against the walls under the balcony.

"Be seated, gentlemen."

The chairs scraped softly. As was his custom, Ullrich Bohlen remained standing, watchful for the slightest gesture of authority—or betrayal.

For a moment the room was given over to silence. The twelve men were listening to what lay beyond it. They were like surgeons counting the heartbeats of a delirious patient.

The man in the carved chair, since he sat in their midst, could not see their faces without turning to the right or left. And this he did not deign to do.

"Gentlemen," he said, "you know why I have summoned you. There have been rumors, spread by our enemies, of a serious breakthrough—of a disastrous situation along our whole front. You should have crushed such fabrications—"

"My Leader," one of the men said, "they are not fabrications."

"Nor are they the truth—not so long as I am alive. You should have more faith, gentlemen. My star may seem dimmed to your eyes. Actually it is approaching its brightest hour. Have patience. Tomorrow you will see it again. There will be a miracle."

They sat forward, each trying to catch a glimpse of his face. They were like marionettes whose strings have slipped from the controlling hand and who assume spontaneous grotesque attitudes of their own. It was true, of course. He had performed miracles.

He drew the casket closer to him and opened it.

"But first, gentlemen, I require a great act of sacrifice and courage from one of you. I trust you all. The honor is in the hands of destiny."

A faint gleam of ironical amusement spread over the frozen faces. They knew the ritual. As each man dipped his hand into the casket, it was with resignation to an already accomplished fact. By some unfathomed legerdemain, destiny would now confirm it.

"Ullrich—"

The man Ullrich Bohlen came forward and drew his number and laid it on the table. It corresponded to the number in the soft small hand outstretched as though to meet his own. His face was blank.

"As ever—I am at your orders, my Leader."

"Gentlemen, you are dismissed. You may reassure the people. While I live, they shall not be cheated of the fruits of their heroic sacrifices."

Old phrases—shopworn. They were hard, distrustful men. Still, it was true about those miracles. It would not be wise to lose faith too soon.

The room emptied. The two soldiers withdrew, closing the doors after them. Bohlen had taken up the little slip of paper and was twisting it between his fingers.

"Ullrich—it was my wish that you should be chosen. And you see—destiny is still my servant. I knew I could trust you. The others are like hovering vultures. But I know your metal. I have tested it a hundred times."

"Yes, my Leader."

" 'I tried it in fire,' I said to myself. 'I will test this man's love as no love has ever been tested.' I ordered men who pretended to be my enemies to capture and torture you. Do you remember? Yes—I see you do. But they could not make you betray me. I was listening, Ullrich. I was without mercy. I exulted in your pain—and in your fidelity. I had your father shot without trial. Your mother, I believe, died insane. Your fiancée killed herself. You did not even plead for them. You had no father, no mother, no love—only me."

The voice thrilled with a sort of ecstasy. The man Ullrich bowed his head in assent.

"No greater love— But then, Ullrich, in all history there has never been a greater man. If I died now, history would acknowledge me. It would say, 'He died undefeated and undefeatable.' "

"Yes, my Leader. Indeed, it would be in all the history books."

"And it would be true. No one could have defeated me if I had had a people worthy of me. But then, perhaps no people could have been worthy of me. Ullrich, the weapon in my hand was flawed. In the hour of trial it has broken—"

"So, my Leader, it is not a rumor—"

"No. Everything is finished. Napoleon and I—" The voice, that had been pitched too high, cracked. Bohlen turned his face away from what he did not want to see. "Ullrich, do you remember what they did to Napoleon? It was nothing to what they would do to me. They would drag me through the mud, cage me like an animal, hold me up to the world's ridicule. You must not let that happen, Ullrich. You must save me. You must put me out of reach of those filthy hands stretched out to tear me down. You must put me among the martyrs and the immortals. History will say of me then, 'In the hour of his greatest victory, when he was about to fling his enemies from their moment's triumph to final defeat, he was shot down by a traitor—' "

Bohlen turned again. There was something on the table that had not been there before—a neat silver-handled revolver. On the butt his initials had been inlaid in gold. "Do you remember? I gave it to you on that June night—nearly nine years ago."

"Yes, I remember."

"You used it faithfully—on your best friend. Use it faithfully now. Save me, Ullrich—save my legend."

Bohlen balanced the weapon in his hand.

"How often, my Leader," he said softly, "have I sat opposite you, looking at your heart, yearning to hold just such a little thing as this—just for an instant. I have imagined the blood oozing through your tunic—the pain and horror on your face. It was like the ecstasy of love, the hate I felt for you—a lust of hatred. But I had planned your safety too well. Only you could have entered this room with such a weapon—" He looked up. The white aghast face opposite him seemed to be disintegrating—to be falling to pieces like a long dead thing exposed suddenly to light and air. "Did you really think, my dear Leader, that you could do such things to a man who had loved you as he should have loved his God, and that he would not live to punish you—biding his time?"

The face whispered: "Very well, Judas. Your time has come. Shoot."

Bohlen cocked his head. He went over to the windows and tore them open. The murmur became a roar—savage, torrential, filling the room with menace. The man in the chair recoiled from it—throwing up his hands as though to ward off an invisible assault. Bohlen sauntered back.

"My Leader," he said, "in all my imaginings I never imagined how sweet it would be"—he laid the revolver gently on the table—"to let you live."

When the Japs Bombed Michigan

by Jerry MacMullen

*Japanese Parachute Bombs Were a Bigger Threat
Than the Enemy Knew or We Could Admit. Here's
the Hitherto Secret Story of How They Worked, Why
They Fizzled, and What Not to Do If You Find One*

IF YOU'RE THE outdoor type and like to scramble around in the rocks and trees and cactus, it's entirely possible that some day you may stumble upon a huge tattered bag of creamy-white paper with a tangle of rope attached. If you do, watch carefully where you walk.

Should you then come across an odd-looking four-spoked aluminum wheel about two feet in diameter, all festooned with insulated wire and dynamite fuse, don't try draping it over your campfire as a support for the coffeepot. Instead, get word immediately to the nearest Army or Navy installation, to the F.B.I., the sheriff, or police. *Don't fool with it yourself.* You may be smart, but you aren't smart enough to disarm a Japanese balloon safely, and that's exactly what you will have found.

As a substitute for the buzz bomb, which was definitely out of their reach, the Japs hit upon the paper balloon as a good cheap way to destroy the American homeland. Of the large numbers they sent off amid touching ceremonies, some 300 have been recovered in the United States, Canada, and Alaska. How many more are still lying around on inaccessible crags and in remote forests is anybody's guess.

Those balloons really got around, too; in fact, two of them actually crossed the Pacific, the Rockies, and the great central plains and came down in Michigan. And they can be lethal yet, if they're not left for the experts to handle. In fact, the six deaths they caused in this country occurred when curious youngsters, picnicking in Lake County, Oregon, found one caught in a tree. In some way they detonated the fifteen-kilogram antipersonnel bomb which the balloon carried—all the balloons had them—blasting five children and an adult into eternity.

Aside from this tragedy, the Japanese did little damage on the American continent. The submarine which lobbed a few wild shells into an oil installation near Santa Barbara was merely a nuisance, and probably stimulated war bond sales. The balloon idea had some merit, except that it didn't work. True, one dying balloon got into a power line and shut off the electricity for a few hours, and another one set fire to a railroad tool house, but not even Tojo could call that a major victory—even if he added, for good measure, the two or three small grass fires which were started.

However, it wasn't entirely the fault of the Japs that those balloons weren't a king-sized headache. You see, most of them fell during the winter and spring, when things were pretty damp. But suppose they had dropped during the late summer or autumn months? Fires in the West Coast's tinder-dry forests and brushlands would have consumed countless thousands of otherwise productive man-hours, wiped out critically needed timber, and probably taken a toll of lives.

No doubt this occurred to the Nips; the Doolittle raid on Tokyo irked them no end, and the forests of the Pacific slope must have looked inviting indeed. So at an outlandish expenditure of yen—more than 9,000,000 of them, in fact, or some $2,000,000 in prewar days—they started the balloon project. It took two years to whip into final shape, and by that time things were not going at all well in Honshu. But the womenfolks patiently cut and pasted the paper balloon envelopes, the young squirts soldered the wires, and the kids and old men filled the bombs. In all, they eventually sent off some 9,000 balloons. Even if more are found, the percentage of hits never will exceed ten, and that isn't very good. However, it's enough to embarrass those folks who felt that several thousand miles of ocean constituted a defense from all comers.

They were weird things, those paper balloons—weird and ingenious. Japan must have had a man with a veritable Rube Goldberg approach to physics and chemistry, for the gear he designed for the balloons was outlandish. In fact, the whole screwball business was typical of Japanese psychology. To begin with, there was the use of paper, in a land where paper is used for everything from umbrellas and raincoats to gaudy kites. Then again, there was the wind angle. The Japanese are definitely wind-happy; you'll find that in their history and their mythology. Was it not *kamikaze*—the "divine wind"— which worsted the fleet of the Mongolian invaders centuries ago? If now the wind would be so kind as to carry paper weapons to harass the wicked enemy across the sea—ah, so nice! So very nice!

At this point Dame Nature deals herself a hand in the contest. And, sad to relate, she slips the face cards to the Sons of Heaven; the Allies must be content with a pair of deuces or, at best, treys. For, immutably, "weather" moves around the world from west to east. And if you go high enough, you'll find yourself in a wind current which comes across from Asia straight to the Americas, and loses no time doing it. *Banzai!* Shoot something up into the air, and let Honorable Wind carry it to your foe. That something, obviously, is a balloon.

It is idle to assume that General MacArthur's current charges do not know their weather. As meteorologists the Nipponese are tops, and have been for a long time. They knew that up around 28,000 feet a constant wind stream raced eastward at 100 knots or so, at least during the fall and winter months. Past performance charts showed the paths of these currents, and simple arithmetic proved that a balloon kept in this stream would cross the Pacific in about four days. The Japs had only to design a pilot-

less balloon that would keep a constant level and carry a pay load of incendiary or fragmentation bombs—or both.

Inventing such a balloon would be a lot of trouble, but by the summer of 1944 a little more trouble didn't matter much to the Nips, one way or the other. The thing would have to be susceptible of mass production and it should be cheap—being intended for one lone flight. Labor being Japan's cheapest commodity, each balloon set them back only about $220 American.

The scientists got busy. The problem of keeping the balloon from going too high was simple—it called merely for a spring-controlled escape valve, which would let out some of the gas when the balloon reached the lowered atmospheric pressure at its service ceiling. Much more thought was needed to rid the balloon of ballast when it got too low, as it would do occasionally from the natural leakage of gas through the envelope, or from running into a layer of colder air, which would reduce its lift. There was much knitting of brows, much sad shaking of heads, much troubled sucking in of breath. And then Rubesaki Goldbergiyama let out a happy bleat and waved his slide rule in the air—he had it! Aneroid barometers would control the dropping of ballast, letting a series of sandbags fall, one at a time, whenever the balloon dropped to a predetermined level.

It was a good idea, but it needed refinement. If the balloon were to carry thirty or forty sacks of ballast— which it would need—that would mean a like number of barometers, a lot of added weight, and a reduced pay load of bombs. So, with ingenuity worthy of a better cause, they made three or four barometers take care of everything. And they meant just that—everything.

The first public intimation of all this patient hocus-pocus came early in December of 1944, when the little community of Kalispell, Montana, shouldered itself into the nation's headlines with an account of a mysterious bomb which had gone off with a bright flash and a lot of noise, but hadn't hurt anyone. Fragments were identified as coming from a Japanese Army fifteen-kilo (thirty-three-pound) antipersonnel bomb—and if the Japanese Army happened to be around Kalispell in November of 1944, neither the sheriff nor the F.B.I. had heard of it.

Then someone found nearby a strange-looking paper balloon with Japanese characters; the source of the bomb immediately ceased to be a mystery. Forthwith there was a lot of gumshoeing and hypothesis and drawing of diagrams by the Army, the Navy and the F.B.I., with a view to determining just what gave. At first there was some official willingness to believe that the thing had come from a submarine somewhere off the coast. This was ruled out, however, when the size and unwieldiness of the balloon were studied. To inflate and launch a thirty-three-foot paper balloon from the tiny deck of a submarine, even in a calm sea and with little wind, would be a bit of a chore. And as our own meteorologists are no dopes, it wasn't too

One of about 300 Jap balloons that reached this country with 33-pound bombs. Made of mulberry paper, they cost $220 each in American money.

hard to figure out that it came all the way over from Japan. Simultaneously, the American newspapers began to clam up, and the subsequent thunderous silence about balloons became one of the bright pages in the history of voluntary censorship. It was a silence which must have driven the Japs completely nuts.

Right away everyone wanted one of those balloons intact, for study and analysis. And one fine day a Navy pilot came face to face with one. His machine gun, unfortunately, chose that moment to go temperamental, and it looked as if the thing would get away. But he was a resourceful lad. Unable to shoot it down, he did the next best thing. He took a swipe at it with his plane, passing close and then banking away sharply to let the slipstream from his propeller strike it. To his delight, one side of the balloon flattened out momentarily, and he figured that he had squeezed out some of the hydrogen. Sure enough, the balloon settled slightly. So he did it again— and again—and again. As a result of this aerial badmin-

ton, he finally batted the thing down in a snow-clad forest, where ground crews recovered it. The young man didn't know it then, but all the time he was jockeying that balloon, he was living on borrowed minutes. That, however, is getting ahead of the story.

The balloon itself proved to be a spherical bag of two-ply mulberry paper, intensely tough—in fact, you can't tear it with both hands unless you start it, exactly right, at an edge. Small hemp lines, dangling from a scalloped skirt at the balloon's equator, supported an outlandish-looking device some thirty feet below the bag. And it was upon this device that the government Dick Tracys concentrated, for that was what made the whole thing tick.

The pendant affair was the previously mentioned aluminum wheel, its thick rim studded with seventy-two plugs. It rode horizontally, and a few inches above it was a smaller aluminum ring with half the number of plugs. Back and forth across the big ring and running to the plugs in the smaller one was a network of dynamite fuse. Each plug was connected also with a fantastic array of insulated wires, and on top of the whole business, to energize it, was a battery, mounted on the wooden box that held the aneroids.

Here is how it worked: When the balloon got down to around 22,000 feet, an aneroid closed a circuit and fired a tiny charge of black powder behind each of a pair of plugs in the bottom ring; this dropped a sandbag weighing about five pounds and simultaneously ignited a fuse running up to a single plug in the upper ring. This didn't drop anything, but it set up the contacts of a switch controlling the circuit to fire the next pair of plugs below. So when the balloon dropped to its new critical level, two more plugs would blow out and another sack would drop.

And so, high above the rolling wastes of the North Pacific, this grotesque paper ballet danced eastward, rising and falling, sputtering and popping its little squibs of powder, spinning in those wild 100-knot currents and moving ever closer to the American coast. The thing was so arranged that when the last sandbag was dropped and, the General Staff hoped, the balloon was over a nice fat aircraft plant or a war housing project, the final circuit was closed. This did several interesting things. First, it dropped the pay load of fifteen kilos of sudden death. Then it lighted off two more fuses, of which one—a short one—ran to a two-and-one-half-pound block of picric acid, an explosive of which the Nipponese are inordinately fond. The longer fuse ran up along one of the ropes to the side of the balloon, ending in a bag of flashlight powder cemented to the fabric itself. The object was obvious; the picric acid would destroy the ballast gear, and the balloon, thus freed of weight would leap skyward to be itself destroyed half an hour later—and many miles away —by the flash bomb. The stupid Yankee pigs would, therefore, remain ignorant of what was hitting them. *Banzai!* Two *banzais!* Or anyhow one and a half. Because it didn't always work.

Balloons trickled into North America in November and December. In January the trickle increased several hundred percent. February was three times as bad as January —but only half as bad as March. Meanwhile our own weather people were doing some interesting things with maps and with predictions which later proved to be right on the beam. They said that April would show fewer balloons than March, and that from then on business would drop steadily as the 100-knot winter wind became the mere thirty-five-knot wind of midyear. Late summer, they said, would see an upsurge—and by November again it would be Kitty, Bar the Door. Sure enough, April saw the balloon curve breaking sharply downward.

The various governmental agencies charged with such duties as worrying about enemy balloons heaved a small sigh of relief; it looked like a breathing spell, and so far no great harm had been done. But how about the other half of the prediction—the return of the balloons in quantities by late autumn? Even by April, the wily Nips had substituted, in place of the four last sandbags to be released, incendiary bombs—no doubt on the theory that by the time these last loads were ready to go, the balloon might be over the Boeing factory or some nice lush oilfield. Up until now, the forests had been damp and green—but what of late autumn, when they would be dry?

A number of remedies came to mind, and although a few balloons were shot down, all defensive measures ran up against the same inescapable fact: from the ground, a thirty-three-foot paper sack five miles in the air is invisible, unless you happen to be looking in exactly the right spot and have excellent vision. Get up in a plane, and it's even worse. The balloons were no longer funny.

Meanwhile, in one of the mountain states a band of horses came across a deflated balloon whose block of picric acid had failed to go off and had worked loose. It looked good to eat, and an eager horse snapped his teeth into it. You will note that the past tense is used in referring to those horses.

A sheriff brought one balloon down with his trusty rifle, and there was a tale of a group of ranchers who lassoed one as it dipped close to the ground. Another rancher and his Indian cowhand chased a balloon for miles, thinking that it was a parachute with someone hanging from it—for as a balloon neared the end of its life, the lower part would collapse, up inside the bag, and the thing looked remarkably like a parachute. A thermite bomb fell in an apple orchard and hours later the charred remnants of what probably was the same balloon assembly came down many miles away—also in an apple orchard.

"The answer to this balloon business," said a veteran Navy officer, "is to bomb the hell out of Japan. Get 'em where they originate." And it looked as if he was right; not even the milder winds of spring and early summer could have produced the slump in the balloon business which was noted. It couldn't have been coincidence that the virtual cessation of the balloon attack coincided with the frightful mauling which the B-29s and their lesser playfellows were handing out to the little brown men.

And so passed the mulberry-paper barrage—9,000 balloons which killed six noncombatants and a band of horses, broke a power line and set a few fires. And they cost $220 apiece.

Tojo—you were had.

The Bombing of New York

an installment of a serial by Fred Allhoff

With the Advice and Counsel of Lieutenant General Robert Lee Bullard, Rear Admiral Yates Stirling, George E. Sokolsky, and Many Others

Late in August, 1945, after Seattle and other northwestern cities had fallen to the Russian and Japanese invaders America's east coast was still awaiting Hitler's attack. In some respects the nation was now in better shape for self-defense. The invasion had prompted Congress to sanction the creation of a unified command, and Japanese outrages in occupied

Tacoma had aroused the dormant fighting spirit of the whole people.

By Rear Admiral O'Shane's order, Lieutenant Doug Norton and his cameraman Rodgers were flown east to the national capital. There, in one of Rodgers' films of refugees from Seattle, federal agents spotted a German spy named Grubel, known to be an old-time co-worker of the vanished von Holtz, with the result that Grubel was caught and executed.

Peggy O'Liam wrote Doug that she was busy in Baltimore but hoped soon to go home to Illinois. Doug longed for an assignment to Baltimore! Instead, he and Rodgers were sent to New York City. They found Manhattan Island surrounded with barrage balloons, elderly men or young women driving the buses and the few taxis that gasoline could be spared for, Central Park full of trench shelters, and the entire city childless after hurried precautionary evacuations.

That night a siren's shrieks warned of an air raid. Searchlights swept the cloud-layered skies. In from the ocean southward came Hitler's bombers by the hundred. Explosions rocked the downtown tall buildings. Overhead, the defending fighter planes went for the Nazi fighters. From a high window, Norton and Rodgers saw a great yellow flare as gas tanks on the Jersey shore blew up.

Then Rodgers pointed southwestward over Manhattan and shouted, "Doug! Look!"

DOWN OUT OF the layer of clouds had come the first squadron of a wing of 250 huge new Wulf bombers to brave the blinding glare of searchlights and the antiaircraft fire. Leveling off at 9,000 feet, the leading plane, its belly bomb-bay doors open, flew in a straight line toward its bomb-release point.

Norton and Rodgers could actually see the falling bombs as a swinging searchlight caught them in mid-air for an instant. They seemed tiny things, those huge fourteen-foot, two-ton missiles. They let go a moment later with a window-shattering blast that reverberated amid the silhouetted downtown skyscrapers and was audible far uptown.

One by one the great bombers dropped down out of the clouds. At varying altitudes above the balloon barrage and hugging the western rim of Manhattan Island, they flattened out for the forty-five seconds of dangerous straight-line flying necessary to align their sights and drop their eggs. Each plane released its bombs, salvo, just north of the plane that had preceded it. Then, banking sharply, it turned to roar toward the Jersey meadows, and thence toward the open sea and safety.

From the clouds above them, smaller Nazi and American pursuit ships were dropping in flames out of a raging dogfight. Other American pursuit planes fought their way toward open sea, where, without having to hurdle the fire of their own antiaircraft batteries, they might meet and bring down incoming enemy bombers.

From the ground the sleek Wulf bombers were absorbing terrific punishment. The first Nazi plane to be caught in a hell of antiaircraft fire jettisoned its bombs and wheeled desperately to get away. A merciless searchlight pinned it against a backdrop of clouds, and up that shaft of light an antiaircraft battery sent a burst that scored a direct hit, ripping off one wing and spinning the plane crazily into the North River. Another Nazi bomber, struck before it could release its tons of high explosive, blew to flinders in the air with a terrific spurt of flame.

Still they came on, and by now the skies over lower Manhattan were a sullen, shivering red. Methodically, precisely, and with uncanny accuracy, the bombers were blasting and setting ablaze the wooden piers and covered pier sheds along West Street. The great Pennsylvania Railroad terminal for perishables had been struck. Washington Market and West Washington Market were in flames, their tons of foodstuffs ruined.

To the eerie scream of the "whistling" bombs, the roar of their explosions, the deep drone of planes, and the clatter of antiaircraft fire, was added the whine of fire trucks and the clang of ambulances.

Norton and Rodgers made for the roof. The elevators were not running, but they found the staircase door. On the roof, a gray-haired man—a civilian "spotter"—pointed southwest.

"Looks like the whole of downtown's afire," he said. "Jersey's getting it, too."

They looked in that direction, across the North River. They were in time to see a sheet of flame leap 2,000 feet into the air. The storage tanks of the Bayonne oil refineries had been struck. Other bombs were bursting in New Jersey, and Norton guessed what their objectives would be; warehouses, sheds, stockyards, and factories, from the Ford plant (now manufacturing warplane engines) near Edgewater to the floating grain elevators beyond the Black Tom flatlands. But primarily the target of the Nazi bombers in New Jersey would be the twelve great trunk lines over which New York's food came in.

The bombers fought their way toward uptown Manhattan. Waterfront property was burning furiously from as far south as the United Fruit Line piers to the great piers at Fiftieth Street, where, before the war in Europe, the luxury liners *Normandie* and *Queen Mary* had docked.

A squadron of German fighting planes swooped down and riddled three barrage balloons, which collapsed, slowly deflated, and fell earthward. But ground crews instantly sent aloft new balloons, and an American fighting squadron fell upon and destroyed the attacking planes.

A Nazi bomber pilot, attempting to sneak between a pair of barrage balloons, was blinded by a searchlight. His left wing struck a balloon's mooring cable and was sheared off. The pilot crashed in his plane.

All that night the raid continued with undiminished fury. Wave after wave of Nazi bombers came over. The Fifth Coast Artillery battery at Fort Hamilton was blasted out after downing an estimated fifty enemy planes.

From the hotel roof Norton and Rodgers watched the assault upon a blacked-out city from whose chimneys rose blankets of smoke and artificial fog. Once a screaming bomb fell so close that instinctively the two dropped on the roof and curled up in the smallest possible space. The bomb missed the hotel, exploded with a roar in the street. And though that explosion was twenty-seven floors below them, they could feel the building tremble.

Uptown, beyond the piers, new fires raged as incendiary bombs plunged through the roofs of brownstone houses in the side streets off Riverside Drive. Striking inland, the bombers chose as targets some of New York's greatest skyscrapers, whose upper floors towered above the smoke. The great RCA Building in Rockefeller Center suffered a direct hit that ripped out its east wall from the seventieth to the sixty-fifth stories. A bomb directed at the Chrysler Building struck, instead, the near-by Chanin Building, ripping off a corner of its fifty-fourth to fifty-second stories.

In Brooklyn the Bay Ridge Terminal, stored with food, was set afire and the tracks of the New York Connecting Railway were twisted and uprooted by bomb hits that knocked out the New York, New Haven and Hartford service linking the city with New England. Directly across the upper bay, the Greenville railroad yards in New Jersey—main artery by which Manhattan received freight from the West—were demolished.

Brooklyn's army piers and the Navy Yard suffered bomb hits.

Before dawn, roaming bombers had demolished the huge Sunnyside yard of the Pennsylvania Railroad in Queens, had severed three of the five bridges across the East River, and had put out of operation the Point Morris and Hell Gate electric plants.

Low-flying Nazi mine layers, operating outside Manhattan's balloon barrage, had skimmed up the East and North Rivers during the night, sowing scattered fields of floating mines. On their return flight, close to the New York shore, they had raked fireboats with machine-gun fire, killing crew members who were trying to save the burning piers.

It had been around dawn when Nazi bombers, flying beyond range of ear or eye, had come over New York City to release tens of thousands of tiny parachutes which floated down to alight on roofs and window ledges and in streets, and in buildings already bombed. Not until later were Norton and Rodgers to learn their significance.

At seven o'clock of the sultry morning of August 27 a siren sounded the "all clear" signal. New Yorkers, shaky from a sleepless night, came out into the streets to inspect the damage done. It had been strategic rather than intensive. Subways had stalled, surface lines had stopped running. Thousands of persons had spent a night of terror in subway tubes, some of which ran fairly close to the surface.

Morning found the city without power or gas, its transportation disrupted, its population virtually isolated. Faced with an immediate shortage of food, the army had taken control of every restaurant in New York. Army planes with loud-speakers flew over Manhattan advising people that it had been necessary for the moment to ration food; that they should apply to the restaurants nearest their homes for individual allowances.

Other warnings were issued: Since electrical refrigeration had broken down, civilians were cautioned against tainted meat; since water mains had been smashed, all water must be boiled before drinking; and the utmost conservation of any available water was ordered.

Rodgers and Norton had gone down to their room from the hotel roof when the "all clear" signal had sounded. They found the telephone dead. No water came from the faucets in the bathroom.

"No shave this morning," said Rodgers.

Norton shrugged.

Secretly each man wondered whether the hotel's high-pressure pump had failed or whether the lack of water was caused by something far more serious.

They walked down the many flights of stairs to the street level. There was a long line of hotel guests waiting to enter the coffee shop. They took their places in the line. Breakfast—in a dining room presided over by a watchful army sergeant—was skimpy: one slice of toast, one egg, fruit juice, and one cup of tea or synthetic coffee.

A waiter dropped a knife upon the tiled floor. A woman at the table next to theirs half rose from her chair,

screamed. Civilian nerves were on edge. But if the merciless bombardment had made New Yorkers jumpy, it had also served to bring them closer together than they had ever been in their hurried peacetime lives. Men and women in the line were exchanging experiences of the night before in easy conversations with perfect strangers. Potbellied business men who had been digging trench shelters were inordinately proud of their newly calloused or blistered hands, as steel-helmeted members of Home Defense units were of their arm bands. Elderly men and women who came patiently to take their places at the foot of the waiting line were promptly smuggled up near its head—and no one complained. Jock Rodgers grinned, said to Norton:

"There's nothing like an air raid to bring people together."

And it was true. In days long past these same people would have squabbled among themselves over defense measures and policies. Their seeming disunity had incurred only the contempt of the "virile" dictatorships. One night of bombs—of bombs that blasted rich and poor alike—had united them in the cause of democratic freedom.

They were nervous and shaken, true. Unshaven men were hollow-eyed, women pale. But there was about them a new dignity. They had not asked for this war, but now that it had come they were bearing it uncomplainingly. Norton, as he watched them, felt a surge of pride. Since they had never known the grim fanaticism of Hitlerian regimentation, they accepted whatever was in store for them with confidence and easy good will. A man sitting at a nearby table told his companion:

"The more damn noise they make, the better I'll like it! Then I'll know our own antiaircraft guns are in there banging away!"

Norton and Rodgers set out for a walk about the Times Square section. Along Broadway were great queues of people lined up awaiting their turns to enter restaurants. Before the Paramount Theater, where Jimmy Durante was making a personal appearance, a huge crater had been blasted in the street by high-explosive bombs. A crew of the Disaster Control Board's 100,000 emergency workers had roped off the gaping hole, from which a cloud of live hot steam issued. New Yorkers, natural-born "sidewalk superintendents," had lost none of their insatiable curiosity. They were crowded three deep about the gully in which workmen struggled with shredded wires, pipes, mains.

The two turned west on Fiftieth Street and headed toward the still smoldering docks along the North River. They were opposite a citizens' food line when sirens overhead shrilled warnings of a new raid. Part of the line broke to seek shelter; part of it stubbornly remained huddled against building walls. Norton saw a man look aloft and thumb his nose. Ten squadrons of bombers, trailed by their higher-flying fighter escort, came over in open V formation. American fighter planes were seeking to get above them.

Rodgers halted in midstreet a moment to aim his camera above. Then, at the wail of a "scream" bomb, he ran with Norton for shelter in the doorway of Polyclinic Hospital.

The bomb exploded in the street, close to the line of waiting people.

A man in a surgeon's apron said to half a dozen men standing by with stretchers, "When you get the 'all clear,' go out and get 'em, boys." To Norton he said, "Got a cigarette?"

He proved to be a military surgeon. Norton noticed that his hands trembled.

"Operating all night?"

"Yes. By candlelight."

"Casualties very heavy?"

"Heavy enough. Our people are pretty reckless. Lot of them stay outside to watch the raids and get hit by pieces of our own shells."

"How's civilian morale?" Norton inquired.

"Incredibly good. Half of those we have to operate on are proud of their wounds. Makes 'em feel they're taking part in the war. And the place is cluttered up with would-be blood donors. We've got plenty of blood banks—don't need them. But we can't very well turn them down. They're so pathetically eager to do something—especially for the other fellow who is worse off than they are. I guess that's as good a brand of democracy as we'll need to see us through this hellish war."

The air raid had moved farther uptown. Occasionally the dull boom of a bomb burst came to them. The surgeon said:

"You saw the parachutes come down last night? They're giving us a headache. Brought down delayed-action bombs —explosive, incendiary, and some gas, chiefly mustard and Lewisite. They go off unexpectedly. The firemen and mop-up squads have been getting it. That isn't our most serious problem, though."

"What is?"

"Water. We had sense enough, thank God, when the alarm sounded last night, to fill every bathtub and wash-basin in the hospital. We can still sponge off the burn victims—but what are we going to do for them when the water's all gone?"

"I don't know whether you know it or not, but New York City is without water. The Germans are trying to stampede seven million people into panic. Day before yesterday I'd have said it might be done. Not any more! In the next two days people are going to be dropping like flies. But they're not going to stampede! Raids won't split us apart, they'll drive us together."

"Where," Norton asked, "did they hit the water supply?"

"At its source. They bombed our water systems last night, knocking out reservoirs from Kensico to the Schoharie Reservoir. They even got to our new Delaware System, just completed this year. They'll be around now after the few bridges and tunnels we have left, and then they'll have us both isolated and thirsty. How we're going to evacuate our people I don't know, but it'll have to be done—somehow."

The water shortage had created a ghastly situation. By the second day, civilians standing thirstily in line to receive their water rations refused to break up their lines when Nazi planes came over. Some of those who did run for shelter dropped exhausted. Those who remained were often struck by bombs. Casualty figures began to sky-rocket.

Between raids, efforts were made to evacuate some of New York's millions. It was difficult and dangerous work. Civilian owners of small motorcraft—members of the United States Power Squadron—volunteered to clear the East and North Rivers of floating mines dropped there by Nazi planes. They succeeded, but only at a heavy cost due to the mines and to raiding Nazi dive bombers.

Most of New York harbor's shipping had gone up in flames; but at night, between raids, lighters, tug-drawn barges, and such ferryboats as had not been destroyed in their slips worked with the privately owned fleet. All bridges over both rivers had now been destroyed.

Staten Island's pumping stations, too, had been wrecked, and the water famine in all of Greater New York became a hideous problem. Cholera broke out on the lower West Side.

Small boats braved the bombs and machine guns to lay a water line across the North River from New Jersey—itself feeling the pinch of bombed pumping stations. But this proved to be but a slight alleviation of the suffering.

They left the city between air raids. A car took them to the shore of the Hudson, where a motor launch was waiting. They were in midstream when Nazi planes swooped down on the city for the fourth time that day. The planes, their formation broken up by a terrific barrage of antiaircraft fire, dispersed and were turning back when one escort plane sighted the launch threading its way through a field of floating mines and came roaring down. Norton could see the machine guns protruding from its nose and wings.

He thought, This is it!

Suddenly a burst of antiaircraft fire ripped across the sky. It tore away part of the German plane's tail assemblage. The plane rocketed upward in a crazy zoom, power-stalled, and came whirling down in a tail spin to hit the water and sink.

"We seem to be learning how to fight their kind of war," O'Shane grunted dryly.

Replacement for Pinky

a short short story by S. L. Gomberg

It Was His First Mission As a Tail Gunner. The
Crew Was Hostile and He Was Lonely and Afraid
—Until He Remembered the Song in His Heart

FREDDY looked up from the V-mail letter he was writing. A loud murmur had come from the men playing poker on the bed across the barracks. One of them—the waist gunner named Martino—wanted a round of draw instead of stud. He was voted down, and the game went on.

Freddy picked up the letter and reread what he had written.

"Dear Mary," it said: "Today I met the crew of the ship I am assigned to. It is a B-24 called *Bloomer Girl,* and I am to be the tail gunner. The fellows are nice and must be a good crew since they have already flown twenty missions together. It should be great, flying with them."

What else could he say, he wondered. It would only worry her if she knew that the gunner he was replacing—a New Jersey boy called Pinky—had been killed two days ago on a China Sea mission. And it would be foolish to write about the cold reception the crew had given him when he reported in. Not that he expected to be greeted with a brass band. But they could have been friendly, at least. It wasn't his fault their buddy had gotten it, or that he had been assigned to them right from a replacement base.

Yet they seemed so uninterested, so stone-faced, when he was introduced, as though he was horning in where he didn't belong. Even the officers—pilot, co-pilot, navigator, and bombardier—even they acted the same way.

Freddy glanced over at the men around the bed. They still weren't smiling or laughing. Just playing cards, not talking much at all. It was easy to understand how they felt about Pinky. But they didn't have to hold it against him, did they?

He was just writing Mary about how different the Chinese kids were from the kids in India, when Feinstein, the ball turret gunner, tapped him on the shoulder. Freddy jumped up so fast he dropped his pen.

"We're going over to the PX for awhile," Feinstein said. A warm glow poured right through Freddy. "And that's where we'll be in case the lieutenant or somebody wants us." Feinstein picked up his flight jacket from the next bed and joined the others, who were already starting for the door. Freddy watched them leave, then reached down for his pen. Maybe he should write something about the funny-smelling market places in China. Mary might enjoy that. . . .

They were briefed for the mission just after midnight. Outside, engines were coughing and getting "run-ups." Freddy listened hard to everything. Their target was an important railroad bridge, and the Intelligence officer warned of ack-ack defenses and maybe some fighter opposition. It would be cloudy part of the way, but not around the target area. If they stayed on schedule, they would unload their bombs at dawn. Take-off time was in an hour. Freddy's throat was dry and his legs trembled a little when he got up to follow everyone else out of the room. The *Bloomer Girl* loomed like a crouching winged monster in the darkness as her crew arrived in a truck. Freddy almost fell, hopping down with his parachute and extra equipment in his arms. Lieutenant Novack, the pilot, watched his men climb into the B-24. He spoke a few low words to some of them or patted their backs. But all he said to Freddy was, "Keep your eyes open. Japs are tricky." Nothing else. No other hints for a guy on his first mission. Not even a little encouragement for a guy who felt alone and scared.

There wasn't much to see on the way to the target. The night was heavy with clouds. Over the intercom, Freddy could hear the rest of the crew talking. Thomas, the radio operator, complained about static trouble. Feinstein reported that number two engine sounded rocky. The co-pilot checked and said it would be all right. After a while Lieutenant Schultz, the navigator, mentioned that he had mailed the letter to Pinky's folks. Nobody else said anything then.

Freddy strained his eyes to see against the lightening sky behind them. Maybe they missed Pinky so much because he had been the first one to spot fighters coming their way and always warned them in time. That kind of gunner was valuable to any crew. Or it could be that Pinky had never missed any Jap coming in for a tail attack. He might have been a deadeye, a gunner his buddies could depend on, no matter how rugged the going was.

Freddy gripped his gun handles until his hands trembled. He swung the turret up and down, back and forth. And he prayed for a Jap, even a whole formation of Japs, to try coming in at him. He was ready to prove anything they'd want.

Then he began feeling doubts. Supposing he didn't spot the Jap fighters coming in? What would happen then? Or he might miss his aim entirely and let the crew down that way. Scanning the skies, Freddy tightened his grip on the guns and tried his microphone button and prayed, hard.

Over the target vicious bursts of flak rocked the *Bloomer Girl*. Freddy stared with helpless fascinated eyes as the black puffs just missed them. Lieutenant McCabe, the bombardier, yelled, "Bombs away!" Then they turned east, into the new sun, homeward bound.

As they roared toward friendly territory, Freddy relaxed just a little. If only the crew would break down—laugh, or joke, or anything. His first mission was almost over, and so far they were all safe. Down below, the gray night mist was rolling back from the land as the day took hold. So he planned a new letter to Mary.

Mary—sweet, warm Mary who loved him. He hadn't seen her in a year, but he had only to close his eyes and she was there, always. Even after a year away from her, twelve long months. Yes, he'd write that. . . . Freddy stiffened on the gunner's seat. He had said good-by a year ago, on Easter Sunday, 1944, on the last day of his last furlough. And today was Easter Sunday again; he had just realized it.

They had walked to the station together that Easter Sunday, at about this same time of morning. They were holding hands and she wanted to cry. He knew it. But they sang, instead:

"In your Easter bonnet, with all the
    frills upon it,
You'll be the grandest lady in the
    Easter parade. . . ."

Freddy looked down in horror. His thumb was on the microphone button. They had heard him singing! Everyone in the crew had heard him! His throat became dry suddenly, and he released the button.

"What's the matter back there?" It was Lieutenant Novack.

"Why'd you stop singing?" Feinstein wanted to know. "Anything wrong?"

Freddy stuttered that he was all right.

"Then go ahead, kid," Lieutenant Schultz broke in; "finish it."

"Sure, finish it, and sing more," Martino called. "Pinky always sang back there—especially on the way home!"

"Let's hear it, Freddy," somebody else yelled. "Sing out!"

So Freddy sang to his new crew. Then they all harmonized, with Feinstein singing a pretty good bass.

"It's Gonna Be Tough,"
by Drew Middleton

Others May Doubt the Invasion's Success, but Not the Men Who Have to Do the Fighting. They're Calmly Sure They Can "Take" the Germans and Anxious to Prove It

Somewhere in England
with the United States Army.

WE WERE STANDING on a green hill looking out across the sea toward Europe. There were four privates, a sergeant, and a lieutenant—all of a combat company of one of the finest regiments in the United States Army. They looked for a long time at the rough gray sea as the wind tore at their faces. From a nearby field where troops were working out a "problem" came a faint popping of rifles. Overhead, a Spitfire on coastal patrol buzzed angrily.

Finally one of the privates spoke. "It's gonna be rough," he said, "but I think with the British and the bombers and the Navy we can pull it off. But it's gonna be rough."

This calm determination and knowledge of dangers ahead seem to me to symbolize the attitude of the American Army in Britain toward its greatest task—invasion of Europe. And, along with the realization of the magnitude of the operation, there is growing among our soldiers a feeling of unity with the tens of thousands of their British allies—the soldiers, sailors, and airmen who'll do the fighting and dying with them.

These are serious men, these soldiers from New York and the Carolinas, the farms of the Middle West and the seaports of the Pacific coast. They do not boast as they did two years ago, nor are they as boisterous as they were then. They are soldiers now, experienced fighting men, with the calm, sure faith in their own ability that marks the veteran. They are, as a senior British officer said as he watched a retreat in the square of a British barracks,

"a magnificent weapon—a tribute to democracy." He added, "You in America have shown all our enemies what the United States can do in the face of danger. I hope it is a lesson to them and to the rest of the world."

Probably no American Army in history has been better trained or equipped than this one. Training has continued by night and by day since the Invasion Army began to take form. It varies from large-scale exercises, wherein British and American soldiers, tanks, guns, planes, and ships work together as one team, to small "problems" involving a company or a battalion at the most. Since the former involve techniques which must be secret until they are sprung on the enemy, it is best to describe one of the "problems" which occupy so important a place in training.

A battalion was scrambling across a series of windswept, rock-strewn hills toward a ridge commanding the surrounding country. In a small clump of trees mortars were pounding the ridge, while infantrymen "froze" flat on the turf, waiting for the mortars and heavy machine guns to "fix" enemy positions.

The sergeant explained. "We are getting enemy positions on this side of the ridge, and trying to get the ones on the reverse slope," he said. "You can see the targets if you use field glasses. When they're really knocked out, those guys up there will go forward. They're just inside the safety zone now, but at that they're working a lot closer to the fire than we used to back at home." He smiled proudly. "We know our job now," he said.

Suddenly the fire ceased, and the doughboys rose from the ground and surged forward, moving smoothly. They reached the top of the ridge and were outlined on the sky line for a moment. A captain hollered, "Get off that sky line, you boneheads!" Then they went on down the other side of the ridge to "get" positions there.

"That's not so bad—but they still haven't got it quite right," said the captain. "We'll try it again tomorrow, and get it perfect."

On the other side of the hill, the doughboys, machine-gun and mortar crews had gathered to listen to criticism of their work. They listened seriously, gazing out at sea or at the ground. Some one said, "O. K. Let's get back," and they formed in threes and marched off to their billets. The "problem" was an impressive performance. Except for the absence of Germans, it might have been any one of a dozen small attacks in Tunisia, attacks which no one reports but which eat up men and equipment as surely as Stalingrad or Alamein, and contribute as greatly to victory.

The equipment with which American soldiers are training now is to a great extent the equipment with which they will attack Hitler's European Fortress. Two years ago, when the Army first came to Britain, it was a common-place to say that it was the best equipped in the world. This was true as far as clothes, food, and engineering material were concerned, but combat revealed some weaknesses in the weapons. These weapons have now been improved or replaced. Some of the new field guns are far ahead of anything the Germans have yet used in any theater, and they are served so well that the gun crews look like automatons as they go about their tasks.

But there is the feeling among officers and men alike that the last two years have taught that, good though material may be, it is no better than the physical and mental condition of the men who use it.

Mentally and physically, our troops here are superior to any others I've seen in four years of war, not excepting the panzer grenadiers of crack German armored divi-

sions, the durable Britons of the Guards, or veteran tank outfits like the Seventh Armored Division. They have a mental keenness which exceeds that of European soldiers, and after a training which in some cases has gone on for four years they've developed a remarkable physical stamina.

This latter is being built up to peak for the invasion. Infantrymen tramp winding English roads every day, and there is not a company which can't do its twenty-five miles a day or its sixteen miles in four hours. Artillerymen rattle off with their guns in the middle of the night to ford English trout streams and plow across the soft English countryside until the dawn finds their big guns on a hilltop covering a quiet English cathedral town. Engineers, the handymen of modern war, bridge rivers, "delouse" mock mine fields, and sharpen their rifle eyes for the business to come—which inevitably must bring its full share of fighting and building and destroying for this ubiquitous corps.

As a result of all this, the soldiers are as fit as they've ever been, and healthier than those in the Mediterranean theater. You see them in the English market towns without their overcoats, reassuring anxious English mothers: "Why, this ain't cold. Why, ma'am, out in Duluth this time of year. . . ." The hospitals have been gratifyingly empty of patients from among the soldiers training in the field, although there have been a number of cases of flu among headquarters troops.

Generally, the Army is healthy and fighting fit, and one sergeant confided sorrowfully, "These guys are so fat and sassy it's gonna be hard to hold them, once they get going." He thought for a moment and then added, "They got to be that way, I guess. It's gonna be tough."

This theme runs through all the soldiers' talk, coupled with the unquestioning belief that, tough though it may be, they can "take" the Germans. None of them talks of honor or glory or freedom, and any interested person who does is greeted with cold cynicism. The soldier knows vaguely that beyond sweat, mud, and blood, he is fighting for certain principles. But he feels this personal knowledge is enough, and he's usually unfriendly toward politicians or chaplains who attempt to enlarge on the principles.

One thing that struck this correspondent was the immense pride which so many of the soldiers have in the Army. Many of them entered the service four years ago, when the Army was using stovepipes for mortars and trucks for tanks in maneuvers. Today they find themselves well armed, well drilled, and well led, and they're immensely proud not only of themselves for changing from civilians into soldiers, but of the government's ability to do the job.

Because of this, most of the G. I.s with whom I talked had a profound admiration for both President Roosevelt and General Marshall, to whom they ascribe the mounting efficiency and power of the Army in which they serve. It is not a political sentiment but one compounded of the

realization of the distance they've come in four years and pride in service.

Toward the invasion they display a seeming indifference. They make none of the bloodthirsty remarks which are commonly attributed to soldiers before a great offensive. But they are absolutely confident that they are better fighters and soldiers than the Germans, although in the next breath they will borrow an English phrase and concede that "old Fritz is a soldier."

Combat experience in Tunisia, Sicily, and Italy has raised the standard of our noncommissioned officers and our officers. Some of the officers with whom I've talked recently were "noncoms" in Tunisia and have been commissioned to new outfits.

These new officers have distinguished themselves in training for invasion. One general told me, "They may be a bit short on theory, but they're damned good when it comes to keeping men moving under fire—and that's one of the arts of war just as much as moving divisions on a map."

They are civilian soldiers, but it must not be thought that all of them are in field commands. The intelligence officer of one of our finest infantry divisions was publicity man for a wine growers' association before the war. Many other staff officers of proven ability came into the Army from important civilian jobs. There are publishers, lawyers, newspapermen, and municipal officials serving in positions of great important in this Army which, perhaps more than any other ever raised, represents the American nation in arms.

As a counterbalance there are West Pointers who, despite the gags and ribbing from the civilian soldiers—they call West Point "the Trade School"—are looked up to by the rest of the corps of officers. Now that a great part of the Army is trained, one finds more and more "Pointers" in field units rather than in the training centers. I met one twenty-six-year-old lieutenant colonel who will go far if his reckless gallantry doesn't end his career. As

professional soldiers they are far ahead of their counterparts in the British Army, although they naturally lack the experience of both British and German officers.

The ordinary soldier's attitude toward West Pointers is a revealing change from that of two years ago. Over the last beer before the pub closes, G. I. Joe will admit that although West Pointers "are hell" on discipline, drill, and dress, they "don't make many mistakes and they don't get you killed for nothing."

Relations between the ordinary fighting man and the High Command are not, of course, intimate. Since the Supreme Command of the Allied Expeditionary Force was set up in London, General "Ike" Eisenhower, supreme commander, General Sir Bernard Law Montgomery, commander of British ground forces, and Lieutenant General Omar Bradley, senior commander of U. S. ground forces, have done their utmost to make their figures familiar to the man who'll pull the trigger. Eisenhower is an almost legendary figure, commanding as he does the entire operation, but Montgomery is much closer to our troops. They like him even though they are amused at his penchant for publicity.

The reason for their affection is simple, and it is not that Montgomery is the only senior general of the Western powers who in a long series of battles has never been defeated. It is that Montgomery is known as a soldier who never strikes until he is fully prepared. Our soldiers, like the British, know that Montgomery is not a "waster" and that he has the habit of victory.

Bradley is an austere, somewhat distant figure who has earned the admiration of many by his classic calm during the bombardments in Tunisia and Sicily. He is very popular among the officers, who attribute to him almost supernatural ability to solve tactical problems in a few hours by ordering a series of attacks which with mathematical precision bring about the desired answer to the tactical situation.

Generally, however, what affection the men have for their generals is centered in the divisional commanders. Each has his own nickname, and it is frequently scurrilous, but for those for whom they have a genuine liking the troops will do anything.

At present, despite the intensity of their training and and the prospect before them, our soldiers are enjoying life. They are living in a pleasant quarter of England; their chow is, by field standards, good, and their billets are comfortable.

Some of them are living in schools and hotels, others are in Nissen huts or British barracks. With typical American ingenuity they've gone about making even the barest Nissen hut more comfortable. They give dances for the local girls, adorning the bare walls of the barracks or town halls with Rabelaisian frescoes which they fondly believe imitate those of El Morocco.

It is a small unit which doesn't have its own dance band, and the night air round any camp is lively with songs of quartets.

Our people have made a tremendous impression in a section of Britain traditionally conservative and hostile to foreigners. For one thing, they are much better behaved than the English expected. A man who ran a tobacco shop in one small town said, "They are the best behaved soldiers I ever saw," and an elderly woman who ran an isolated pub added, "They're so polite." The chief complaint is that the soldiers are addicted to sorrowful ballads at such advanced hours as ten o'clock at night, when most rural Englishmen and their wives are in bed. But that is a minor point—and, as one farmer said, "That song they sing about the railroad is quite nice!"

On the other hand, most of our Americans are impressed by the generosity of the British. "You get asked to dinner on Sunday," said a corporal of artillery, "and you get turkey and pudding an lots of beer and whisky. Maybe at first you don't realize that's all they have for the week, and even if you do you don't want to hold back, for fear of hurting their feelings."

Many of our divisions are quartered in agricultural sectors which suffered heavily from casualties in the first grim year of the war. Kids from all over America have been welcomed by English families whose sons died at Dunkirk, Trondheim, Calais, Narvik, or Louvain, or are in prison camps. "I feel as though I were really doing something for my Bert," one farm wife said when she told me how she walked a quarter mile each morning with a handful of fresh eggs for an American battery.

Out of this intermingling and the fighting of the last two years has come a new respect for the British as soldiers and civilians. The soldier has heard too much about Africa and Sicily to believe the old story that the British aren't fighting—or he's been there himself and has learned on the battlefield that they certainly are.

On top of that has come kindness from British civilians. It's no wonder that even the most rabidly anti-British soldier of two years ago now admits, "These guys are O. K. to fight beside."

Today our troops are healthy both mentally and physically, and are exceedingly well trained and equipped and well led. They have the correct mental attitude toward what is coming. "It's gonna be tough—but we can do it!"

The Bottom
of the Mountain
a story by Jerome Weidman

Someone Was Giving the Enemy Information. Intelligence Suspected the Band Leader — An ex-American Who Had Found Fame and Fortune in London. He Had a Secret, Yes! But It Wasn't What the Officials Thought

"WILL YOU HAVE one with us, sir?" The second lieutenant was not drunk, but he was not completely sober, either. He looked very young, twenty-one or twenty-two. The Airborne flash on the shoulder of his unpressed American uniform told Crayne almost as much about the young officer's recent movements as a less carefully trained observer could have learned from reading all the papers in his pockets.

"It's real chartreuse, sir," he went on. He was holding a tall, dark green, dusty bottle. The girl with him looked even younger than he did. She was very pretty in a shy, breathless, British way. The couple had stopped at Crayne's table, probably because the lieutenant had noticed Crayne's obviously American clothes.

"That's very nice of you, but thanks," Crayne said. "I'm drinking whisky."

"It's real chartreuse, sir," the lieutenant repeated. "I just brought it over from Normandy this morning."

D Day was not so many weeks old that the boy's pride could be considered unjustified.

"Thanks again," Crayne said. "I'll stick to my whisky."

The boy looked hurt as they walked away. Crayne had a moment of anger with himself. Why had he refused to take the drink? The fact that he disliked chartreuse and casual drunks was not the answer. Crayne finished his drink in a gulp. Apparently it was not so easy as he told himself it was, to be facing your thirty-ninth birthday in civilian clothes after being invalided out of the Army, among kids who wore khaki.

"Waiter," Crayne said. "Bring me another one of these. Double, please."

The waiter brought the drink. Crayne put the young lieutenant out of his mind. He was not here for fun, even though it was supposed to look that way. Under cover of his regular job as a member of the American press corps, Crayne had taken on this special work for the Colonel. He went back to watching the thinning crowd from his side table.

The Small Downstairs Ballroom of the Crescent Hotel in London was not small and it was not downstairs. It was called the Small Downstairs Ballroom to distinguish it from the larger restaurant at the other side of the lobby. When somebody rang you up and asked you to be in "the Small Downstairs" at nine, it meant the Crescent in the Strand. And you went there for the expensive rhythms of Cedric Hummert's orchestra. All of London, or rather those parts of it that could pay the price, had been dancing to his music for twenty years.

"Time, sir," the waiter said. "We're closing the bar. Another, sir?"

364

Crayne looked at his watch.

"Thanks, no," he said. "Bring me my check, please."

Crayne paid his check, gave the room a final glance, and moved toward the door. As far as the information the Colonel wanted was concerned, the evening had been a failure. But Crayne was glad to be going. For almost an hour the two small electric signs in the center of the mirrored panels that flanked the orchestra had been lighted. Crayne didn't think he was more afraid of the raids than most people in London. It was just that he did not like to be in the Small Downstairs Ballroom of the Crescent when they were coming over. There was something unsettling about being warned that death was overhead by two unobtrusive bits of neon tubing that flashed, discreetly and silently, the almost innocent word "Alert."

Crayne retrieved his coat from the cloakroom and turned for a last look through the doorway. Three or four couples were still on the dance floor. The waiters were stripping tables of empty glasses and crumpled napkins. The band was playing with the soft finality that meant the next number would be *God Save the King*. A young American officer, holding the hand of the girl beside him, stood at the foot of the bandstand. He was talking to the conductor. Cedric Hummert leaned down from the platform, then grinned and nodded. The young officer turned. It was the boy with the Airborne flash and the dusty bottle.

"Would you take this back for a moment?" Crayne handed his coat to the cloakroom attendant. "Some friends I want to say good night to."

He walked back into the room and sat down. The band broke into *Night and Day*. When the lieutenant and his girl reached the table, they stopped short. They looked at Crayne in surprise.

"I changed my mind about that drink," Crayne said. "May I?"

The surprise in the boy's face turned to pleasure.

"You bet, sir." He took an empty glass from the next table, set it beside the two in front of him, and filled all three from the dusty bottle. "To our side, sir."

"To our side," Crayne said, "and to our allies."

"To our side," the girl said, "and to *our* allies."

Crayne noticed that she touched the glass to her lips but did not drink. He didn't blame her. The stuff was vile. "It isn't much to do for one's country in time of war," the Colonel had said when, months before, he urged Crayne to take on his curious assignment. It wasn't, and Crayne had taken it on. It had not occurred to him then that drinking bad chartreuse would be a part of the odd duties that nobody in all the world except the Colonel and Crayne knew Crayne was performing. Under the table the lieutenant and the girl were holding hands. The orchestra stopped playing.

"Great tune," the boy said. "I asked Mr. Hummert to play it for us."

"It's terribly sweet of him," the girl said shyly. "He's such a nice man."

"Yes," Crayne said. "Very."

The orchestra stood up to play *God Save the King*. Crayne and the lieutenant and the girl rose. When it was over, Hummert jumped down from the platform and came across the deserted dance floor toward them.

"I asked him to have a drink with us," the boy said. He moved forward and took Hummert's extended hand. "Thank you, sir. That was really swell."

"Glad you liked it," Hummert said. "Hello, Crayne."

"Oh," the boy said. "You know each other?"

"Know each other!" Hummert laughed as he sat down. The laugh was like his clothes and his manner: very good, very smooth, yet just a shade too flashy. "I've known Crayne for donkey's years, long before he got to be a big-shot Broadway columnist. Why, I knew Crayne when he was just a cub reporter around the big street." The lieutenant looked at Crayne with awe. "I'm just a New York boy myself," Hummert said. He wasn't. He came from Mapleton, Ohio, but, after twenty years in London, he pretended that he was a native New Yorker. Most people mistook him for an Englishman. Hummert did not correct them unless someone like Crayne, who knew he was not, happened to be present. "We're old, old friends, aren't we?"

"Yes," Crayne said, "we are."

They weren't. Crayne had heard about the older man only vaguely in his cub reporter days, when Hummert was just beginning to be known around Broadway. His name was Charles Hummert in those days. Twenty years later, when Crayne came to London as a war correspondent, Hummert had looked him up. He looked up all the American newspapermen. Three years had gone by, however, since it had been Crayne's business to be friendly with orchestra leaders.

During those first months in London he had not returned Hummert's enthusiastic overtures. He didn't know why he disliked him, but the feeling was strong enough to cause him to stay away from the Crescent's Small Downstairs Ballroom. But since the Colonel had assigned him to this job, Crayne regretted his earlier coolness. The chances of his coming up with what the Colonel wanted depended almost entirely on Hummert's belief that he and Crayne were really close friends.

"Are you an American, sir?"

"I'll tell the cockeyed world," Hummert said. "American as apple pie."

He wasn't. There was something wrong about him. Even his slang was dated and false. Crayne wondered if that was why he disliked Hummert. That, plus the fact that Hummert was a naturalized Englishman.

"You'll have another drink, then, sir, won't you?"

"You bet your life I will."

The boy tipped the chartreuse bottle. It was empty. The boy looked embarrassed.

"Never mind. We'll have one on me," Hummert said. "For old times' sake, eh, Crayne?" He snapped his fingers at a waiter. "How about a quick round for me and my friends, Victor?"

"I'm sorry, sir. The bar is closed, sir."

"To hell with that," Hummert said. "Just tell them it's for me, will you?"

"I'll try, sir."

"Step on it, Victor. My friends are thirsty." Hummert laughed. "They always say that," he said confidentially. "That's the British for you. You've got to know them. Me, I know them like a book."

The waiter came back.

"I'm sorry, Mr. Hummert. The steward's locked up and gone off, sir."

"That's one hell of a way to treat me and my friends, Victor. What's his rush?"

"There's an alert on, sir. Been on for a couple of hours. I imagine he was anxious to get home, sir."

Hummert scowled. He looked quickly at the lieutenant and then at the girl. Crayne was aware that the unprofitable evening had suddenly and unexpectedly taken a turn that might lead to what the Colonel wanted.

"Tell you what," Hummert said. "How about everybody coming over to my place for a couple? I've got plenty of liquor in the house. What do you say?"

Crayne crushed out his cigarette.

"That's awfully nice of you," he said. "But it's very late and we wouldn't want to disturb your family."

"You won't be disturbing them," Hummert said. "The wife and kids are in the country. Sent them down two weeks ago, when these bloody things started coming over. Come on. I've got some interesting things to show you."

"Well, if it's all right with these two youngsters," Crayne said. During his few months in the Colonel's strange business that was now his business, too, Crayne had learned that while you could only rarely shape the events with which you had to work, it was always possible to take correct advantage of them when they shaped themselves for you. "I certainly could use a drink."

There were only five or six people in the queue waiting at the bus stop on the Edgware Road when Crayne came down the street. It was midafternoon, too early for the shoppers and office workers to be going home to Willesden and Maida Vale.

He walked past the queue, crossed the road, and stopped to buy a paper. Then he walked around the block, and came out once more into the Edgware Road. The length and character of the queue had changed. Now the line included several women with shopping bags, half a dozen schoolboys, and among others an American officer with a white mustache.

Crayne took his place at the end of the queue. A few minutes later a bus stopped in front of the queue. Crayne got on behind the women with shopping bags and the American officer. A few passengers found seats downstairs. The American officer and Crayne climbed to the top deck. The last seat in the rear, a double one next to the stairs, was empty. Crayne took it. The bus lurched sharply. The American officer staggered and dropped into the vacant space next to Crayne. He smiled apologetically.

"Sorry."

"Quite all right, sir," Crayne said. Sitting like that, side by side in the rear seat next to the stairs, there was nobody behind or on either side of them. The clippie came upstairs. Crayne took a shilling from his pocket. "Two five-penny tickets, please."

'Where to, sir?"

"The Gaumont cinema," Crayne said. "Kilburn High Road."

She took the coin, punched a couple of tickets, dug two coppers out of the leather wallet at her side, and gave the tickets and the change to Crayne.

The clippie moved on down the aisle toward the other passengers. In a low conversational tone Crayne said, "We're after the wrong man, sir."

"We can always be mistaken," the Colonel said. "We frequently are. But we can't close our files on him until we're certain."

"I think you can close them, sir," Crayne said. "I'm certain."

"Why?"

Crayne looked with quick interest at the handsome white-haired man beside him. He had first met the Colonel six months before, when the Intelligence officer had sent for Crayne and asked the surprised newspaperman to work for him secretly. Then, as now, the Colonel seemed to know everything about him. During those six months Crayne had grown to like the older man. It was a liking based solely on his respect for the Colonel's ability. Crayne had nothing else to go on. Their meetings were infrequent. They were arranged by telephone and held in odd places, to discuss a new assignment for Crayne or to hear Crayne's report on a current job. Nobody, not even the members of the Colonel's own organization, was aware that Crayne was in any way connected with their work.

The Colonel never talked about personal matters. Consequently Crayne knew almost nothing about his chief. There were times when this made their business relationship a difficult one for Crayne. He was certain that the Cedric Hummert case was closed. He was not certain that his reasons would be accepted by the Colonel.

"I finally got to his house," Crayne said. "Last night, sir."

"Alone?"

"No. With a second lieutenant just back from Normandy, and his girl. Hummert picked them up in the Small Downstairs. I happened to be with them. He asked me to go along.

It was Hummert's practice of taking young American officers to his flat late at night, after the Crescent's Small Downstairs Ballroom closed, and feeding them more liquor than was good for them that had aroused the suspicions of the Colonel's organization. For a couple of months before D Day, and during the weeks that followed, there had been a number of small security leaks in London. Several had been traced back to the Small Downstairs Ballroom of the Crescent.

The Colonel had no real evidence to go on. Merely a hunch. He felt there was something peculiar about an American band leader who had left his own country, settled in London, and remained there for twenty years without going back even once for a visit. It looked, the Colonel said, as though Hummert had renounced his native land. Such men made good enemy agents. So the Colonel had assigned Crayne to the Hummert case.

"How did it go?" he asked, after a pause.

"Very well," Crayne said. "There was a hell of a raid on."

Crayne told the Colonel about his three hours in Hummert's house with the young lieutenant and the girl. Hummert had spent most of the time showing them his possessions: the piano that had once belonged to the King of Rumania, the set of Swinburne with the poet's autograph on each flyleaf, the liquor cabinet that was a present from someone related by marriage to the royal family, the portrait of his wife by a member of the Royal Academy.

While Hummert showed and described his treasures, Crayne had gradually remembered all that he had known and forgotten about him in those early days on Broadway. Hummert had never been a really big name on the big street. He had been just another young man with a band that worked fairly regularly and was paid fairly well. One day he had disappeared. A few questions were asked about him, but not many. Charles Hummert was not missed. Soon he was forgotten.

At four in the morning the lieutenant and his girl and Crayne had said good night and left Hummert's house. Crayne put the youngsters into a taxi, walked through the blackout to his own flat, and lay awake until dawn thinking the thing out. By the time he pulled the sleep mask over his eyes and rolled his face away from the morning sun to get some rest, Crayne was sure he had the problem solved.

"I see," the Colonel said.

"I may have it figured wrong," Crayne said. "I don't think so sir."

The Colonel did not answer. He stared out the window at the queues in front of the fish and vegetable hucksters' carts on the Kilburn High Road. He seemed absorbed in the teeming scene.

Crayne was irritable. It was his job to get information. He had performed that job well on previous assignments. On this one he had come up not with information but with a theory. It had been an embarrassing theory to explain, in an undertone on top of a bus. It was annoying to see that his theory was not even interesting enough to distract the Colonel's attention.

"Of course, all this is based on only one visit to his home," Crayne said. "Hummert could hardly be expected to try to get information out of an Army officer while I was present. He wouldn't have invited me to come along if he'd wanted to do that. Just the same, I don't think he's the man we're looking for."

"I think I'll get off at the next stop," the Colonel said casually. "I must get back to my office." He smiled suddenly, a broad, friendly grin. "I'll buy your theory," he said. The bus began to slow down. The Colonel stepped over to the stairs, and turned back for a moment. "I'm going to close my files on Hummert."

The phone rang on the desk at the other side of the office. Crayne was trying to finish a dispatch. There had been two heavy raids that morning and his secretary, an English girl who had been blitzed out of three different dwellings in four years, had rushed off to Putney to see if she would have a place to sleep that night.

The phone continued to ring. Crayne remained at the typewriter. His paper in New York did not know about his work for the Colonel. He could offer no explanation if he fell behind in his coverage of the London news. The phone rang shrilly on his secretary's desk. He stood up, finally, and went across the room.

"Hello." It was a woman's voice. "Mr. Crayne, please."

"Speaking."

"Oh." She sounded upset. "This is Mrs. Hummert. Mrs. Cedric Hummert."

"Yes," Crayne said. "How do you do?"

"Could you come around to our flat right away? It's frightfully important."

"I'm sorry. I can't right now."

"Please, Mr. Crayne."

The flat, impersonal, superior cadence of the voice had not changed, but there was a small, almost desperate increase in pitch. It was enough to cut through Crayne's divided attention.

"What's wrong?"

"Our flat's been hit. This morning's raid. My husband is asking for you, Mr. Crayne."

"For me? Why me?"

"Yes. I don't know. He keeps calling your name."

"Is he badly hurt?"

"Yes, rather. They rang me in the country at noon. I came up by the first train. He wants you, Mr. Crayne. Do say you'll come."

"I'll be right over."

"Thank you so much. We're at Westminster Gardens. If you'll just ask any taxi driver."

"I know Westminster Gardens."

In the taxi Crayne could not decide whether he was more annoyed by the tone of Mrs. Hummert's voice or by her husband's upsetting summons. The files on Hummert were closed. The Colonel had ended the case the day before. Why should Hummert send for Crayne now? He could not possibly know that he had been under suspicion.

Crayne sat up straight on the taxi seat. There *was* a way by which Hummert could have known he was under suspicion. It was the only way: if Hummert was guilty. The taxi stopped. The street in which Westminster Gardens stood was roped off. Crayne paid the driver, walked up to the policeman on guard, and showed his press card.

"Right, sir. You'll have to use the side entrance. I'm afraid the front has been knocked out, sir."

Westminster Gardens was a gaudy modernistic block of flats, with vast sheets of seamless glass instead of windowpanes.

The robot had landed in the street, fifty yards or so beyond the entrance. The blast had knocked out the front of Westminster Gardens and sliced away sections of flats on either side. A. R. P. men with "Heavy Rescue" patches on their sleeves were working in the rubble. Crayne picked his way through the debris. He showed his card to another policeman near the door.

"You'll have to walk, sir. The lift's gone. Back stairs are over there, sir, to your left."

Crayne walked up three flights. The door of the Hummert flat was ajar. The blast had sprung the hinges. Crayne pushed the pearl button on the jamb. He was not surprised to hear the buzzer sound inside. Blast damage was unpredictable. It could wreck a roomful of bronze statues and leave a delicate vase intact in the middle. The door was opened by a smartly dressed woman of about forty with a hard, lined face and blonde hair.

"You're Mr. Crayne?"

"Yes."

"I'm Mrs. Hummert. It's frightfully kind of you to come. This is Dr. Farquarson."

"Mr. Hummert keeps calling your name," the doctor said. "Mrs. Hummert and I were wondering if you know why?"

"I have no idea. Do you want me to ask him?"

"I'm afraid it's impossible to question him," Dr. Farquarson said. "Mr. Hummert's condition is very grave."

"That's too bad," Crayne said. "Is there anything I can do?"

Mrs. Hummert and the doctor exchanged glances. She nodded slightly.

"If you will come this way," Dr. Farquarson said. "I must ask you not to excite him. He is very weak."

"Of course."

Crayne moved toward the bedroom door and stopped. Dr. Farquarson had moved toward the door of the living room.

"The bedrooms are almost completely gone," Mrs. Hummert said. "That's why Cedric was injured. He was asleep when the bomb landed. They found him a couple of hours later and sent for me. We've put him in the drawing room. It's the one room that wasn't hit so badly."

"We must be very quiet," Dr. Farquarson said. "He must not be disturbed."

Crayne nodded. The doctor opened the door. Crayne stared at the room which, when he had seen it three nights before, had been so carefully and laboriously arranged that it had resembled a room in a museum. The piano that had belonged to the King of Rumania was cracked wide open. The priceless autographed set of Swinburne was torn to bits. The portrait of Mrs. Hummert by the Royal Academician lay on the floor, the frame broken, the canvas slashed in several places as though with a knife. Hummert, his head propped up on two pillows, lay motionless in a large bed that had been moved into the middle of the ruined room.

"He's asleep," Dr. Farquarson whispered. "I gave him a sedative an hour ago."

Crayne nodded. He was shocked by Hummert's appearance. His head was bandaged and his left arm, bound in splints, lay stiff and straight at his side. His eyes were closed. His heavy irregular breathing was painful to hear. Each breath was a struggle. The large blustering band leader now looked small and frail under the thin covers. He opened his eyes.

"Crayne." His voice was hoarse. "Get Crayne."

Crayne stepped over to the bed.

"Here I am."

Hummert's eyes were closed again.

"Crayne," he said. "Get Crayne."

"Here I am. It's me. I'm Crayne."

Hummert opened his eyes. A gleam of recognition shot through them. His parched lips cracked apart in a horrible approximation of a smile, and then, as his eyes fell on Dr. Farquarson and Mrs. Hummert, the smile stopped.

"Alone. Want talk Crayne alone."

Crayne turned to the others.

"I won't upset him," he said quietly. He wanted them to get out. He did not want any witnesses to what Hummert was going to tell him. "Of course, if you'd rather I didn't—"

The doctor hesitated, then nodded and took Mrs. Hummert's arm. They went out and closed the door softly. Crayne turned back to the man on the bed. Hummert's eyes were closed.

"We're alone now," Crayne said. "What did you want to tell me?"

The band leader did not answer. Crayne bent over the bed. Hummert's breathing was weaker. He seemed to be resting, gathering strength for what he wanted to say. Crayne pulled over a broken chair and sat down beside the bed.

"Take it easy," he said. "I've got plenty of time."

Crayne found it hard to suppress a mounting feeling of excitement. The Colonel had closed the files on Hummert because of Crayne's analysis. It was true that Crayne would look foolish if Hummert, afraid that he was about to die, had sent for Crayne in order to make a complete confession. But Crayne knew that only one thing was important now: to correct a mistake he had caused the Colonel to make.

"Whenever you're ready," Crayne said.

Crayne watched the man whose life was slipping away before his eyes and wondered where his analysis had gone wrong. He had seen it all so clearly three nights before. Hummert was like most of the men Crayne had known on and around Broadway. He had wanted success. More than anything in the world he had desired fame, money. His ambition had been larger than his talent.

Hummert never really reached Broadway in the full meaning of that phrase. His ability was too small. He reached the fringes of fame and money. He touched the edge of success. He never really held it firmly. Success

was the pinnacle of a tall, tall mountain. He had come close, but never close enough. He knew finally that, like most men, he would never reach the top. But Hummert differed in one respect: he faced the reality that if he remained on Broadway he would never have what he wanted. He made a decision. He left Broadway. He came to London.

In the British capital the competition was not so great. The mere fact that he was an American was an asset. Here he achieved fame, earned money, became a success. He reached the top of the mountain. The air was sweet. It was as he had always dreamed it would be. It was difficult to give it up.

Hummert stayed on. And the longer he stayed, the more difficult it was to go back. He set about the task of making it impossible for himself to return. He changed his name from Charles to Cedric. He married an English girl. He sent his children to British schools. He deliberately lost touch with his relatives in America. He cultivated a British accent. And finally he became a naturalized British subject.

Twenty years had gone by. They were good years. He was happy. He was respected. He was successful. He had everything he had ever wanted. Everything except the one thing he had always had but no longer possessed: his own country.

"I want you to take a look at this liquor cabinet." Crayne could hear Hummert's voice again as he showed his possessions. "It was presented to me by a member of the royal family."

There had been a pathetic eagerness in Hummert's voice. For all his hearty British manner, he had looked and sounded like a small boy explaining how, in spite of his black eye and bloody nose, he had really won the fight from which he had just come home in tatters.

Long before Crayne left Hummert's flat at four o'clock that morning, he knew that the band leader did not take young American officers from the Small Downstairs Ballroom of the Crescent to his house and fill them with liquor to pry military secrets for the enemy.

The war, the air raids, the young men in uniform from his own country, all of these things in combination had shaken Hummert's belief in the decision he had made twenty years ago. He was too old to have his belief shaken. He was forty-seven. When the robots started coming over, he sent his wife and children to the country. He had to remain in London. He was an Englishman now. Englishmen did not run away from bombs. He was alone much of the time, in spite of the many people by whom he was surrounded in his work.

He had done a good job on himself in twenty years, but it was not perfect. The British knew he was American, and the Americans thought he was British. He was comfortable with neither. He began to entertain young American officers at his house. To ingratiate himself with them, he told them he was a native New Yorker.

For Hummert this entertaining had become a necessity. The admiration of the young men for his possessions was reassuring. The roomful of treasures was the symbol, the price he had received for giving up his own country. Hummert needed reassurance. That was how Crayne had figured it.

That was the basis on which the Colonel had closed Hummert's file. Where had the analysis gone wrong?

"Want you do me favor."

Crayne leaned over the bed. Hummert's eyes were open. They were the only things alive in that shrunken body.

"Anything at all," Crayne said. He tried not to sound eager. The confession could clean up the case for the Colonel. It would not answer the question that kept drilling in the back of Crayne's mind: Why had Hummert chosen him, an American newspaperman who had never taken any pains to conceal his dislike for Hummert?

Hummert closed his eyes. He was gathering together whatever was left in him for the final effort. Crayne waited. His glance slid across the room toward the door. He did not want the doctor or Mrs. Hummert to interrupt.

Crayne's eyes skipped across the fragments of the shattered room. It was all worthless now, of course. But it had been quite a price. Crayne had known men in his time who had sold more of themselves for less. It was not his business to judge. It was his business to pay close attention and hear clearly what Hummert had to say. He would have to repeat it to the Colonel.

Hummert opened his eyes again. His dry lips were moving. Crayne leaned down.

"Family owns plot—in Mapleton, Ohio," Hummert said, forcing the words out one at a time. "Please send cable." His body arched upward in a final, desperate effort. Crayne put his arm under the thin shoulders. "Cremate," Hummert gasped. "Send ashes Mapleton. Family will pay. Bury ashes home. Not here. Home."

The stiffness went out of him. It was as though Crayne had been holding one of those inflated rubber figures with which children play on the beach and suddenly, without warning, all the air had escaped. Crayne lowered the limp body to the bed and straightened up. The Colonel's files would not have to be reopened. Charles Hummert had started his journey back home at last.

Everybody Knows La Guardia

by John Dos Passos

Here's a Typical Day in the Hectic Life of New York's LaGuardia, a Stick of Dynamite in a Double-Breasted Suit Who Is Never Out of the News for More Than a Day

AS I SLOSH up through the dripping park to the Gracie Mansion, a tall cop in a rubber raincoat steps in my path to ask if I have an appointment and leads me up to the front door under the high white porch of the old-time country house. There he turns me over to a maid, who ushers me through the white-paneled hall into a side room that looks spacious and empty in the gray morning light that comes in off the river.

A small, broad-shouldered, heavy-faced man, buttoned into a double-breasted blue suit, sits behind the desk at the end of the room. He is smoking a long cigar while he goes over a pile of papers. He has the look of a man who has enjoyed his breakfast. His dark eyes, behind black-rimmed horn spectacles, are eating up the typewritten sheets. He gets to his feet to say How do you do, pulling off his glasses as he does so. His manner is absolutely without pretension. He offers me one of his cigars, saying a friend sent them from Jamaica, then sits down again.

A marvelous place for a quiet interview, I think to myself as I light my cigar. The first question I'll want to ask is just forming in back of my lips when the Mayor hops to his feet. "Well, it's time to go to work," he says. "Come along."

Following him out into the hall, I say something about what a handsome old house the city has given him to live in. He stops in his tracks and looks up at the elab-orate moldings of the ceiling. "It's tough on my wife," he says, "keeping it up. The Metropolitan Museum fixed up these lower rooms in good taste. They gave me a rare old antique carpet for the hall. When the King of Greece came to call, he dropped right down on his knees to feel it with his hand, and said it was so valuable it ought to be hung on the wall." The Mayor drops down to the floor and imitates the way the king put on his eyeglasses to see better. "I told the museum to take it away because the kids got the habit of running down the stairs and jumping on it."

He snatches up his broad-brimmed rancher's hat of light tan felt and we duck into the driving rain. While the tall cop holds open the car door, we squeeze in beside the driver of the white single-seated police roadster. Speeding down the East River Drive, we start to talk about children. Obviously the Mayor likes to talk about children. One thing he feels he can boast about, he says, is that the children of the city are better fed, better clothed, cleaner and healthier today than they were ten years ago.

This is great, I think; he's really going to talk. But he has hardly started when a voice begins to croak out of the two-way radio. He reaches for the telephone receiver on the dashboard and is lost in a conversation with his office. When I am able to get his attention again, we're already way downtown opposite the Navy Yard, speeding toward the old bridges that hum with early traffic. The Mayor points out parks and playgrounds and the staggered blocks of the new housing. "People live better. There's no doubt about it," he says. I begin to say something about missing the excitement of Manhattan's old swarming East Side.

"You never had to live in it," he answers.

Before I can explain what I mean, the car turns in through a brick-paved street lined with warehouses, around the tall marble buildings that house the law courts of the city and state, and draws up in the middle of the park before the arched entrance of the old City Hall.

The Mayor jumps out of the car and runs at a jog trot up the steps into the vestibule. Reporters in raincoats converge on him there and hold him in a huddle for a second. He breaks away and darts off past the desks of the receptionists, then turns into a narrow passage clogged with typewriters. Handing his hat to a tall man in uniform with gilt braid on the shoulder, he waves me to a chair and plops down behind his enormous desk. We can talk later; first, he's got to go over the day's mail. Three girl stenographers, who have followed him into the office, sit alert and smiling on the edges of their chairs.

Immediately there's a hush of concentration in the room. There is no sound but the jangle of downtown traffic filtering through the closed windows. From the walls, portraits of former mayors in their silk stocks look down out of their gilt frames. The Mayor sits under a great crystal chandelier. On the desk in front of him stands his calendar. Both sides of the desk are piled with reference books and folders full of documents. A small gavel lies handy. On the wall opposite there's a large-scale civilian defense map with a diagram of an enemy bomb bursting in Brooklyn and the resulting action. Around the walls, chairs and settees wait for visitors. Over to the right of the desk a group of armchairs still hold the attitude of respectful attention of those who last sat in them the afternoon before.

The Mayor looks up from the pile of various colored sheets, pulls on his half-smoked cigar, and starts dictating replies in a low quiet voice. Now and then a serious-looking man comes in with an old-fashioned black ledger and opens it under the Mayor's nose to check on an appointment. A young fellow with pencils in his breast pocket shows the Mayor clippings pasted on cardboard. When there's someone on the phone he ought to speak to, a young woman secretary comes in and whispers in his ear. He trots out into the other room and is back in an instant at his dictating again. While the minutes tick into hours I sit there, feeling like a man who has found himself by some accident on the stage after the curtain has gone up on a play.

At ten thirty the stenographers slip out. I begin to phrase a question, but already city officials have moved into the room and into the group of armchairs. Two small

dark men have slid silently onto the settees in the back of the room. The Mayor starts reading a document in a rapid perfunctory voice. The words "statutory public hearing" stand out. It's something about changing the name of a street somewhere in Queens. In three minutes it's over. The little men in back vanish as silently as they came.

Now maybe there'll be a lull, I think, and start stirring in my chair. But the secretary is already introducing a visitor. The period of conferences has begun.

"What have you got?" the Mayor asks sharply as the visitor settles in his seat. This gray-haired man can't seem to disentangle himself from the details of the problem surrounding an easement for a sewer. The Mayor's voice goes shrill as he cuts him off in the middle of a sentence: "All right. That ends that." The visitors come thick and fast. Two men and a woman chat about how the borough presidents are going to vote in the Board of Estimate. The chief of police reads a report. A red-faced man in uniform goes over the Fire Department's troubles in getting enough men to man the stations at the beaches. A brisk young man is asking whether they shouldn't plant apple trees at the reform school. A young lady with glasses is talking about relief clients, case loads, limited employability.

The Mayor pushes his glasses up on his forehead and leans back in his chair to listen. "Nobody ever sees these people." He drags the words out. "Are you sure they are unemployable?" His face wrinkles up. "Why I'm so worried is, one morning we are going to wake up and be hit between the eyes. That's why I want to save every cent I can, to be ready when the time comes."

When he talks he gestures with the hand that holds the cigar. Often there's a coaxing whine in his voice as he ends a conversation. "We've got to go in with one eye open and know what we're doing." Or a sharply phrased question: "Is it on the level?" Or admonishingly he shakes the surprisingly long forefinger of his stubby hand. "Be alert on this, won't you, please?"

I keep forgetting my questions as I watch the show. As the morning goes on the feeling of pressure rises. Business has to be speeded up, decisions hastened. Secretaries and assistants run in and out. The Mayor looks down, sometimes frowning or pouting, at papers laid down in front of him. Now and then he pulls off his glasses and chews on the earpieces. Wisps of black hair begin to shake down on his forehead.

At twelve o'clock a secretary brings him a cup of black coffee in a heavy white porcelain cup. The visitor gets a sandwich with his cup of coffee. Now this ought to be a good time for a talk, I think. But somebody sets the typewritten copy of a speech on the desk before the Mayor. "Just a minute," he says abstractedly as his eyes run over it fast. Meanwhile he sips his coffee. "Sure, give it out."

But before I can begin, his assistant appears with an armful of lawbooks. All morning there's been talk about the leakage of city employees into war jobs. Some people are holding two jobs at once. He has been finding out whether or not it's a crime for a man to use another man's Social Security card. Passing my chair, the assistant whispers, "I've been with five mayors. On all questions of law I was the authority. Now he knows more about it than I do."

As one o'clock approaches, the pressure relaxes. Just as I'm opening my mouth, the Mayor starts dictating in Italian. The dark girl who is taking it down in shorthand corrects him over the form of a verb. As he warms up he begins to talk fluently with very little accent. He gets to his feet and walks back and forth behind his chair as if he were addressing a meeting. Meanwhile the secretaries are fussing about a letter that's been lost in the files. Folders are hurried in and out. Documents rustle impatiently. A young man hurries in with a Bible and a reference book. The Mayor wants to look up something to use in the speech he is scheduled to make at a luncheon. The secretary starts a rambling explanation. "I don't want any explanations. Give me the passage, will you?"

"And this is a quiet day," whispers the assistant as he brushes past my chair. "You ought to see a busy day."

For a second the big office is empty. I straighten up and clear my throat. But already five young soldiers are being ushered in. "We didn't know whether you'd remember us or not," says the redheaded sergeant who leads the way. "Makes us feel better about government when a man like you can find time for guys like us." The Mayor says, laughing, that sure he remembers that talk in Kodiak in Alaska. How are things out there anyway? Stationed down in North Carolina now, they say. They've got a couple of days' leave and have come to take a look at New York. "Going overseas soon?" the Mayor asks. They shrug. "Well," he says cheerfully, "if there's one sight prettier in the whole world than steaming out of the port of New York, it's steaming in again."

Suddenly it's time to go to the luncheon. I trail close behind him as he bolts out through the secretaries' room. The officer with the gold braid on his shoulder is running after him with the broad-brimmed rancher's hat, and catches up halfway down the steps. City Hall reporters crowd around asking if there's anything cooking. Two women are standing on the pavement outside looking up at the City Hall. "Sure that's the Mayor! Everybody knows what he looks like!" one of them shouts excitedly.

"I'm the only executive in the whole country," he says with some pride, as we squeeze into the single-seated police car again, "who hasn't got a car of his own."

Driving uptown, the Mayor is recognized on every street corner. Men on trucks, people in the backs of cars, taxi drivers, groups at crossings waiting for the traffic lights smile and wave to him as he passes. They know him. He's their Mayor.

The luncheon is on Park Avenue. Sitting on gilt chairs amid a profusion of potted palms and not a little incrusta-

tion of diamonds and real lace, women dressed for the afternoon and elderly men are listening to a talkative toastmaster. When the little Mayor takes the microphone, he brings a breath of the real life of city streets and tenements into the stuffy room. We mustn't forget that the girls we are trying to help are real people like your own daughters, he tells them. He talks indulgently and understandingly about the need for romance these girls feel, about their craze for uniform and for the young men who may not have very long to live. To help them we must look to the heart more than to the head.

While the lunchers are still applauding, while the photographers' bulbs are still flashing, he is making for the door. Well, that's over, I think as I hurry after him. Going downtown will be the ideal time . . . But there is a young woman already sitting in the car with whom the Mayor has got to talk about juvenile delinquency on the way downtown.

Back at the office, appointments have piled up. A delegation from Harlem has been waiting—a colored clergyman, a lieutenant, several neatly dressed women, photographers. They are posed in a jiffy. Bulbs flash. Handshaking. Before they are out of the room he has settled down for a long talk with a nautical-looking man about the employees of the city's ferries and sludge boats.

All the while the assistant is standing by the desk, smiling, with his finger in a lawbook. "Mayor, I've got a statute for you," he whispers in the first break in the conversation. The Mayor snatches the book and reads the passage greedily. He grunts and hands it back.

The talk switches to plans for a new ferry station on Staten Island. A number of men are studying the big maps of the five boroughs against the wall opposite the desk. It is all about the flow of traffic, tunnels after the war, appropriations. They are warming up. Everybody's excited. They seem to be making their point.

Leaning back at his desk with his glasses pushed back on his forehead, the Mayor is playing with a gold pencil case. He frowns with pursed lips. "That's money in a different order of magnitude. . . . Can't you do it in two or three bites? . . . I'm a little timid—I'm a little scared of it."

As the men say good-by and walk out, there's a general stir in the office. I manage to get in a word about postwar planning. The Mayor hands me a cable he's just received from a committee of the English House of Commons asking the same question. As if by magic, one of the pleasant-faced girl stenographers has reappeared. The Mayor throws himself into dictating a reply. "Forging forward . . ." In the middle of it he leans over and hands me the last cigar on his desk. "You smoke this. I've still got my old butt," he says. "I oughtn't to smoke too much anyway."

Before he's finished his reply to the House of Commons a group of city officials have clustered round the big desk waiting to discuss the budget. "Gee whiz, Thursday's the first of the month!" the Mayor blurts out in the midst of it. There is a flutter of secretaries. The black ledger is spread out in front of him. "I've got to change my whole schedule. Tomorrow I'll do my thinking. Don't crowd me in the morning so I'll be all tired out. Call off everything else Monday so I can do that."

An education headache is waiting, a committee on medical insurance, a truck drivers' strike, the Department of Health, research, the incidence of measles, the quarantine against rabies in the Bronx. . . .

At four thirty he's signing his mail, while the secretaries who have brought the letters in hang over his shoulders. He grumbles over the letters as he turns them over. His face wrinkles up. "What's this? Where did you get those facts? I won't sign that one. . . . Let me look at that." He sticks out his lip. His eyes go very black. "I think they are playing politics with that. It's just an outrage to play politics with that." A spike of hair shakes down on his forehead. "Cheap bastards."

Before he's finished, the man with the gold braid comes in to report that the Mayor is late for his appointment in Brooklyn. We go charging out, somebody again running after him with the broad-brimmed rancher's hat. He talks over his shoulder with the newspapermen as he runs down the steps. On the pavement outside we tangle with an elderly man with blank eyes, carrying a suitcase under one arm, who announces in a loud voice that he is waiting to remind the Mayor that he's promised that today he'll appoint him Commissioner of Bugs and Poisons Dropped from the Air.

"Tomorrow!" shouts the Mayor and ducks into the police car. "Who the devil's that?" I ask. He answers, a little breathless, "Been going on for years. He's bats. He peddles socks and neckties in office buildings. Seems to have enough sense to make his own living."

We whisk across Brooklyn Bridge and pile out of the car in front of a brick building newly converted into a firehouse. The firemen are all lined up. There's a band, a glee club, admirals from the nearby Navy Yard, a small crowd of neighbors. The band strikes up. The glee club sings God Bless America. There are some speeches. Photographers' bulbs flash. Then off we go, speeding through Brooklyn to a clubhouse, where drinks and canapés are laid out on a long table to celebrate the occasion.

A couple of gulps, a few hands shaken, a little low-voiced talk with this man and that, and we are off again, back across the Williamsburg Bridge to Manhattan. On lower Park Avenue we stop for a quiet drink at one of the Mayor's clubs.

In the sudden solitude of the empty bar we sit blinking at each other. Now is the time.

How to begin? I want to ask about his life in Arizona as a kid; what it was like to work in a U. S. consulate in the old days of the Austro-Hungarian Empire; how much he feels he has accomplished since he first charged out into the streets of the Italian sections of Manhattan to defeat Tammany on its home ground; what recollections he has of his years as an insurgent congressman in Washington.

But even now, when the rush of business has let up for a second, there's still no time. We have scarcely begun to talk before the Mayor has to go. He hands me a ticket for the concert that evening and whisks me uptown to drop me politely at my door on the way home. My day with the Mayor is over.

Walking out after dinner into the floor of Madison Square Garden, looking up at the tiers of blurred faces under the crisscrossing spotlights, listening to the hollow rumble of voices muffled by the hugeness of the hall and the strains of the double symphony orchestra tuning up on the platform, it strikes me that this is what Fiorello LaGuardia probably dreamed of for himself when he was a small boy. He loves music. He loves a crowd. There he sits, a small man in a business suit, in his box beside his wife. With the LaGuardias are a modestly dressed group of friends. There are no uniforms or white shirt fronts or ermine. You wouldn't know where he was sitting if you came casually into the hall.

And yet he knows he is the skipper. He's the man who is running the town. He's happy in that knowledge.

Applause beats about the maestro's head as it rises above the ranked violins.

Then the maestro taps with the baton. The hall vibrates to volleys of hand-clapping. The maestro's arms wave. The long strains of Lohengrin, immensely amplified by the augmented orchestra, fill the huge hall. The Mayor sits quiet on the edge of his chair. His face is relaxed. He is drinking in the music and the feeling of expectation in the crowd. This is his life as he likes it.

After the concert I meet a friend in a bar. He knows what I've been doing all day. "Well, did he jump down your throat?" he asks sarcastically.

"No. Quite the contrary. He was a little sharp at times, but he didn't blow up once all day."

"Not once? Amazing. That can mean only one thing," my friend says, laughing. "He's going to run again. He's going to run for a fourth term for Mayor."

Here's Your Country Soldier

by Lt. William Fitzgibbon

What's It Like to Get Home after Two Years? How Are the Dames? Is It Still the Good Old U. S. A.? A Serviceman Reports Back to the Boys Over There

A HIGH-EXPLOSIVE shell, the old Anzio Express, came in with a quick whine and a roaring crash a hundred yards from where we stood. A swirl of gray dust hung over the shattered building like a snagged cloud, and from it came a soldier in a jeep driving fast toward safer regions.

The Navy said to hell with the passenger list; we'd check it out at sea—and the remaining soldiers on the wharf scrambled aboard. The LST closed its jawlike ramp and cast off. The Jerries threw in another round that landed in the water to our starboard, spouting up a huge geyser and killing dozens of fish. Within five minutes we were out of artillery range for the first time in months.

A few weeks later I was in New York City eating a banana split, and the girl behind the counter was telling me how lucky I was to walk in just when they happened to have bananas.

That's the war for you. Sometimes you stay in one spot for months and months, until you're ready for a Section 8; then suddenly the Army transfers you around so fast you think you're on a whirligig.

She was a nice soft-looking girl with amber hair, but I was tired of her talk about bananas and how hard they were to buy. Then she asked what that ribbon was, and I told her it was the European Theater.

"How long were you overseas?"

"Two years," I said. It's funny, but whenever I tell someone that now, I feel as though I'm bragging. Overseas, you flaunt the fact with a mixture of pride and self-commiseration and it gives you rank over the new arrivals. Once you are home, it's merely an incident in your background and it makes you a little self-conscious to talk about it.

"Gee," the girl said, "I'm glad we had bananas when you came in. We're supposed to get a dozen bananas a month, but sometimes we don't get any for months, and even then most of them are overripe and squashy. Slow ships or something, I guess, because of the submarines."

I wondered how I could include a dissertation on bananas in "my first impressions of the United States," which I had promised to write to O'Conner. Private William O'Conner of Brooklyn took me down to the docks that last morning at Anzio. He and I had been on duty together since D plus three, working nights and sleeping days.

"Listen, lieutenant," he'd said. "Don't be like all those other guys when you get back. Tell us what the States is like now. Tell us about the chow you get, and how you're livin', and about the dames, and if the people back there know what we're doing over here and if they give a damn. Do that, willya, lieutenant? Don't forget about us, like those other guys who went back. And tell us how it feels to get home after two years." I said sure I would, for the *n*th time, and he saluted, sloppily as usual, and drove back to the war.

We'd all wondered what the hell when our departed friends failed to write to us from the States. We knew it wasn't carelessness. There was another reason. They were sparing us some ugly truths, we thought: something was wrong at home.

The United States is all right. I know that now, and I know why the men who went home failed to write back to us. But I had to come home to find out.

I plucked a quarter from the collection of American, Italian, and Algerian coins in my pocket and paid the girl before she could begin pumping me about the war. I don't exactly mind talking about my close calls, but after hearing the experiences of some infantrymen in my outfit, I feel like a junior Scout leader relating the adventures of summer camp.

Outside the drugstore I stopped at a corner stand and bought a stack of the latest magazines. The last I'd seen had been two months old. A large display of candy caught my eye and I asked the guy behind the counter how much I could buy.

"All you want," he said, and when I asked if I could buy a hundred almond bars he started to get them. I told him never to mind, I was only investigating. He turned away from me gruffly.

Your mind gets twisted in two years overseas. Your view of the U. S. A. is all out of focus. My wife knows how long I was gone, but occasionally she finds it hard to believe I was shipped out before the gas shortage was felt and before any rationing began. We, overseas, had a distorted view of rationing. We thought there were extreme shortages of candy and cigarettes here at home because we were limited ourselves. Many of our soldiers over there still believe that, and homefront problems of labor, manpower shortages, crowded trains, Victory girls, and housing conditions are subjects for nightlong speculation.

In one of the magazines I bought was a cartoon showing a well-dressed man with a briefcase being accosted by a policeman for sleeping on a park bench. The Washington Monument was in the background.

Those soldiers I left in Italy stare at cartoons such as that, not knowing whether to laugh or take them seriously. A source of fine anticipation, of course, is the cartoonists' satire on women of the U. S. howling wolfishly at the outnumbered male. There's a joke in the Army that says soldiers are required to wear steel helmets in New York City for protection against room keys that girls throw out of hotel windows. The overseas soldier, who has seen the unexpected happen so many times, half believes it.

Purely in the interest of enlightening my friends overseas, of course, I halted a girl on the street by the simple method of standing in her path, and asked her how she was affected by the available-male shortage. She was a classy-looking biddy, except for some slight mustache traces.

"Oh," she said, "you soldiers are all alike."

Next, as a final step in my inquiry into wartime morals, I whistled at a girl—close up. She walked right by with the nose two inches higher. Just like old times.

During the course of my twenty-one-day leave, and afterward in my travels under Army orders to a new post assignment, I visited New York, Durham, North Carolina, Philadelphia, Cincinnati, Indianapolis, and Louisville and walked the main stem in each of these cities. As I did so, I kept an eye peeled to see how the draft was going, and I think if I had a penny for every draft-age civilian I saw I would have enough money to buy a forty-nine-cent necktie. And those I saw looked a mite peaked. I won't venture further along those lines. Comes to mind the story of three G.I.s who attacked a 4F in Chicago, or some such likely place, and he sent the three of them to the infirmary.

At any rate, after my quick look around I judge the average civilian male in the United States today is either in puberty, senility, or war work.

There are exceptions. There are profiteers, loafers, draft dodgers, and disaffectionists in the States today, just as the United States also had these people in the Revolutionary War, the War of 1812, the Civil War, the War with Spain, and World War I. But don't be persuaded by scare stories in the papers that these people are even the Q. in John Q. Public. The genuine American people are solidly behind the war—and I didn't have to be home very long to find that out.

Several weeks after I was home I heard a lady remark on a quiz program that she "never reads the war news." Something like that makes it hard to keep your dinner down, after living the war and thinking only war for months and years, unless you recognize these rare people for what they are. As Thackeray wrote, "You can't have a tempest in a slop bucket."

It's nice to be able to sit here in a comfortable chair and say, "Don't give it a second thought." But I appreciate the overseas point of view. Over there we don't get the true picture of the homefront war effort. Sure, we heard a lot of boasting by big business of how its products were winning the war, and we saw pictures of Army and Navy "E" presentations, but we kind of shrugged it off as propaganda and ballyhoo. The reports we got, usually by curt press items or word of mouth, of boondoggling and haggling in the States were not so easy to shrug off.

Overseas we hear of strikes, not of war plants without strikes; we hear of disgruntled workers and of absenteeism, but not much of those who work hard at their benches every day, month in and year out. It's nobody's fault in particular. Bad news travels faster than good; newspapers deal in the unusual, not the commonplace.

Upon my arrival home I heard a dozen glittering stories of U. S. production. None of them reached us overseas.

One of them, typical of the rest, I'd like to tell for the soldiers overseas who read this. It occurred in a New Jersey war plant. The Reynolds Metals Company found itself suddenly in a manpower shortage which, were it not remedied, would throw the plant off its production level, and consequently leave war contracts unfulfilled. As it was illegal to work women seven days a week (and 98 per cent of the plant's employees were women), the plant managers spread a word-of-mouth appeal for Sunday workers—laborers in other plants, white-collar workers, housewives, students, anybody who would give up his weekly day off. And, for solid proof that America is working, they got twice as many as they could use!

Workers, professional men, bankers, teachers, and housewives answered the call from all over the New York-New Jersey area. These people didn't do it for gain, or to get their pictures in the papers. A bank president who took his place at a workbench refused, when confronted by a reporter, to identify either himself or the institution he heads. A Long Island lawyer got up at 4:30 A. M., traveled by car to a train, by train and subway to a taxi, and by taxi to the Reynolds Metals plant. After he had paid for his lunch and for this zigzag trip he had a profit of two dollars in his jeans—not much for the loss of his Sundays, or for his eight hours of perspiration, or for the five hours of traveling.

The doubts the soldier has regarding the integrity of his country are somewhat mitigated by the sight of supplies flowing into his sector, but human stories such as the foregoing would certainly be reassuring to him. I told a newspaper friend of mine I intended to include the Reynolds war-plant story in this article and he advised against it.

"Don't do it," he said. "It's old stuff. It must have happened two months before you came home, and besides, it never was unique. The same stuff goes on all over the country."

I tell a lot of people here at home what their long-gone boys want to know about the States. It's a one-man campaign to liven up those V mails. Sure, we were interested in politics, in labor and race problems and in shortages, but we got a lot of general news. We wanted to know how the U. S. man on the street actually was living. The old home town is damned hazy after a year or more overseas and any letter that takes a walk down Main Street, pointing out Mason's shoe store, Carter's drugstore (with old man Carter himself jerking sodas because he can't get help), and the civilian clothes in the window of Riggs' men's shop, is a letter your soldier will read and reread until it's smudged beyond recognition.

Give him a G-2 estimate of the hometown situation. Tell him about the girls and if they're suffering a man shortage; tell him what the restaurants have to eat and drink and how a steak costs a dollar fifty to two bucks almost any place now; tell him what a man's suit (a civvy!) would cost him these days. Tell him how many bonds your town bought in the last drive. Tell him about old men and girls delivering telegrams, and about women driving taxis and delivering milk and working on the railroads. That's old stuff to you, but it sure isn't to the guy with Ireland, Algeria, Tunisia, Italy, and France (or Australia, New Guinea, and Guam) between him and Main Street.

If you would try to picture yourself in the soldier's shoes, living his boring, loathsome life, then letters going overseas would improve enormously. There would be fewer cases of guys sweating out mail call, feeling the excitement of receiving a letter, and then experiencing the awful letdown that comes with reading dry nothingness.

But to get back to the business of coming home: would that be a letdown, too? Certainly I don't think any of the boatload of us returning to the United States on rotation really expected it to be. True, at times our glowing anticipation was mixed with apprehensions about homefront apathy, but the moment we stepped ashore those endless foreign years telescoped, and our fears of U. S. indifference fell dead away. Our country and our people hadn't changed. All at once we were home. All at once our bleak worries were foolish and groundless. All at once we had never been away.

The kids on the streets spoke English and didn't tag along after us for chewing gum or bonbons or cigarettes as did the Algerian ragamuffins; nor did they, as do their Neapolitan contemporaries, attempt clamantly to interest us in a shoeshine or their sister or both. Cars lined the clean streets and no one threw slop from the windows with a "Gardyvoo!" At least you guessed they didn't.

It was nighttime and still the city was brightly lit. Shop windows were filled with luxuries of civilian peacetime life, though some items demanded coupons. Drugstores served soft drinks, ice cream and ices, sodas, milk shakes, sundaes, fruit cups, and, if you happened along at the right time, banana splits. Restaurant menus displayed just about everything they had had to offer before Pearl Harbor, except occasionally steak was crossed off. You can get whiskies, liqueurs, and domestic wines in bars, we found out, though there is a little difficulty in buying whisky by the bottle. Some of it may not be of best quality, but the worst of it is nectar compared with the European and African products.

All the beds I've been in since we invaded these shores have had clean sheets and good mattresses, and I think it safe to presume the same is true with most of the others. I haven't seen my Victory girls that I recognized as Victory girls. The story depicting girls whistling at men is the bunk. They don't. Well, not at me, anyway.

Soldiers, no place in the States is crowded, by overseas standards. True, trains are jammed; frequently people have to stand up. Hotel rooms can't always be had. But even in Washington taxicabs are not as difficult to patronize as the tabloids and movies would have you believe. You can't walk to a curb and have a jinnee appear in a cloud of smoke with a taxi at the mere snap of your fingers. Sometimes you have to wait ten minutes. In the United States, war is heck.

I know now it was the task of describing *just how it feels to get home* that proved too much for our friends who came home first. The writing of the answer is simple enough. That's the trouble. The answer is so simple it will sound unconvincing to the overseas soldier, who has thought, talked, and dreamed so much of home that he is prepared only for drama and emotion surpassing anything he has ever experienced. I expected the same. It's not that way.

Suddenly you are home. You are Jack back in the pulpit; you are the man back in the moon. Your return is a great feeling of naturalness; you belong here, you are a part of it—you have never been gone. More than exultation or gripping tensity, you experience a surge of comfort and contentment. Perhaps that's hard for you guys overseas to believe, but that's the way it is.

It may come to you as you catch sight of the U. S. shore line, or you may feel it when you first set foot on the pier, or days later when you walk down your own Main Street.

It may even sweep over you while you're still two days out at sea—as with us. At ten in the morning someone turned on the radio. A smooth announcer's voice, coming over the domestic wave length, punctured the quiet of the ship without warning.

"All you have to do is send us a dollar," the voice said, "and we will send you a dozen rosebushes."

The ship's main lounge burst into laughter. We were home.

V
Peace, It's Wonderful
(1946-1950)

Liberty

MAR. 29, 1947   10c

**An Exciting New Story
by Margaret Culkin Banning**

Book: OUR OWN KIND — A Novel of Life
on the Wrong Side of the Tracks

Another Big Picture Section

(See THE EISENHOWER STORY)

Liberty

JULY 5, 1947   10 CENTS

Book: **DULCIMER STREET**
the great best seller

THE NEW TRUMAN by Alden Hatch

COME UNTO ME a short short story
you will never forget

WASHINGTON MISSOURI

ROUTE '48

AT THE WAR'S end, the nation set about reestablishing the patterns of peacetime living.

One of them seemed to decree that *Liberty* revert to its old status of nonprofit publication. A lot of Americans continued to read the magazine, with the circulation standing at 2.5 million. But with rival periodicals again well supplied with paper, *Liberty*'s charms for the advertising fraternity began to fade.

Still, its editors indefatigably scanned the horizon for up-to-the-moment subjects like acid-tongued Oscar Levant and Earl "Madman" Muntz, the West Coast auto dealer who cheerfully branded himself insane for offering cars at such a low price. The possibilities of the infant television industry were an especially rich source of provocative pieces. Emphasis on photos lessened as the magazine began an orgy of quizzes, word games, and cock-eyed crossword puzzles. However, the backbone of the magazine was still the book condensation—"Reading Time: One Evening."

Liberty also placed greater emphasis on fiction. Its short stories ran longer, while editors hunted for fresh talent. Some were new to the magazine, others new to the world. Among them were Jerome Weidman, Ernest Lehman, Robert Ruark, and William Saroyan.

During the war, financier Floyd Odlum of the Atlas Corporation had bought part ownership of the magazine; the other major stockholder being John R. Cuneo, of the Cuneo Press. The magazine now faced a new era with these two in control. For Odlum, participation was largely an operational device. "He used his losses favorably, tax-wise," as one of his associates recalls.

The new owners took two steps. First they made the magazine a bi-weekly, thus cutting operational costs in half. Then they picked as publisher Franklin S. Forsberg, a man of magazine experience who had recently been colonel-in-command of *Yank: the Army Weekly*. "Cure the magazine or kill it," Cuneo said to him.

But Forsberg, who had hoped to devote his considerable energies to the magazine, found his main occupation was to act as referee between the two owners. Odlum suffered from arthritis and liked to operate from the warmth of a heated swimming pool on his estate in Indio, California. At one point, Forsberg had to cross the country in order to ask him for an additional $1,500,000 for *Liberty*. He found the tycoon immersed in warm water, discussing transactions of tens and hundreds of millions over his poolside phone. Forsberg finally got a chance to request his paltry million and a half. Odlum brusquely refused.

In 1947, the magazine announced that thereafter, it would appear only once a month. It was an unhappy decision, a confession of impending defeat. Looking around, Forsberg saw an editorial staff still hopeful of a miracle. But the advertising department was despondent, as was the circulation office, where figures had tumbled to 1.5 million.

Forsberg had begun with orders to cure or kill. Unable to do either, he resigned and would later hark back philosophically on "an interesting if not a profitable experience."

Liberty celebrated its twenty-fifth birthday in May 1949. In the magazine wars, it had become one of the walking wounded. But in 1945, as this section begins, it was still alive and if not well, at least read by two-and-a-half million people. . . .

The skipper and the exec were shooting a little proxy crap, using their high-powered binoculars to bring the dice right up to their eyes.

We Remember This
by Robert Ruark

These Are the Kind of Stories You'll Hear When Your Fighting Man Comes Home. Not Stories of Violent Combat, but the Funny Things, the Touching Things, the Incongruous Things . . . the Little Things That Go to Make Up a War

YOU SIT ON the window ledge of a London hotel, swing your feet, and watch the antiaircraft guns, listen to the clap of the bombs as they splatter the docks. You are swimming in the Mediterranean off Bizerte, and a dead Italian soldier washes almost into your lap. Your transport brings a four-striper skipper back from Guadalcanal, and you find out, months later, that he lives right under you in an apartment house in Washington, D. C.

You sit down in the Officers' Club at Espiritu Santo, and there is a man you used to drink beer with in Casablanca. You say good-by to a guy in New Orleans, and you both turn up months later in a hospital in Oakland, California —he by way of Saipan, you via a jeep accident in the Solomons.

After getting around for a couple of years in this war, nothing seems real any more. Experiences resolve into a jumble of faces and places. The things that stand out sharply in a much-traveled serviceman's mind are little isolated events and sensations. And these are what millions of men will be talking about when they have forgotten the paralyzing feel of fear and the hot, confused unreality of combat. They will recall running into an old schoolmate on a Normandy beach when they have long forgotten that they ever shoved a bayonet into a German.

The following is, I believe, typical of what wives and children will hear until the next world war sweeps away the vet's right to remember aloud:

The big transport, outbound, shivered and plunged in a heavy swell. Her ports were tightly closed to maintain blackout, and it was hotter than blazes there below decks. The air of the casual officers' chow hall was thick with greasy cigar smoke, and into the midst of the murk plunged the chef, bearing a pink-and-blue birthday cake in each fat hairy hand.

This was the most poignant party I ever attended—a birthday party for two babies who, for all their fathers knew, were not even born. The fathers, Marine second lieutenants bound for some undefined island in the Southwest Pacific, had shoved off a couple of weeks before the kids were due. Estimating that both babies were scheduled for the same day, the two harried papas—smooth-faced kids hardly out of their teens—had paced the decks all day, fretting themselves sick. To divert them their fellow passengers had tossed a party for the two new babies, some 6,000 miles away in the United States.

One section of the mess had been laid out lavishly, with a white tablecloth on the splintery plank tables and much cutlery and glassware. There were big bowls of green salad (we had stopped off in Panama), cold cuts, olives, celery, and apples. The steward had broken out two boxes of powder-dry cigars, and there were a couple of big jugs of lemonade. Most of the ship's company was there, in addition to a dozen or so transient officers.

The chef, hardened by too many months of frying and boiling, still had managed a very creditable pair of cakes. Instead of candles, each cake bore a paste zero in the center—one pink, one blue. Each carried the pastry messages: "Don't worry, Pop.—JUNIOR," and "All my love," signed with the name of each man's wife.

It was very corny, of course. It was very corny when the lieutenants got up and stammered "Unaccustomed as I am to public fatherhood" speeches, and fumblingly opened the silly presents their buddies had brought. It was corny until the chaplain got up, took the cigar out of his kisser, and offered a short prayer.

Very simply, the Holy Joe asked for protection and consolation for the two scared young mothers back home. He asked that the new babies be granted a chance to see their fathers some day in the future. And then he said he hoped the babies never would have to repeat their par-

ents' experience—of being separated by war at the one time when men and women most need to be together.

Maybe that was corny, too. But it didn't seem so then, and it doesn't seem so now, when, for all I know, both fathers may be dead on Guam or Saipan. Maybe the babies weren't even born at the time. It was not the kind of party I would like to make a habit of.

The man with the caul was third assistant engineer on the Liberty ship on which I made my first run as a gunnery officer. He was a big loud-mouthed fellow with an irritating knowing glint in his eye, always able to top any story with gems from his own personal background. And he had this caul thing.

According to his interpretation, a man who was born with a caul was gifted with second sight. This supernatural power made our third assistant an authority on anything and everything, but he specialized on the possibility of our ship being blown out from under us.

He claimed to have been torpedoed six times—three in World War I and three in the current unpleasantness. He said he had been in a daylong fight with two German raiders, and once had been machine-gunned by Nazi submariners while he was floating among the wreckage of his ship. He had a lot of other gruesome stories.

This first trip of ours was a very rugged deal. The weather was colder than a banshee's breath, and you could practically walk on the periscopes. We lost several ships. Once a tanker was tagged and blew up at high noon, right in the middle of the convoy. Depth charges rattled and thumped all day and all night. The third assistant was as nervous as a fox in a forest fire. But he stoutly maintained that, through the good offices of his caul, we would all get back all right.

And we did get back, after a couple of near squeaks. As we came into the Narrows, the Third launched an orgy of self-congratulation. It ran like this:

"I been going to sea ever since the war started, and I can always tell when a ship is going to get it. Once in Jacksonville I got off a tanker I'd made three trips on, just because I had a hunch she was going to get bumped. I signed on another ship and we hadn't hardly passed the sea buoy before the ship I just left caught a fish and blew up. Nobody got off her, either.

"The last time I had that feeling I decided I'd just test it out, and stay on the ship anyhow. We were running along off Cuba when a sub let us have two fish and blew me over the side. Only three of us lived through that one, because the submarine captain machine-gunned us in the water. That's where I got this here scar." And the Third ripped open his shirt to expose a long, dirty-white slash from collarbone to shoulder blade.

"So, lieutenant, you want to mind what I say. As long as I feel good about this ship, nothing is going to happen

to her. But if you see me getting off you better get sick or something and get off too."

In New York I got a few days' leave and went home. I got back the day before we were supposed to sail, and there was the third assistant, still feeling mystic.

"Everything's all right, lieutenant," he said. "I don't like the looks of all this high explosive we're carrying, but I still feel good about the ship."

That was fine. I went ashore to the convoy conference and deduced that, with the Tunisian campaign just terminated, we would shortly be in business in Sicily. I had one last shore-going steak and returned to the ship, which was still taking high explosive. As I went to my cabin on the boat deck, I looked across at the third assistant's quarters, and there was a dark stranger unpacking his gear. My stomach bumped a little bit.

"I'm the new Third," he said. "Just came aboard. I understand your old Third got off this afternoon."

"What was the matter?" I asked. "He was O. K. this morning."

"I dunno," the new boy said. "Somebody said he got sick."

"So am I," I said, and went to my sack. That night I dreamed about a caul.

I almost wish I could report that they blew the ship out from under us, but I can't. All I can tell the old Third is that we were shunted accidentally into Casablanca, and that a few hours later subs knocked off most of the ships in our outboard column. I can report that we got to Bizerte the day after a big German air raid, and left the day before another one. Whoever handled the Third's destiny must have thought he was still aboard.

It was only on the next trip, into Italy, that the news seeped through to the Luftwaffe that our man with the caul was no longer with us. The Luftwaffe made the most of it.

One day in the late fall of 1943 a battered transport steamed away from the Italian beach, her shrapnel-spattered decks crammed with weary troops, mostly casualties. The ship's captain and executive officer stood wearily on the bridge, their whiskered faces drawn and smudged. Each man held a pair of binoculars, which he focused straight down at a cluster of soldiers on the deck. Suddenly the captain lowered his glasses and his lips moved profanely. He reached into his pocket, dragged out a wad of dirty bills, and passed them to his exec. Both men again stared fixedly at the deck.

In a minute or so the exec laughed and extended his hand. The skipper dug more deeply into his pants and came up with some more limp bills, which he passed over. Both kept looking through their glasses. Then the executive officer dipped into *his* pocket and paid some money to the captain. This mystifying interchange of currency kept up for the better part of an hour, until general quarters sent all hands to their stations.

The explanation was really very simple. An old-fashioned Army crap game was going on down below. Navy regulations forbid gambling aboard ship, but in most cases involving Army passengers, the regulation is winked at. The skipper and the exec merely were shooting a little proxy craps, using their high-powered binoculars to bring the dice right up to their eyes.

To the inmates a Navy hospital is one of the funniest places in the world. This is because everybody has something fairly horrible the matter with him, and there is no inclination toward mutual sympathy. And nobody ever gets out of Navy hospitals except the doctors, who funnel through at a terrific clip. We used to average three doctors a week in my ward, and the nurse turnover was something fierce. But none of the patients ever left. We were a very gay bunch in Ward 40-A, out in Oakland, California. We had the sublime and the ridiculous of all war casualties. One was an aviator who'd fallen 2,000 feet from his plane into the drink. His chute had failed to open, but he'd succeeded in breaking only a hip. The other was a lieutenant who'd been laid up for almost a year with a leg broken in a volleyball game at Noumes. Nearly everybody had been around a year or so, and we bitterly resented any seriously sick newcomer who might bust up our playhouse.

Here's an example of what we thought was funny as hell: We were flinging a quiet party one night, behind nursie's back, and we ran out of beer. We had a car, a tavern was only a mile away, and everybody had unlimited liberty. Refueling seemed simple.

We took a quick poll of the party: Two Marine majors, shot up in New Britain, with both legs in casts. Robbie, a Navy ensign, also with a couple of bum gams from a torpedoed LST. Another ensign's arms were still *hors de combat* from an LCT explosion. A Marine flier was sound in limb, but both eyes were full of glass from a crash. Another guy had a hand blown off by a 20-mm.-gun explosion. My arms were encumbered by ten pounds of structural steel. We scoured the ward without finding anyone whole enough to drive a car a mile to the beer joint and back. This we thought was uproariously funny.

We finally solved the problem by routing out a Wave ensign, confined with bronchitis, and sending her off to forage for us. Never try to tell us the Waves haven't justified themselves in this war.

Just before I left Oakland—congratulated by my friends as the only Navy man ever to leave the joint alive—an order was issued which strictly forbade pharmacists' mates having races with their wheel-chaired and wheel-stretchered patients. Nothing can be more shocking than a squadron of wheel chairs tearing down the hill while their maimed occupants whoop and cheer their ricksha boys on. I understand these makeshift sweepstakes seriously endangered the life and limb of several visiting civilians.

There is one thing you can say about Navy hospitals. The only people who feel sorry for themselves are the doctors, and this is merely because most of the doctors wish they could go to sea. Everybody else, blind, one-legged, and shell-shocked, is mighty tickled to be back home at any cost.

To prove that this is the screwiest war of all time, let me cite a recent happening in Union Station, Washington, D. C. An Army captain and a Navy lieutenant appeared at the ticket gate with a little, pert, graying lady. The men both carried heavy bags, and they hurried to the train with the little woman trotting at their sides.

As they reached the train, the little lady tiptoed and kissed them each soundly. She said:

"Now, I want you boys to take good care of yourselves, and don't worry about me. I'll be all right. I'll be fine. You just take care of yourselves."

So Mrs. Elizabeth May Craig climbed on the train, to cover the war in Europe for a newspaper syndicate, while her son, the Army captain, went back to his desk in Tempo "B" and her son-in-law, the Navy lieutenant, went back to *his* desk in the Navy Department.

I will always remember a bizarre church service I attended one morning in Bari, Italy, which was a nice town until the Luftwaffe came over and blew a good half of it into the Adriatic. This particular church service was being held on the flying bridge of a Liberty ship on which I was gunnery officer.

My gun crew was feeling the need of a preacher, because the past couple of weeks had been very strenuous and the next few promised to be even more so. I rounded up an Army chaplain and we set up a portable organ just aft of the No. 6 Oerlikon cannon. We were lifting our voices in song when a couple of Jerry planes came over and the guns began to go off. The congregation evaporated in a headlong dive for the guns, and the organist did his best to crawl under the organ. The chaplain began to scrabble around for his iron hat. After a bit the planes went away, and the guns quit. Church opened for business again.

It made a strange picture: the cocked and loaded 20-mms. reared against the soft-blue Italian sky, and the sun glittering on the dust of the sky pilot's helmet as he prayed for a quick end of the war and the coming day when once again man could love his neighbor as himself. He had just reached the "love thy neighbor" part when the planes came back and church broke up again as the flock went about its gunnery chores.

This continued for an hour or so. Every time the poor chaplain would get going good, the shore batteries would open up and then the ships' guns would chime in, the solid slap of the Bofors making queer harmony with the bump of the 20s and the nasty crack of the three-inchers. The chaplain, who had undergone similar difficulties in Africa and Sicily, decided we had had enough church for one day.

"Even in the old Wild West days," he said somewhat bitterly, "the congregation used to leave the guns at the door."

There are many other little memories: the ridiculous figure cut by a skinny Navy radioman, dressed in a big German coalscuttle helmet and nothing else, as he yelled *"Kamerad!"* at the searchlit skies during an air alert; a tough Scots paratrooper, still bloody from the business at Termoli, weeping freely as he sang Annie Laurie in a rowdy Italian bistro; the way some of the captive supermen of the Afrika Korps kicked and screamed when forced aboard our troopships, because they had been told that German subs sank everything that put to sea; the way prices skyrocketed when the Yanks took over a town. . . .

These are the kinds of thing you will be hearing when your fighting man comes home—not the violent tales of killing and blood and muck. These are the things he will remember from the war.

Miss Moffatt Steps Out

a story by Marjorie Kinnan Rawlings

*For the First Time in More Years Than Miss Moffatt
Cared to Remember, a Man Had Talked to Her. It Was
an Event in a Day of Events. Is It Surprising That She
Was Inspired to Do Things She had Never Done Before?*

MISS MOFFATT WENT to bed excited. She had corrected all the history papers, and the next day, Saturday, was to be festive. She had decided definitely to go downtown to watch the parade. History was being made, and she could bring a greater enthusiasm to her classes if she shared in the city's moment of glory. The state division was home from the wars. She expected to be wakeful; but she slept soundly after all. The band woke her up at nine o'clock. She put on her rayon dressing gown and took the curlpapers out of her hair before going to the window.

The parade itself would not leave the courthouse until eleven. She moved the burlap screen from one corner of her bedroom, unscrewed the light bulb in a standing lamp and screwed in the two-cup coffee percolator. She looked out in the hall to see if her neighbor, Mrs. Gwynn, who went to her office at eight o'clock, had put out her newspaper for her. The newspaper was not in sight. The morning paper with her breakfast, on holidays, was a luxury, and she could not help being disappointed. She thought, If I get a raise some day, I'll *subscribe* to the paper. She made her bed and cleared the rickety card table on which she worked and ate, made two pieces of toast on a grill over the single-burner gas plate, hesitated, then spread the table with her best linen cloth and brought from the clothes cupboard the jar of strawberry jam she had brought back from her week in the country.

If only she had the newspaper, breakfast would be a real party. But Miss Moffatt would not allow her disappointment to spoil the morning. And what a lovely October morning! The maples were turning, and one branch, yellow and red, stretched close enough to her window so that by sitting a little to one side she could see it. The sky was robin's-egg blue, the air was crisp

without being cold, the sun touched one corner of the window sill, and sparrows twittered as though the season were spring. She pulled the card table to the far side of the window so that she could watch the maple bough, then she set the percolator and the plate of toast on the table, and replaced the screen to hide the corner.

I do like things *nice*, she thought, and she had a moment of pride that she managed to live so nicely. She considered combing her hair before sitting down, but decided that was carrying things too far. She ate slowly, greatly enjoying the strawberry jam. It was a very small jar indeed, and reluctantly she ate only half of it, saving the rest for another occasion. "Something else may happen, and I'd feel so badly if I had eaten *all* the jam."

She changed to her old wool dressing gown before washing the dishes. The roominghouse maid would probably skip her room, as she often did on Saturday, and she brought out her broom and dustpan from the cupboard and brushed up and dusted, although there was really no dirt in the room. But she would hate to come back from the parade and not have things neat. She took clean underwear from the dresser and tiptoed down the hall to the bathroom, since others might be sleeping late on Saturday. The hot water had had time to catch up after the early baths. She scrubbed the tub, then drew it full of steaming water. She tied her hand towel around her head so that her hair would not come uncurled.

She dressed carefully, hesitating between her brown everyday suit and her print dress. She decided on the print, although her topcoat was shabby. The day would probably be warm and she could carry the coat over her arm. She was ready a little after ten. If she had had the paper to read, she would have come out exactly even. She looked at herself in the small mirror over the dresser. She felt pleasant, she felt almost pretty, and then the mirror betrayed her. The gold spectacles were unbecoming, no question of it, but buying new ones was unthinkable. The hair was so thin that she seemed all face. The face was bony, gray from the years of eating cheap foods that could be warmed up over the one gas burner. She thought, I just don't believe I eat properly. I'm such a strange *color*. But her salary was small, and fear of losing her job always hung over her, so that she saved most of her pay for a rainy day. She seemed to remember a time when she had been pretty. That had been in grade school, at the age of the children she now instructed. She had even had two beaus who competed to walk home with her and carry her books. It was a long time ago. She was fifty-two. That would make it more than forty years ago.

Interrupting her soliloquy, suddenly she thought, Why, I don't have to wait! I can go now.

She gave a final straightening to the tufted bedspread, locked the door behind her, and set out to walk downtown. She strolled along slowly, looking in shop windows. The day was surely warming up, and she took off her coat and hung it over her left arm and felt neat and proper in her print dress. She decided not to go all the way to the courthouse. It seemed as though the parade would last longer if she met it halfway. It would be horrid to see it start out, then trail away into nothingness. The crowd was gathering and she took a place at the front of the curb. Two of her pupils raced by. She called gaily, "Hello!" The boys seemed not to recognize her. One jostled the other and they laughed boisterously. One did not speak at all. The other said, "Hey, Miss Moffatt," and they ran on.

She heard a thumping of drums far up the street. Then a flute began an air, thin and high, and the heavier instruments of the band came in, and there was music, a march of Sousa's. Miss Moffatt shivered with pleasure. It seemed ages before the parade appeared, but it was enough to know it was coming and to listen to the stirring march. A drum major came first, twirling his baton. Then the band. Then a group of WACs, trim and marching well. And now—now, the home division was coming! She should have noticed, being a history teacher, whether they were in battle garb or in dress uniform, but she saw only that they were grinning from ear to ear as the crowds cheered.

People pressed close behind her, and she was pushed off the curb into the street.

Ordinarily she would have been in a panic, to be out alone, practically with the parade, but there were such roars, such hand clapping, that she was caught up in the tumult. She pulled her handkerchief from her coat pocket and waved it wildly. The marching columns passed her. She called out, "Hurray! Hurray!" From the mass of men a sergeant noticed her, alone on the street, waving, calling. He was a little drunk and extremely happy. He stepped out of formation, bowed in front of her, chuckled, "Hiya, babe," and stepped back.

She was suddenly conscious of her position and pushed back against the people on the curb. They yielded, for the parade was almost over, and they were already turning away. Her heart was pounding. She felt her way through the crowd and walked, unseeing, home to her room. She sat down on the edge of the bed. Oh, I am so silly, she thought. I'm trembling, and she leaned back on the pillow and took off her stiff felt hat. "It didn't mean anything. Why am I so upset?"

As she lay, and her pulse slowed, it seemed to her that she began to understand.

"It's my own fault that I'm so lonely. I don't *go out* to people. When I did, today, it happened. Someone *responded* to me. I must *participate*."

Why, she had found the answer to everything. She sat up straight.

"I'll go to a hotel for dinner. A *good* hotel. Everyone will be celebrating, and I'll celebrate too."

She did try to be honest with herself, and so she inquired if she had it in mind that a man would speak to her, perhaps the sergeant again, but she denied it indignantly.

"It's only that I'm going to stop being such a *hermit*."

She took off the print dress and put on faded gingham and made a pot of tea and a peanut-butter sandwich for her lunch. She washed the cup and teapot, putting the tea leaves in a paper bag and then in the wastebasket. She lay down to take a nap, to be fresh for the evening. Sleep would not come, and she was suddenly alert, deciding what to wear. Her one evening dress, of course. All the women would be dressed. The dress was many years old, but she had worn it only once, at the Board of Education banquet, and there was really nothing about it to go out of style.

She was glad to have something to occupy her and she got up and took the dress out of its cotton bag, brought out the ironing board, and pressed it carefully. It was an uglier gray than she had remembered. The afternoon dragged. At four o'clock she had another bath. She dressed as slowly as possible. Her white summer purse would have to do, and there was nothing for it but to wear the shabby topcoat. She would take it off and carry it the moment she reached the hotel door. And she would take a taxi. She took five dollars from an envelope hidden under her flannel nightgowns.

"I sha'n't even *think* about money tonight."

She put a few drops of perfume on her handkerchief. The perfume was old and brown and had a peculiar smell. Her class had given it to her for Christmas ten years ago, the only class ever to give her a present. Why, some of those boys were probably in the parade today. Perhaps they had thought of her as they fought through Africa, Italy, France, and Germany. She put another drop of perfume under the net ruching outlining the neck of the gray evening dress. Six-thirty would surely not be too early to arrive at the hotel. At six she sauntered, elegantly, she felt, down the stairs, and called a cab from the telephone in the lower hall. It came almost at once.

"The Buckingham Hotel," she said, but the driver did not seem at all surprised.

It was a magnificent hotel. The stripped awning reached out to the cab to welcome her. The doorman rushed out to swing open the door. She fumbled in her purse and paid her fare and tipped the driver five cents. She was in the lobby before she realized that she had forgotten to take off her coat. She struggled with it and dropped her purse. A bellboy picked it up for her.

"Check your coat, ma'am?"

"Oh, yes. Thank you." It was such a relief to see him take it away.

"I should have tipped him, too," and she looked around, but he was not in sight.

The hotel was a confusion of large rooms, gilt and crystal and elegant. The dining room could be any one of them. She wandered around and found it in a distant wing. It was empty, except for dozens of waiters, white-coated, idle, and arrogant. She had strayed halfway across the great room before one appeared beside her and inquired, "Madam is alone?"

Yes, she was quite alone. Yes, a table just anywhere. Thank you. Thank you so much. The table was in the farthest corner. Far away was the raised stand for the orchestra. But it was better not to be too near the music. The waiter flourished a menu and laid it in front of her.

She said firmly, "I'll have a cocktail first, please."

"Yes, madam. What will madam have?"

He was probably deaf.

She said loudly, "A cocktail, please."

"Madam, there are a hundred cocktails, a thousand. A Martini, a Manhattan, a Daiquiri—"

"Yes, yes, please. Any one. Thank you."

She was red and hot. Her spectacles were opaque with steam. She took them off and wiped them with her handkerchief. Of course, she knew there was more than one kind of cocktail. How stupid. The cocktail was before her. They did have quick service, but she would have liked a little time to get herself together. The drink was pale and a trifle bitter. There was an olive at the bottom of the glass and she ate it gratefully to take away the horrid taste. So that was a cocktail. How could anyone get down enough to be drunk? But she felt a warm glow and was calm when the waiter leaned over with pencil and order pad. She would have liked to choose slowly, for there was a long list of wonderful dishes, all unbelievably expensive. Three dollars and a half for steak, two dollars and a half for broiled chicken. Against her will, she looked hurriedly down the column of prices. There, a dollar and a half, which was not so appalling.

"I'll have the country sausage with apple rings," she said.

"And what else, madam?"

"Oh, nothing, nothing at all. That's all I care for."

Why, if she had anything else, her five dollars might not be enough. She really was not hungry, anyway. She saw with pleasure that a man and woman had come into the dining room and were headed her way. They took a table near her, the only one more remote than hers. She had felt for an instant that her being there had attracted them to the corner, out of the vast empty room, but they were lovers and leaned their heads together and began to murmur softly. When she caught their eyes, she smiled brightly, but they looked through her and once they kissed. She might not have been there at all, sitting stiffly in the old-fashioned gray dress with net ruching, her streaked gray hair coming out of curl and hanging limply.

There was a candle on her table. She struggled to light it, looking forward to dinner by candlelight, but a draft kept blowing out the matches. "Oh, dear," she said, and gave it up. The waiter put a plate before her. On it were two small patties of dark brown sausage, each topped with a pale fried apple ring. How could they have cooked the sausage so quickly? It almost seemed as though the waiter were trying to hurry her away. Well, she would not be hurried. She was paying for this and she intended to enjoy it.

The waiter said, "Madam understood that the price of the entree included other things, soup, vegetables, rolls, dessert?"

His tone was bland but his eyes were malevolent. She believed he knew she had not understood. He could have told her in time. She could not send him back now across that great room. And she was hungry, terribly hungry.

"Nothing else. I'll have dessert—and coffee," and she bent her head over her plate. Her eyes smarted.

She thought, If I went out oftener, I wouldn't be so *foolish*.

She ate as slowly as possible and drank all her water, but the waiter did not come to fill up the glass again. She didn't even have bread and butter, and she was accustomed to eating a great deal of bread. It was too provoking. The dining room was beginning to fill. The sausage was good and she felt more cheerful. She looked up between minute bites to watch the people coming in, laughing and joking. Not one of the women had on an evening dress. They were either in sports clothes or wore very brief black dresses. She looked up and smiled when a party passed her table. No one noticed. She could not divide the last morsel again. The waiter took away her plate and handed her the menu. She was hungrier than when she began, and she would have the richest dessert possible.

"Biskit Tortinny," she said, "and coffee."

"Bisquee Tortoni," said the waiter. "Coffee." And again it was before her before she could say Jack Robinson. The dessert was a tiny thing in a fluted paper basket. The coffee was good and she used all the cream and four teaspoons of sugar. She sipped slowly. For a moment she thought it was her sergeant of the morning who sat down at the table next to her, but of course it was not. He was a much younger sergeant. He looked around uncertainly. The coincidence raised her spirits.

Why, he was alone, too! He was probably far from home and feeling as forlorn as she. I don't *have* to let myself be cheated, she thought. All I have to do is *go out* to people. Like this morning. Her heart beat rapidly. I'll invite him to have dinner as my guest, and I'll have ice cream. She wiped her forehead. Now. Speak to him now.

The young sergeant lifted one hand high and his face shone. A girl with a corsage and a little perky hat was making her way to him, smiling as luminously as he. Miss Moffatt felt suddenly faint and dizzy. The cocktail, of course, was responsible for this dreadful feeling of collapse. She looked about desperately and the waiter shoved before her the check on a silver tray. The cocktail had cost a dollar. She counted out two dollar bills and two quarters. There was fifteen cents left in change in her purse. She added that to the tray and pushed back her chair clumsily. The waiter ignored her.

The crossing of the room was endless. The long gray dress wrapped itself around her ankles. The dining room was nearly full, the orchestra came in, the violinist tuned his fiddle, and applause sounded from the gay company. The music began as she reached the lobby. She found her way to the checkroom and described her coat. She folded it over her arm.

The doorman said, "Taxi, madam?"

She hesitated. Another thirty-five cents would be an insane extravagance. Then she lifted her chin and pulled the shabby coat around her.

"If you please," she said.

She would go home in glory, as the state division had returned. She had shared in history, and she would tell her class on Monday that they had shared, too. And she would tell them—oh, she would tell them again and again —that the battle was not yet won, that one human being must be kind to another, one race, one nation to another, or the world was lost.

"But, mother, it's for indoors—think of the coal we'll save!"

Can-You-Keep-A-Straight-Face Quiz

by W. C. Fields

How many of these 40 questions can you answer?

Grade yourself as follows:

35 correct	....	Excellent
30 correct	....	Good
25 correct	....	Fair
20 correct	....	Passing
Under 20	....	Failing

1—What brilliant comedian's real name is Claude William Dukinfield?

1—Me.

2—What close friend of mine, today a Hollywood legend, once said, "As a writer I am a stylist, and the most beautiful sentence I have ever heard is, 'Have one on the house' "?

2—The fabulous Wilson Mizner.

3—Can you name the chubby ex-burlesque funny man who became renowned for the expression, "I'm a ba-a-a-ad boy"?

3—Lou Costello of Abbott and Costello.

4—What comedian, part Indian, said, "My folks didn't come over on the Mayflower, but they were there to meet the boat"?

4—Will Rogers.

5—List the three nationally known radio stars who, as a gag, ran for President of the United States.

5—Eddie Cantor, Gracie Allen, and yours truly, W. C. Fields.

6—When Lincoln was puzzled about a Cabinet, what humor writer advised him, "Fill it up with showmen, sir. Showmen is devoid of pollertics. They hain't got any principles. They know how to cater for the public. Showmen, sir, is honest men. Ef you doubt their literary ability, look at their posters. Ef you want a Cabinit as is a Cabinit, fill it up with showmen"?

6—Artemus Ward, great American humor writer, who died in 1867.

7—What sensational comic, appearing in a picture called The Great Man, when asked if he liked little children, replied, "Yes, if they're well cooked"?

7—Ahem—me.

8—"When I was a boy of fourteen," said a famous American humorist, "my father was so ignorant I could hardly stand to have the old man around. But when I got to be twenty-one, I was astonished at how much the old man had learned in seven years!" Who was the famous American humorist?

8—Mark Twain.

9—Who penned an uproarious book about outhouses that made a profit of fifty dollars a word and caused his daughter to cry from embarrassment?

9—Chic Sale. And the book was *The Specialist*.

10—A man called the Perfect Fool contended, "What this country needs is a good five-cent nickel." Who was the Perfect Fool?

10—Ed Wynn.

11—And, by the way, what is the popular radio name of F. Chase Taylor?

11—Colonel Lemuel Q. Stoopnagle.

12—Who killed Technocracy with the bright crack, "Nothing you can't spell will ever work"?

12—The one and only Will Rogers.

13—Can you recall two make-believe comedy feuds similar to the Ben Bernie-Walter Winchell one?

13—Feuds? What about Fred Allen and Jack Benny, or Rudy Vallee and John Barrymore, or any of eight other teams plus W. C. Fields and Charlie McCarthy?

14—Who's responsible for the famous gag line, "Oh, I know Clark Gable, very well. I call him Clark—and he calls me 'Hey you!' "?

14—Bob Hope.

15—What rotund comic, handsome, intelligent, kind, tells a famous story which begins, "Mister, don't kill Tom the Old Fly! Why, once, in Upper Sandusky, I was placed in durance vile at the behest of a local blackguard . . ."?

15—Me. And it was Tom the Old Fly who released me from durance vile.

16—What renowned wit, upon being introduced to Garbo, said, "Pardon me, I didn't catch the name"?

16—Sharp-tongued Oscar Levant.

17—Can you name the abusive runt who weighs only forty pounds, yet owns forty-five suits worth seventy-five dollars each, and says of his boss, "Ah, he is a man of rare gifts—very rare"?

17—Charlie McCarthy. Grrr!

18—List three popular radio comedians whose wives play opposite them on the air. And their wives, please.

18—Jack Benny, Fred Allen, George Burns. And their wives—Mary Livingstone, Portland Hoffa, and Gracie Allen.

19—What immortal comic stated that, if he were elected President, he would bring these two items before Congress: (*a*) Political baby-kissing must come to an end —unless the size and age of the babies can be materially increased. (*b*) Sentiment or no sentiment, Dolly Madison's wash *must* be removed from the East Room?

19—Ahem—me.

20—The expression "straight man" means (*a*) a person who refuses to take part in a crime; (*b*) a member of a comedy team who acts as stooge and feeds jokes; (*c*) a comedian who refuses to tell off-color stories. Which is correct?

20—(*b*) is the answer.

21—Can you name the bearded sage who spouted the line, "Youth is a wonderful thing—it's a shame it has to be wasted on children"?

21—George Bernard Shaw.

22—And, in everyday life, just who is Baby Snooks and who is her much harassed daddy?

22—Fanny Brice is Baby Snooks. Hanley Stafford is her graying father.

23—What swell storyteller, who often writes for *Liberty Magazine*, repeats the gag about the radical speaker who, in the heat of a debate, cried, "I am an atheist, thank God"?

23—Your own Harry Hershfield. And not a bad gag either.

24—Who is an ex-vaudevillian with the first name of George, who courted and proposed to what female screwball for three years before she finally said "Yes"?

24—George Burns proposed to Gracie Allen for three years.

25—Do you recall the movie executive credited with saying at a pep meeting, "Gentlemen, I want you to know that I am not always right—but I am never wrong"?

25—Good ol' Sam Goldwyn.

26—One of America's truly great funny men was a professional drowner in his youth. That is, he'd pretend to drown in the ocean, then, when a crowd gathered to watch him being revived in the beach beer garden, the owner would sell more hot dogs, ice cream, and drinks, and split the profit. Know whom I'm talking about?

26—I think W. C. Fields is your man.

27—Can you name the actress (she was once a sexational leading lady of mine) who gave this classic advice, "Girls, the best way to hold a man is—in your arms"?

27—Mae West.

28—What rotund Supreme Court judge used to tell the one about the boy who killed his mother and father—then pleaded for mercy on the ground that he was an orphan?

28—Judge William Howard Taft.

29—Two rib ticklers have been on the radio for sixteen years, and they first got realistic ideas about Negro life by walking the streets of Harlem. Who are they?

29—Amos 'n' Andy.

30—Einstein's theory of relativity was once explained this way: "When you sit with a nice girl for an hour, you think it is only a minute; but when you sit on a hot stove for a minute, you think it is an hour." Who did the explaining?

30—Albert Einstein himself!

31—What syndicated humorist once stated, "The narrower the mind, the broader the statement"?

31—Ted Cook of King Features.

32—Can you identify the humor writer who said, "There are only three basic jokes, but, since the mother-in-law joke is not a joke but a very serious question, there are only two"?

32—George Ade. Hiya, George!

33—A certain Governor of New York, asked to speak at Sing Sing, began with, "My fellow citizens," then remembered the convicts weren't citizens, and said, "My fellow convicts." But that was worse. Finally he gulped and said, "Well, anyhow, I'm glad to see so many of you here." Who was he?

33—Governor Al Smith.

34—Who authored this dedication on a very funny book about golf: "To my daughter, without whose unflagging interest and constant assistance this book would have been written in half the time"?

34—P. G. Wodehouse wrote that dedication in Golf Without Tears.

35—What comedian, who speaks in a dry drawl, writes his own stuff, chews tobacco, drew $100,000 for his last movie, once labeled his fellow comedians, "Intellectual midgets living on borrowed minds"?

35—Fred Allen.

36—Recently some one misled American youth by advising them, in applying for a job, as follows: "Never show up for an interview in bare feet. Do not read a prospective employer's mail while he is questioning you as to qualifications!" Do you know the blackguard who spouted this advice?

36—Oh, I wouldn't call him a blackguard. His name is Fields—W. C. Fields.

37—Let's also see if you know the famous and humorous epitaph on an atheist's tombstone in Thurmont, Maryland. Well?

37—The epitaph reads, "Here lies an atheist—all dressed up and no place to go."

38—What publisher, insisting the word "news" was plural, wired a reporter, "Are there any news?" and received the prompt reply, "Not a new"?

38—The one and only Horace Greeley.

39—Match a comic to each of the following bits of anatomy that have made the comics popular: (*a*) Nose; (*b*) mouth; (*c*) hands.

39—(*a*) Schnozzle Durante or me; (*b*) Joe E. Brown or Martha Raye; (*c*) ZaSu Pitts.

40—What gossip columnist, creator of Mr. Mefoofsky, once confessed, "I usually get my stuff from people who promised somebody else that they would keep it a secret"?

40—Walter Winchell.

41—Sure, there are only forty questions, but this extra answer is in case you missed one. You can fill in with this answer to better your score, and the answer is—Me.

Mrs. Roosevelt

by Irwin Ross

The Former First Lady Is Still a Human Whirlwind, But
Now She Writes and Says Exactly What She Pleases

ON APRIL 20, 1945, eight days after her husband's death, Eleanor Roosevelt left the White House for the last time. As she stepped from the train in New York she was met by a group of reporters. They pleaded for a statement. Mrs. Roosevelt walked straight past them, looking neither to the right nor the left. "The story," she said firmly, "is over."

It wasn't. Instead of going into retirement, Mrs. Roosevelt has become a public figure in her own right.

Her U. N. duties take up the bulk of her time. She is one of the most popular, and one of the most unusual delegates in the Assembly. A tall, ramrod-straight, gray-haired matriarch, dressed in black, Eleanor Roosevelt seems to speak for the voiceless millions. Amid the pol-

ished, skilled diplomats of the world's mightiest powers, she is simple, straightforward. It is inspiring to see her in action—as when she stands up to the devious, tough-minded debaters of the Soviet Union. For months, for example, she has successfully fought the Russian attempt to force displaced persons now in Germany to return, against their will, to Soviet-dominated countries.

While she adopts a firm line toward the Soviets, Eleanor Roosevelt displays her statesmanship in her understanding of their difficulties. She explains their present truculence in terms of history, war sacrifices, internal difficulties.

Although she never appeases, Mrs. Roosevelt strives mightily for unity among the former war allies. As first chairman of the U. N. Human Rights Commission, she discreetly mediated the acrimonious disputes between the Russian and western blocs, salvaging enough agreement to set up a functioning organization.

It is also as a unifying force that Eleanor Roosevelt plays her major role in domestic affairs. She is friendly to all the liberal factions, a member of none. In the recent blowup between Wallace and Truman she stood neither for Wallace nor against him. She is, simply, for the cooperative effort. And her prestige has never been higher. All the former New Dealers keep in close touch with her—Ickes, Wallace, Morgenthau, Bob Sherwood, Sam Rosenman. The Democratic senatorial nomination was hers for the asking in New York this year; but Eleanor Roosevelt has no desire, at sixty-two, to assume the burdens of elective office.

Despite this reluctance, she is an indefatigable worker. Further, she can now be outspoken without fear of embarrassing the President—an important advantage. Mrs. Roosevelt took an active part in the 1946 election campaign, delivering the keynote address at the New York State Democratic Convention, appearing at innumerable radio broadcasts, and publicity rallies.

All in all, she has turned in a bewilderingly dynamic account of herself since leaving the White House. She has twice been appointed a delegate to the U. N. Assembly. She has toured Germany, lectured widely, given a course in civic events at the Women's Trade Union League, continued to turn out her daily newspaper column and her monthly question-and-answer page for the *Ladies' Home Journal*. This year she published a book of these pages, and she is now at work on the second volume of her autobiography.

Weekdays when the U. N. is in session, Mrs. Roosevelt lives in her six-room New York apartment at Washington Square West. She rises at six-thirty or seven, and frequently starts out with a breakfast conference. If she doesn't have one, she will take Fala for a brisk walk around Washington Square. She trots him along into the grocery and butcher shop and does the day's ordering, for no matter how strenuous her schedule, Mrs. Roosevelt always keeps a firm hand on her household affairs. She is a familiar figure in the neighborhood. Her neighbors greet her on the street but don't trespass on her privacy. She has an equally congenial time on the subways, which she uses frequently.

Following the morning constitutional, Mrs. Roosevelt goes by car to U. N. headquarters. There follows a daylong, fatiguing stretch of oratorical harangues, endless bickering over procedural points, all the storms and birth pangs of creating an enduring world organization. During the lunch hour Mrs. Roosevelt eats a light meal and dictates My Day to Falvina Thompson, her long-time friend and secretary, who takes the copy straight onto the typewriter. Then back to the committee sessions. Mrs. Roosevelt doesn't get home till 7 P.M. She is usually up till one or two in the morning.

Her schedule is lighter over the week-ends, which she spends—always with two secretaries on hand—at her seven-room cottage in Hyde Park. But she devotes at least half of each day to work. Recreation takes the form of long walks or swimming.

Her entertaining is simple. In the city she occasionally gives small, quiet parties, and in the country she goes in for sizable picnics. She spends a great deal of time with her family, dotes on her grandchildren.

Since the President's death, Mrs. Roosevelt has been besieged by souvenir hunters. At Hyde Park, many people who visit Roosevelt's grave feel compelled to see his widow or Fala. Mrs. Roosevelt is not as troubled by this problem in the city, as the doormen at her building keep uninvited callers away.

There are, however, occasional slip-ups—such as the time two New York students decided to cross the Square and call on Mrs. Roosevelt just when she had told the doormen that she was expecting a large group of people for a committee meeting. The students breezed right in and cornered her for nearly ten minutes before, in her deftly polite way, she was able to extricate herself.

In both New York and Hyde Park, Mrs. Roosevelt has unlisted telephone numbers, but everybody seems to know them.

In spite of being no longer in the White House, Mrs. Roosevelt is more than ever the great mother confessor to thousands of troubled, bewildered folk in this country and abroad. She receives an average of 150 letters a day, with a bewildering variety of pleas: G.I.s wanting to import their girl friends from Germany or Japan; parents trying to locate sons' graves in Europe; applications for jobs on her personal staff or with the United Nations; appeals for assistance from estranged husbands and wives; requests for food, coal, clothing from impoverished citizens of Greece, Germany, Austria, Azerbaijan.

In the case of every letter, the writers are referred to the proper governmental or United Nations agency, and whenever she can, Mrs. Roosevelt sends along a helpful word of advice. Once or twice, when the mail has been particularly heavy, Miss Thompson has prepared form-letter answers. The complaints were immediate—"We always heard personally from Mrs. Roosevelt before"—and the effort had to be abandoned. Her mail today is as heavy as it ever was in the White House—and there, Mrs. Roosevelt had a staff of twenty-six to handle correspondence, etc.

Mrs. Roosevelt's principal sources of income these days are her column and her page in the *Ladies' Home Journal*. She gives a half dozen paid lectures a year. Unlike other Presidents' widows, she receives no pension. A bill was drafted in the last session of Congress to pay her the customary $5,000 a year, but it was not enacted. Her expenses are high. She employs three secretaries and maintains an office in the apartment of Malvina Thompson. Annual cost: approximately $20,000.

Mrs. Roosevelt gets from 50 to 100 speaking invitations a week, the vast majority of which she has to refuse. As much as possible she limits herself to organizations with which she is affiliated: the National Association for Advancement of Colored People, the Wiltwick School for delinquent children, the Union for Democratic Action, the Democratic Party, the Women's Trade Union League, the Hudson Shore Labor School, the United Jewish Appeal, the Citizens' Committee on Children of New York City. For all these groups Mrs. Roosevelt speaks, appears at board and committee meetings, signs money-raising appeals.

No amount of activity seems to daunt her. She persisted in her work despite flu during the London meeting of the U. N. Assembly in January, 1946; an attack of shingles in May couldn't stop her. She was badly battered in her auto accident last August—a tooth knocked out, knees bruised, and a general black-and-blue bodily condition—but she didn't take a day off. Her comment in her column was characteristic: "I myself am quite well, though for some time I shall look as though I had been in a football game without having taken any training. . . ."

From time to time Mrs. Roosevelt likes to beguile herself with a quaint vision of her future: an old lady in a lace cap, knitting quietly in a rocking chair. It is a vision which her friends know will never come true.

"That's enough of that, Lundberg!"

LIBERTY

Some People Have All the Luck
by Booth Tarkington

Henry Had Carried His War Bride's Picture With Him During All Those Lonely Months Overseas—But Now That He Was Back, He Saw a Lot That Wasn't in the Picture. A Tale of Wisdom and Hope for Every War Bride and Groom, Spun with Tenderness by America's Master Storyteller

AFTER TWO YEARS and five months of martial service abroad, much of it violent, Henry Wharton Brown, twenty-four years old, formerly infantryman (pfc.) found himself wearing store clothes and looking out of a kitchen window.

"Found himself" is the truth of his state of mind. He found himself to be seated in that blue-painted wooden chair and to be looking out that four-paned window at rain and a dismal outskirt of the midland town of Emmonsville, population 15,000. He was also finding himself to be married, to have abruptly a wife, a child, and a father-in-law.

For three days Henry had been more or less aware that this was his new condition; but now he seemed for the first time to be realizing its full actualness. That was why he preferred to look out of the window, even at some of Emmonsville, rather than at his wife or his child or his father-in-law. A kindhearted boy made into a soldier, Henry had taken a long series of jolts during the past three years, and here, in peacetime, was another. He was far, far from sure that he liked having a wife, a child, and a father-in-law.

On the other hand, it was plain that his wife and his father-in-law liked having him. His store clothes looked wrong on him; but he was leanly big and brownly handsome, a highly pleasing young man even though his honest eyes and good features were now more perplexed and reticent than affable. His wife and his father-in-law were doing their best to mollify this expression.

"Might take you a few more days to get used to the romance of it, Henry," Mr. Mern, the father-in-law, said.

"Maybe." Henry didn't turn his head as he spoke. He didn't care much for this fat and genial middle-aged stranger who seemed to be settled down in the small house to live there the rest of his days.

"Why I name it a romance, Henry," Mr. Mern went on placatively, "it's because I look at it that way in regards to myself, me having a daughter that let a soldier get married to her only five days after she happened to set down by him on a train. By and large, that's the way it was, wasn't it Mattie?"

Mattie, the girl Henry was just now fully discovering to be his actual wife, sat peeling potatoes and at the same time skillfully holding upon her lap the fattish pink child, Henrietta, twenty months old. "What, father?" Mattie asked, for in addition to peeling potatoes and holding Henrietta, she was looking rather anxiously at Henry.

"By and large," Mr. Mern repeated, "what I says was it looks to me like romance because I'm the father of you and the grandfather of Henrietta; but it wouldn't happened except Henry and you being on that train together and getting married in five days and him leaving for Europe inside the same week to be in the war all this time before he ever laid eyes on his own child. That's why I says by and large, I'd have to call it a romance. Wouldn't you apply that expression to it, too, Henry?"

" 'By and large'?" Henry said vacantly. "What's by and large got to do with it?"

Mr. Mern and his daughter exchanged a surreptitious, serious glance.

Henry continued to look forth at the three muddy vacant lots between the cottage and its nearest neighbor, a filling station with wet pumps gleaming through gray drizzle.

"Up around Ashtabula, where I and Mattie's always hailed from, Henry," he said, "there was considerable Browns. You might been related to 'em or not, as the case may be. Take the Frank Forrest Brown family, for instance; they had kin in Chicago and Milwaukee and as fur east as Allegheny City. Was you related to any of—"

"I wasn't and I am not." Henry's posture was unrelaxed. "I already said not."

"Well, anyways," Mr. Mern ventured, "they're nice people, them Ashtabula Browns, good farmin' stock. They had a minister in their family. Reverend Ed Brown and wife. They lost their only child and Reverend Mrs. Ed Brown come straight to me. 'Oh, Mr. Mern,' she says, 'I don't know what to do! If it could only been me that was taken, Mr. Mern—if it could only been me instead!' Well, I put my hand on her shoulder. 'That ain't the way to look at it, Mrs. Brown,' I says. 'The only thing for you to consider,' I says, 'it's it was not so to be.' That's what I put my hand on her shoulder and told her, Henry: 'It was not so to be.' "

"No kin of mine," Henry said. "Never heard of her."

Mr. Mern made another effort. "Well, likely not," he assented. "Take Frank Forrest Brown himself, though, for instance. Did he have a temper! In point of facts, he was the profanest man anywheres around Ashtabula that I ever listened to. Cuss? Even during the Army I bet you never heard the beat. I put my hand on his shoulder one day when he was carryin' on because he'd busted his tractor. 'Listen, Frank Forrest Brown,' I says. 'I want to ask you something, Frank,' I says. 'What good,' I says— 'what good did such language ever do you or any other man? Think it over,' I says. 'Think it over.

As Henry gave no sign that the moral anecdote had reached his mind or even his ears, the young wife spoke up to save her father from feeling too flattened. "Did that stop Mr. Frank Forrest Brown's swearing?" she asked. "*Did* he think it over and stop, father?"

"Well, not right then, maybe," Mr. Mern admitted honestly. "I couldn't hardly say so. Maybe it did afterwards—some."

"We'll certainly hope so," Mattie said. "We'll all three hope it did, won't we?"

Then she tried to think that the averted Henry hadn't heard her; but she was afraid he had. He drew a deep breath and his nostrils widened like those of a person striving to endure pain—or excessive boredom—in silence. Mattie and her father looked at each other again, this time emptily, and for the moment seemed to have exhausted their conversational resources. A fog of baffled stillness filled the room; then it was the immobile Henry who spoke.

"There's that dog and cat, both of 'em, again," he said. "They're out in the rain and all over mud. Prob'ly goin' try and get in. They look terrible."

Mattie bent her head over Henrietta and the potatoes. "I thought you'd like 'em, Henry," she said. "I did think a cat and dog'd be kind of homelike for you when you got back. They're real nice, if you could just get used to

397

'em a little. That's why I named 'em for you—him Hen and her Henny—so you'd have all three of 'em to amuse you, Henrietta and Hen and Henny."

Her voice was sweet as it seemed to plead with him to like Henrietta and Hen and Henny—and herself and her father, and the cottage she'd bought with her earnings at the Emmonsville electronics plant. Henry, who was from the hills of New Hampshire, hadn't seen much of Emmonsville in the three days he'd been there, but he didn't care for this flat country. He thought of it as "out west" because it was west of New England. "Oh, I like dogs well enough," he said, with unfortunate implications.

"But not cats or—or babies?" Mattie's voice had a tremble in it.

Henry's response, still from his profile, was only, "Aw, now!"

"I had to come to Emmonsville," Mattie said, as if explaining a fault. "I had to, Henry, to get the job they advertised for at the plant. Then it got to seeming a right nice place to live, so I commenced paying for the house, like I wrote you, and I thought you'd like it."

"There's the cat," Henry said, referring to a miaow from just outside the rear door of the kitchen. A scratching upon the door followed the miaow. "It's not him scratching; it's that dog. Great team—tomcat and a she-dog!"

"I guess if you wouldn't mind they ought to get dry maybe," Mattie said apologetically, and nodded to her father.

Mr. Mern, obedient, went to the door, admitted the damp tomcat, Hen, and the drenched she-dog, Henny. Hen, the cat, at once went thoughtfully to sit behind the kitchen stove; but Henny, both long-haired and short-haired by acute miscegenation, was tumultuously affectionate. In a burst of gratitude she rushed upon Mattie and made a devoted attempt to kiss her face, a muddy effort upsetting to Henrietta and the pan of potatoes in Mattie's lap. Henrietta, previously dozing, outdid tin horns; potatoes rolled upon the floor and were stepped upon by Henny's hind feet while her forepaws continued to disfigure Henrietta and Mattie's dress and apron.

"Oh, my!" Mattie said. "Please don't, Henny! There, there, Henrietta! Henny just wants to show she loves you. Please stop jumping, Henny. Please get dry with Hen. Look how nice he's sitting there. Please, Henny, please!"

Henny controlled her transports, seated herself beside the stove as if she'd done nothing at all, and the young wife, after an uncertain glance toward Henry, placed the weeping Henrietta in Mr. Mern's arms. "Just hold her for me a minute, father." Then, on her knees, Mattie began to restore the potatoes to the pan.

Her husband's face and voice were both expressionless. "Dog's muddy feet been all over those potatoes. We supposed to eat 'em?"

"I'll wash 'em off, all fresh and nice," Mattie said. "You wouldn't know it after they're boiled. Father, if you'd

recite 'Hey diddle-diddle, the cat and the fiddle' to Henrietta, she might quit. Kind of sing it to her; she likes that."

"She does?" Henry asked, as Mr. Mern complied unmusically and Henrietta screamed, though not with pleasure. "She likes it, does she?"

Mattie looked desperate. A fallen strand of brown hair hung over her left eye and the fellow of that eye threatened to become watery. She set the pan of retrieved potatoes upon the kitchen table and took Henrietta from Mr. Mern. "There, there, Henrietta! Maybe you'd better stop singing now, father. Henry, would you and father mind if you'd just go and sit in the living room a little while? I'll call you soon as dinner is ready. There, there, Henrietta!"

"Dinner?" Henry repeated the word thoughtfully. "At our house up home my mother always had lunch in the middle of the day. We had dinner in the evening."

"So'll we, then," Mattie said. "There, there, Henrietta! We'll call it lunch if you like that better; but just now, honey, maybe you wouldn't mind sitting in the sitting room with father till I get things a little straightened out?"

Henry, following Mr. Mern into the only other room downstairs, looked back from the doorway but didn't seem to feel encouraged by what he saw and heard—wet cat, muddy dog, muddy potatoes, wet and muddy floor, Mattie spotted with muddy pawprints, hair over one eye, and walking up and down, stroking Henrietta's vociferous head. "There, there, Henrietta! There, there, Henrietta!" Mattie varied her soothing with softly sung snatches from "Hey diddle-diddle, the cat and the fiddle," but Henrietta had been too much annoyed to settle down. Thus far she was a plain child, inheriting more from fat Mr. Mern, apparently, than from either of her parents, and what was disclosed by her noisily open mouth Henry found unattractive.

In the sitting room he asked a question of his father-in-law, who was seated and lighting a cigar. "When do they get their teeth?"

"What?" Mr. Mern asked; then comprehended. "Ain't she already got a couple or so, four or five maybe? Seems to me I've noticed—"

"I mean a full set," Henry said. "When they open up like that, they look terrible inside without 'em." He sat down across the small room from his father-in-law, whose cigar seemed of lowly origin. "She's hollered like that most the time that I been here. Who's been bringing her up?"

"Why, Mattie." Mr. Mern was surprised by the question. "Of course during her office hours at the plant she had to pay a woman to look after the baby, but not since couple weeks ago when she commenced lookin' for you home, and quit. It's nice she could fix it with the boss you can take her place at the plant for the reconversion— piece o' luck I'd call it! I expect you're lookin' forward to goin' in there next Monday morning right eager, ain't

398

you, Henry? Mattie says it'll be easy for you to pick up right where she left off."

"She says so, does she?" Henry's eagerness was not in evidence. He did not look upon himself as "the Common Man"—anything but. Since his return, though, he'd heard more than one broadcast allusion to the dignity of that myth and it didn't seem to him very dignified to be taking a woman's place in industry or to have had her arrange such a substitution. "Guess it's better than nothing," he muttered.

"Better than nothin'!" Mr. Mern echoed timidly. "Right good pay, Henry! Why, if I'd made that much off the farm when I was startin' out in life, I'd thought I was in a dream! It's a good way to look at it, though—better than nothin'. It's what I told my Uncle Carlos one nice day along about 1924 after he got laid up with arthritis. He complained he only had board and clothes from his Spanish war pension to look forward to. 'Ain't that better than nothin', Uncle Carlos?' I says to him. 'Think it over, Uncle Carlos,' I says."

Henry was cold to this. "Didn't you put your hand on your Uncle Carlos' shoulder when you told him that?" he asked.

"What?" Mr. Mern was puzzled. "Yes, come to think of it, guess I did. I put my hand on his shoulder and I says—"

"You already told me that," Henry said.

"I did?" Mr. Mern looked blank. He seemed to feel a little rebuffed.

Henry was staring at the mantelpiece ornaments (from the five-and-ten) over the gloomily vacant fireplace, and he was wondering what his mother and father and sisters and small brother were doing in the nice old house on a White Mountain hillside. He was also wondering how it happened that he wasn't there instead of here. Mattie didn't seem to be the same girl he'd got into such a whirl about almost the first time he looked at her on that darn train. He'd carried a snapshot of her all through the war, and in his mind's eye, too, a picture of her, vague but gaily pretty—she didn't seem to look anything like that, the way she was now.

He could hear her doing metallic things in the kitchen, and she'd quieted Henrietta; but Henrietta'd break out again before long. He couldn't remember ever knowing a noisier baby—no, nor a homelier. For that matter, he thought all babies pretty homely. He didn't know that he'd ever expected to care to have one. The little sitting room was kind of chilly and he'd had enough of that in Germany.

Mr. Mern's cigar smelled worse and worse; he always smoked those foul cigars of his right down to the wet part, and his son-in-law wondered where he got the money to buy 'em. Claims he owns a farm somewhere, Henry thought. Bet he doesn't. Bet he expects to live on

Mattie and me the rest of his life. Talk, talk, talk! Have I got to smell those cigars and listen to him forever?

Mr. Mern, in fact, had already begun hopefully to talk again.

As was well known in the farming neighborhood near Ashtabula, where Mr. Mern came from, his little narratives were all of the same pattern—all tributes to himself and his fatherly wisdom—but now, in particular, in his son-in-law's company, he was only doing his best, in a manner really humble, to be appreciated a little. He didn't know any better way; nobody else was going to point out the likable things about him—except Mattie maybe, and Mattie was never a talker; she was always more a busy kind of girl. She was busier now than she'd ever been, working hard to get Henry used to herself and to Henrietta and Henny and Hen. But Mr. Mern thought the way to get people used to anything was to talk 'em into it. In a voice as appealing as he could make it, he continued to recall all the best things about himself and his sayings that he could remember.

I can't take it! I'm just not going to be able to! Henry was thinking when Mattie opened the door and told them that dinner—"I mean lunch," she said—was ready.

Some of her hair was still over one eye and she looked worriedly hot; but Henrietta was asleep on the cushions in a clothesbasket, the kitchen floor had been mopped, and Hen and Henny looked dry.

"What's cozier," Mr. Mern asked heartily, "than a nice cold rain outdoors where it can't slosh you, and setting down to good old fish and boiled potatoes and a nice cold goblet of water in a nice hot kitchen?"

Henry, taking his seat at the table, looked misgivingly at the plate before him on the white oilcloth. "Old fish?" he asked. "How old?"

"It isn't," Mattie assured him. "Father only means he likes fish."

"So do this cat and dog," Henry said. "Do they always behave starved while a person's trying to eat?"

"They're affectionate," Mr. Mern explained. "It shows they like you, Henry, wanting you to hand 'em something from your plate. They wouldn't do it except they'd took a notion to you. They trust you."

Henry believed himself not finicky; but even in the Army he hadn't enjoyed listening to people who went on talking while they had a good deal of food in their mouths.

"It must feel like you're almost in a dream, Henry. After all the bang-bang and shootin' you been through with them Nazis, to come back and get out here to God's country, the land of broad fields and blue skies, instead of havin' to start in again way up there in them cold New Hampshire mountains among all them New England people—it must seem like magic! I expect you feel it's pretty wonderful havin' a nice house like this in a nice busy town and a sweet-lookin' little wife and a lovely child and a splendid job all waitin' for you, whilst all you had to do was just walk in and set down and enjoy 'em! Why, when I was your age if some angel from heaven or the President of the United States had of offered me a set-up like this—"

He was interrupted. "Get off o' me!" Henry said, as the cat jumped upon his lap and tried to attach himself there when ill received. "Got claws like a grizzly bear's. This fish sets him crazy. He—*ouch!*" The former soldier, though anything but hardhearted, spoke as profanely as if still in the Army, and made impulsively a wide-armed sweep that sent the intruder half across the room.

Hen, tail up in alarm, jumped into the clothesbasket, bringing Henrietta a fright greater than his own. Naturally Henrietta called in her own way for help, and went on calling for it after she'd been rescued. In her mother's arms and brought to the table, she still suffered from shock and made her condition known to the very rooftree. Mattie tried to comfort her and eat a little at the same time. Henny, either excited by Henrietta's noise or merely supplicating for food, barked and barked. Mr. Mern somehow made his mild voice heard:

"I'm afraid the coffee acts like it's boiling over, dearie."

"Oh, my soul!" Mattie cried, and, losing her head, dumped their distressed child into its father's lap, he being next to her; Mr. Mern was across the table. She upset her chair as she sprang up; the clatter made both Henrietta and Henny louder, coffee spilled and hissed on the stove, and the cat came back from behind the clothesbasket, again interested in Henry.

"Take this baby back," Henry begged. "I can't handle her. I got no experience with 'em. Look out—she's going to be sick, too; she acts like it."

Mr. Mern spoke pacifyingly: "No, no; that isn't sickness. Hen landing on her that way just give her a surprise. They don't like gettin' surprised. Kind of rock her up and down, Henry, and she'll feel quieted. Just rock her and—"

"Rock her? She won't let me. Look the way she's squirming. She don't like me! She's going to be sick, I can tell that much! I can't—"

"Just a minute!" Mattie snatched scorched fingers from the coffeepot's handle. "Just one min—"

"She's going to be sick, I tell you," Henry insisted. "She don't like me and she don't like the smell of this fish. She's going to be sick."

"But it's fresh, honey. Haddock always smells that way. The fishman told me it's—"

"She is sick!" Henry said. "Listen to how she sounds. My gosh, can't you take her?"

"But, Henry, just let me bring your coffee—"

"Thanks, but I don't want 'ny." Henry was in great pain of mind. He rose, pushed the more-than-ever-clamorous Henrietta upon his wife, and turned away from the table.

"Know where you put my raincoat?"

"Your—your raincoat, honey?"

"Yes. I need it."

"But, Henry, you haven't finished your— You haven't even had your coffee yet."

"Said I didn't want 'ny."

"But, honey, you don't want to go out in the rain, do you?"

"Don't worry, looks like I'm maybe kind of in the way here. Anyhow I just got to—I mean I forget where I put my raincoat."

Both Mattie and Mr. Mern were looking at him with a pitiable apprehension. "There, there, Henrietta; there, there!" Mattie said. "I hung it up in that little hall closet where your hat and empty suitcase are, Henry, if—if you think you got to—got to go somewhere."

"Well I—" Henry walked to the inner door. "Don't worry. I guess I'll just go take a look around uptown." He spoke gently but with an elaborate casualness that intensified the anxiety in the gaze of his wife and his father-in-law.

Mr. Mern loosened from his neck his tucked-in napkin, got to his feet. "Expect you're maybe right, Henry. Good idea for us menfolks to take a little walk outdoors while Mattie gets things straightened up. I might just as well see if I can find an umbrella somewhere and go along with you. I got plenty time and so—"

"Nope," Henry said. "I mean, thank you, but— I mean, if you don't mind, I wasn't just looking for any company exactly. I mean, I—well, just excuse me, please. Goodby."

He passed hurriedly through the sitting room into the little hallway, took his raincoat and hat from the shallow closet there, and went out by the front door, scrabbling his way into the raincoat as he met the weather. He didn't turn his head to look back; but when he'd closed the white picket gate behind him, the side of his eye informed him of four faces at the front window of the cottage. In the center of the small lawn was a tiny wet bed of bedraggled asters, Mattie's special disappointment because she'd hoped they'd be a cheery welcome to him when he came from the war; but they'd been frostbitten, so they wilted before the great day.

Two of the faces at the window, Henrietta's and Henny's, showed merely a little curiosity; but Mattie's and Mr. Mern's were wistful. Mattie's and Mr. Mern's faces weren't frightened exactly; Henry hadn't packed his suitcase; he hadn't even taken his new cloth overcoat with him—and it had been hanging right on his raincoat in the hall closet—so it looked as if he'd be pretty sure to come back.

Henry, striding, head down, by the dismal filling station beyond the three muddy vacant lots, didn't care about his suitcase or his new overcoat.

All he wanted right now was to be on that bus and headed for New Hampshire.

Opposite the street corner that was the bus station in the midland town, Emmonsville, stood a one-story building cheerily painted apple green and labeled accordingly, The Apple-Green Tavern. Henry Wharton Brown halted before the tavern door. His raincoat gently dripped chilled drops bestowed upon it by November clouds; his hatbrim did the same, and shadowed under it, his lips moved, forming soundless words. "Just too tough for me, that's all. No, I couldn't take it. I tried—I did try; but no. Her old man—talk and eat and talk, talk, talk, all about how noble he is himself! Oh, my, that baby! Just squeal and holler and make faces—and noise and confusion—and dogs and cats! I expect maybe Mattie's good as gold—but no. I—"

He slowly entered the Apple-Green Tavern.

Its interior also was apple green, a large inviting room spotted symmetrically with apple-green small tables, apple-green chairs, and the glistening variation of two silverlike chromium bars, one a milk bar, the other just a bar. Henry, wincing under more and more kickings of conscience the nearer he came to liberty's door, sat down droopingly at one of the tables.

The tavern was just emptying out upon Main Street the few last business men of Emmonsville who had snack-lunched in the place, and no bartender stood behind the bar—Emmonsville plainly didn't drink this early in the afternoon. The only attendant remaining was the agreeable-looking girl, apple green of both dress and apron, who took Henry's order for coffee and a fried-egg sandwich. When she brought them, he asked, "Know if the eastbound bus is pretty regularly on time?"

"Most days it is," she replied. "The one you mean's the four-fifteen through bus that goes all the way to Albany, isn't it?"

"Yes, that's it."

"Quite a trip," she said affably. "Just going home from the Army, aren't you? I bet your folks'll be glad to see you."

"Guess they will."

"Sure will, soldier! Better eat your sandwich before it gets cold." Still she lingered; something about him seemed to puzzle her. "Look," she said suddenly. "Aren't you—I mean, I think you must be the same fella I saw going into Hebber's grocery yesterday with that nice quiet girl that worked in the electronics and's bought the cottage way down at the end of South Street—Mattie Brown. Listen. Aren't you married to her?"

"Guess so." Henry drank his coffee botheredly, and the girl, after a musing, final glance at him, went to the milk bar and, taking a small ledger from a drawer there, occupied herself with mathematics and a fountain pen. Henry looked at her from time to time and thought she seemed neat, competent, and rather pretty. Probably she'd have talked to him longer if she hadn't happened to find out that he was married.

It's the way dames are. I guess, if they decide you're married, he thought. Skip right off and don't give you a chance to take any interest in 'em. Well, it's one more. He meant that it was one more reason a man ought to know he'd been haywire, going plumb nuts over a girl on a train and getting himself all married up just because he was in the Army and didn't know if he'd ever get back from overseas. What had been eating him to make him do such a thing? He could think of four or five girls back home in New Hampshire he maybe wouldn't much mind being married to—if he'd only waited till after the war, when he could take a good look around.

For that matter, he could likely enough not have got all so upset over being married to Mattie if she'd stayed the way she was those few days before he got shoveled onto the ship. She was a right attractive girl then—just terribly devoted and sensible. How many thousands of times he'd hoped he wouldn't be shot up too much to get back to her! But gosh! when he did—that homely baby, that father-in-law, those pet animals, and settling down in that cottage in this flat country to a job a woman had held—no, he couldn't; he couldn't take it!

He was slowly finishing his second fried-egg sandwich when the bartender emerged from an interior door and, humming loudly I Gotta Have Love, slapped the apple-green waitress coquettishly on the back as he passed her. She seemed pleased, and the lone customer envied the bartender. Bachelor, Henry thought. They like single men to make passes at 'em. He looked at his watch, then ordered beer and drank it glumly.

By three o'clock several more apple-green waitresses had appeared. Two or three people were upon the stools alongside the bar, three or four were at the milk bar, others sat at tables; then, when across the street a bus rolled in from eastward and its long inside released some twenty or thirty passengers, business in the Apple-Green Tavern began to be fairly brisk.

Some of the bus passengers crossed the street and came into the tavern to drink or eat, or both. Through a window Henry was looking languidly at these as they approached, when he was alerted by a pang of manly interest. What gave it to him was, most naturally, a most beautiful girl.

The rain had stopped and a sudden temporary great shaft of sunshine enveloped her gloriously as she walked, laughing, across the street. Thus she was all rosy gold: her fair hair, her beaver coat, her tan stockings—even her tall-heeled sandals on the reflecting wet asphalt of Main Street—seemed of sparkling gold. She was tall, richly outlined, almost startlingly graceful. Her eyes, once seen, were unforgettable—radiant cornflower blue.

"*What* a dame!" he said, almost aloud. He had no eyes at all for her companion, a brown-faced small young man who wore new clothes and carried three heavy suitcases and a large pigskin satchel.

The pair came through the doorway—Henry's rosy-gold girl still laughing—and moved toward a table not far from him. He stared, and she, approving, gave him a nice glance; but her companion gave him more than one; then advanced upon him shouting heartily.

"Big Harry Brown! Big Harry! Well, of all the—" Suitcases and pigskin bag were dropped upon the floor; Henry's shoulders were beaten uproariously. "Whatch doin' in Emmonsville, Big Harry, of all places in the world?"

It was a comrades' reunion. Henry, on his feet, explained not more than that he was in Emmonsville waiting for an eastbound bus, and his happy friend said that he, too, was connecting here with a bus, not Henry's but one for Cincinnati. "Why Cincinnati?" he asked uproariously. "Going to visit the wife's grandma there, that's all! The wife's, I said, didn't I? That's all, just the wife! Big Harry Brown, meet Grace. Meet Grace on her honeymoon. With who? With me, that's all! Married Tuesday night!"

Henry, well roused from his deep gloom, warmly congratulated them both, especially Grace, newly Mrs. Horace Cooper, whose shapely hand he was unduly pleased to find cordially reciprocative of his clasp.

"How simply wonderful;" she cried. Could you let us sit at your table?"

When they were seated, with the bags under the table, a waitress carried a lavish order to the bartender—champagne cocktails for three, the jovial bridegroom's invitation. The beaming, beautiful bride, however, had little more than sat down when she jumped up. "Just two minutes," she said with an affectionate touch of her fingers upon a shoulder of each of the gentlemen. "I just have to put through a call to my grandmother and then us three chums'll have a real chin, Big Harry! I'll be right back."

The bridegroom's brow was abruptly shadowed. "Listen," he said. "That jerk's not going to turn up here, too, is he? It ain't him—"

She filliped pretty fingers against his cheek. "Silly boy! My grandmother's got to know we're on time up to now, don't she, darlingest?"

Horace Cooper's brow unclouded and he slapped Henry's knee. "How's that for the prize of the world, old rugged? Look how she moves! Wait till she takes that fur coat off! Look at everybody in the place staring at her! Look, now, all trying to get a gander at her through the glass of the booth. How'm I for a picker?"

"Some people," Henry admitted grudgingly, "have all the luck."

"You said it! All the luck! 'Some people?' Me!" Horace's elation knew no bounds. "Have I got all the luck? Wow-wowie! Y'ought to hear her sing! Boogie-woogie absolute tops. Dance? Oh, boy, oh, *boy!* Day they let me out didn't I head for my old burg of Cleveland, Ohio. First evening home, me for the night spots! Walked right in on her doing a turn at the biggest of 'em all—and did I grab her? Right spang out of the claws of the wolf pack! Boy! Fell for her first look she gimme and her for me!"

"Her for you, too?" Henry asked wonderingly; then made amends: "Well, after all, you're no such badlookin' little Joe, and you always got money to throw around, and—"

Horace hadn't listened; he was doing the talking. "Got her in a taxi after the show. 'I bet you're already married, doggone it,' I squeals, ribbin' her. 'Want to count my alimony?' she comes back at me, and y'ought to heard her silvery laugh! Showed her to my folks right the next day and they all hollers hurrah, nothing's too good for us heroes out o' the Army, go to it! Boy! Wish I could show her to some more of our old good Joes like you, Big Harry. They might be sore they didn't see her first themselves; but they'd be glad for their good old buddy Horace, wouldn't they?"

"Sure, Horace," Henry said.

Horace was so busy with self congratulation that he didn't feel any interest in anything else. The bride, however, returning and followed by every entranced male stare in the place, was more altruistic. When Horace, with perhaps too much of the air of a showman, had removed her beaver coat, she sat down between him and Henry and at once asked why her new husband hadn't told her he had such a marvelous-looking ex-G.I. buddy.

"You are; you're marvelous—so big-mannish and yet so wistful. I adore wistful men," she said to Henry. "Don't blush! I don't know, though; maybe you'd better go on blushing. It's intriguing; it's terrific! Do you think Horace'd mind if I and you saw a good deal of each other?" Her shoulder touched Henry's and her alluringly laughing face was close to his. "Not by any chance you aren't going to be on our bus to Cincinnati, are you?"

"Listen," Horace said, sobered. "He ain't. I'd trust him, though. Honest I would. Anyway, I'd trust him better than I would a plaid-coated, blue-pants, fat-necked, fat-faced old married man named Ackers from Cleveland."

Mrs. Cooper laughed musically and patted not her husband's hand but Henry's. "Isn't he a pet, though!" she cried. "Goes bang like a firecracker every time he gets jealous. Mr. Francis Ackers may be married but he isn't old and he isn't really fat, either. He was divine to me in Cleveland."

"Yeah!" the volatile Horace said, openly sulky. "Divine on our wedding trip, too! Funny how, right now, his business requires him to take that automobile trip and turn up in every hotel we've hung up at."

The bride denied this. "He did not! We didn't see Mr. Ackers in Bellefontaine at all, and that's where we were only last night."

"Yeah," Horace said. "Thought it'd be slicker to skip at least one place, I guess!" He leaned toward the new wife. "Listen! On the level, was it honest your grandma you phoned to just now?

"Jealous of grandma now!" Mrs. Cooper clapped her hands. "First my old friend, Mr. Ackers, and then grandma! Did you *ever* see anything like him?" she asked Henry; then added cozily, "Now let's talk about you, Big Harry. Tell me all about yourself."

"Not much to tell," Henry said, trying to be modest, but proving himself to be only and simply a man. "I don't usually have much to say about myself; I wouldn't know where to begin. Of course I was glad to get out of the Army, like everybody else. I was born and grew up in New Hampshire, where my folks always lived. It's nice there—hills and lakes and good food—and I went to school there and got along about the same as other pupils. Maybe I got better marks than some; I expect likely I did. It wasn't so much that I was any great amount smarter than the rest, though, I guess. Well, so when I got through high school, I—"

He paused, perceiving that her attention wandered. At a table about ten feet distant a young man with thin hair and an earnest thin face was looking fixedly at Mrs. Cooper.

"Oh," Henry said. "Friend of yours?"

"I got a good many," Mrs. Cooper responded frankly. "Seems like I do remember that face from somewhere." She laughed and gave Henry's chin a frolicsome little slap. "Listen. You aren't going to be jealous, too, are you?"

"Maybe I could," Henry said almost gaily and was gaily rewarded.

"I think you're cute!" she whispered, and for a dazing moment Henry's simple heart seemed bursting into a shower of flowers and music. The sensation was brief. The thin-faced, thin-haired, earnest young man who'd been staring at Mrs. Cooper had come forward.

"Look. I beg your pardon," he said, "but don't you remember me, Vance T. Johnson? You were one of the Gilded Giddies in that Silver Show Boat floor show at Milwaukee, Christmas week, and we all had a big party Christmas Eve. It was you got me to sing Mandalay, don't you remember?"

"Why Vance Johnson!" Mrs. Cooper cried, and couldn't have been more gracious. With exclamations of wonder and welcome she gave him her hand across the table, while he, all aglow and apparently unaware of the introductions she was performing, sat down, facing her ardently.

"I didn't get to see half enough of you in Milwaukee, Grace," he said. "Not half. Not a quarter! It was my last night there, you see, because I had to make Rochester the day after Christmas. Ever since Milwaukee I been wondering I don't know how many times if I wouldn't pair up with you again somewhere." He laughed companionably, seeming to include Messrs. Cooper and Brown now in a pleasant fellowship, and chattered rapidly on.

Sloppy simp! Henry thought, revolted. His recent automatically produced heartful of music and flowers vanished out of him, leaving behind it a slight mortification and a tendency to regard Horace as a pathetic figure. Horace, meanwhile, was truculently regarding himself as an offended figure. He proved this when Mr. Johnson paused after a too personal inquiry.

"See you got your baggage under the table, Grace. Where you going from here?"

"Cincinnati," Horace replied for her harshly. "Cincinnati, see? To visit our grandma, hers and mine, see?"

Mrs. Cooper explained: "Maybe you didn't understand, Vance. I was introducing my bridegroom, Mr. Horace Cooper." She pressed a forefinger into Horace's cheek. "This one."

"Bridegroom? Am I sunk?" Mr. Johnson made mournful outcry. "Of all the luck! Just when I—" Then he rallied surprisingly. "Cincinnati? On the bus? Well, isn't that something, anyhow? Emmonsville took me only half a day. *I'm* going to Cincinnati myself. Us waiting for the same good old bus! Married or single a guy doesn't get a chance to sit next to a girl like you every day."

"Listen!" Horace tried to sound jocular. He didn't. "Whatch mean, next to a girl like you? Just how next are you expecting to—"

He was interrupted. A curly-haired man, middle-aged but chubbily jaunty in a plaid tweed jacket, blue slacks and brown suède shoes, had entered the tavern and, apparently looking for just the right table, halted himself conspicuously. With gestures of amazement. "Well, of all the series of coincidences!" he exclaimed loudly. "Me sitting around the Emmonsville House all day waiting for a phone call from—from Cleveland—and here was this jolly party going on and I never—"

"Why, Francis Ackers!" Mrs. Cooper jumped up to extend her all-welcoming hand. "How on earth did you happen to hit Emmonsville today of *all* days? Just think, this makes actually the third place we've been you happened to turn up at! Join the party! This is Mr. Brown that's been in the Army with my Horace, and that's Mr. Vance T. Johnson of Boston—and I think you already know my husband."

"He ought to," Horace said, "by this time!"

"Horace, presh—" Mrs. Cooper with gay good-fellowship still retained Mr. Ackers' hand. "Put another chair at the table and order another round. Make it five this time, Horace, hon."

"Me? No soap!" Horace rose. "Look at the time! That Cincinnati bus is two and a half minutes overdue already. Yes, by golly, look there!" He pointed toward a window. "She's rollin' in right now and she only stops here about a minute and a half. Get a hustle on!"

Mrs. Cooper made a cheerful lamentation as he more than brusquely put her fur coat upon her. "Think of breaking up such a party just when it's getting so good! All right, honey, don't jerk me. You're coming too, aren't you, Vance?"

"You said it, babe!" Mr. Johnson was retrieving a hat, overcoat, and small traveling bag from the table at which he'd previously sat. "On to Cincinnati!" he cried, rushing to join her. "The city of my dreams!"

The bride, however, was now holding Henry's hand. "Not your bus? But isn't there somebody you ought to see in Cincinnati?" she urged. "It's a lovely city. Really, aren't you coming, too?"

"No. I—"

"Can't possibly?" She spoke in a low voice. "Ah, too bad! But don't look so down, Big Harry! Something tells me you and I are meant to meet again some day. Don't forget me!" Then, accompanied closely by Mr. Johnson and also by Mr. Francis Ackers, who said he'd just see them off, she made her laughing way to the door. Horace contrived to get the handles of the four pieces of luggage into his two hands and followed bumpingly.

Through the window Henry watched the group. Crossing the street, Mr. Ackers and Mr. Johnson kept as close as they could to Mrs. Cooper—that is, one against her right side, the other against her left—while Horace, struggling after them, first made efforts to intervene between his bride and Mr. Ackers, then to dislodge Mr. Johnson.

A loud tweed cap, removed from a round curly-haired middle-aged head, waved toward a beautiful face beaming down through a bus window and the great machine moved smoothly away toward Cincinnati. Smiling fatuously, Mr. Ackers strolled back and invited Henry to join him at the bar.

When Henry declined, remaining seated at his table, "Why so morose?" the chubby man inquired. "You *could* get a train for Cincinnati that'd land you there less'n an hour after the bus.

Henry was brief: "What I want with Cincinnati?"

"So? She didn't give you her grandma's address?"

"What use I got for it?"

"You didn't fall for her?" The chubby man's surprise increased. "Strange! We all do. My mistake." He went to the bar, came back with a filled glass and, standing, spoke benevolently: "Wonderful creature she is—quite beyond words!" He laughed down at Henry ingratiatingly. "You'd think so, too, if you knew her better. Whoosh! Can she make the money fly! I ought to know. I was her second husband."

"Her what?"

"Her second. Oh, not the one just before this one," Mr. Ackers said, and became serious. I was the only one she ever really loved, though"—he paused; then, with solemn idiocy, he added—"or ever will."

Henry made no response. He was more or less stupefied. But one sharp emotion pierced his numbness; it was the emotion of pity—pity for a once moderately intelligent comrade. Poor old Horace! He used to have *some* sense sometimes—in the Army.

He sat and sat, staring down at the apple-green table until an apple-green waitress—she who'd first served him —came impulsively to his elbow. "Listen, fella," she said. "I thought you wanted that eastbound bus. Look there! You better run."

Again Henry glanced through the window. "No, I was expecting maybe a couple Joes I know would come in on it. I see they didn't. So long."

He went out to Main Street, turned to his left, and frowning deeply under a down-bent wet hatbrim, walked slowly through a renewed drizzle all the long way to a filling station separated by three muddy vacant lots from a small white cottage at the end of South Street. Beside the oil pumps he halted and looked through November early twilight toward the cottage.

There was a long back yard behind it, and against the rear fence a small wooden shed. From the door of the shed there came forth the slender figure of a smallish girl who held in her arms a larger load of firewood than she should have tried to carry.

She was little, but walked sturdily, and somehow it was visible that she had patience and acceptance—as if she steadily did her best, no matter what, and if no reward at all could be looked for; but there was a loneliness about her that went to the heart.

Henry came on, walking even more slowly than before. The scrawny asters his wife had planted for him were dim in the wet twilight as he opened the gate. He stood looking fixedly at the dead little flower bed for some moments, then entered the cottage by the front door, left his raincoat and hat in the closet, and went into the sitting room. Mattie was always quick. A new fire had already begun to crackle under the mantelpiece; the room was rosy, the one easy chair in the house had been drawn up to the blaze, and a pair of large slippers warmed on the hearth. Everything was quiet—Henrietta was surely asleep —and peace was upon the small house.

Mattie came in from the kitchen. Her hair was neat, and under a white apron she wore a trim pink dress. "Get your wet shoes off and your feet to the fire, dear," she said. "I'll have sup—dinner—ready in half an hour. There'll be fried chicken, Henry."

He looked at her troubledly. "Where's—where's Mr. Mern?"

"Father? He told me to say goodby for him. He was sorry you didn't come back before he had to catch his train. He waited as long as he could."

"Where's he gone?"

"Why, home to Ashtabula." She was surprised. "He only came down to help me get things ready for you, but he couldn't stay away from the farm except these few days. I thought you knew that." She pushed him down into the easy chair, knelt, and began to remove his shoes.

He leaned forward, staring at her so hard that she was worried. "What's the matter? What are you thinking?"

Henry smiled at last. 'Oh, nothing," he said, took one of her busy hands, held it, and kissed it. "Nothing—except I was just thinking some people have all the luck. I mean me, honey."

WINDBLOWN—Norma Jean Daugherty pauses prettily during an autumn stroll on Santa Monica Beach, California.
RAPHO-GUILLUMETTE

What Do You Know About 1948?

a quiz by Ted Shane

1. *(a)* Who murdered whom in the Rose Bowl on New Year's Day? *(b)* What happened in the Salad Bowl? *(c)* Fruit Bowl?

2. Josip Broz startled the world by defying Josef Dzugashvili. Explain. Did he get away with it?

3. Who entered a doghouse because they had unleashed "a cacophonic and chaotic heaping of sounds which strongly smells of the spirit of current modernistic bourgeois music"?

4. What was known as the Bandaid Song and who wrote it?

5. Nicknames made news. Identify: *(a)* Henry the Ache. *(b)* Idaho's Hot Potato. *(c)* The Bitch of Buchenwald. *(d)* Jersey Joe. *(e)* Ol' Satchelfoots.

6. After being fined $20,000, and his union $1,400,000, who had his salary raised to $50,000 a year?

7. It was a year of romance. There were pairings and repairings. Who did what to whom?

Irene Selznick	Margaret Ellen Almquist
Jane Wyman	David Selznick
Artie Shaw	Henry J. (Bob) Topping
Maria Jeritza	Henry J. (Bob) Topping
June Haver	Ronald Reagan
Arline Judge	Irving J. Seery
Gypsy Rose Lee	Julio de Diego
Dennis Day	Jimmy Zito
Franchot Tone	Kathleen Winsor
Hedy Lamarr	
Jean Wallace	
John Loder	

What happened to Lana Turner?

8. It was a year of sensations. *(a)* Who is alleged to have said in a Washington restaurant, "Waiter, there's a spy in my soup!"? *(b)* The son of what well-known writer sued his ex-employers for more than $1,000,000? *(c)* Who confessed to dyeing her hair to betray her country? *(d)* Who Hissed in whose Chambers?

9. Having already claimed the invention of the steam engine, penicillin, steel girders, and radar, what nation also added the electric bulb, the transformer, and electric welding?

10. On the field of muscular battle: *(a)* What ancient enemy of Brooklyn was retired? *(b)* What bombshell fell on New York fans in midseason?

11. In the world of sport: *(a)* Who won the Kentucky Derby, Preakness, Belmont Stakes? *(b)* The U. S. Men's National Singles tennis crown? *(c)* Poughkeepsie Intercollegiate Regatta? *(d)* Olympic decathlon? *(e)* World's chess championship? *(f)* Little World Series? *(g)* Golf National Open? *(h)* What Dutch housewife starred at the Olympics?

12. Identify *(a)* Virus X. *(b)* Virus Sex.

13. *It Took Nine Tailors* appeared and made very little impression. It was *(a)* A play about Wallace's Vice-Presidential running mate? *(b)* The autobiography of Adolphe Menjou written by A. A. Musselman? *(c)* The Life of Dubinsky?

14. What was the Bell X-1?

15. Who said, "Because of the economy wave in Hollywood they've had to lay off nine of Bing Crosby's makeup men"?

16. The Allies' air line began flying the Rainbow Route to Berlin. Describe.

17. Stephen J. Supina, war hero, made the U. N. look upward as well as forward. How?

18. The ECOSOC got into the headlines because it was *(a)* The Emptyheaded Communists of Seattle Overthrowing Capitalism? *(b)* The sound made by Lou Boudreau's bat? *(c)* The Economic and Social Council of the U. N., meeting in Geneva to establish human rights?

19. Who was WHO in '48?

20. What *(a)* movie got the Academy Award for '47? *(b)* Whose performances snagged ditto? *(c)* What was the deflationary move of Hollywood in '48? *(d)* What movie bad man was arrested as a bad man? *(e)* What Hollywood star became a terrific Broadway hit in what? *(f)* Britain and Hollywood made peace. What were the terms?

21. Who was said to be slated for the positions of Toastmaster General and Secretary of Eggriculture if Dewey had won?

22. They figured in popular movies. Name the pictures: *(a)* A mermaid's tail. *(b)* A man trapped on a bridge.

(c) A metal obstruction to peace. *(d)* Timepieces and magazine executives. *(e)* A man named Blandings. *(f)* 777. *(g)* A pair of red shoes.

23. What senator was most indiscreet during '48?

24. Five famous people celebrated their fourteenth birthday on May 28 entirely unnoticed. Who are they?

25. On receipt of a pair of spurs, who said, "I really can take Congress for a ride now"? And how did he do it?

26. *(a)* Who was Heels Beals? *(b)* What was Konitsa? *(c)* Who was the shy, enchanted boy folks sang unshyly about?

27. What $87,000 peach turned out to be a World Series lemon; and what Lemon turned out to be a peach? (Yuk-yuk)

28. The micro-plankton organisms around Bikini were still how active?

29. What was Operation Sandstone?

(Answers will be found on next page)

"I didn't get my man, sir, but I have a fascinating story to tell . . ."
LIBERTY

ANSWERS to What do you Know about '48 — — —

1. *(a)* Michigan 49, USC 0. *(b)* At Phoenix, Arizona: Nevada 13, N. Texas 6. *(c)* There is no Fruit Bowl.

2. Tito defied Stalin as the Iron Curtain trembled. Tito's still alive—he hopes!

3. Soviet Hit Paraders Dmitri Shostakovich *(cf. Shostakovich Small by a Waterfall)*, Sergei Prokofieff, and Aram Khachaturian were rebuked by the Communist Central Committee.

4. The "Sabre Dance," because you broke a finger playing it; Khachaturian.

5. *(a)* Truman's name for Henry Wallace, Democratic Party splitter. *(b)* Senator Glen Taylor, Henry the Ache's running mate. *(c)* Ilse Koch, whose life sentence was commuted by the army. *(d)* Joe Walcott, with whom Joe Louis finally caught up. *(e)* Leroy (Satchel) Paige, ancient colored pitcher.

6. John L. Lewis.

7. Selznick divorced Selznick. Wyman d. Reagan. It became Unforever Artie with Winsor. Jeritza married Seery. Haver d. Zito. Judge unloaded Topping (her fifth). Lee m. de Diego. Dennis Day (Eugene Patrick McNulty) m. Almquist. Tone d. Wallace. Lamarr and Loder unlocked—here's your chance, fellas! Turner grabbed off Bob Topping. She's no fool!

8. *(a)* Congressman J. Parnell Thomas (né Thomas Feeney). *(b)* Screenwriter Ring Lardner, Jr., sacked by Twentieth Century-Fox for alleged Commie activities. *(c)* Brunette Elizabeth Bentley, alleged beauty, dyed for dear old Russia—becoming an alleged blonde spy. *(d)* Hiss, ex-State Department employee, said Time editor Chambers was off his rocker about his Commie activities! So there!

9. Russia—who else, comrade?

10. *(a)* Umpire George Magerkurth—yet Brooklyn still losted. *(b)* Durocher replaced Ott as manager of the hated Gi'nts.

11. *(a)* Citation (and we didn't bet on him!). *(b)* Richard (Pancho) Gonzales of L. A. *(c)* The U. of Washington, *(d)* Robert Bruce (Bob) Mathias, 17, of Tulare, Calif. *(e)* Mikhail Botvinnik, Soviet engineer. *(f)* Montreal.

(g) Ben Hogan. *(h)* Mrs. Fanny Blankers-Koen. (She copped the 100-, 200-, and 80-meter hurdles.)

12. *(a)* Flue germ which leveled 200,000 Los Angeleños. *(b)* Evil germ detected by Supreme Court in Wilson's novel, *Memoirs of Hecate County*, after Boston banning.

13. *(b)*.

14. Supersonic rocket plane flown by war pilot Captain Yeager faster than sound.

15. Bob Hope

16. When Russia clamped the blockade on Berlin, the Allied air lift went into action.

17. With a homemade bomb from a small plane he bombed the U. N. at Lake Success to get its mind on peace.

18. *(c)*.

19. World Health Organization, agency of U. N. (Would that it could cure the disease of war!)

20. *(a)* *Gentleman's Agreement.* *(b)* Loretta Young in *The Farmer's Daughter*; Ronald Colman in *A Double Life.* *(c)* Sam Goldwyn and his top executives took a voluntary 50-percent cut (leaving them with a mere $100,000 or so a year). *(d)* Robert Mitchum, for allegedly smoking marijuana. *(e)* Henry Fonda helped make *Mister Roberts* a sell-out. *(f)* Britain agreed to drop the 75-percent import duty on American films; let Hollywood take $17,000,000 a year out.

21. Lowell Thomas and Henry A. Wallace.

22. *(a)* *Mr. Peabody and the Mermaid.* *(b)* *Naked City.* *(c)* *The Iron Curtain.* *(d)* *The Big Clock.* *(e)* *Mr. Blandings Builds His Dream House.* *(f)* *Call Northside 777.* *(g)* *The Red Shoes*, made from a fairy tale.

23. William Powell in the movie *The Senator Was Indiscreet.*

24. The Dionne quintuplets.

25. President Truman. He called Congress in special session.

26. *(a)* A would-be harasser of Dick Tracy. *(b)* A place the Greek Communists couldn't take by siege. *(c)* "Nature Boy."

27. Bob Feller, who lost two games; and Bob Lemon, who didn't, for Cleveland.

28. Radio–radioactive. (Get it?)

29. A test of three new atomic weapons at Eniwetok. The operation was a success (?).

"America, What a Country!"
by Eddy Gilmore

*What Happened When a Single Sears Roebuck Catalogue Reached
Russia, and Why, As a Propaganda Agent, Nothing Can Beat It*

TWO INNOCENT ENOUGH articles of American life —the Sears Roebuck catalogue and the phonograph record—are the most powerful pieces of foreign propaganda in Russia. The catalogue comes first. I returned to the United States last summer after almost five years in the Soviet Union, so I believe I've had a good chance to judge.

About two years ago a friend sent me the latest volume of the Messrs. Sears, etc. I showed it to my Russian wife, who canceled all engagements for the evening and bedded down with the book. Late that night, she passed it on to Nura, our usually skeptical-of-anything-foreign cook. By teatime next day Nura had passed the word to the neighborhood that another American phenomenon had hit Moscow.

Forgetting all about the catalogue, I went downtown to work. When I returned for lunch, the volume also had been working—on the wife of a Red Army general.

"Do you mean to tell me," she said, "that whoever wrote this wonderful book is asking people to buy all these things?"

"I do," I answered.

"And that he has all these things I see photographs of?"

"All but a few," I explained, "and you'll see that he's announced the items that he doesn't have."

"These things," she continued, "are selling in dollars and cents. What do they mean in rubles?"

I referred her to the international exchange rate—5.2 rubles to the dollar. After a moment's pause she gasped, "A new dress for eighty rubles!"

The Russians were then carrying out Stalin's orders— "Everything for the front"—and there were no new dresses. Secondhand dresses were bringing about 2,000 to 3,000 rubles, or $400 to $600 each.

I told a couple of Russian friends about the catalogue. They came home with me the next day to see it.

"Where is it?" I asked my wife.

"The general's wife borrowed it from Nura while I was out," she said. "She's going to show it to some more generals' wives."

I apologized to my friends. They said they'd come back. And they did. The book was getting pretty dog-eared by the time Mrs. General returned it, but they didn't seem to mind. It was still a golden thing.

Next it got into the hands of a dressmaker through a one-time schoolmate of my wife. This friend came in shortly to tell us:

"The dressmaker says if she can keep the book for a week she'll make me a dress for nothing!"

"What does she want it for?" I asked. "She can't buy anything out of it. None of you Russians can."

"Oh, we know that, but she copies these latest American styles."

And peddled them at high premiums to customers, I later discovered.

"I can't let her have it for a week," I bargained, for the line of people who wanted to see it was forming on the left. "Five days is all I can spare."

The dressmaker agreed to five days, and our friend got her free frock. Since then I've never had to "sell" America. The catalogue does that for me.

The phonograph records are played almost daily over the Moscow, Leningrad, Kiev, Odessa, and Kharkov radios. They are also given, or lent, to Soviet agencies that get them to Russian musicians, singers, producers, composers, and actors. One result has been a mighty admiration for such persons as Jerome Kern, George Gershwin, Stephen Foster, Richard Rodgers, and Victor Herbert, to mention a few. There's also growing praise for Benny Goodman, Teddy Wilson, Harry James, Tommy and Jimmy Dorsey, Duke Ellington, Lionel Hampton, Pee Wee Russell, Gene Krupa, etc., etc.

Recorded music from the first group is convincing more and more Russians that America has and has had sane, gifted composers. The second group has made an overpowering impression on the music played by dance and concert orchestras. "Amerikanskie Djhaz" is now regarded as the only jazz. Jitterbug, pronounced "jeetaboug," has kicked itself into the Russian language.

For the records, thank the one-time Office of War Information and its astute director in Moscow, Joseph Phillips, now of *Newsweek*, and Elizabeth Eagan, his successor in handing out recorded Americana. Miss Eagan holds regular jam sessions. I've attended two or three, and each time, when the party broke up, the pronouncements from the Russians followed the same pattern: "America, what a country!"

Movies have their say, but the Russians regard even a perfectly normal American street scene as "costumed" and hence as propaganda. Furthermore, only a few American movies ever get shown in Russia.

The United States has in the U.S.S.R. two magazines in Russian. The last I knew, the circulation of each was limited to 10,000 copies. Ten thousand among 193,000,-000 Russians isn't much. The British do better with their *Russian Ally*—a weekly Russian-language newspaper. Its circulation is about 40,000.

The British Broadcasting Corporation's three daily half-hour shortwave broadcasts in Russian are reaching a growing group of people. If we're going to have American broadcasts in Russian beamed to the Soviet Union, as some have proposed, the stations should be in central Europe or the BBC will simply drown them out. The American station in Frankfurt, Germany, can be heard clearly in Moscow.

The Sears Roebuck catalogue is still my choice, however. If there were some way to get a couple of million copies to the Russian people, I believe they'd have a better impression of the United States than that created by all the other high-priced pieces of propaganda.

"All right, all right—we'll go to Florida!"

LIBERTY

Col. Stoopnagle's Fictionary
(Unabashed)

JOLLYGIST: A guy who's happy digging up ancient ruins.

DRYDRANT: No water in this one.

OINKMENT: Salve for a sick pig.

WICKTORIOUS: Finally getting the kerosene lamp lighted.

BRICKFIST: Joe Louis' morning meal.

SNORECHESTRA: A bunch of musicians sound asleep.

BOYSTEROUS: Any healthy twelve-year-old lad.

MAYORTRIMONY: Marriage by Fiorello.

LAPPETITE: A desire to have your secretary on your knee.

LAUGHADAVIT: A sworn statement made by a comedian.

SNACKROBAT: A guest who leaps over the bar to get at the hors d'oeuvres.

AX-RAY: Something used to look through an egg to see if the hen is going to hatchet.

WHAMBITION: What every prize-fighter must have to win.

OURTHRITIS: Me and you; we got gout.

WAXIDENT: A broken record.

MINNIE-ATURE: What Mickey Mouse carries in the back of his watch.

SUPPLEMEN: The stag line.

PRAYDIO: What we listen to on Sunday morning.

FLATLAS: A map of the world before Columbus.

CORPS-NET: The bugle that wakes the marines.

SEA-ESTA: A sleep in the deep.

KIN-ETIQUETTE: A state in which one behaves properly toward one's relatives.

NAUGHTZI: A German general who amounts to nothing.

OPPRONENT: Your adversary when he is floorizontal.

HELLOCUTIONIST: A telephone operator.

Fred Allen:
Never Without a Gag
by Irving Wallace

WHENEVER HE OPENS his mouth, Fred Allen breathes brightcracks. The cream of them add up to his weekly radio hour, which grosses his troupe $10,000 and nets him personally $4,000 a week.

Barbs dipped in satire and timely nonsense—a rare blend of humor, that! Its exponents in modern times have been few. James McNeill Whistler, Mark Twain, Wilson Mizner, Will Rogers. Today the species is extinct—except for Fred Allen.

Mr. Allen is not the matinee-idol type. His face is somewhat a cross between the elder Jukes' and Charlie Chan's. His teeth are chipped—the result of a juggling act back in the Dark Ages of Vaudeville when he held a fork in his mouth and caught turnips thrown from the audience. Of his voice, O. O. McIntyre once said, "Allen sounds like a man with false teeth chewing on slate pencils." This voice, variously described as a "vinegar drawl" and a "parched, unhappy singsong," actually sounds like the dry crackle of brown wrapping paper.

It is told that almost a decade ago a sponsor of household commodities, desiring to hire a comedian for radio advertising, listened an entire afternoon to recordings of applicants. Finally, when it was over, the weary sponsor rose and sighed, "I've decided on the one I want. Get me the guy with the flat voice. He's the best."

Thus, on October 23, 1932, Fred Allen first assaulted the eardrums of radio listeners—and he kept up his barrage of wit until today between fifteen and twenty million people listen to his brilliant dronings.

More than most comedians, Fred Allen has retained a fearless honesty and integrity. When he dislikes something, he tells the world. His pet aversion currently is the Pompous Executive. "I hate vice-presidents," he told me. "Those maestros of confusion!"

However, his aversion of longest standing is radio censorship. He has an almost monthly joust with the Demon Taboo. Once he prepared a joke about a dog in a hotel room that barked whenever the man next door came home, because the man was a Pole. This was blue-penciled lest it insult the Polish people. So with great patience, Allen changed "Pole" to "Mr. Post"—and got his laugh anyway.

Because Allen doesn't pull his punch lines, his gags often miss the funny bone and fall on the corn. There was the time he spun a story about "the poor fellow who wanted to be a pharmacist but who flunked in chow mein." The drugstore heads raged at that one. Another time he sighed, "Ah, those Philadelphia hotels! Why, I know one where the rooms are so small the mice are humpbacked!" The Philadelphia Hotelkeepers Association almost lynched him.

Perhaps the biggest fuss resulted from a program over a year ago when for his weekly Guest Star or the Person You Didn't Expect to Meet, he interviewed Mr. Lawrence Duffy, aged doorman of the Hotel Astor. "Now, in the good old days," sighed Doorman Duffy, "I once got a tip of a hundred dollars!"

"Yes," agreed Fred Allen; "back in '28, some of those Wall Street men used to think nothing of buying the restaurant and throwing it to the waiter as a tip. I guess some of those boys still chuckle about their financial pranks as they're sitting around up in Sing Sing today."

This brought all of Wall Street (that wasn't in Sing Sing) down the comedian's throat. There was much gruff talk of suing. Every one was out of temper except Allen, who sat down to his 1921 portable typewriter (which doesn't type capital letters because the shift key has been broken for years) and pecked out this note:

to the president of the new york stock exchange.
gentlemen,
no malice was intended and i am sorry to have incurred the disfavor of the gentlemen. i have considered committing

hari-kari on the two points recently gained by bethlehem steel. i have also thought about calling a conference, since a conference is a gathering of important people who, singly, can do nothing but together can decide that nothing can be done. both ideas were abandoned in favor of this letter to you.

sincerely,

fred allen.

The Stock Exchange didn't sue. It posted the letter on its bulletin board and got a week of laughs free.

Fred Allen was born with, or to, the name John Florence Sullivan. He still uses it when he signs his income tax and radio contracts. He has also had at different times the names of Paul Huckle, Fred St. James, Freddie James, and finally, borrowing the last name of a theatrical agent, Fred Allen. Every week he gets letters from people named Allen who claim to be relatives and want money.

His father was a bookbinder in the Boston Public Library, and he finally got a job there stacking books. To relieve monotony, he juggled the volumes—and this led naturally to amateur vaudeville. When I asked him about those early days, he reminisced with a few rib ticklers:

"My first real appearance took place at the Hub Theater. Billed as a 'talking juggler,' I was too frightened to talk and too nervous to juggle. The idea of the act was commendable for those days. If you listened to my monologue, it would take your mind off my juggling. And if you were intent on the feats of so-called dexterity, it saved wear and tear on your ears. You paid your money and took your choice!

"Anyway, I must have scratched myself on a nail in the dressing room, because the following morning I awakened with the theater in my blood.

"In 1916 a friend of mine concocted a formula for a seasickness cure, which he wanted me to try out. Accordingly, billed as 'The World's Worst Juggler,' I set sail for Australia—and for fourteen months appeared in vaudeville theaters throughout Australia, Tasmania, New Zealand, and Honolulu. I sailed so much and juggled so little that I finally wrote my agent: 'Listen. Did I sign for vaudeville—or before the mast?'

"Then back to America and more years of vaudeville, under the name Freddie James, from California to Nova Scotia. So many theater managers had mistaken me for one of the James boys on salary days that I reluctantly changed my professional name to Allen as a tribute to Ethan Allen, who had stopped using the name shortly after the Revolution."

His early days, he now admits, were a cavalcade of gags. At sixteen he was saying, "I could tell you a secret about a can of condensed milk, but I'm afraid it would leak out." At nineteen he was cracking, "I don't have to look up my family tree. I know that I'm the sap!" At twenty-five he was mailing ten-per-centers a twelve-page booklet labeled What I Know About Show Business, by Fred Allen, and all the pages were blank. At twenty-seven, dressed in a suit ten sizes too large for him, he'd amble out on the stage and explain, "You see, my suit was tailored in New Rochelle. And, of course, I'm a much bigger man in New Rochelle than I am here in New York."

In those days, whenever a quip got only weak or light applause, Allen would turn in the direction of the applause and say touchingly, "Thank you, Mother."

During his hectic career Allen was involved in two major feuds—one fact and one phony. The real one occurred when he was doing Broadway musicals with Clifton Webb and Libby Holman. For a while he teamed with comic Jimmy Savo, until little Jimmy began to feel that Allen's acid quips were making him appear sillier than was necessary. He finally challenged Allen to an alley fight. That was the end of the team. But Fred Allen still can't help giving his ex-partner the verbal hot-foot. Recently, when asked about Savo, he flipped:

"Jimmy Savo had given a piece of his mind to so many people that by the time he got working with me he had only a fragment left!"

Allen's other feud, pure fiction, began with gags about Jack Benny's inability to play "The Bee" on his violin, greatly increased the Crossleys of both funny men, and culminated in Paramount starring both in *Love Thy Neighbor*, which earned Fred Allen $100,000.

The feud with Benny has shaken some of Allen's best gags out of his system. Typical anti-Benny barbs:

"The only girl that ever looked twice at Jack Benny was Robert Ripley's secretary. And she didn't believe it. Benny a great lover? He's set Cupid back two hundred years! Oh, yes, indeed, Jack is a very funny man. Five minutes with him and your sides ache. Every time he tells a joke he punches you in the stomach."

While Allen hates Hollywood sham and front, he can kid about the town, too. "I'm always afraid I'll wake up at twelve o'clock in Hollywood and find the place turned back into a pumpkin! I went to the Brown Derby while there. It's a popular café where people from Iowa mistake each other for movie stars. And Ciro's, the Brown Derby with White Tie, where movie stars mistake each other for movie stars. It's where you meet the producer, a dynamic ulcer in charge of making a picture—and where you don't meet the assistant producer, the man who gets fired when the producer makes a bad film!"

Radio is Allen's first love. He sets each gag for each show like an architect planning the Taj Mahal. As a result, he keeps his nose inside his apartment, out of his 4,000 collected joke books, but sniffing nine daily newspapers and four weekly magazines for comedy news and leads. "My week is budgeted like a recipe for a nervous breakdown," he says.

And it really is. He will spend three entire nights writing copy that will last only five minutes on the air.

Three fifths of the show's dialogue is spoken by him, and the rest belongs to Guests and to the Mighty Allen Art Art Players. Every gag is his own, and no other comedian in the United States can say that! Once he tried hiring gag writers. Even hired Frank Sullivan. But no use. Today he hires four idea men who suggest skits for him to build up.

He goes out only two nights a week, either to dinner and theater or to a prize fight. He takes boxing lessons on Tuesday afternoons, and spends another two-hour session in the gym during the week. "Exercise?" he will laugh. "Well, I like long walks—especially when they're taken by the people who annoy me."

He works solid week-ends, except for Sunday Mass. A good Catholic who doesn't drink, doesn't gamble, and who once supported thirty poor families ("The WPA saved him," says his wife), he has been married to Portland Hoffa since 1927, when he was on the stage and she was in George White's Scandals. "As a result," he says, "we had no extended honeymoon, but spent a few days in Waterbury, Connecticut, to make it seem longer!"

Many of Allen's friends are newspapermen. Not long ago one of them, H. Allen Smith, wrote a healthy sacrilege entitled *Low Man on a Totem Pole*. Fred Allen wrote the introduction to the book. One of his passages on his pal Smith goes like this:

"His current hobby is reading quickly. If a story in *Liberty* specifies 'Reading Time, 12 minutes,' Smith will read it in five and save several minutes. Last year the minutes saved reading *Liberty* stories under par added up to six days and enabled Smith to enjoy almost an extra week on his vacation (which he spent practicing). In a recent speed-reading exhibition Smith sat in a dark room and a news photographer set off a flashlight bulb. During the ensuing split second of glare Smith read the entire 'My Day' column and got halfway through Pegler. . . .

"He enjoys looking at people who are looking at excavations. He stands in long lines outside of movie theaters and, at the crucial moment, doesn't go in. . . . Smith's face, which seems to be receding (from what, I am not prepared to say), hangs down from his hair and rests on his Adam's apple."

Fred Allen told me his three favorite comedians are Jack Benny, Bob Hope, and Colonel Lemuel Q. Stoopnagle. He told me the gag he originated that had been most repeated for years was, "How much would you charge to haunt a house?" He refused to pass on any Hitler jokes, insisting, "I don't know what I could say about Hitler that would be printable. He doesn't inspire laughter in any form."

There Was This Girl

a story by F. Hugh Herbert

There Are Some Things a Man Can Never Explain
to His Wife Or to Himself. This Is One of Them

I NEVER INTENDED to go to this cocktail party in the first place. I finally decided to go because I had the jumps. I'd been sitting at my desk all afternoon thinking about Janie, and wondering when the baby would come, and figuring that it must be hell for a girl to be pregnant. Poor little Janie. For the past few months she'd had a pretty bad time, but never a peep out of her. She was really happy about having a kid. Not simpering-happy, like in the layette advertisements, but quietly, shining-happy in her eyes. She's wonderful.

I was actually on my way home when I decided to stop off at this party. Janie likes me to come home early and I like to be home with her, and that's where I should have gone. So instead I called Janie up from a drugstore and asked if she'd mind if I went to this party for an hour or so, and she said of course not. She's been swell about things like that. Says that one pregnant parent in a family is plenty.

There must have been fifty or sixty people at this party and I knew hardly any of them. Someone took me over to the bar, got me a drink, and then mooched off. So then I looked around the room, and over by the fireplace there was this girl.

I'd never met her before. Never seen her. But we looked at each other across that crowded, smoky, chattering room, and right away I knew that she'd been watching me from the moment I came in. Right away I knew she wanted me to come over and talk to her.

Matter of fact that was almost the first thing she told me. Said it very simply and directly. She wasn't putting on an act or being cute.

She wasn't exceptionally pretty, but she was very young. Probably about nineteen or twenty, I figured.

She was badly dressed. She was wearing a suit. It looked quite expensive and it was simple, but it was wrong for her. I couldn't say where, or why, or how, or even what would have been right for her, but this suit wasn't right and neither was her foolish hat. Janie could have told you. Janie has an instinct for the right clothes.

Anyway, there I was, stuck at this party, and there was this girl. She was pretending to sip an old-fashioned. It was obvious she didn't like it. She would raise the glass to her mouth, barely moisten her lips with the drink, and then she'd lick the taste off, the way kids do when they're being forced to drink something. She had pretty lips. They looked cool and soft, like a little girl's.

She told me her name was Lois. I didn't ask her; she just told me. She didn't give me her last name. She pretended to take another sip of her drink, and then, as she licked her lips, she smiled at me. She smiled with her eyes more than with her lips. She had lovely eyes.

There are some things you can never explain to yourself or to anyone else. This is one of them. Why I suddenly gave her a phony name I'll never know. There was no reason on earth why I should have. She hadn't even asked for my name. I said, "My name's Cary."

She said, "Are you having fun here, Cary?" You could tell right away that she wasn't having fun and that she hoped I wasn't. It was a hint, all right, but it was the sort of blunt, endearing hint you often hear in the voice of a kid trying to get a grown-up to leave a museum or some place where it's boring. I lowered my voice and said I was having a lousy time. She was glad to hear that. You could tell it from her eyes. I was just going to suggest that we blow, but again she beat me to it. She started pulling on her gloves. She said, "Please, will you take me somewhere else?" She didn't really have to ask. She knew I would. I think that childish "please" really got me, though. She was blushing. She had a lovely skin. She wasn't blushing because she was fussed or embarrassed. She was blushing because she was excited and happy. She told me that later, but I knew then.

I knew, too, that I wasn't going to tell her a thing about Janie or the baby. I think I must have known that much when I first walked across the room to talk to her. Maybe that's why I gave her that phony name. I don't know.

She was hungry. She hadn't eaten since breakfast. We took a taxi and I gave the driver the address of a little French café on West Fortieth Street. I hadn't been there in years. I'd never taken Janie there.

It was snowing and extremely cold. As we got into the cab she said, "This is fun." I never made a pass at her all the way downtown. I sat in one corner of the cab, with my hands in the pockets of my coat, and she sat in the other corner, and our shoulders never even touched. She put her feet up on the jump seat. She had cute ankles, and her shoes were the one thing right about her.

I don't know why I didn't make any passes in the cab. It would have been all right with her. She told me that later, but I knew it then without being told. I don't know why I held off. We both knew that sooner or later I'd be making love to her. Maybe I was figuring that the longer we waited the better it would be. Maybe I was thinking of Janie. I don't know. Some things you can never explain.

When we got to the café, the place was empty. It was only about half past five, I guess. They gave us a table in a corner by the fire. They have good food at this place, and she loved it. She really was hungry, too. She ate quite a meal, and had several glasses of that red wine they always serve in joints like that. And all through the meal she talked, happily, excitedly, charmingly, like a school kid.

I'd guessed wrong about her age. She wasn't even quite eighteen. She was a born New Yorker. She worked in the stenographic department of a big advertising agency. At night she studied music—piano. She had very pretty hands.

She was a distant relative of the people who gave the cocktail party, and that's how come she was there. It was the first real cocktail party she'd ever been to.

At first I didn't do much talking. I just let her rattle on. There was something awfully sweet about the way she was telling me everything. Once in a while I got in a few licks on my own. I gave this girl the damndest line. It wasn't enough that I'd lied about my name. I lied about everything—my profession, my birthplace, my age, marital status, income—everything. Earlier she'd said something about being fascinated by architecture, so all of a sudden I'm an architect. I'm a wealthy bachelor and I've never been married, or even engaged, and I've never yet met a girl I could really fall in love with. Except maybe tonight —with a soulful glance at her. That sort of line.

I sat there and I let this girl talk, and I kept on piling lie upon lie. There was this girl, obviously a sensitive, charming kid, shyly and eagerly telling me of a dream, her simple, touching romantic dream of the kind of man she'd always hoped to meet some day, and I fed the dream with my senseless lies. Whatever she admired, I was it. Whatever she'd hoped for, that was just what I happened to be.

And as we sat there by the fire, filling up with food and wine, I watched a change coming over her. There was now a tremulous, melting quality to her voice, and it was in those big eyes of hers, and on those soft, little-girl lips. She wasn't falling for me any more—she'd fallen. She'd fallen in love with me. She'd always cherished a dream in her heart, and now suddenly I was it. I was in, solid. I was the knight in shining armor.

A lie should have some point, some benefit to be gained, some disadvantage to be avoided. By now my stupid lies had lost whatever point they might have had when I left the party with this girl. Back of my mind, I suppose, when we got into the cab, I was figuring that it should be possible to seduce her. It seemed reasonable and quite feasible. I could tell she liked me. And a girl doesn't leave a party with a man she's just met, the way we did, unless she's figuring on something like that happening, and unless she's prepared to handle it.

Now, after the line I'd given her, that was clearly out. There was this girl with her soft, childish lips, looking at me with eyes of wonder as if I were the answer to all her prayers. She said, "This is so wonderful. This is the way I hoped it would be." She blinked a tear onto her long lashes and let it run down her cheek. She said, "I'm not even going to pretend to wipe it off. With you I'm not ashamed to be happy enough to cry." Then she moistened her lips and blew me a little kiss.

I suppose I should have told her then that I'd been feeding her a line. I didn't. I'd lied myself onto a dizzy, sentimental plane, and I was stuck there. I went on lying. I poured it on even thicker. I told her everything I thought she'd like to hear. I sank my voice to a whisper and I picked up her hand from the checkered tablecloth and I kissed her fingers one by one and I told her that I loved her. I gave her the damndest line. There was this girl who didn't mean a thing to me one way or the other, and I was making her tremble with a clean, shining happiness, and wherever it shone through I polished it some more with some more lies.

I looked at the clock and it was almost seven. I realized I'd have to phone Janie. I gave some excuse to this girl and went into the phone booth in the rear of the café. I told Janie I was still at this party and that some people had asked me to dinner and I was checking to find out if that was all right with her. That one lie to Janie bothered me far more than all the lies I'd given to this girl. I really felt like a heel. Janie told me she was very comfortable in bed, and felt fine, and said for me to stay as long as I liked.

416

There are some things you can never explain. I stayed in the phone booth several minutes after Janie hung up. I knew I ought to go home to Janie right away. Not that the baby was due any minute or anything like that. It wasn't due for three weeks but, after all, anything can happen. Anyway, I knew I ought to go home.

But there was this girl, waiting for me at our table. I could see her through the glass in the door of the phone booth. Suddenly she got up, walked around the table, leaned over my place, and started tearing paper matches out of a couple of matchbooks. I saw her arranging the matches on the tablecloth. She was spelling out something with the matches and I knew right away what she was spelling out. I knew then that I wasn't going home to Janie right away. I was going to spend the rest of the evening with this girl, telling her more lies, and I hypnotized myself into thinking there was no harm in it.

I was right about the matches. She had spelled out "I love you." I stared at it for a moment and then I smiled at her and she caught her breath in a little contented sigh. She said, "You know I mean that, don't you?" I nodded and told her it went double. She crinkled her nose at me like a rabbit. She whispered, "Isn't it wonderful?"

I took her to the Roxy. I don't remember what the picture was. We never looked at it. We sat there in the dark, her hand in mine, and for a couple of hours longer I was this Cary, the man she'd always hoped for, the boy of her dreams come true. I'd only met her a few hours ago, and I had no intention of ever trying to see her again. But I sat there and kissed her fingers and I gave her the damndest line.

She lived way up on Two Hundred and Thirty-ninth Street. She said, "With most boys I'd suggest the subway, but you're rich, so let's take a cab." I'd told her I had a big income.

She was leaning against me. Her head was thrown back and she was looking out of the skylight of the taxi. It was still snowing. Without looking at me she said, "Aren't you *ever* going to kiss me?"

We kissed, and her lips were as soft and sweet as I knew they would be. She pulled off her silly little hat that was all wrong, and put her head on my shoulder, and snuggled up against me. She was sweet. I felt like a heel. I went on lying to her. I knew I'd never want to see her again, but I asked her for another date. For tomorrow night. I knew that was what she would want. She wrinkled her nose at me again. She said, "Any day. Any time. Always." Just like that. With a little catch in her breath between each phrase.

She shared an apartment with two other girls. She had no folks. She said it was too late to invite me up. We stood in the snow and said good night. I kissed her again and I knew how Judas must have felt.

She opened her purse, scribbled something on a card, and gave it to me. She said, "You'll need my telephone number." She didn't ask for mine, or for my address. She never doubted me for one second.

She said, "Good night, darling," and then went into the apartment house. I paid off the cab and went home by subway.

Janie was still awake, reading in bed, when I got home. She has a funny little crooked smile that means she's specially glad to see me. I sat on the bed, and she put her arms around me and pulled me over onto the pillows. She said, "Did you have fun, darling?"

I think I could have told her the whole story then and she would have understood. She'd have tried to anyway. Janie's very understanding. Instead, I lied to her. I told her I'd had dinner with some men I hadn't seen in a long time. I told her we sat around for hours afterward chewing the rag.

Janie said she was hungry and I told her I'd fix her a cup of cocoa and maybe a sandwich. She wanted to get up and help me, but I wouldn't let her get out of bed. She couldn't be leaping up and down in her condition. Janie settled back comfortably against the propped-up pillows and clasped her hands across her stomach. She said, "He's very active tonight. He's kicking up like crazy." Janie's always been convinced it'll be a boy.

I went into the kitchen and put some milk on the stove. I rooted around in the icebox for stuff to make sandwiches. I still felt sick at my stomach, the way you feel when you've done something shabby or dirty or unpardonable. I kept on thinking about this girl. Even while I was fixing sandwiches for Janie I was thinking about this girl. I knew, too, that she was thinking of me. I'd fixed that all right by giving her this line.

There are some things that you just can't explain. It was over, and I was sorry that it ever happened, but I just wanted to hear this girl's voice once more. Or maybe I wanted her to hear my voice. I don't know. I thought of her lying there in bed in her apartment, in the dark, lying there awake, thinking about me, wishing that maybe I'd telephone. I suddenly felt sure that was why she'd given me her number.

I went back into the bedroom to see what Janie was doing. She was reading a magazine very contentedly. She lowered it for a moment and smiled at me. She said, "Hello. Do you like being married as much as me? I bet you couldn't possibly." Then she went back to her reading.

I went back to the kitchen and very quietly closed the door. We have an extension telephone in the kitchen. I just had to talk to this girl. I didn't know what I was going to say, but I had to hear her voice.

She answered the telephone herself. I was right. She told me she'd been staring at it for an hour in the dark, praying that I'd call her up. She said, "I *knew* you'd call. I just *knew* it." Her voice was the ecstatic whisper of a child. I don't know exactly what I said. I swear I don't remember. All I know is that I was in a sweat, shaking

417

all over, getting a certain thrill out of the happiness and excitement of this girl who didn't mean a thing in my life.

We spoke for maybe three or four minutes. Just before she hung up, she said, "I love you for calling. I love you for loving me. I love you for just being you." Then she whispered good night and the phone clicked. I tore up the card with her telephone number and threw the fragments into the wastebasket. Now it was over. I was never going to see her or speak to her again. I made the cocoa, fixed up a tray for Janie, and went back to the bedroom.

Janie was staring at me, wide-eyed and very pale. She had the telephone extension still in her hand. She could have pretended that she hadn't listened in, but that isn't like Janie. I hadn't forgotten we had an extension by the bed, but it never occurred to me that she'd listen in.

Janie said, "Tom—who was that girl? What does it mean?" She told me she'd heard the telephone tinkle when I dialed, and that she'd picked it up and heard the whole conversation. I didn't know what to say. I didn't know what to do. I never felt quite so awful in my life. I stood there holding the tray, and the cup of cocoa rattled and spilled over, and I thought I was going to faint.

Janie said, "Who was that girl? You'd better tell me."

It was too late then, but I told her the whole story, just as I've written it down now. I told her the whole crazy, meaningless story. Janie never took her eyes off mine once. She never interrupted. She never asked one question. Quietly, calmly, and very directly, Janie said, "Are you in love with this girl?"

I told her, truthfully, that she didn't mean a thing in the world to me. Nothing. Not a thing.

Janie said, "All right. Let's not ever talk about it any more."

While I got undressed Janie drank her cocoa and ate a sandwich. I was afraid to look at her. I never looked at the bed once. I don't know what she was thinking.

When I was ready for bed, she handed me the little tray, and while I was setting it down, she turned off her bed light and settled down for the night.

I was ashamed to kiss her good night and started turning down my bed, but she held her arms out to me just the way she always did and kissed me good night. I started to say something, but she wouldn't let me. Janie said, "Go to sleep. It's all right."

I couldn't sleep. I heard Janie tossing around, too. She couldn't sleep either. I held my breath several times to listen, because I was afraid she might be crying, but she wasn't.

After about an hour Janie suddenly said, "Tom—was she very pretty?" Before I could answer she stopped me. She said, "No—never mind. I said we'd never talk about it any more. Let's don't." She squirmed around some more, and the bedsprings creaked, and then I heard her give a long, tired sigh. She said, "Never mind, darling. After the baby comes I'll be young and pretty again. You wait and see."

Nothing more was said, but I could hear her stirring uneasily for hours. I never slept at all. I was busy thinking.

There was Janie, lying by my side, doubting me for the first time in her life. And uptown, never doubting me, there was this girl.

The Kid Grows Up

a short short story by Ernest Lehman

It Was a Tough Spot for a Promising Young Ballplayer—
Damned if He Lost the Game and Doomed if He Didn't

GEE, I MISS the kid.

That's the trouble with baseball—one mistake and they chase a guy back to the minors.

It was something like living my whole career over again, rooming with the kid and nursing him along, feeding him every little trick I had picked up in eighteen years of major-league campaigning and seeing him become the greatest rookie first baseman since Lou Gehrig. Too bad I couldn't teach him to stay away from the gambling joints across the river.

I still remember how startled I was that night, when I woke up and saw him at the open window of our hotel room, staring out at the rain.

"What is it, kid, what is it?"

"Nothing," Petey muttered. "Go on back to sleep."

"How much they got you hung up for this time, Petey?"

He whirled around. "None of your business! Why don't you lay off?"

"Sure, kid, sure." He was right.

"Aw, I'm sorry, Mike. They really got me over a barrel for good!"

"Frankie Ray?"

"Who else?" He shrugged hopelessly.

"Much?"

"He just—yesterday he tore up my I O U for ten Gs."

I felt my heart sink. "Nice of him."

"Yeah. Nice of him." The kid strode to the phone and asked the desk for WE 6-1212. He listened to the weather report and then banged the phone back on the cradle. "Tomorrow—sunny and mild." He pounded a fist into his palm.

"O.K., sunny and mild. Then what do you say we turn in? The Sox are throwing McFadden at us tomorrow and I got enough trouble seeing that curve ball of his without bloodshot eyes." I snapped off the light.

"Mike?"

"Yeah, kid?" I yawned.

"Aren't you going to ask me why Frankie Ray tore up the I O U?"

"Look, Petey," I said, "maybe I can't bat my weight any more, but I can still add two and two. It's tomorrow's game, isn't it?"

He flopped down on his bed, and then I heard him bawling quietly into his pillow and I was glad for his sake that the lights were out. You know, when a guy hits at a .346 clip and leads the league in RBIs his first season in the big time, and is a dead cinch for the Rookie-of-the-Year award, you tend to forget that he can still be just a baby at heart.

"I should've listened to you, Mike," he was choking. "I should've quit the first night they nicked me. Now it's too late."

"It's never too late," I lied.

"But—but he said if I don't lay down for him tomorrow and make sure we blow it to the Sox, he'll louse me up with the commissioner or he'll have his gorillas break my arms some night when they catch me alone on a dark street. You don't know this Frankie Ray. He'll kill if he has to. He'll—"

"Take it easy, kid. The fellows in the next room—"

"It's only one game, Mike," his voice pleaded with me. "We're not going any place and the Sox are stuck in the second division too. What's one game more or less?"

I had to think about that for a long time. Finally I said, "Sometimes a guy finds he don't want to live with himself any more, once he's done something like laying down out there for dough. But I don't know. Maybe you're the kind of guy who wouldn't be damaged by his own crookedness. Maybe you could get away with it and *not* be ruined as a ballplayer."

"But they'll ruin me if I *don't!*" he cried out.

"Look, I'm not saying you're not on a spot. But remember, no one got you on it but yourself."

But before I went to sleep I prayed it would rain tomorrow and every day. And I prayed that the team would fall apart.

It didn't rain. And the club didn't fall apart.

McFadden was having one of his hottest days for the Sox, but old Lew Sickelman was matching him every inch of the way. I couldn't bear to watch the kid in the dugout. He looked sick with fear and he couldn't keep his eyes off the box behind third, where Frankie Ray and his boys were chewing on their cigars and waiting patiently for who knows *how* much dough to fall into their laps on a sure thing.

Twice the kid came up with men on base and twice he went down swinging. But that could have been nervousness. About what happened in the seventh, I don't know. The kid was supposed to be one of the best fielding first basemen in the majors, but he dropped an easy third-out throw and allowed Bleeker to score from third for the Sox with the first run of the game.

Anyway, we went into the last of the ninth trailing one to nothing on the kid's error, and you couldn't get him to look you in the eye.

Sukey Lyons struck out to start the last half of the final frame. Tammerock tried to drag a bunt and was nipped by a whisker. And that left it up to me. As I stepped to the plate I glanced at the kid kneeling in the batter's circle waiting to follow me if I drew a life. Our eyes met for a moment, and then I was up there waving a stick at McFadden. I was the last out. If I died, the game would be over and the kid would be off the hook.

The first pitch was high and wide and I missed it by a foot for strike one. I must have been in a fog. The second pitch cut the outside corner before I even saw it. I was too busy wondering if the kid had actually been laying down and destroying himself, or if he had just blown up under the strain. I didn't get time to think about the third pitch at all, because McFadden hit me with it and I trotted down to first.

The kid strode to the plate.

I glanced over behind third base. Frankie Ray and his boys weren't sitting calmly in back of their cigars now.

They were standing up like everyone else, only they *weren't* hollering for the kid to belt one.

McFadden came in with his curve ball, the kid took a wild swing and missed for strike one. Hanson cocked his arm and I hustled back to the bag. Stealing second on *that* guy's arm would be suicide. McFadden's next delivery was a pitchout but I wasn't moving. Then he slipped his fast ball past the kid's knuckles for a count of one and two, and the kid was only one strike away from freedom.

McFadden went to the resin bag and Petey fingered his cap nervously. His face was as white as the foul lines. He glanced at the box where Frankie Ray was watching him. He looked into the dugout where our guys were shouting and pleading for a long one, and then he looked down to first where I was inching off the sack, and I could almost feel him trying to come to a decision—the toughest decision a twenty-year-old kid would ever have to make inside a ball park.

McFadden toed the rubber. He took a half wind-up. Then he shot a quick glance at me and blazed one toward the plate. I saw the kid's shoulders hunching. I saw those powerful arms whipping the bat around. I heard the crack of the bat against that speeding fast ball, and I knew then, even as I saw the pill rising up, up, up, far out toward the left-field bleachers and the crowd let out a mighty shout, that the kid had made his decision and made it well. And as the ball landed up in the stands and I jogged past second, I knew that the kid had finally come of age and I felt a thrill go through me like it was I who had made that decision and belted the homer.

Above the roar of the crowd I was aware of Frankie Ray standing there in his box behind the dugout, his face dark and violent, and if there was any doubt in my mind as to what was in store for the kid, the doubt was erased when I saw that face.

I don't know. I guess I must've been thinking about the great years that might have stretched ahead for Petey. I must've been thinking what a shame it was that a kid like that, who had become a man with one swing of his bat, could be ruined by a hood like Frankie Ray. I certainly must've had *something* on my mind. Why else would I have done what I did?

Anyway, I'm down here with the Norfolk club now, and the kid's up there having himself another great year in the majors. That's good enough for me. And who knows, maybe all I wanted, really, was to get my name in the record books: Mike Kagel, the guy who lost a ball game by forgetting to touch third on the way to the plate.

Ten Famous Hollywood Laughs

by Sidney Skolsky

Goldwyn, Chaplin—An All-Star Short Subject Wherein
Any Resemblance to Real Persons or Places Is Intentional

I HAVE BEEN covering the Hollywood beat for some years and during that time I have heard many stories. The following are my favorites.

Stories about the cinema city start with Sam Goldwyn. This astute producer of fine pictures has been quoted more than any person in Hollywood. Remarks such as "include me out," and "a verbal contract isn't worth the paper it's written on," are now classics. However, my favorite Goldwyn story is no one-line snap Goldwynism. It's a yarn that throws a spotlight on the man.

Goldwyn summoned Edward Chodorov to his office to discuss writing a scenario. Chodorov had read the original story, didn't like it; didn't think it would make a good picture, and told Goldwyn so. Of course he didn't get the job. The story was made under the title, *Woman Chases Man*, and was one of Goldwyn's few failures.

Fade out. Fade in, several years later. Goldwyn was in search of a writer to work on *The Real Glory*. The new story editor suggested Eddie Chodorov. Goldwyn almost hit the ceiling. "Never mention that name to me," he said. "I won't have him around. He was connected with one of my worst flops!"

Another Hollywood character is the former prizefighter, who turned into a good comedian, Maxie Rosenbloom. "Slapsie Maxie" had made a name as a clown in the ring, and when he started to work in pictures, directors realized that he hadn't been kidding. He once told me to be careful of a certain fellow, that "he would punch me in the nose behind my back." Of the many Rosenbloom yarns, the one I consider priceless is the time Maxie was on his way to the Twentieth Century-Fox studio to work in a picture. The prizefighter was driving along Santa Monica Boulevard in his car when he almost collided with another car. In it were two young collegiate lads on their way to U. C. L. A., and Maxie shouted at them. The two boys hollered right back and threatened to beat him up. Maxie leaned out of his car and said, "You wouldn't talk that way to me if I were in condition!"

Dorothy Parker has long been famous as one of the wits of the nation. One of my favorite Parker stories concerns Jimmy Cagney.

Cagney invited Dorothy Parker and her husband, Alan Campbell, to a yachting party on his boat, the Martha. His guests didn't know it, but Cagney gets seasick when he is on a moving boat, and so this particular Sunday he kept the boat anchored at the dock all day. Toward evening he took Dorothy and Campbell ashore and treated them to dinner in a nearby restaurant. A couple of Sundays later, Dorothy Parker and Alan Campbell invited Jimmy Cagney to join them on an automobile party. When Cagney arrived, he was ushered into Dorothy Parker's auto, which was parked near the house. She and her husband were sitting in the back seat, and they had Jimmy join them. They chatted for a couple of hours, and Cagney got restless. "Well," he said finally, "when do we get going?"

"Oh, we're not going any place," answered Dorothy Parker. "This is an automobile party, like your yachting party."

Joe Frisco is a natural comic. A book should be written about him, and it should tell of the time he was summoned to the Los Angeles City Hall concerning back income taxes. He owed about $25,000. "Go ahead," said Frisco to the income-tax collector; "put the handcuffs on me. I can't pay it."

The income-tax man said, "We're not going to send you to jail, Mr. Frisco. We know you'll be working soon. All we want to do is to make an arrangement where you will begin to pay us so much a week." This was agreed. On the way out, Joe Frisco met his best friend, Pat Rooney, Jr., waiting in the anteroom.

"Why are you here?" asked Joe.

"I've got to pay two hundred and fifty dollars in back taxes, and I haven't got the money."

"Come with me," said Joe. "The collector's a great friend of mine."

Frisco and Rooney, Jr., walked into the room where the tax collector was sitting. Frisco introduced Pat Rooney, Jr., and said, "This fellow is my best friend. He owes you two hundred and fifty dollars. Put it on my tab."

The highest award Hollywood can give one of its workers is the Academy Award gold statuette, personally known as "Oscar." Actors, actresses, directors, and producers strive annually to win an Oscar. Here is an incident that illustrates the effect of an Oscar on a career: Leo McCarey got the Academy Award for his direction of *The Awful Truth*. McCarey next started to prepare another picture, which turned out to be *Love Affair*. He struck a snag in the story and phoned his brother, Ray, also a director, and asked him to come over and talk story with him.

Leo and Ray kicked the story around in Leo's den, where the gold Academy Award statuette stood proudly on Leo's desk. They talked story for two hours but couldn't get anywhere. Finally Leo McCarey realized what was holding him back. He called in the colored maid and shouted, "Throw that damn statuette out of here so I can write a picture!"

Wilson Mizner was a fabulous character. He was in on the beginning of every "Klondike" in America. He was there for the gold rush in Alaska, and he was there for the real-estate boom in Florida. He was on Broadway during the halcyon days of Jack's and Rector's. He was in Hollywood when the movies started to talk and the modern "gold rush" was on. He mingled with society and prizefighters. (He was once married to the wealthy Mrs. Yerkes. When he applied for a divorce, the judge asked him on what grounds. Mizner answered, "Marriage is sufficient.")

One of Mizner's favorite citizens was Stanley Ketchell, the prizefighter, whom he managed. There are many, many stories about Mizner, but I have a special fondness for one that concerns him and his affection for this pugilist. Mizner was with a bunch of his cronies, playing cards, when he heard that Stanley Ketchell had just been shot in a saloon brawl. Mizner put down his cards and said, "Let them start counting ten over him. He'll get up."

There are many stories about actors, but there has never been a better criticism of the acting profession than the one Frank Moran, a former prizefighter, made to Gene Fowler. Fowler was at home, recuperating from an automobile accident, and Moran visited him. Gene showed Frank a stack of telegrams he had received, and said, "I got telegrams from Jack Dempsey, Gene Tunney, Jim Jeffries, and a number of fighters. They're so nice they sound as if they were written by sissies. And the telegrams I got from actors—well, they try to wisecrack, and they

sound as if they were written by tough guys. I can't understand that."

"I can explain it," said Moran. "Whenever you don't understand anything about an actor, always remember that it was an actor who shot Lincoln."

Orson Welles is the latest addition to the crop of Hollywood geniuses. Soon after he arrived in Movietown, Welles consented to lecture for a women's club in Santa Monica. When it came time for the lecture, there were so few people in the auditorium that the lady who was to introduce Welles fled. Welles was forced to introduce himself. He said:

"Ladies and gentlemen, since there is no one here to give you the highlights of my life, I will tell you about myself. I am a director of plays. I am a producer of plays. I am an actor on the legitimate stage. I am a motion-picture actor. I write, direct, and act on the radio. I am a magician. I also paint and sketch, and I am a book publisher." Here Welles paused for a second. Then he leaned toward the small audience and said, "Isn't it a shame that there are so many of me and so few of you?"

Charlie Chaplin is, without a doubt, our greatest entertainer. A visitor to Chaplin's Beverly hilltop house is usually treated to a one-man show that lasts for hours. One evening Konrad Bercovici and his daughter were Chaplin's guests. Chaplin was in good mood, and started to give imitations. He imitated writers, actors, political figures, his Jap servant, everyone. Then he took Bercovici and his daughter to dinner.

It was past midnight when the three left the restaurant. Chaplin was still imitating people. Suddenly, on the street, while his car pulled up to the curb, he sang at the top of his voice an aria from an Italian opera. He sang it superbly.

"Why, Charlie," Bercovici's daughter exclaimed, "I never knew you could sing so beautifully."

"I can't sing at all," Chaplin answered. "I was only imitating Caruso."

Hollywood is my beat, and I have seen and heard strange and unbelievable things. My favorite tale about fantastic Hollywood concerns Max Gordon, the noted theatrical producer. Max Gordon is the only man I know who held two important jobs in two studios at the same time. Max Gordon was hurried from the East and hired by Warners to act as official adviser to Mervyn LeRoy, who was then busy making a Rodgers and Hart Musical picture, *Fools for Scandal*. At the same time Max Gordon was hurried from the East by Radio Pictures, where he was "to learn the business" at one thousand dollars a week. Gordon went to work at one studio every morning to learn the business, and at another every afternoon to teach the business. But don't get me wrong. I love Hollywood.

TV Show of the Future
by Nora Hammesfahr

Television Will Have One Thing in Common with the Circus—It Will Be the Greatest Show On Earth, with Everything from Basement Bargain Sales to College Courses.

TELEVISION HAS ALREADY given some indication of how it will revolutionize many aspects of our way of life. But this is just the beginning.

To get an idea of some of the fabulous possibilities that lie ahead, let's go behind the television screen and talk with the presidents and vice-presidents, the official and technical heads of this romping infant industry; let's find out how far they think TV will be advanced by 1955.

A billion-dollar-a-year industry today, television will be one of the ten major U. S. industries six years hence and will affect every phase of American life.

Dr. Allen B. Du Mont, president of Du Mont Laboratories, Inc., says that "For the approximate 70 TV stations on the air today, well over 1,000 will serve all the important metropolitan areas of the nation by 1955." But millions of Americans—farmers and country folk out of reach of city TV stations—are saying, "What about us?" To which NBC's president Niles Trammell replies that eventually 80 per cent of the nation will be within range of telecast stations. The experts also say ways will be found to provide additional channels for blanketing the nation with TV services of all sorts.

As for international television, the United States will be linked to Canada, Cuba, and Mexico by 1955. Further than that, a start will have been made toward transatlantic television either by planes, providing an airborne lift for signals, as envisaged by General David Sarnoff, chairman of the board and president of the Radio Corporation of America; or by radio relay through the Far North, beginning in Labrador, as Dr. Du Mont suggests. In either case, both industry leaders are agreed that it is only the tremendous cost involved that prevents us from enjoying international TV now.

Television of the future, judging by the elaborate programs being planned now, will have one thing in common with the circus—it will be the greatest show on earth! And it will be in color, too.

How much of video fare will be films? John L. Van Volkenburg, CBS vice-president in charge of television, estimates 20 per cent; NBC's President Trammell says, "30 per cent to 40 per cent."

Backing up these forecasts, adman Jack Warwick, vice-president of Warwick & Legler, Inc., explains that "Since Americans spend more money for movies than for any other form of entertainment, that is obviously what they want the most—and what they will get."

Paramount, Twentieth Century-Fox, and Warner Brothers are planning right now to televise news as it happens in place of their three-day-old newsreels.

But Hollywood's use of television will go much farther than newscasts and will result in giving home video serious competition. Joining forces with their theaters, the major studios would be in a position to buy the exclusive rights to such sports events as the Rose Bowl Game, the World Series, fights, special events, etc., and to supplement these with other video features of their own. Whether or not, as seems likely, video will prove to be the solution to greater movie attendance remains to be seen. Opera performances and many other productions too lavish for a small screen may find a new medium in theater video.

In any event, you will see more on your living-room screen than films of live shows and movies. You will see improved productions of all your favorite programs, plus sports and special events. These, together with the movies, will be your video entertainment.

But all this is the entertainment side of your life. Television promises much more by 1955. Take Mother's bargain hunting, for instance. Through service programs she will sit comfortably in her living room and "teleshop." Let's say it's dollar day in her town and her favorite store is videocasting its biggest bargains. After the show she orders by telephone. That is teleshopping for Mother. But Dad will be able to save valuable time too. For instance, he can watch televised demonstrations of automobiles, thus eliminating the showroom-to-showroom ordeal. Enthusiastic response to a few such experimental service programs shows they fill a vital need.

But television goes to business too. If, for instance, Dad is a top executive, foreman or superintendent in a large plant, he will be able to oversee assembly lines from his office. Regulating traffic, policing prisons, guarding banks and jewelry stores are only a few of the possible ways video can serve business.

Perhaps no single contribution that video can make is so important as what it will be able to do for our children. By 1955, according to all predictions, it may be that renowned educators, eminent scientists, and great professors like Einstein through video will offer hundreds of college students simultaneously the best of their learning. Only supplementary instruction would be needed from local teachers.

As Commander Mortimer W. Loewi, director of television at Du Mont Network, says. "Television is your window to the world."

An evening's entertainment, daytime service programs, improved industrial techniques, better education for children—all these television has to offer. But perhaps not one of them is half so important as TV's potential for promoting the unity of mankind.

"That's my husband. He's insanely jealous."

LIBERTY

425

LIBERTY WAS PUBLISHED for the last time in July of 1950.

Up to that unhappy moment its editors had struggled valiantly to keep the magazine alive and interesting. One of their final ideas was a series called "What Liberty Means to Me," to be written each month by a famous person.

Eleanor Roosevelt contributed to this series a few months before the magazine died, and it seems fitting to conclude with her words as our last ones.

What Liberty Means To Me
by Eleanor Roosevelt

America's Most Distinguished Stateswoman Says Real Liberty in a Democracy Can Exist Only As Long As the Control of the Government Remains in the Hands of the People

I HAVE JUST flown over some of our midwest plains and the mountains of the west coast and the deserts that one flies over as one approaches them. This part of our country always seems to me nearest to the pioneer days, and as I think of those men who came west and settled the land, I realize how much the concept they had of liberty has changed. To them liberty meant the right of every man to defend and protect himself; to go where he wished; to settle where he wished; to believe and act as he wished. There was really little interference with the individual's desires.

That was a kind of liberty which can no longer be enjoyed by the average citizen of our country. As populations grow more dense, it becomes necessary for liberty to be conditioned by the liberty of all people, and in order to achieve a common standard, people must accept to live under law. In a democracy, however, with a representative type of government, people always retain their power over their representatives. They allow them to make the laws, and if the majority of the people concur in the decisions of their representatives, the laws will remain and be increasingly well enforced as time goes on. If the majority disagrees, the law will be less and less obeyed; and if the feeling is important enough against any law, it will not only be ignored but it will actually be rescinded.

Liberty in the world of today lies largely in the hands of those people who wish to govern themselves and who are willing to subordinate individual freedom to the kind of freedom which gives consideration to the desires of other people. For instance, in our big cities we have a police force in order that people may not be permitted to commit crime and prey upon their neighbors or to make nuisances of themselves in public places. But those of us who care about real liberty are jealous that the laws so safeguard the individual that there is as little as possible interference with his personal life. We make sure that all people have liberty of thought and of conscience;

426

that they are allowed to practice their religion freely, and that they have the right to freedom of expression; freedom to come together peaceably to discuss or to organize as they wish, as long as they do not disturb the peace or threaten the collective security of the whole people.

We are careful to insure that the law shall provide for the protection of the individual against any arbitrary use of the law, even by government itself. Liberty must also include security from outside aggression so that it is the right of the people to take such measures, either alone or collectively, as will assure them a peaceful existence.

Lately we have also come to recognize that liberty can only exist where a government, controlled by the people, creates an economic atmosphere in which all people willing to earn a living can do so, because slavery can be imposed on people through fear of want, just as it can be imposed on people by an aggressor nation which is allowed to gain physical control of another people.

The only thing that is essential in our modern concept of liberty is that it always be the majority of the people who make the laws and who are willing to abide by them. The moment that a government becomes so strong that this power is no longer in the hands of the people, or that they become afraid to exercise it, then the people have lost their liberty and are slaves as surely as they ever were in the days gone by.

It is for this reason that I feel real liberty can only exist in a democracy where the people accept their responsibility, consider their citizenship as a trust, and see to it that they never let the control of their government slip into the hands of any individual or any group, but keep it always in the hands of the people themselves and function under the will of the majority. The majority may be wrong, but it is safer for the people themselves to have to recognize that they have made a mistake and to make the change through their own acceptance of error than it is for people to abdicate their own judgment and their power at any time.

Liberty is precious to us all, no less now that it is conditioned by the rights of all men than when it was the liberty of one individual living on an island alone.